STRENGTH OF MATERIALS

STRENGTH OF MATERIALS

Ferdinand L. Singer

PROFESSOR OF ENGINEERING MECHANICS
NEW YORK UNIVERSITY
COLLEGE OF ENGINEERING

HARPER & BROTHERS, PUBLISHERS
NEW YORK

Contents

CHAPTER V.   STRESSES IN BEAMS

CHAPTER VI.   BEAM DEFLECTIONS

CHAPTER VII.   RESTRAINED BEAMS

CHAPTER VIII. CONTINUOUS BEAMS

CHAPTER IX. COMBINED STRESSES

CHAPTER X. REINFORCED BEAMS

CHAPTER XI. COLUMNS

CHAPTER XII. SPECIAL TOPICS

APPENDIX A. MOMENTS OF INERTIA

APPENDIX B. TABLES

Preface

Successful machine or structural design is practically impossible without thorough mastery of engineering mechanics and understanding of strength of materials. This book attempts to present the fundamental principles of strength of materials in a form that will transmit these principles easily to the student for his complete understanding and permanent possession.

In *Strength of Materials* we are concerned with the analysis and design of members subjected to various combinations of loadings. These combinations may be resolved into three basic types of loadings. These types consist of axial, torsional, and flexural loads, and, in this sequence, each is discussed separately before considering their combined effects. In each, the student is led progressively from the simpler applications to the more complex cases of statically indeterminate loadings. This complete exposition of the three basic types of loading is followed by applications to various combinations of loadings. The author's experience has shown that this arrangement helps the student to grasp more readily the significance and application of the general study of combined stresses.

Among the topics to which special attention is directed are the following: statically indeterminate members subjected to axial loads; eccentrically loaded connections; the construction of shear and moment diagrams, and their application to beam design; deflections by the area-moment method, preceded by a full discussion of moment diagrams by parts; the treatment of continuous beams by means of both the general three-moment theorem and a short but complete presentation of the moment distribution method; Mohr's circle as applied to combined stresses, strain components and strain rosettes, and to moments of inertia; such special topics as shear flow, shear center, unsymmetrical bending, thick-walled cylinders, etc., which serve as an introduction to advanced study.

It is hoped that these topics, as well as the others in the text, are presented in a manner that will relieve the instructor of the burden of detailed explanations. But primarily, the student's point of view has been retained and his special problems kept in mind. Words have not been spared to make a fundamental principle perfectly understood. On the other hand, excess verbiage has been eliminated. Principles are developed using a consistent plan which first relates stresses to deformations, then applies the equations of static equilibrium, and finally satisfies the boundary condi-

ix

tions. The physical significance of fundamental concepts, and the assumptions and limitations made in developing them, are carefully discussed so that memorization is reduced to a minimum. Rules of sign have also been simplified by assigning the positive sense to all quantities to which the adjectives up, above, or similar terms may be applied; for negative signs, the converse is true.

Numerous illustrative problems show in detail how principles are applied. The explanations are complete — nothing is taken for granted. Throughout, the equation or theory to be applied is stated at the left-hand side of the page. In the solution, numerical values are substituted in the respective order in which the symbols appear in the equation. This procedure enables the student to follow readily the various steps of the solution without continually referring to the body of the text.

Problems for assignment have been chosen carefully to give wide variety in type and difficulty. They have been arranged approximately in the order of their difficulty, and answers to two-thirds of them have been given. All of the problems are intrinsically practical, although some of the loadings are more complex than those ordinarily encountered; nevertheless, such academic loadings serve to emphasize a basic principle. As a rule, numerical values have been selected which simplify arithmetical computations.

The numbering plan used in the book enables one to locate quickly any cross-reference. With this plan, all articles, figures, equations, tables, and problems are preceded by the chapter numeral in which they appear and are numbered consecutively through each chapter. Figures for assigned problems are given the same number as the problem to which they refer in order to simplify correlation of a problem figure with the corresponding problem data. The summaries appended to most chapters are intended to give the student a coördinated picture of what he has studied. It is hoped that they will be helpful in review and post-college work.

The author wishes to acknowledge his indebtedness to the various textbooks consulted during the preparation of this book. Collectively these books have been a source of many ideas and problems. Grateful acknowledgment is due to Dean Emeritus William R. Bryans and Professor Charles E. Gus (since resigned) for their inspiration, influence, and advice. Thanks are extended to many others, especially Professor William G. Plumtree, for their helpful suggestions.

FERDINAND L. SINGER

New York, New York
January, 1951

List of Symbols and Abbreviations*

A	area
A'	partial area of beam section
$\bar{a}, \bar{b}$	coördinates of centroid of moment diagram caused by simply supported loads
b	breadth, width
c	distance from neutral axis to extreme fiber
D, d	diameter
E	modulus of elasticity in tension or compression
e	eccentricity, natural base of logarithms
f_c	unit compressive stress in concrete
f_s	unit tensile stress in reinforcing steel
G	modulus of rigidity (i.e., modulus of elasticity in shear)
g	gravitational acceleration (32.2 ft per sec²)
h	height, depth of beam
I	moment of inertia of area
$I_{\text{N.A.}}$	moment of inertia with respect to neutral axis
I_o	centroidal moment of inertia
J	polar moment of inertia
J_o	centroidal polar moment of inertia
K	stress concentration factor
k	spring constant, radius of gyration
L	length
M	bending moment, moment of force
N	normal force, factor of safety
n	revolutions per minute, ratio of moduli of elasticity
P	force, concentrated load, hoop tension
P_{cr}	critical load for columns
P_{uv}, P_{xy}	products of inertia
p	pressure per unit of area
Q	statical or first moment of area
q	shear flow
R	reaction, resultant force
R, r	radii

* With very few exceptions these symbols and abbreviations agree with those approved by the American Standards Association.

S	unit stress
S_b	unit bearing stress
S_c	unit compressive stress
S_{cr}	critical unit stress in column formulas
S_f	unit flexural stress
S_n	unit normal stress
S_r	unit radial stress
S_s	unit shearing stress
S_t	unit tensile stress, unit tangential stress
S_x, S_y, S_z	unit normal stresses in x, y, and z directions respectively
S_{xy}	unit shearing stress on x and y planes
$S_{y.p.}$	stress at yield point
T	torque, temperature
t	thickness, tangential deviation
u, v, w	rectangular coördinates
V	vertical shearing force
v	velocity
W	total weight or load
w	weight or load per unit of length
X, Y, Z	orthogonal components of a force
x, y, z	rectangular coördinates
$\bar{x}, \bar{y}, \bar{z}$	coördinates of centroid or center of gravity
y	deflection of beam (positive upward)
$Z = \dfrac{I}{c}$	section modulus
α	temperature coefficient of linear expansion
$\alpha, \beta, \gamma, \text{-\,-\,-}$	angles
γ	unit shearing strain, weight per unit volume
δ	total elongation or contraction; deflection of beam (positive downward); maximum deflection of column
δ_{st}	static deflection
ϵ	unit tensile or compressive strain
$\epsilon_x, \epsilon_y, \epsilon_z$	unit tensile or compressive strain in the x, y, and z directions respectively
θ	total angle of twist, slope angle for elastic curve
ρ	radius of curvature, variable radius, mass density
μ	Poisson's ratio, coefficient of friction
ω	angular velocity
deg	degrees
DF	distribution factor
FEM	fixed end moment
ft	feet

hp	horsepower
hr	hour
K	kips (1000 lb)
lb	pounds
min	minutes
psf	pounds per square foot
psi	pounds per square inch
rad	radians
rev	revolutions
rpm	revolutions per minute
rps	revolutions per second
sec	seconds

STRENGTH OF MATERIALS

Chapter I
Simple Stress

1–1. Introduction

Strength of Materials extends the study of forces that was begun in *Engineering Mechanics*, but there is a sharp distinction between the two subjects. Fundamentally, the field of mechanics covers the relations between forces acting on rigid bodies; in *statics*, the bodies are in equilibrium, whereas in *dynamics*, they are accelerated but can be put in equilibrium by applying correctly placed inertia forces.

In contrast to mechanics, strength of materials deals with the relations between externally applied loads and their internal effects on bodies. Moreover, the bodies are no longer assumed to be ideally rigid; the deformations, however small, are of major interest. The properties of the material of which a structure or machine is made affect both its choice and the dimensions that will satisfy the requirements of strength and rigidity.

The difference between mechanics and strength of materials can be further emphasized by the following example. It is a simple problem in statics to determine the force required at the end of a crowbar to pry up a given load (Fig. 1–1). A moment summation about the fulcrum determines P. This statics solution assumes the crowbar to be both rigid enough and strong enough to permit the desired action. In strength of materials, however, the solution must extend further: We must investigate the bar itself to be sure

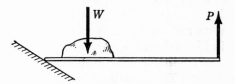

FIG. 1–1. — Crowbar must neither break nor bend excessively.

that it will neither break nor be so flexible that it bends without lifting the load.

Throughout this book we shall study the principles that govern these two fundamental concepts of *strength* and *rigidity*. In this first chapter we start with simple axial loadings; later we consider twisting loads and bending loads; and finally we discuss simultaneous combinations of these three basic types of loadings.

1

1–2. Analysis of Internal Forces

Consider a body of any shape acted upon by the forces shown in Fig. 1–2. In engineering mechanics, we would start by determining the resultant of the applied forces to determine whether or not the body remains at rest. If the resultant is zero, we have static equilibrium — a condition generally prevailing in structures. If the resultant is not zero, we may apply inertia forces to bring about dynamic equilibrium. Such cases are discussed later under dynamic loading. For the present we shall consider only cases involving static equilibrium.

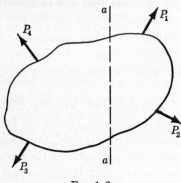

Fig. 1–2.

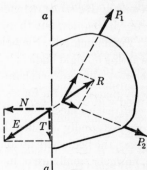

Fig. 1–3. — How normal and shearing forces are produced.

In strength of materials, an additional investigation is made of the internal distribution of the forces. This may be done by assuming the body of Fig. 1–2 to be at rest (or, if accelerated, by applying the necessary inertia forces to put it into dynamic equilibrium). We now pass an exploratory section a–a and consider the free-body diagram of the right segment shown in Fig. 1–3. This segment is acted upon by the applied forces P_1 and P_2, plus a resisting force E equal and opposite to the resultant R of the applied forces. This resisting force is the force actually being transmitted across section a–a. The value of this force is determined by the condition that it must maintain the free-body diagram of the right segment in equilibrium; that is, its value is determined from the fact that it must balance the effect of the applied forces. Therefore, we extend the lines of action of P_1 and P_2 as shown in Fig. 1–3, and put in the equilibrant E to balance the resultant R of the applied forces.

We observe now that E may be resolved into its components N and T, directed normal and tangent respectively to the exposed surface a–a. The normal component N is the resultant of the tearing action over section a–a; the tangential component T measures the resistance of the left seg-

ment to sliding past the right segment. T is
called the resisting shearing force.

A little reflection will show that if the exploratory section *a–a* had been oriented differently, as in Fig. 1–4 where it is perpendicular
to the equilibrant E, the shearing effect on
the section would have been reduced to zero,
and the tearing effect would have been at a
maximum.

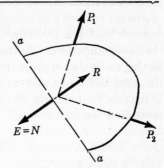

This discussion has two conclusions: (1)
The effect of applied forces depends upon the
selection of the exploratory section, and (2)
the maximum pull (or push, if the forces are
reversed) is exerted over a section that is per-

Fig. 1–4. — When exploratory
section *a-a* is perpendicular to
R, only normal forces are produced.

pendicular to the resultant of the applied forces.

The purpose of studying strength of materials is to insure that the structures used will be safe against the maximum internal effects that may be
produced by any combination of loading. We shall learn as our study proceeds that it is not always possible or convenient to select an exploratory
section that is perpendicular to the resultant load; instead, we may have
to start by analyzing the effects acting on a section like *a–a* in Fig. 1–3, and
then learn how these effects combine to produce maximum internal effects
like those on section *a–a* in Fig. 1–4. This procedure we shall study later
in Chapter IX, dealing with combined stresses. For the present, we restrict our study to conditions of loading in which the section of maximum
internal effect is evident by inspection.

1–3. Simple Stress

One of the basic problems of the engineer is to select the proper material
and correctly use and proportion it so as to enable a structure or machine

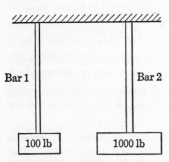

to do most efficiently what it is designed to
do. For this purpose, it is essential to determine the strength, stiffness, and other
properties of materials. A tabulation of the
average properties of common metals is
given in Appendix B, Table B–1, on page
447.

Let us consider two bars of equal length
but different materials, suspended from a
common support as in Fig. 1–5. If we knew
nothing about the bars except that they
could support the indicated maximum loads,

Fig. 1–5. — Bars supporting
maximum loads.

we could not tell which material is stronger. Of course, Bar 2 supports a greater load, but we cannot compare strengths without having a common basis of comparison. In this instance, the cross-sectional areas are needed. So let us further specify that Bar 1 has a cross-sectional area of 1/100 sq in., and Bar 2 has an area of 1 sq in. Now it is simple to compare their strengths by reducing the data to load capacity per unit area. Here we note that the unit strength of Bar 1 is

$$S_1 = \frac{100}{\frac{1}{100}} = 10,000 \text{ psi}$$

(the abbreviation *psi* represents *pounds per square inch*) and Bar 2 has a unit strength

$$S_2 = \frac{1000}{1} = 1000 \text{ psi}$$

Thus the material of Bar 1 is 10 times as strong as that of Bar 2.

We usually define the unit strength of a material as the stress[1] in the material. It is expressed symbolically as

$$S = \frac{P}{A} \tag{1-1}$$

where S is the stress or force per unit area, P is the applied load, and A is the cross-sectional area. Observe that maximum stress in tension or compression occurs over a section normal to the load, as indicated in Fig. 1–4. Shearing stress is discussed in the next article.

However, even as simple an expression as Eq. (1–1) requires careful discussion. Dividing load by area does not define the stress over all the area; it merely determines the average stress. A more exact definition of stress is obtained by dividing the differential load dP by the differential area over which it acts:

$$S = \frac{dP}{dA} \tag{1-1a}$$

Next let us see under what conditions $S = \dfrac{P}{A}$ will accurately define the stress at all points of the cross-section. The condition under which the stress is constant or uniform is known as *simple stress*. We shall show now that a uniform stress distribution results when the resultant of the applied loads passes through the centroid of the cross-section.[2]

---

[1] Some engineers use *stress* or *total stress* as synonymous with load or force, and *unit stress* or *stress intensity* when referring to the intensity of load per unit area. In this book, *stress* will always denote *force per unit area*.

[2] There are certain exceptions to this rule; they are caused by stress concentration (see p. 379) and by abrupt changes in cross-section, and at points in the vicinity of the applied loads (see p. 5).

Suppose that a cutting plane isolates the lower half of one of the bars in Fig. 1–5. Then, as shown in Fig. 1–6, the resisting forces over the cut section must balance the applied load P. A typical resisting force is dP. Applying the conditions of equilibrium, we obtain

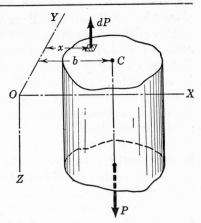

$$[\Sigma Z = 0] \qquad P = \int dP = \int S\,dA$$
$$[\Sigma M_y = 0] \ \ Pb = \int x\,dP = \int x\,(S\,dA)$$

If we specify that the stress distribution is to be constant over the cut section, S may be written outside the integrals in the above equations to obtain

Fig. 1–6. — For uniform stress, P must pass through the centroid C.

$$P = S\int dA = SA$$

and therefore,

$$Pb = (SA)\,b = S\int x\,dA$$

Then, canceling the common factor S, we obtain

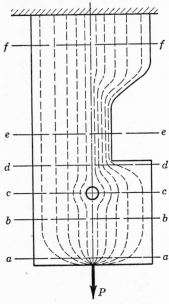

$$b = \frac{\int x\,dA}{A} = \bar{x}$$

from which the coordinate b of the point C is recognized as being the x coordinate of the centroid of the section. By taking a moment summation about the X axis, we could similarly show that $\bar{y}$ defines the y coordinate of C. We conclude that a uniform stress distribution is obtained only when the resultant of the applied loads passes through the centroid of that surface.

It does not follow, however, that positioning the load through the centroid of the section *always* results in a uniform stress distribution. For example, in Fig. 1–7 is shown the profile of a flat bar of constant thickness. The load P is applied at the center line of the bar. At sections b–b and f–f, the stress distribution is uniform and illustrates the principle discussed

Fig. 1–7. — Exceptions to uniform stress distribution occur at sections a–a, c–c, d–d, and e–e.

above; but at the other indicated sections the stresses are not uniform.

At section e–e, the stress distribution is not uniform because the line of action of P obviously does not pass through the centroid of the section. Nor are the stresses uniformly distributed all across sections c–c or d–d because, although the action line of P does pass through the centroids of these sections, here there are abrupt changes in section. At such sections, the stresses are usually highly localized and can be determined only by the mathematical theory of elasticity or some experimental method such as photoelasticity. Also, the stress is not uniform across section a–a because here the section is too close to the point where the load is applied. Unless a section is located at a distance from the end of the rod at least equal to the minimum width of the rod, we will not obtain a uniform stress distribution.[3]

In order to visualize why sections c–c, d–d, and a–a do not have uniform stress, imagine that the applied force P produces stress lines which radiate out from the load and distribute themselves throughout the body as indicated by the dashed lines in the figure. Although this concept is not actually correct, it does indicate the existence of stress concentration wherever the shape of the body interferes with the "free flow" of the stress lines. The bunching of these lines about the hole in section c–c, and around the sharp corner of section d–d, which indicates stress concentration, contrasts with the relatively smooth flow of stress around the radius between sections e–e and f–f.

PROBLEMS

101. Determine the cross-sectional areas of bars BD, CD, and CE necessary to carry the loads on the given truss without exceeding a tensile stress of 20,000 psi or a compressive stress of 12,000 psi. A reduced stress in compression is specified here to avoid the danger of buckling.

Ans. $A_{BD} = 3.0$ in.²; $A_{CD} = 1.67$ in.²; $A_{CE} = 2.4$ in.²

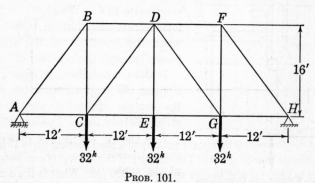

PROB. 101.

[3] See S. Timoshenko, *Theory of Elasticity*, McGraw-Hill, p. 51

102. Using the allowable stresses specified in the preceding problem, compute the necessary cross-sectional area of bars *DF*, *EF*, and *EG* in the cantilever truss shown.

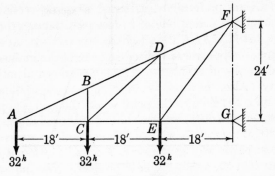

PROB. 102.

103. A short steel tube is subjected to an axial compressive load of 64,000 lb. Determine the inside diameter if the outside diameter is 6 in. and the limiting compressive stress is 16,000 psi.

104. Determine the outside diameter of a hollow steel tube that will carry a tensile load of 100,000 lb at a stress of 18,000 psi. Assume the wall thickness to be one-tenth of the outside diameter.   *Ans.* $D = 4.44$ in.

105. Part of the landing gear for a light plane is shown. Determine the compressive stress in the strut *AB* caused by a landing reaction $R = 2500$ lb. Strut *AB* is inclined at 53.1° with *BC*.   *Ans.* $S_c = 8100$ psi

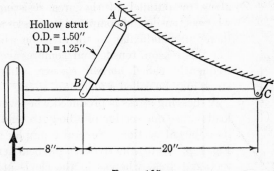

PROB. 105.

106. A timber post 8 in. square rests upon a steel bearing plate 12 in. square on top of a concrete pier as shown. Determine *P* if the allowable compressive stress in the timber is 1200 psi and that in concrete is 600 psi. What is the dimension *d* at the base of the pier if the soil pressure must not exceed 4500 lb/sq ft?

Ans. $d = 49.6$ in. square

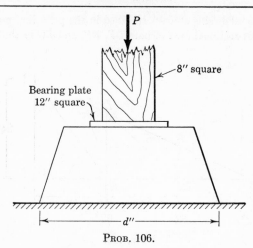

PROB. 106.

107. An assembly used in drilling a well consists of three different sections of steel tubing, each 500 ft long and supporting a weight $P = 30,000$ lb at the bottom, as shown. Compute the cross-sectional area required for each section if the maximum stress in each is limited to 6000 psi. What is the total weight of the assembly? Assume that steel weighs 490 lb/cu ft.

Ans. $A_1 = 6.98$ in.^{2}; $A_2 = 9.73$ in.^{2}; $A_3 = 13.58$ in.^{2}; $W = 51,500$ lb

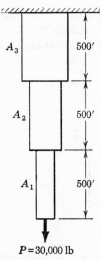

PROB. 107.

1–4. Shearing Stress

Shearing stress differs from both tensile and compressive stress in that it is caused by forces acting along or parallel to the area resisting the forces, whereas tensile and compressive stresses are caused by forces perpendicular to the areas on which they act. For this reason, tensile and compressive stresses are frequently called *normal stresses*, while a shearing stress may be called a *tangential stress*.

A shearing stress is produced whenever the applied loads cause one section of a body to tend to slide past its adjacent section. Several examples are shown in Fig. 1–8. In (*a*) the rivet resists shear across its cross-sectional area, whereas in the clevis at (*b*) the bolt resists shear across two cross-sectional areas; case (*a*) may be called *single shear* and case (*b*) *double shear*. In (*c*) a circular slug is about to be punched out of a plate; the resisting area is similar to the milled edge of a coin. In each case, the shear occurs over an area parallel to the applied load. This may be called *direct shear* in contrast to the *induced shear* that may occur over sections inclined with the load, as was illustrated in Fig. 1–3 on page 2.

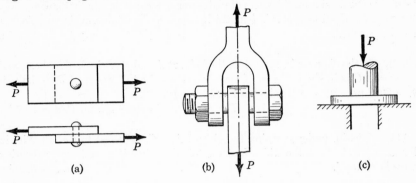

Fig. 1–8. — Examples of shear.

The discussion concerning uniform normal stresses in Art. 1–3 might lead us to conclude also that uniform shearing stress will exist when the resultant shearing force passes through the centroid of the cross-section being sheared. If this were true, the shearing stress could be found from

$$S_s = \frac{P}{A} \tag{1–2}$$

Actually, the shearing stress is practically never uniformly distributed, so Eq. (1–2) must be interpreted as giving merely the *average* shearing stress. It is shown later (Art. 5–7) that the maximum shearing stress over a rectangular section is 50% greater than the average shearing stress, and that for a solid circular section it is 33% greater. However, the problems in this article are intended to be solved by Eq. (1–2) and the shearing stresses specified are the *average* stresses.

PROBLEMS

108. The end chord of a timber truss is framed into the bottom chord as shown. Neglecting friction, compute the dimension b if the allowable shearing stress is 120 psi. Determine the dimension c so that the bearing stress does not exceed 1000 psi.

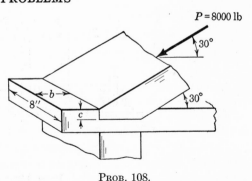

Prob. 108.

109. A hole is to be punched out of a plate having an ultimate shearing strength of 40,000 psi. (*a*) If the compressive stress in the punch is limited to 60,000 psi, determine the maximum thickness of plate from which a hole 2 in. in diameter may be punched. (*b*) If the plate is $\frac{1}{2}$ in. thick, compute the minimum size of hole that may be punched.   *Ans.* (*a*) $t = \frac{3}{4}$ in.; (*b*) $d = 1.33$ in.

110. In the diagram in Prob. 105, the bolts at A and B are in double shear, and the one at C is in single shear. Compute the required diameter of these bolts if $S_s = 8000$ psi. Strut AB is inclined at 53.1° with BC.
        Ans. For A and B, $d = 0.59$ in.; for C, $d = 0.67$ in.

111. A 24-in. pulley carrying the given belt pulls is keyed to a shaft 2-in. in diameter. Determine the width b of the 3-in.-long key if the allowable shearing stress is 8000 psi.   *Ans.* $b = 0.40$ in.

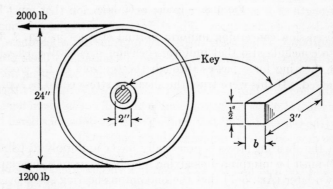

PROB. 111.

112. For the bell crank shown in equilibrium, determine the area of the bar AB if the tensile stress in it is limited to $\frac{3}{2}$ the shearing stress in the 1-in.-diameter pin at D.   *Ans.* $A = 0.618$ in.²

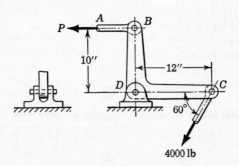

PROB. 112.

113. Two blocks of wood 2 in. wide and $\frac{1}{2}$ in. thick are glued together as shown. Using the concept illustrated in Fig. 1–3, determine the shearing load and from it the shearing stress on the glued joint, if $P = 1200$ lb. Generalize this procedure to show that the shearing stress on a section inclined at an angle θ to a transverse section of area A is $S_s = \dfrac{1}{2} \dfrac{P}{A} \sin 2\theta$.

114. In Prob. 113, assume the glued joint to be at 20° with the axis of the blocks instead of 30°. If the shearing stress along the joint is limited to 200 psi, and the tensile stress across a transverse section may not exceed 1000 psi, determine the safe load P.   *Ans.* $P = 622$ lb

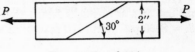

PROB. 113 and 114.

1–5. Stress-Strain Diagram

The strength of a material is not the only criterion that must be considered in designing structures. The stiffness of a material is frequently of equal importance. To a lesser degree, such properties as hardness, toughness, ductility, etc., determine the selection of a material. These properties are determined by making tests on the materials and comparing the results with established standards. Although a complete description of these tests is the province of materials testing and hence will not be given here, one of the tests (the tension test of steel) and its results will be considered because it helps to develop several important basic concepts.

If a specimen of structural steel is gripped between the jaws of a testing machine and the load and the extension in a specified length are observed simultaneously, we shall be able to plot these observations on a graph on which the ordinates represent *load* and the abscissae represent *extension*.

Fig. 1–9 represents such a graph. Notice that we did not plot load against extension; rather, unit load or stress was plotted against unit elongation, technically known as *strain*. Only by reducing observed values to a unit basis can the properties of one specimen be compared with those of other specimens. The diagram in Fig. 1–9 is called a stress-strain diagram, the name being taken from the coordinates.

Strain. To obtain the unit elongation or strain, ϵ, it would seem obvious to divide the elongation δ by the length L in which it was measured, thereby obtaining

$$\epsilon = \frac{\delta}{L} \tag{1–3}$$

The strain so computed, however, measures only the average value of strain. The correct expression for strain at any position is

$$\epsilon = \frac{d\delta}{dL} \tag{1–3a}$$

which determines the average strain in a length so small that the strain must be constant over that length. But under certain conditions the strain may be assumed constant and its value computed from Eq. (1–3). These conditions are:

1. The specimen must be of constant cross-section.
2. The material must be homogeneous.
3. The load must be axial, i.e., produce uniform stress.

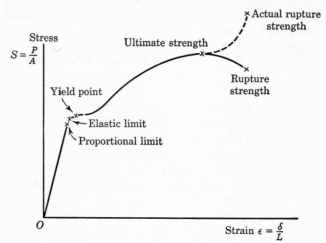

Fig. 1–9. — Stress-strain diagram.

Proportional Limit. From the origin O to a point called the *proportional limit*, Fig. 1–9 shows the stress-strain diagram to be a straight line. From this we deduce the well-known relation, first postulated by Robert Hooke[4] in 1678, that stress is proportional to strain. Notice carefully that this proportionality does not extend throughout the diagram; it ends at the proportional limit. Beyond this point, the stress is no longer proportional to the strain. The proportional limit is important because all subsequent theory involving the behavior of elastic bodies is based upon a stress-strain proportionality.[5] This assumption places an upper limit on the usable stress a material may carry. This is also our first indication that the proportional limit, and not the ultimate strength, is the maximum stress to which a material may be subjected. We shall return to this observation later when we discuss working stress and the factor of safety.

[4] Robert Hooke's famous law *Ut tensio sic vis,* i.e., "As strain, so force," related total strain to total force and did not recognize a limit to this proportionality.

[5] The stress-strain diagram of many materials is actually a curve on which there is no definite proportional limit. In such cases, the stress-strain proportionality is assumed to exist up to a stress at which the strain increases at a rate 50% greater than shown by the initial tangent to the stress-strain diagram.

Other concepts developed from the stress-strain curve are: (1) the *elastic limit*, or the stress beyond which the material will not return to its original shape when unloaded, but will retain a permanent deformation called *permanent set*. (2) *Yield point*, at which there is an appreciable elongation or yielding of the material without any corresponding increase of load; indeed, the load may actually decrease while the yielding occurs. However, the phenomenon of yielding is peculiar to structural steel; other grades of steels and steel alloys or other materials do not possess it, as is indicated by the typical stress-strain curves of these materials shown in Fig. 1–10.

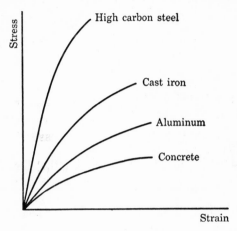

Fig. 1–10. — Comparative stress-strain diagrams for different materials.

(3) Ultimate stress, or *ultimate strength* as it is more commonly called, which is the highest ordinate on the stress-strain curve. (4) *Rupture strength*, or the stress at failure. For structural steel it is somewhat lower than ultimate strength because the rupture strength is computed by dividing the rupture load by the original cross-sectional area which, although convenient, is incorrect. The error is caused by a phenomenon known as *necking*. As failure occurs, the material stretches very rapidly and simultaneously narrows down, as shown in Fig. 1–11, so that the rupture load

Fig. 1–11. — Necking, or narrowing, of steel specimen at failure.

is actually distributed over a smaller area.[6] If the rupture area is measured after failure occurs, and divided into the rupture load, the result is a truer

[6] For reasons that are explained in Art. 12–4, the actual failure is caused by shear, resulting in the cuplike rupture shown.

value of the actual failure stress. Although this is considerably higher than the ultimate strength, the ultimate strength is commonly taken as the maximum stress of the material.

Working Stress and Factor of Safety. The working stress is defined as the actual stress the material has when under load. It is almost synonymous with *allowable stress*, which is the maximum safe stress a material may carry. In actual design, the allowable stress S_w should be limited to values not exceeding the proportional limit so as not to invalidate the stress-strain relation of Hooke's law on which all subsequent theory is based. However, since the proportional limit is difficult to determine accurately, it is customary to base the allowable stress on either the yield point or the ultimate strength, divided by a suitable number N, called the factor of safety:

$$S_w = \frac{S_{y.p.}}{N} \quad \text{or} \quad S_w = \frac{S_{ult}}{N} \tag{1-4}$$

The yield point is selected as the basis for determining S_w in structural steel because it is the stress at which a prohibitively large permanent set may occur. For other materials, the allowable stress is usually based on the ultimate strength.

Many factors must be considered in selecting the allowable stress. This selection should not be made by the novice, as will become apparent in a moment; usually the allowable stress is set by a group of experienced engineers and embodied in various building codes and specifications. A short discussion of the factors governing the selection of an allowable stress starts with the observation that in many materials the proportional limit is about one-half the ultimate strength. To avoid accidental overloading, an allowable stress of one-half the proportional limit is usually specified for dead loads gradually applied. The term dead loads generally refers to the weight of the structure, or to loads which, once applied, are not removed. An allowable stress set in this way corresponds to a factor of safety of 4, and is recommended for materials that are known to be quite uniform and homogeneous. For other materials, like wood, in which unpredictable non-uniformities (such as knot holes) may occur, larger factors of safety are desirable. The dynamic effect of suddenly applied loads also requires higher factors of safety. As a rule, factors of safety are not directly specified; rather, allowable stresses are set for different materials under different conditions of use, and these stresses are used by the designer.

1-6. Hooke's Law

Let us return now to a consideration of the straight-line portion of the stress-strain diagram in Fig. 1-9. The slope of that line is the ratio of stress to strain. It is called the *modulus of elasticity* and is denoted by *E:*

$$\text{Slope of stress-strain curve} = E = \frac{S}{\epsilon}$$

which is usually written in the form

$$S = E\epsilon \tag{1-5}$$

In this form it is known as Hooke's law. Originally Hooke's law specified merely that stress was proportional to strain, but Thomas Young in 1807 introduced a constant of proportionality that came to be known as Young's modulus. Eventually this name was superseded by the phrase *modulus of elasticity*, which conveys the impression that it is a measure of the elastic properties of the material, although it actually is a measure of the stiffness. A better choice would have been modulus of stiffness.

A convenient variation of Hooke's law is obtained by replacing S by its equivalent $\frac{P}{A}$ and replacing ϵ by $\frac{\delta}{L}$, so that Eq. (1–5) becomes

$$\frac{P}{A} = E\frac{\delta}{L}$$

or

$$\delta = \frac{PL}{AE} = \frac{SL}{E} \tag{1-6}$$

Eq. (1–6) expresses the relation among the total deformation δ, the applied load P, the length L, the cross-sectional area A, and the modulus of elasticity E. The unit of deformation δ has the same unit as length L, since the units of S and E, being equivalent, cancel out of the equation. Note that Eq. (1–6) is subject to all the restrictions previously discussed in connection with the equations it combines. For convenience, let us restate these restrictions:

1. The load must be axial.
2. The bar must have a constant cross-section and be homogeneous.
3. The stress must not exceed the proportional limit.

Shearing Deformation. Shearing forces cause a shearing deformation, just as axial forces cause elongations, but with an important difference. An element subject to tension undergoes an increase in length; an element subject to shear does not change the length of its sides, but undergoes a change in shape from a rectangle to a parallelogram, as shown in Fig. 1–12.

The action may be visualized for the present as equivalent to the infinitesimal sliding of infinitely thin layers past each

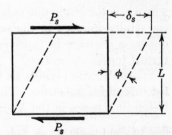

Fig. 1–12. — Shear deformation.

other, thereby resulting in the total shearing deformation δ_s in the length L. The actual action is more complex than that pictured and will be discussed more fully in Art. 9–9.

The shearing strain γ is given by

$$\gamma = \frac{\delta_s}{L} \tag{1-7}$$

and the relation between shearing stress and shearing strain, assuming Hooke's law to apply to shear, is

$$S_s = G\gamma \tag{1-8}$$

in which G represents the modulus of elasticity in shear, more commonly called the *modulus of rigidity*. The relation between the shearing deformation and applied shearing forces is expressed by

$$\delta_s = \frac{P_s L}{A_s G} \tag{1-9}$$

in which P_s is the shearing force acting over the shearing area A_s.

Sometimes the shearing strain is expressed as the angular change between perpendicular elements. Then from Fig. 1–12,

$$\tan \varphi = \frac{\delta_s}{L} = \gamma$$

from which, if φ is small as it usually is, the angular change between perpendicular elements is measured by γ expressed in radians.

Poisson's Ratio. Another type of elastic deformation is the change in transverse dimensions accompanying axial tension or compression. Experiments show that if a bar is lengthened by axial tension, there is a reduction in the transverse dimensions. Poisson showed in 1811 that the ratio of the *unit* deformations or strains in these directions is constant for stresses within the proportional limit. Accordingly this ratio is named after him; it is denoted by μ and defined by

$$\mu = -\frac{\epsilon_y}{\epsilon_x} = -\frac{\epsilon_z}{\epsilon_x} \tag{1-10}$$

where ϵ_x is the strain due only to stress in the X direction, and ϵ_y and ϵ_z are the strains induced in the perpendicular directions. The minus sign indicates a decrease in transverse dimensions when ϵ_x is positive, as in the case of tensile elongation.

Poisson's ratio permits us to extend Hooke's law for uniaxial stress to the case of biaxial stress. Thus, if an element is subjected simultaneously to tensile stresses in the X and Y directions, the strain in the X direction due to the tensile stress S_x is $\frac{S_x}{E}$. Simultaneously the tensile stress S_y will produce lateral contraction in the X direction of the amount $\mu \dfrac{S_y}{E}$, so the resultant unit deformation or strain in the X direction will be

$$\epsilon_x = \frac{S_x}{E} - \mu \frac{S_y}{E} \tag{1-11}$$

Similarly the total strain in the Y direction is

$$\epsilon_y = \frac{S_y}{E} - \mu \frac{S_x}{E} \tag{1-12}$$

If desired, Eqs. (1–11) and (1–12) can be solved to express the stresses in terms of the strains as follows:

$$S_x = \frac{(\epsilon_x + \mu\epsilon_y)\,E}{1 - \mu^2}; \quad S_y = \frac{(\epsilon_y + \mu\epsilon_x)\,E}{1 - \mu^2} \tag{1-13}$$

A further extension of the above discussion results in the following expressions for strains caused by simultaneous action of triaxial tensile stresses:

$$\left.\begin{aligned}
\epsilon_x &= \frac{1}{E}\,[S_x - \mu\,(S_y + S_z)] \\[4pt]
\epsilon_y &= \frac{1}{E}\,[S_y - \mu\,(S_z + S_x)] \\[4pt]
\epsilon_z &= \frac{1}{E}\,[S_z - \mu\,(S_x + S_y)]
\end{aligned}\right\} \tag{1-14}$$

All the above equations are valid for compressive effects also; it is only necessary to assign positive signs to elongations and tensile stresses, and, conversely, negative signs to contractions and compressive stresses.

An important relation[7] between the constants E, G, and μ for a given material is expressed by

$$G = \frac{E}{2(1 + \mu)} \tag{1-15}$$

which is useful for computing values of μ when E and G have been determined. Common values of Poisson's ratio are 0.25 to 0.30 for steel, approximately 0.33 for most other metals, and from $\frac{1}{8}$ to $\frac{1}{12}$ for concrete.

ILLUSTRATIVE PROBLEMS

115. Compute the total elongation caused by an axial load of 10,000 lb applied to a flat bar $\frac{1}{2}$ in. thick, tapering from a width of 3 in. to 1 in. in a length of 30 ft, as shown in Fig. 1–13. Assume $E = 30 \times 10^6$ psi.

Solution: Since the cross-sectional area is not constant, Eq. (1–6) does not apply directly. However, it may be used to find the elongation in a differential length for

[7] This relation is proved in Art. 9–11.

which the cross-sectional area is constant. Then the total elongation is the sum of these infinitesimal elongations.

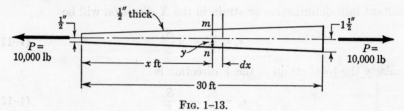

FIG. 1–13.

At section m–n, distant x ft from the small end, the half width y is found from geometry to be

$$y = \frac{1}{2} + \frac{x}{30}$$

and the area at that section is

$$A = \frac{1}{2}(2y) = \left(\frac{1}{2} + \frac{x}{30}\right) \text{ sq in.}$$

At section m–n, in a differential length dx, the elongation may be found from Eq. (1–6).

$$\left[\delta = \frac{PL}{AE}\right] \qquad d\delta = \frac{10,000\,dx}{\left(\frac{1}{2} + \frac{x}{30}\right)(30 \times 10^6)} = 10^{-2} \cdot \frac{dx}{15 + x}$$

from which the total elongation is

$$\delta = 10^{-2} \int_0^{30} \frac{dx}{15 + x} = 10^{-2}\Big[\log_e(15 + x)\Big]_0^{30}$$

$$= 10^{-2} \log_e \frac{45}{15} = 0.010986 \text{ ft} \approx 0.011 \text{ ft} \quad Ans.$$

116. Two steel bars AB and BC support a load $P = 6000$ lb, as shown in Fig. 1–14a. Area of AB is $\frac{1}{2}$ sq in.; area of BC is $\frac{3}{4}$ sq in. If $E = 30 \times 10^6$ psi, compute the horizontal and vertical components of the movement of B.

Solution: We begin by computing the deformations produced in each bar by P. From statics, we obtain $P_{AB} = 10,000$ lb T and $P_{BC} = 8000$ lb C. The corresponding deformations are

$$\left[\delta = \frac{PL}{AE}\right] \qquad \delta_{AB} = \frac{10,000(15)}{\frac{1}{2}(30 \times 10^6)} = 0.010 \text{ ft lengthening}$$

$$\delta_{BC} = \frac{8000(12)}{\frac{3}{4}(30 \times 10^6)} = 0.00427 \text{ ft shortening}$$

To analyze the effect of these deformations on the movement of B, imagine first that bars AB and BC are disconnected at B so that they undergo the defor-

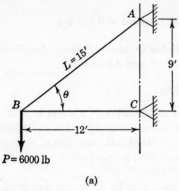

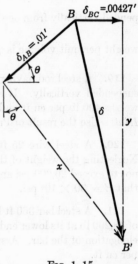

(a)   (b)

FIG. 1–14.

mations pictured (greatly exaggerated) in Fig. 1–14*b*. To refasten the bars, rotate them about *A* and *C* to meet at *B″*. However, the arcs generated in these rotations are so small that they may be effectively replaced by straight lines drawn perpendicular to *AB* and *BC* respectively; these lines, intersecting at *B′*, determine the effective final position of *B*. The deformations δ_{AB} and δ_{BC} are drawn to a larger scale in Fig. 1–15, in which the total movement of *B* is the vector *BB′* or δ directed as shown.

From Fig. 1–15 it is evident that the horizontal component of δ is

$$\delta_h = \delta_{BC} = 0.00427 \text{ ft rightward} \quad Ans.$$

However, δ_h is also equal to the algebraic sum of the horizontal components of δ_{AB} and the unknown length *x*, so that

$$\delta_h = (x)\sin\theta - (\delta_{AB})\cos\theta$$

from which

$$0.00427 = x\left(\tfrac{3}{5}\right) - 0.01\left(\tfrac{4}{5}\right), \qquad x = 0.0204 \text{ ft}$$

FIG. 1–15.

This value of *x* is used to determine δ_v, which is the sum of the vertical components of δ_{AB} and *x*:

$$\delta_v = \delta_{AB}\sin\theta + x\cos\theta$$
$$= 0.01\left(\tfrac{3}{5}\right) + 0.0204\left(\tfrac{4}{5}\right) = 0.0223 \text{ ft down.} \quad Ans.$$

If we return to Fig. 1–14*b*, we may now compute the magnitude of the angles through which bars *AB* and *BC* rotate. We obtain

$$\left[\theta = \frac{s}{r}\right] \qquad \alpha_{AB} = \frac{x}{L_{AB}} = \frac{0.0204}{15} = 0.00136 \text{ radians} = 0.078 \text{ deg}$$

and

$$\alpha_{BC} = \frac{y}{L_{BC}} = \frac{0.0223}{12} = 0.00186 \text{ radians} = 0.107 \text{ deg}$$

These rotations are so small that it is justifiable to assume that the directions of δ_{AB} and δ_{BC} coincide with the original directions of bars AB and BC.

PROBLEMS

117. During a stress-strain test, the unit deformation at a stress of 5000 psi was observed to be 0.000167 in. per in. and at a stress of 20,000 psi it was 0.000667 in. per in. If the proportional limit is 30,000 psi, what is the modulus of elasticity? What is the stress corresponding to a strain of 0.0002 in. per in.? Would these results be valid if the proportional limit were 18,000 psi? Why?

$Ans.$ $E = 30 \times 10^6$ psi; $S = 6000$ psi

118. A uniform bar of length L, cross-sectional area A, and weight W is suspended vertically from one end. Show that its total elongation is $\delta = \dfrac{WL}{2\,AE}$. If its weight per unit volume is γ, show also that $\delta = \dfrac{\gamma L^2}{2\,E}$.

119. A steel rod having a cross-sectional area of 1 sq in. and a length of 400 ft is suspended vertically. It supports a load of 5000 lb at the lower end. If steel weighs 490 lb per cu ft and $E = 30 \times 10^6$ psi, find the total elongation in the rod. *Hint:* Use the result of Prob. 118. $Ans.$ $\delta = 0.909$ in.

120. A steel wire 25 ft long, hanging vertically, supports a load of 1000 lb. Neglecting the weight of the wire, determine the required diameter if the stress is not to exceed 20,000 psi and the total elongation is not to exceed 0.18 in. Assume that $E = 30 \times 10^6$ psi. $Ans.$ $d = 0.266$ in.

121. A steel bar 360 ft long, suspended vertically from one end, supports a load of 48,200 lb at its lower end. If the maximum stress is 6020 psi, determine the total elongation of the bar. Assume that $E = 30 \times 10^6$ psi and that steel weighs 480 lb per cu ft. $Ans.$ $\delta = 0.781$ in.

122. An aluminum bar having a cross-sectional area of $\frac{1}{4}$ sq in. carries the axial loads applied at the positions shown. If $E = 10 \times 10^6$ psi, compute the total deformation of the bar. $Ans.$ $\delta = 0.0192$ in.

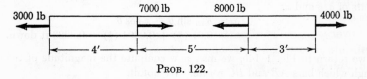

PROB. 122.

123. A rigid bar hinged at A and supported by a steel rod at B carries a load of 6000 lb at C. Using the data shown, compute the vertical displacement of the end C.

124. A uniform concrete slab of total weight W is to be attached as shown to two rods whose lower ends are on the same level. Determine the ratio of the areas of the rods so that the slab will remain level.   *Ans.* $\dfrac{A_a}{A_s} = 9$

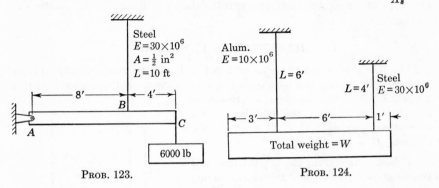

PROB. 123.   PROB. 124.

125. A round bar of length L tapers uniformly from a diameter D at one end to a smaller diameter d at the other. Determine the elongation caused by an axial tensile load P.   *Ans.* $\delta = \dfrac{4\,PL}{\pi EDd}$

126. Two aluminum rods AB and BC hinged to rigid supports are pinned together at B to carry a vertical load $P = 6000$ lb. Assume $\alpha = \theta = 30°$. If each rod has a cross-sectional area of 0.6 sq in. and $E = 10 \times 10^6$ psi, compute (*a*) the elongation of each rod and (*b*) the horizontal and vertical displacements of point B.

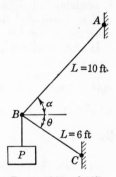

Ans. (*b*) $\delta_h = 0.0023$ ft; $\delta_v = 0.016$ ft

127. Solve Prob. 126 if rod BC is of steel with $E = 30 \times 10^6$ psi. Assume $\alpha = 45°$ and $\theta = 30°$; all other data remain unchanged.

Ans. (*b*) $\delta_h = 0.00358$ ft; $\delta_v = 0.00913$ ft

PROB. 126 and 127.

1–7. Statically Indeterminate Members

There are certain combinations of axially loaded members in which the equations of static equilibrium are not sufficient for a solution. This condition exists in structures where the reactive forces or the internal resisting forces over a cross-section exceed the number of independent equations of equilibrium. Such cases are called *statically indeterminate* and require the use of additional relations which depend upon the elastic deformations in the members. The cases are so varied that they can best be described by sample problems illustrating the following general principles:

1. To a free-body diagram of the structure, or a part of it, apply the equations of static equilibrium.

2. If there are more unknowns than independent equations of equilibrium, obtain additional equations from the geometric relations between the elastic deformations produced by the loads. To define these relations clearly, draw a sketch that exaggerates the magnitudes of the elastic deformations.

ILLUSTRATIVE PROBLEMS

128. The short concrete post shown in Fig. 1–16 is reinforced axially with six symmetrically placed steel bars, each 1 sq in. in section. If the applied load P is 228,000 lb, compute the stress developed in each material. Assume the following moduli of elasticity: for steel, $E_s = 30 \times 10^6$ psi; for concrete, $E_c = 2 \times 10^6$ psi.

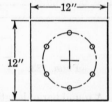

Solution: As shown, the applied load and the resisting forces on any transverse section m–n form a collinear force system. From statics, we have

$$[\Sigma F = 0] \qquad P_s + P_c = 228,000 \qquad (a)$$

Since no other equation of static equilibrium is available to indicate in what proportion the load is distributed to each material, we consider the elastic deformation of the structure. It is evident that the bearing plate causes the steel and concrete to deform equally. Hence, applying $\delta = \dfrac{SL}{E}$ to these equal deformations, we obtain

$$[\delta_s = \delta_c] \qquad \left(\frac{SL}{E}\right)_s = \left(\frac{SL}{E}\right)_c$$

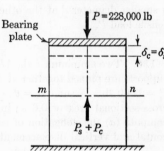

Fig. 1–16. — Reinforced concrete post.

from which, by canceling out the equal lengths of steel and concrete and substituting the moduli of elasticity, we have the following relation between the stresses:

$$S_s = \frac{E_s}{E_c} S_c = \frac{30}{2} S_c = 15 \, S_c \qquad (b)$$

Eq. (b) may be called the governing equation for stress. Note that it depends only upon the fact that both materials deform equally. This stress relation is independent of the loads or areas, and remains valid provided the proportional limit of either material is not exceeded.

We may now use $P = AS$ to rewrite Eq. (a):

$$6 \, S_s + (144 - 6)S_c = 228,000$$

whence, replacing S_s by $15 \, S_c$ as defined in Eq. (b), we obtain

$$6(15\,S_c) + 138\,S_c = 228{,}000$$
$$S_c = 1000\,\text{psi} \quad Ans.$$

and from Eq. (*b*)

$$S_s = 15\,S_c = 15{,}000\,\text{psi.} \quad Ans.$$

129. In the preceding problem, assume the allowable stresses to be $S_s \leq 18{,}000$ psi and $S_c \leq 800$ psi. Compute the maximum safe axial load P that may be applied.

Solution: The unwary student may substitute the allowable stresses only in the equation of static equilibrium. This is wrong, for it does not consider the equal deformations in the materials. From Eq. (*b*) of the preceding problem, we saw that equal deformations produce the following governing relation between the stresses:

$$S_s = 15\,S_c$$

From this relation we observe that if the concrete is stressed to its limit of 800 psi, the corresponding stress in the steel is

$$S_s = 15(800) = 12{,}000\,\text{psi}$$

In other words, the steel could not be stressed to its limit of 18,000 psi without over-stressing the concrete. The actual working stresses are thereby determined to be $S_c = 800$ psi and $S_s = 12{,}000$ psi. These values are substituted in the equation of static equilibrium

$$[\Sigma F = 0] \quad P = P_s + P_c = A_s S_s + A_c S_c$$
$$= 6(12{,}000) + (144 - 6)(800)$$
$$P = 182{,}400\,\text{lb} \quad Ans.$$

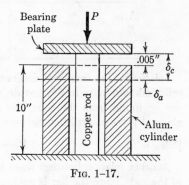

130. A copper rod is inserted into a hollow aluminum cylinder. The copper rod projects 0.005 in., as shown in Fig. 1–17. What maximum load P may be applied to the bearing plate? Use the data in the following table:

Fig. 1–17.

	Copper	Aluminum
Area	2 sq in.	3 sq in.
E	17×10^6 psi	10×10^6 psi
Allowable stress	20,000 psi	10,000 psi

Solution: To find a relation between the stresses, consider the elastic deformations shown exaggerated in Fig. 1–17. We obtain

$$[\delta_c = \delta_a + 0.005] \qquad \left(\frac{SL}{E}\right)_c = \left(\frac{SL}{E}\right)_a + 0.005$$

$$\frac{S_c(10)}{17 \times 10^6} = \frac{S_a(10)}{10 \times 10^6} + 0.005$$

from which

$$S_c = 1.7\, S_a + 8500 \qquad\qquad (a)$$

Eq. (a) is the governing relation between the stresses. It is evident that using $S_a = 10,000$ psi overstresses the copper to 25,500 psi. Therefore copper governs, and the corresponding stress in the aluminum is determined from Eq. (a) to be

$$20,000 = 1.7\, S_a + 8500, \qquad\qquad S_a = 6770 \text{ psi}$$

The total safe load is given by

$$P = P_c + P_a = A_c S_c + A_a S_a$$

whence, substituting the working stresses just determined, we obtain

$$P = 2(20,000) + 3(6770) = 60,300 \text{ lb } Ans.$$

131. A horizontal bar of negligible weight, hinged at A in Fig. 1–18 (a) and assumed rigid, is supported by a bronze rod 8 ft long and a steel rod 3 ft long. Using the data in the following table, compute the stress in each rod.

	Steel	Bronze
Area	1 sq in.	$\frac{1}{2}$ sq in.
E	30×10^6 psi	12×10^6 psi
Proportional limit	35,000 psi	20,000 psi

Solution: The free-body diagram of the bar in Fig. 1–18(b) shows it to be statically indeterminate to the first degree; i.e., there is one more unknown force than can be found from the equations of static equilibrium. A moment summation about A gives one relation between the loads in the rods:

$$[\Sigma M_A = 0] \qquad\qquad 3\,P_s + 8\,P_b = 12(12,000) \qquad\qquad (a)$$

Another relation between these loads is obtained from the elastic deformations of the rods, since the bar is assumed rigid. From the similar triangles formed in Fig. 1–18(b) we obtain

$$\frac{\delta_s}{3} = \frac{\delta_b}{8} \quad \text{or} \quad \frac{1}{3}\left(\frac{PL}{AE}\right)_s = \frac{1}{8}\left(\frac{PL}{AE}\right)_b$$

$$\frac{1}{3} \times \frac{P_s(3)}{(1)(30)} = \frac{1}{8} \times \frac{P_b(8)}{(\frac{1}{2})(12)}$$

whence

$$P_s = 5\,P_b \qquad\qquad (b)$$

Note that the lengths need not be expressed in inches, since a conversion factor of 12 will merely cancel out of the equation. Similarly the factor 10^6 in the modulus of elasticity is omitted.

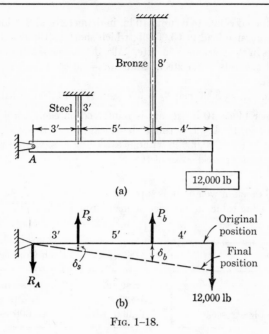

Fig. 1–18.

Solving equations (*a*) and (*b*), we obtain

$$P_s = 31{,}350 \text{ lb}$$
$$P_b = 6270 \text{ lb}$$

Computing the stresses, we apply

$$\left[S = \frac{P}{A} \right]$$

$$S_s = \frac{31{,}350}{1} = 31{,}350 \text{ psi} \quad Ans.$$

$$S_b = \frac{6270}{\frac{1}{2}} = 12{,}540 \text{ psi} \quad Ans.$$

Since both stresses are less than the proportional limits, the answers may be accepted. If the steel stress, for example, had exceeded the proportional limit, the results would not have been valid and a redesign would be required. Perhaps the simplest redesign would be to increase the length of the steel rod, thus making it less rigid. It may be noted here that generally the most rigid parts of an indeterminate structure carry the most load. This is a fundamental principle in the theory of indeterminate structures and is known as the *principle of rigidities*.[8]

PROBLEMS

132. A cast-iron bar 2 in. in diameter and 5 ft long is surrounded by a shell of structural steel 0.25 in. thick. Compute the load that will stretch the combined bar a total of 0.02 in. in the length of 5 ft.   *Ans. P* = 33,300 lb

[8] See Parcel and Maney, *Statically Indeterminate Stresses*, Wiley, 2nd ed., p. 109.

133. A reinforced concrete column 10 in. in diameter and 8 ft long is subjected to an axial compressive load of 60,000 lb, which shortens the column by 0.016 in. Find the stresses in the steel and concrete. Also determine the cross-sectional areas of the steel and concrete. For steel, assume $E = 30 \times 10^6$ psi, and for concrete, $E = 3 \times 10^6$ psi.

Ans. $S_s = 5000$ psi; $S_c = 500$ psi; $A_s = 4.62$ sq in.; $A_c = 73.9$ sq in.

134. A timber block 10 in. square is reinforced on each side by a steel plate 10 in. wide and t in. thick. Determine the thickness t of the steel plates so as to support an axial load of 200,000 lb without exceeding a maximum timber stress of 600 psi, and a maximum steel stress of 16,000 psi. E for timber is 1.5×10^6 psi and for steel it is 30×10^6 psi.   Ans. $t = 0.292$ in.

135. A rigid block of weight W is supported by three rods as shown. Using the data in the following table, determine the maximum safe load W.

Ans. $W = 56,700$ lb

	Steel	Each Copper Rod
Area	2 sq in.	1.5 sq in.
E	30×10^6 psi	15×10^6 psi
Allowable stresses	16,000 psi	10,000 psi

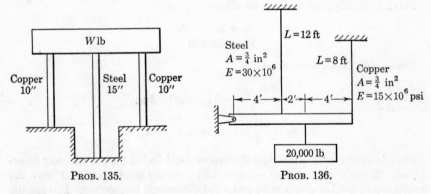

PROB. 135.   PROB. 136.

136. A rigid beam is hinged at one end and supported by two rods, as shown. Compute the stress produced in each rod by a load of 20,000 lb.

137. Three steel eyebars, each 30 ft long, are to be assembled side by side by passing rigid bolts through holes drilled in their ends. If the middle bar is 0.03 in. shorter than the outer bars, what will be the load in each bar after assembly? Each bar is 6 sq in. in area and $E = 30 \times 10^6$ psi.

Ans.   Load in middle bar $= 10,000$ lb

138. Three steel wires, each 0.03 sq in. in area, are used to lift a load of $W = 1200$ lb. Their unstressed lengths are 59.98 ft, 59.99 ft, and 60.00 ft. (a) What stress exists in the longest wire? E = 30×10^6 psi. (b) Determine the stress in the shortest wire if W = 390 lb.

Ans. (a) S = 8330 psi; (b) S = 9000 psi

139. A copper bar is mounted between a bronze bar and a steel bar, as shown. Each bar is 2 in. wide and of the thickness indicated. Compute the safe load P and its location d from the left edge of the assembly if the maximum allowable stresses are S_s = 18,000 psi, S_c = 16,000 psi, and S_b = 12,000 psi. What elongation is produced in a length of 12 ft? Assume E_s = 30×10^6 psi, E_c = 17×10^6 psi, and E_b = 12×10^6 psi, and that the bolts do not bend or otherwise deform.

Ans. P = 45,600 lb, d = 1.18 in.

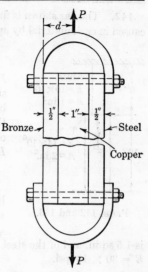

PROB. 138.

PROB. 139.

140. A homogeneous rod of constant cross-section is attached to unyielding supports. It carries an axial load P applied as shown. Prove that the reactions are given by $R_1 = \dfrac{Pb}{L}$ and $R_2 = \dfrac{Pa}{L}$.

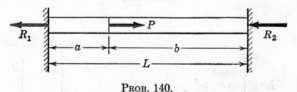

PROB. 140.

141. A homogeneous bar with a cross-sectional area of $\frac{3}{4}$ sq in. is attached to rigid supports. It carries the axial loads P_1 = 5400 lb and P_2 = 4500 lb applied

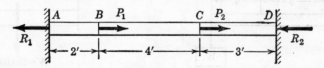

PROB. 141.

as shown. Determine the stress in the segment BC. *Hint:* Use the results of Prob. 140 and compute the reactions caused by P_1 and P_2 acting separately. Use the principle of superposition to compute the reactions when both loads are applied.

142. The bar shown is firmly attached to unyielding supports. Find the stress caused in each material by applying an axial load $P = 24,000$ lb.

Ans. $S_a = 8960$ psi; $S_b = 7520$ psi

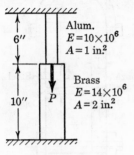

6″

Alum.
$E = 10 \times 10^6$
$A = 1$ in.^{2}

10″　P

Brass
$E = 14 \times 10^6$
$A = 2$ in.^{2}

PROB. 142 and 143.

143. Referring to Prob. 142, what maximum load P may be applied without exceeding an allowable stress of 10,000 psi for aluminum or 14,000 psi for brass? Can a larger load P be carried if the length of the aluminum rod is increased while keeping the length of the brass rod constant? If so, to what value should L_a be changed?

Ans. (a) $P = 26,800$ lb; (b) $L_a = 10$ in.

144. In the assembly of the bronze tube and steel bolt shown, what stresses are caused by $\frac{3}{4}$ of a turn of the nut if $L = 40$ in., the pitch of the bolt thread $p = \frac{1}{16}$ in., and the cross-sectional area of the bronze tube is 1.5 sq in. and of the steel bolt $\frac{3}{4}$ sq in.? For bronze, $E = 12 \times 10^6$ psi; for steel, $E = 30 \times 10^6$ psi. *Ans.* $S_s = 15,600$ psi; $S_b = 7810$ psi

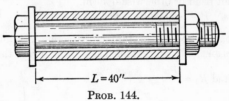

$\longleftarrow L = 40'' \longrightarrow$

PROB. 144.

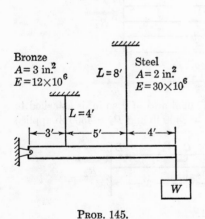

Bronze
$A = 3$ in.^{2}
$E = 12 \times 10^6$

$L = 8'$

Steel
$A = 2$ in.^{2}
$E = 30 \times 10^6$

$L = 4'$

$\leftarrow 3' \rightarrow \leftarrow 5' \rightarrow \leftarrow 4' \rightarrow$

W

PROB. 145.

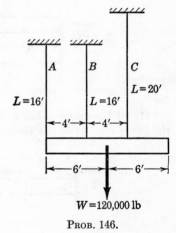

A　B　C

$L = 16'$　　$L = 16'$　　$L = 20'$

$\leftarrow 4' \rightarrow \leftarrow 4' \rightarrow$

$\leftarrow 6' \rightarrow \leftarrow 6' \rightarrow$

$W = 120,000$ lb

PROB. 146.

145. A rigid bar of negligible weight, hinged at one end, is supported by a bronze rod and a steel rod, as shown. What maximum load W may be applied without exceeding a stress in the bronze of 10,000 psi, and a stress in the steel of 18,000 psi? *Ans.* $W = 28,050$ lb

146. The figure represents a section through a balcony. The total uniform floor load of 120,000 lb is supported by three structural steel rods A, B, and C, each 2 sq in. in area. Compute the stress in each rod and its elongation. $E = 30 \times 10^6$ psi. Assume the floor to be rigid, but not necessarily to remain horizontal.

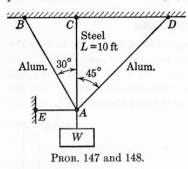

PROB. 147 and 148.

147. Three bars, AB, AC, and AD, are pinned together to support a weight $W = 4000$ lb. Horizontal movement is prevented at joint A by the short horizontal strut AE. Determine the stress in each bar and the force in the strut AE. For the steel bar, $A = 0.20$ sq in. and $E = 30 \times 10^6$ psi. For each aluminum bar, $A = 0.60$ sq in. and $E = 10 \times 10^6$ psi.

Ans. $S_{AC} = 10,000$ psi; $S_{AB} = 2500$ psi; $S_{AD} = 1670$ psi

148. Referring to the data in Prob. 147, determine the maximum value of W that will not exceed an aluminum stress of 5000 psi or a steel stress of 18,000 psi.

Ans. $W = 7200$ lb

1–8.   Thermal Stresses

It is well known that changes in temperature cause bodies to expand or contract, the amount of the linear deformation, δ_t, being expressed by the relation

$$\delta_t = \alpha L \, (\Delta T) \tag{1-16}$$

in which α is the coefficient of linear expansion, usually expressed in units of inches per inch per degree of temperature change, L is the length, and ΔT is the temperature change. Substituting these units in Eq. (1–16) shows the dimensional unit of δ_t to be the same as that of the length L.

If a temperature deformation is permitted to occur freely, as by the use of expansion joints, no load or stress will be induced in the structure. But in some cases it may not be feasible to permit these temperature deformations; the result is that internal forces are created which resist them. The stresses caused by these internal forces are known as *thermal stresses.*

A general procedure for computing the loads and stresses caused when temperature deformation is prevented is outlined in these steps:

1. Imagine the structure relieved of all applied loads and constraints so that temperature deformations can occur freely. Represent these deformations on a sketch, and exaggerate their effect.

2. Now imagine sufficient loads applied to the structure to restore it to the specified conditions of restraint. Represent these loads and corresponding load deformations on the sketch for step 1.

3. The geometric relations between the temperature and load deforma-

tions on the sketch give equations which, together with the equations of static equilibrium, may be solved for all unknown quantities.

The following examples illustrate these steps applied in several different types of problems.

ILLUSTRATIVE PROBLEMS

149. A steel rod 100 in. long is secured between two walls. If the load on the rod is zero at 70° F., compute the stress when the temperature drops to 0° F. Assume the cross-sectional area to be 2 sq in., $\alpha = 6.5 \times 10^{-6}$ in./in./° F., and $E = 30 \times 10^6$ psi. Solve, assuming (a) that the walls are rigid and (b) that the walls spring together a total distance of 0.02 in. as the temperature drops.

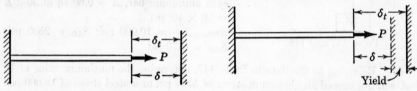

FIG. 1–19.—Rigid walls.   FIG. 1–20.—Nonrigid walls.

Solution: Part a. Imagine the rod disconnected from the right wall. Temperature deformations can then freely occur. A temperature drop causes the contraction represented by δ_t in Fig. 1–19. To reattach the rod to the wall will evidently require a pull P to produce the load deformation δ. From the sketch of deformations, we see that $\delta_t = \delta$, or, in equivalent terms,

$$\alpha L(\Delta T) = \frac{PL}{AE} = \frac{SL}{E}$$

whence

$$S = E\alpha(\Delta T) = (30 \times 10^6)(6.5 \times 10^{-6})(70) = 13,650 \text{ psi}$$

Note that L cancels out of the equation, indicating that the stress is independent of the length.

Part b. When the walls spring together, Fig. 1–20 shows that the free temperature contraction is equal to the sum of the load deformation and the yield of the walls. Hence

$$\delta_t = \delta + \text{yield}$$

whence, replacing the deformations by equivalent terms, we obtain

$$\alpha L(\Delta T) = \frac{SL}{E} + \text{yield}$$

or

$$(6.5 \times 10^{-6})(100)(70) = \frac{S(100)}{30 \times 10^6} + 0.02$$

Multiplying by $(10)^6$ and rearranging terms gives

$$S = 13,650 - 6000 = 7650 \text{ psi}$$

Notice that the yield of the walls reduces the stress considerably, and also that the length does not cancel out as in part *a*.

150. A rigid block weighing 12,000 lb is supported by three rods symmetrically placed, as shown in Fig. 1–21. Assuming the block to remain horizontal, determine the stress in each rod after a temperature rise of 100° F. The lower ends of the rods are assumed to have been at the same level before the block was attached and the temperature changed. Use the data in the following table:

	Each Steel Rod	Bronze Rod
Area	$\frac{3}{4}$ sq in.	1.5 sq in.
E	30×10^6 psi	12×10^6 psi
α	6.5×10^{-6}	10×10^{-6}

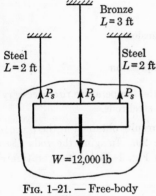

Fig. 1–21. — Free-body diagram.

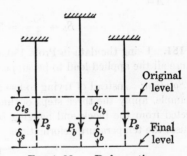

Fig. 1–22. — Deformations.

Solution: With the load detached, the original lower position of the rods is as shown in Fig. 1–22. With the rods free of any constraint, a temperature rise will cause the temperature deformations δ_{t_s} and δ_{t_b} in the steel and bronze respectively. When the rods are attached to the rigid block after the temperature change has occurred, assume their final horizontal level to be as shown. To attach them to the block, it will be necessary to pull their expanded ends through the load deformations δ_s and δ_b by means of the loads P_s and P_b in the steel and bronze respectively. The free-body diagram of the block in Fig. 1–21 represents the equal and opposite effects of the forces exerted by the rods upon the block.

From the deformations shown in Fig. 1–22, we obtain the following geometric relation between the deformations:

$$\delta_{t_s} + \delta_s = \delta_{t_b} + \delta_b$$

or

$$(\alpha L \,\Delta T)_s + \left(\frac{PL}{AE}\right)_s = (\alpha L \,\Delta T)_b + \left(\frac{PL}{AE}\right)_b$$

whence, substituting the given data, we have

$$(6.5 \times 10^{-6})(2)(100) + \frac{P_s(2)}{\frac{3}{4}(30 \times 10^6)} = (10 \times 10^{-6})(3)(100) + \frac{P_b(3)}{1.5(12 \times 10^6)}$$

Multiplying this equation by 10^6 and rearranging terms, we obtain

$$\frac{8}{90} P_s - \frac{1}{6} P_b = 1700 \qquad (a)$$

Another relation between P_s and P_b is obtained from the free-body diagram in Fig. 1–21.

$[\Sigma Y = 0]$ $\qquad\qquad\qquad 2\,P_s + P_b = 12{,}000 \qquad (b)$

Solving Eqs. (a) and (b) yields

$$P_s = 8760 \text{ lb}$$
$$P_b = -5520 \text{ lb}$$

The negative sign for P_b means that the load P_b acts oppositely to that assumed; i.e., the bronze rod is actually in compression and suitable provision must be made to prevent buckling.

The stresses are

$\left[S = \dfrac{P}{A} \right]$ $\qquad\qquad S_s = \dfrac{8760}{\frac{3}{4}} = 11{,}680 \text{ psi tension}$

$\qquad\qquad\qquad\qquad S_b = \dfrac{5520}{1.5} = 3680 \text{ psi compression}$

151. Using the data in Prob. 150, determine the temperature rise necessary to cause all the applied load to be supported by the steel rods.

Solution: Instead of trying to use any of the results obtained in the preceding example, apply the three steps outlined on page 29. Imagine the rods disconnected from the block and hanging freely, as in Fig. 1–23. A temperature rise causes the temperature deformations δ_{t_s} and δ_{t_b}.

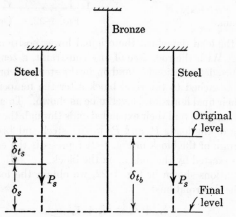

FIG. 1–23. — Bronze rod supporting no load.

Since the bronze rod is to carry no load, the final level of the steel rods must coincide with the unstressed expanded length of the bronze. If the rods are to be at the same final level, the steel rods must go through a load deformation δ_s caused by the pulls P_s, each of which must be 6000 lb to support the 12,000-lb weight of the block.

From Fig. 1–23, the geometric relation between the deformations is

$$\delta_{t_b} = \delta_{t_s} + \delta_s$$

or, with different symbols,

$$(\alpha L \,\Delta T)_b = (\alpha L \,\Delta T)_s + \left(\frac{PL}{AE}\right)_s$$

whence

$$(10 \times 10^{-6})(3)(\Delta T) = (6.5 \times 10^{-6})(2)(\Delta T) + \frac{6000(2)}{\frac{3}{4}(30 \times 10^6)}$$

$$\Delta T = 31.4° \text{ F.} \quad Ans.$$

It is evident that a greater temperature rise will cause the bronze to push against the rigid block, thereby causing compression of the bronze. This confirms the result obtained in Prob. 150, where the temperature rise was 100° F.

PROBLEMS

152. A steel wire with a cross-sectional area of 0.10 sq in. is stretched between two fixed points. The tensile load at 70° F. is 500 lb. What will be the stress intensity at 0° F.? For what temperature will the stress intensity be zero? Assume $\alpha = 6.5 \times 10^{-6}$ and $E = 30 \times 10^6$ psi.   *Ans. $S = 18,600$ psi; $T = 95.6°$ F.*

153. A steel rod is stretched between two rigid walls and carries a tensile load of 1000 lb at 70° F. If the allowable stress intensity is not to exceed 15,000 psi at 0° F., what must be the minimum diameter of the rod?   *Ans. $d = 0.972$ in.*

154. At a temperature of 220° F., a steel tire that is to be shrunk onto a locomotive driving wheel just fits over the wheel, which is at a temperature of 70° F. What stress exists in the tire after the assembly cools to 70° F.? Neglect the deformation of the wheel caused by the pressure of the tire. Assume $\alpha = 6.5 \times 10^{-6}$ and $E = 30 \times 10^6$ psi.

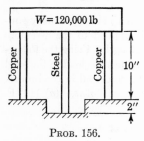

PROB. 156.

155. Steel railroad rails 30 ft long are laid with a clearance of $\frac{1}{8}$ in. at a temperature of 50° F. At what temperature will the ends of the rails just touch? What stress would be induced in the rails at that temperature if there had been no clearance? Assume $\alpha = 6.5 \times 10^{-6}$ and $E = 30 \times 10^6$ psi.

156. A rigid slab weighing 120,000 lb is supported by two copper rods and a steel rod, as shown. Using the data below, determine the temperature change so that all the load will be carried by the copper rods. Does the temperature rise or fall?   *Ans. $\Delta T = 133.3°$ F.*

	Steel	Each Copper Rod
Area	10 sq in.	20 sq in.
E	30×10^6 psi	15×10^6 psi
α	6.5×10^{-6}	9.3×10^{-6}

157. A rigid slab weighing 30,000 lb is supported as shown. Using the data below, determine the final stress in each rod if the temperature rises 200° F. after the load is applied.   *Ans.* $S_s = 1920$ psi compression; $S_c = 9360$ psi compression

	Steel	Copper (Each Rod)
Area	1 sq in.	1.5 sq in.
E	30×10^6 psi	15×10^6 psi
α	6.5×10^{-6}	9.3×10^{-6}

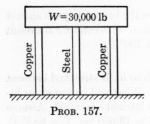

PROB. 157.

158. A bronze sleeve 40 in. long is slipped over a steel bolt, and the nut is turned just snug. The bolt threads have a pitch of $\frac{1}{16}$ in. Using the data below, determine (*a*) what temperature change will produce a tensile stress of 16,000 psi in the steel bolt, and (*b*) at that temperature, how many turns of the nut will completely relieve the stress in the bolt.

	Steel Bolt	Bronze Sleeve
Area	1 sq in.	2 sq in.
E	30×10^6 psi	10×10^6 psi
α	6.5×10^{-6}	10.5×10^{-6}

159. In Prob. 158, determine the stresses induced by a temperature rise of 100° F. Assume that there is no initial stress.

160. A steel cylinder is enclosed in a bronze sleeve; both simultaneously support a vertical compressive load of 80,000 lb which is applied to the assembly through a horizontal bearing plate. Each bar is equal in length. Using the following data, compute (*a*) the temperature change that will reduce the load in the steel to zero, and (*b*) the temperature change that will cause a zero load in the bronze.
Ans.   (*a*) 119° F.

	Bronze	Steel
Area	16 sq in.	6 sq in.
E	12×10^6 psi	30×10^6 psi
α	10×10^{-6}	6.5×10^{-6}

161. A bronze sleeve is slipped over a steel bolt and held in place by a nut that is turned just snug. Using the following data, compute the temperature rise to stress the bronze to 4000 psi.   *Ans.*   152.5° F.

	Steel	Bronze
Area	$\frac{1}{2}$ sq in.	$\frac{3}{4}$ sq in.
E	30×10^6 psi	12×10^6 psi
α	6.5×10^{-6}	10×10^{-6}

162. The nut of the assembly in Prob. 161 is twisted so as to produce an initial compressive stress of 2000 psi in the bronze sleeve. After a temperature rise of 100° F., determine the final stress in each material.

Ans. $S_s = 6940$ psi; $S_b = 4630$ psi

163. A rod is composed of the three segments shown. Using the data below, compute the stress induced in each material by a temperature drop of 100° F. if (*a*) the walls are rigid, and (*b*) the walls spring together by 0.01 in.

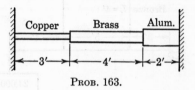

PROB. 163.

	Copper	Brass	Aluminum
Area	$\frac{1}{2}$ sq in.	$\frac{3}{4}$ sq in.	1 sq in.
E	17×10^6 psi	14×10^6 psi	10×10^6 psi
α	9.3×10^{-6}	10.4×10^{-6}	12.8×10^{-6}

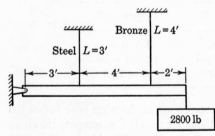

PROB. 164.

164. A rigid bar of negligible weight is supported and loaded as shown. Using the following data, determine what temperature change will relieve the steel rod of all load.

Ans. $\Delta T = 72.8°$ F.

	Steel	Bronze
Area	2 sq in.	3 sq in.
E	30×10^6 psi	12×10^6 psi
α	6.5×10^{-6}	10×10^{-6}

165. A rigid bar of negligible weight is supported and loaded as shown. Using the data below, determine the temperature change that will cause the bronze rod to have a final tensile stress of 6000 psi.   *Ans.* $\Delta T = 23.9°$ F. temperature drop

	Bronze	Steel
Area	3 sq in.	2 sq in.
E	12×10^6 psi	30×10^6 psi
α	10.5×10^{-6}	6.5×10^{-6}

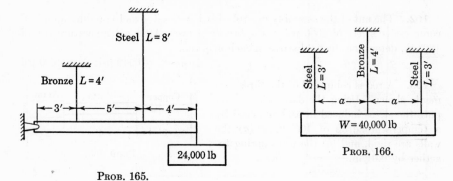

PROB. 165.

PROB. 166.

166. What temperature change acting on the system shown will change the load in the bronze bar to 10,000 lb tension? What are the stresses in each rod before the temperature changes? Use the data below.

Ans. $\Delta T = 35.1°$ F. temperature drop; $S_s = 16,330$ psi; $S_b = 4890$ psi

	Each Steel Rod	Bronze Rod
Area	1 sq in.	1.5 sq in.
E	30×10^6 psi	12×10^6 psi
α	6.5×10^{-6}	10×10^{-6}

167. The lower ends of the three rods shown are at the same level before the rigid block weighing 60,000 lb is applied. Using the data below, compute the stress in each bar if the temperature remains constant. *Hint:* The block does not remain horizontal.

	Steel	Copper	Bronze
Area	2 sq in.	4 sq in.	3 sq in.
E	30×10^6 psi	16×10^6 psi	12×10^6 psi
α	6.5×10^{-6}	9.3×10^{-6}	10.5×10^{-6}

168. In Prob. 167, determine the temperature change that will (*a*) relieve the copper rod of any stress, (*b*) cause a tensile load of 15,000 lb in the bronze rod.

169. In Prob. 145, if W = 24,000 lb, what temperature change will cause the bronze rod to have a final tensile stress of 6000 psi? For bronze, $\alpha = 10 \times 10^{-6}$; for steel, $\alpha = 6.5 \times 10^{-6}$.   *Ans.* $\Delta T = 26.2°$ F. drop

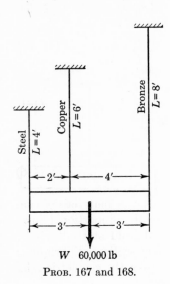

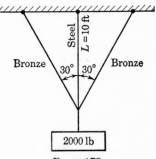

PROB. 170, 171, and 172.

170. The three short bars A, B, and C shown are each $\frac{1}{2}$ in. thick, but vary in width as indicated. They are equally compressed by a plate which is to remain horizontal. Using the data below, find the maximum amount and location of P that will not overstress any bar, yet produce a uniform (although different) stress in each bar.   *Ans.* P = 33,300 lb; e = 3.15 in.

W 60,000 lb

PROB. 167 and 168.

Bar	E (psi)	Allowable Stress (psi)	α
A	30×10^6	20,000	6×10^{-6}
B	10×10^6	10,000	8×10^{-6}
C	15×10^6	15,000	10×10^{-6}

171. In Prob. 170, compute the temperature change, location, and maximum value of P if bar C is to carry no load. The bearing plate is still to remain horizontal, and bars A and B are to have uniform stress.
Ans. $\Delta T = 167°$ F. drop; P = 16,700 lb; e = 1.5 in.

172. In Prob. 170, compute the temperature change, location, and maximum value of P if bar A is to carry no load. The bearing plate is to remain horizontal, and bars B and C are to have uniform stress.
Ans. $\Delta T = 250°$ F. rise; P = 25,000 lb; e = 4.8 in.

PROB. 173.

173. Three rods, each of $\frac{1}{2}$ sq in. area, jointly support the load of 2000 lb shown. Assuming there was no slack or stress in the rods before the load was applied, find (a) the stress in each rod and (b) the temperature change needed to reduce the stress in the bronze rods to zero. For steel, $E = 30 \times 10^6$ psi and $\alpha = 6.5 \times 10^{-6}$. For bronze, $E = 12 \times 10^6$ psi and $\alpha = 10 \times 10^{-6}$.

SUMMARY

Axial loads cause uniform stress distribution that is computed by

$$S = \frac{P}{A} \tag{1-1}$$

and elongations determined from

$$\delta = \frac{PL}{AE} \tag{1-6}$$

Remember that Eq. (1-6) is valid only for homogeneous materials of constant cross-section, axially loaded to stresses below the proportional limit.

Structures composed of two or more materials and statically indeterminate are solved by applying the equations of static equilibrium in combination with additional equations obtained from the geometric relations between the elastic deformations.

Thermal stresses are computed by determining the relations between the thermal deformations

$$\delta_t = \alpha L \, \Delta T \tag{1-16}$$

and the elastic deformations which are used, in combination with the equations of static equilibrium, to solve the various problems that may be encountered.

Chapter II

Riveted and Welded Joints

2–1. Thin-Walled Cylinders

Consider a thin-walled cylinder containing a fluid or gas subjected to a pressure of p psi. This pressure, acting normal to the inside surface, tends to rupture the container in the following way. Let Fig. 2–1a represent the

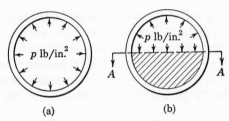

(a)   (b)

FIG. 2–1.

end view of a transverse section through a thin-walled cylinder. The internal pressure distribution on this cylinder is duplicated in Fig. 2–1b, where the cylinder is half full of a fluid. Since a fluid transmits pressure equally in all directions, the lower half of the cylinder in Fig. 2–1b is subject to the same pressure distribution that is shown in Fig. 2–1a.

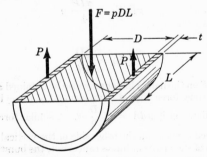

FIG. 2–2.

A free-body diagram of the lower half of the cylinder formed by the cutting plane $A–A$ is shown in Fig. 2–2. It is apparent that the total force F acting on the flat surface of the fluid is resisted by the equal forces P acting on each cut surface of the cylinder wall. Applying a vertical summation of

39

these forces, and noting that F equals the pressure intensity p multiplied by the area DL over which it acts, we obtain[1]

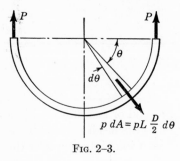

FIG. 2–3.

$$[\Sigma Y = 0] \quad F = p\,DL = 2\,P \quad (2\text{–}1)$$

or

$$P = \frac{p\,DL}{2}$$

The stress in the longitudinal section therefore is

$$\left[S = \frac{P}{A}\right] \quad S_t = \frac{p\,DL}{2\,tL} = \frac{p\,D}{2\,t} \quad (2\text{–}2)$$

This stress is usually called the *tangential stress*, because it acts tangent to the surface of the cylinder; other common names are circumferential stress, hoop stress, and girth stress. The stress computed by Eq. (2–2) is the average stress; for cylinders having a wall thickness equal to $\frac{1}{10}$ or less of the inner radius, it is practically equal to the maximum stress at the inside surface. (See Art. 12–10 for the stress distribution in thick-walled cylinders.)

If we consider next a free-body diagram of a transverse section (Fig. 2–4), we see that the bursting force acting over the end of the cylinder is resisted by the resultant P of the tearing forces acting over the transverse section. The area of a transverse section is the wall thickness multiplied by the mean circumference, or $\pi(D + t)t$; if t is small compared to D, it is closely approximated by πDt. Thus we obtain

$$[P = F] \qquad\qquad \pi DtS_l = \frac{\pi D^2}{4}\,p$$

or

$$S_l = \frac{pD}{4\,t} \qquad (2\text{–}3)$$

[1] The bursting force F on the half cylinder may also be obtained analytically as follows: In Fig. 2–3, the elementary force normal to an element of the cylinder located an angle θ from the horizontal diameter is $p\,dA = pL\dfrac{D}{2}\,d\theta$. A similar force (not shown) acts on the symmetrically placed element on the other side of the vertical centerline. Since the horizontal components of such pairs of forces cancel out, the bursting force F is the summation of the vertical components of these elementary forces:

$$F = \int_0^{\pi} (\sin\theta)(pL\frac{D}{2}\,d\theta) = pL\frac{D}{2}\Big[-\cos\theta\Big]_0^{\pi}$$

which reduces to

$$F = pL\,D$$

as above.

where S_l denotes what is called the longitudinal stress, because it acts parallel to the longitudinal axis of the cylinder.

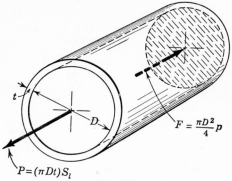

Fig. 2–4.

Comparing Eqs. (2–2) and (2–3) shows that the longitudinal stress is one-half the value of the tangential stress. In effect, this is equivalent to stating that if the pressure in a cylinder is raised to the bursting point, failure will occur along a longitudinal section or longitudinal seam of the cylinder. When a cylinder is composed of two sheets riveted together, as in Fig. 2–5, the strength of the longitudinal joint should be twice the strength of the girth joint. In other words if, as is often the case, the longitudinal joint is not twice as strong as the girth joint, the permissible internal pressure will depend on the strength of the longitudinal joint.

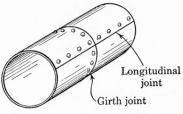

Fig. 2–5.

Eqs. (2–2) and (2–3) have been developed primarily to determine the relation stated in the above paragraph, not as equations to be memorized. It is generally best to compute the stresses by determining the resisting load P from a free-body diagram and then computing the stress by using $S = \dfrac{P}{A}$. The use of Fig. 2–2 for this purpose is shown by the equivalent skeleton diagram in Fig. 2–6, which establishes the relation $2\,P = p\,DL$.

When the ends of the cylinder are not squared off as in Fig. 2–4, but are rounded or dished as in Fig. 2–7, the bursting force on a transverse section may still be computed as the product of the internal pressure multiplied by the projected area of the transverse section. Thus, using the concept discussed in connection with Fig. 2–2, we may imagine the volume between the transverse section A–A and the rounded end in Fig. 2–7 to be full of a fluid. The resultant longitudinal force will equal the product of the pressure intensity multiplied by the shaded area of the transverse section.

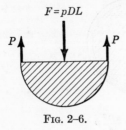

$$F = pDL$$

P P

FIG. 2–6.

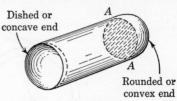

Dished or concave end

A

A

Rounded or convex end

FIG. 2–7.

As another application of the concept of a fluid to transmit pressure, consider a pump chamber cast in several parts, with projecting flanges that are bolted together as shown in Fig. 2–8. The bursting force to be resisted by the bolts in section A–A is proportional to the cross-sectional area at A–A and is expressed by $F_1 = p \left(\dfrac{\pi D_1^2}{4} \right)$; similarly, the bursting force resisted by the bolts in section B–B is $F_2 = p \left(\dfrac{\pi D_2^2}{4} \right)$.

The principles discussed above for determining the tangential stress in thin-walled cylinders may also be applied to computing the contact pres-

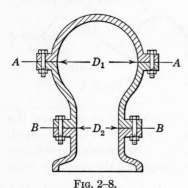

A —————— D_1 ————— A

B — D_2 — B

FIG. 2–8.

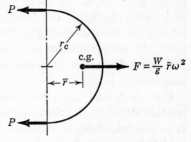

P

r_c

c.g.

$\bar{r}$

P

$F = \dfrac{W}{g} \bar{r} \omega^2$

FIG. 2–9. — Free-body diagram of one-half of rotating ring.

sure exerted by hoops shrunk upon cylinders or the tensile stress developed in a thin rotating ring. In the latter case, for example, the bursting force is generated by the centrifugal force developed on one-half of the ring. Its value may be obtained (Fig. 2–9) by assuming the weight of the half-ring concentrated at its center of gravity, whence we have

$$F = \frac{W}{g} \bar{r} \omega^2 \qquad (a)$$

in which $W = \gamma A \pi r_c$ where γ is the unit weight, A is the cross-sectional area of the ring, and r_c is the radius of the mean circumference. From mechanics, the value of $\bar{r}$ for a semicircular ring is $\bar{r} = \dfrac{2\,r_c}{\pi}$. ω is the angular velocity in radians per sec. Substituting these values reduces Eq. (*a*) to

$$F = \frac{2\,\gamma A\,(r_c\omega)^2}{g} = \frac{2\,\gamma A v^2}{g} \qquad (b)$$

where $v = r_c\omega =$ the peripheral velocity of the ring.

From equilibrium of the free-body diagram in Fig. 2–9 we have

$$2\,P = F$$

hence the stress is

$$S = \frac{P}{A} = \frac{\gamma A v^2}{gA} = \frac{\gamma v^2}{g} \qquad (c)$$

It is seen to vary directly with the unit weight and the square of the peripheral velocity. In applying Eq. (*c*), care must be taken to use consistent units.

ILLUSTRATIVE PROBLEMS

201. At a temperature of 220° F., a steel tire $\frac{3}{8}$ in. thick and 3 in. wide which is to be shrunk onto a locomotive driving wheel 6 ft in diameter just fits over the wheel, which is at a temperature of 70° F. What contact pressure is set up between the tire and the wheel? Neglect the deformation of the wheel caused by the pressure of the tire and assume $\alpha = 6.5 \times 10^{-6}$ and $E = 30 \times 10^6$ psi. If $f = 0.4$, what torque is required to twist the tire relative to the wheel?

Solution: From the condition that the temperature contraction in the tire equals the load deformation, we compute the tensile load in the tire. Hence,

$$\alpha L\,\Delta T = \frac{PL}{AE}$$

or

$$P = AE\alpha\,\Delta T = (\tfrac{3}{8} \times 3)(30 \times 10^6)(6.5 \times 10^{-6})(220 - 70) = 32{,}900 \text{ lb}$$

From a free-body diagram similar to Fig. 2–6, we have

$$p\,DL = 2\,P$$

whence

$$p(6 \times 12)(3) = 2(32{,}900), \quad p = 305 \text{ psi} \quad \textit{Ans.}$$

The total normal force created by this pressure is

$$N = pA = p\pi\,DL = 305\,\pi(6 \times 12)(3) = 207{,}000 \text{ lb}$$

whence the frictional resistance to twisting is

$$F = fN = 0.4(207{,}000) = 82{,}800 \text{ lb}$$

and the required torque is

$$T = F \left(\frac{D}{2}\right) = 82{,}800 \left(\frac{6}{2}\right) = 248{,}000 \text{ ft-lb} \quad Ans.$$

202. A penstock 5 ft in diameter, composed of wooden staves bound together by steel hoops each $\frac{1}{2}$ sq in. in area, is used to conduct water from a reservoir to a powerhouse. If the maximum tensile stress permitted in the hoops is 18,000 psi, what is the maximum spacing between hoops under a head of water of 100 ft?

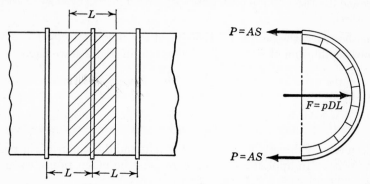

FIG. 2–10. — Spacing of hoops in a penstock.

Solution: The pressure in psi corresponding to a head of water of 100 ft is given by

$$[p = wh] \qquad\qquad p = \frac{62.5(100)}{144} = 43.3 \text{ psi}$$

If the maximum spacing between hoops is denoted by L, then, as shown in Fig. 2–10, each hoop must resist the bursting force on the length L. Since the tensile force in a hoop is given by $P = AS$, we obtain from the free-body diagram

$$[p\,DL = 2\,P] \qquad\qquad 43.3(5 \times 12)L = 2(\tfrac{1}{2} \times 18{,}000)$$

whence

$$L = 6.92 \text{ in.} \quad Ans.$$

PROBLEMS

203. A spherical shell of 8 ft outer diameter and 7 ft 8 in. inner diameter contains helium at a pressure of 1200 psi. Compute the stress in the shell.

Ans. $S = 13{,}800$ psi

204. Find the limiting peripheral velocity of a steel ring if the allowable stress is 18,000 psi and steel weighs 490 lb per cu ft.

205. A flange is used to cap the end of a pipe carrying steam at 500 psi. The pipe has an outside diameter of 14 in. and a wall thickness of $\frac{3}{8}$ in. How many $1\frac{1}{2}$-in. steel bolts must be used to hold on the flange if the allowable stress in the bolts is 12,000 psi, of which 8000 psi is set up initially in the bolts by tightening them? What circumferential stress is developed in the pipe?

Ans. 10 bolts; $S = 8840$ psi

206. A water tank made of $\frac{1}{2}$-in. plate is 30 ft in diameter and 50 ft high. Compute the height of water that will cause a circumferential stress of 5000 psi. Assume that water weighs 62.5 lb per cu ft.   *Ans.* $h = 32$ ft

207. A steel tire $\frac{3}{8}$ in. thick, 4 in. wide, and 72.00 in. inside diameter is heated and shrunk onto a steel wheel 72.02 in. in diameter. Neglecting deformation of the wheel, determine the tensile stress in the tire and the contact pressure between the tire and the wheel. If $f = 0.30$, what torque is required to twist the tire relative to the wheel?

208. A spiral riveted penstock 4 ft in diameter is made of steel plate $\frac{3}{8}$ in. thick. The pitch of the spiral or helix is 8 ft. The spiral seam is a single-riveted lap joint consisting of $\frac{7}{8}$-in. rivets having a shearing strength of 5300 lb each. Determine the spacing of the rivets along the seam for a water pressure of 150 psi. Neglect end thrust. What is the circumferential stress?   *Ans.* 2.74 in.; $S = 9620$ psi

209. A welded steel cylindrical drum made of $\frac{5}{16}$-in. plate has an internal diameter of 4 ft. By how much will the diameter be changed by an internal pressure of 150 psi, (*a*) neglecting the effect of end thrust and (*b*) considering it? Assume that Poisson's ratio is 0.30.

210. A bronze hoop $\frac{1}{2}$ in. thick and with an inside diameter of 25 in. fits snugly at 370° F. over a steel hoop $\frac{3}{4}$ in. thick. Both hoops are 4 in. wide. Compute the contact pressure between the hoops when the temperature drops to 70° F. For steel, $E = 30 \times 10^6$ and $\alpha = 6.5 \times 10^{-6}$. For bronze, $E = 12 \times 10^6$ and $\alpha = 10.5 \times 10^{-6}$. Neglect the possibility that the inner ring may buckle.

Ans. $p = 454$ psi

2–2. Types of Riveted Joints. Definitions

There are two types of riveted boiler joints: lap joints and butt joints. In a lap joint, the plates to be connected are lapped over one another and fastened together by one or more rows of rivets, as in Fig. 2–11. In a butt

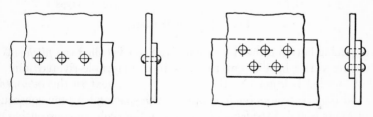

(a) Single-riveted lap joint   (b) Double-riveted lap joint

Fig. 2–11. — Lap joints.

joint, the plates are butted together and joined by two cover plates riveted to each of the main plates. (Occasionally only one cover plate is used.) The number of rows of rivets used to fasten the cover plates to each main plate identifies the joint as single-riveted, double-riveted, etc. (Fig. 2–12). Frequently the outer cover plate in a boiler joint is narrower than the inner cover plate, as in (c) and (d) of Fig. 2–12, the outer plate being wide enough to include only the rivet row in which the rivets are most closely spaced. This type of connection is called a *pressure joint.* Caulking along the edge of the outer cover plate to prevent leakage is more effective in this type.

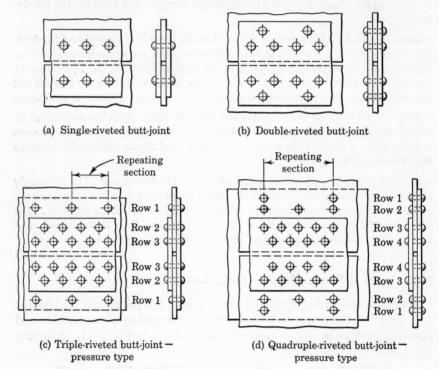

(a) Single-riveted butt-joint

(b) Double-riveted butt-joint

(c) Triple-riveted butt-joint —
pressure type

(d) Quadruple-riveted butt-joint —
pressure type

FIG. 2–12. — Butt joints.

The spacing between the rivets in a given row is called the *pitch.* When the spacing varies in different rows, as in a quadruple-riveted joint, the smallest spacing is known as the *short pitch,* the next as the *intermediate pitch,* and the greatest as the *long pitch.* The spacing between consecutive rows of rivets is called the *back pitch.* When the rivets in consecutive rows are staggered, the distance between the centers of the rivets is the *diagonal pitch.*

In determining the strength of a riveted joint, computations are usually made for a length of joint corresponding to a repeating pattern of rivets. The length of the repeating pattern (more commonly called a *repeating section*) is equal to the long pitch.

Sometimes confusion arises in deciding how many rivets belong in a re-peating section. A study of the repeating section in Fig. 2–12c shows that there are five rivets effective in each half of the triple-riveted butt joint: 2 half rivets in row 1, 2 whole rivets in row 2, and 1 whole and 2 half rivets in row 3. Similarly there are 11 rivets effective in each half of the repeating section of the quadruple-riveted joint in Fig. 2–12d.

The efficiency of a riveted joint indicates how well the joint has been de-signed. It compares the strength of the joint with that of the unriveted plate and is defined by

$$\text{efficiency} = \frac{\text{strength of joint}}{\text{strength of solid plate}} \qquad (2\text{–}4)$$

The rivet holes in boiler joints are usually drilled or subpunched and reamed out to a diameter $\frac{1}{16}$ in. larger than the rivet; however, the rivet is assumed to be driven so tightly that it fills the hole completely. In cal-culations, therefore, the diameter of the driven rivet is considered equal to that of the rivet hole.

2–3. Strength of a Simple Lap Joint

Riveted joints are examples of simple stress governed by the equation $P = AS$. The application of this equation to the elemental types of failure is easily understood by considering a single-riveted lap joint. The failure of a riveted boiler joint is equivalent to any relative movement of the main plates of the joint, because this will destroy its function, which is to main-tain a rigid and leakproof connection.

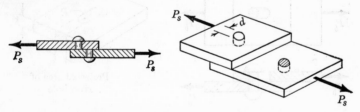

FIG. 2–13. — Shear failure.

In Fig. 2–13, shear of the rivet evidently permits the main plates to separate. The failure load in shear is given by

$$P_s = A_s S_s = \frac{\pi d^2}{4} S_s \qquad (2\text{–}5)$$

where d represents the diameter of both the rivet hole and the driven rivet.

Fig. 2–14 represents a failure caused by the tearing of the main plate. This failure occurs on a section through the rivet hole, this section evidently having minimum tearing resistance. If p is the width of the plate or the length of a repeating section, the resisting area is the product of the net width of the plate $(p-d)$ and the thickness t. The failure load in tension is

$$P_t = A_t S_t = (p-d)t\ S_t \tag{2-6}$$

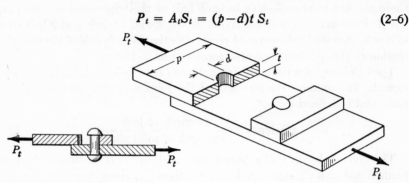

FIG. 2-14. — Tear of plate at section through rivet hole.
$$P_t = A_t S_t = (p-d)t S_t$$

A third type of failure, called a bearing failure, is shown in Fig. 2-15. In this case, relative movement between the main plates may result from a permanent deformation or enlargement of the rivet hole caused by excessive bearing pressure. The rivet itself may also possibly be crushed. In either case, it is assumed that the bearing stress S_b is uniformly distributed over the projected area of the rivet hole.

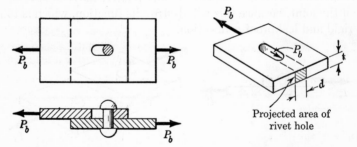

Projected area of rivet hole

FIG. 2-15. — Exaggerated bearing deformation of upper plate.
$$P_b = A_b S_b = (dt)S_b$$

Actually, the intensity with which the rivet bears against the rivet hole is not constant, but varies from zero at the edges of the hole to a maximum directly back of the rivet. It is common practice, however, to assume an average value of the bearing stress as being uniformly distributed. This condition is similar to that when a thin-walled cylinder is subjected to a uniform internal pressure (see Art. 2-1, especially Fig. 2-6); here, as we have seen, the net force is equal to the constant pressure multiplied by the projected area.

The failure load in bearing is expressed by

$$P_b = A_b S_b = (dt)S_b \qquad (2\text{--}7)$$

Other types of failure are possible but will not occur in a properly designed joint. Among them are tearing of the edge of a plate back of a rivet hole, as shown in Fig. 2–16a; shear failure of the plate behind a rivet hole,

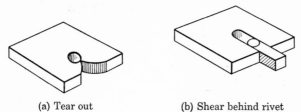

(a) Tear out   (b) Shear behind rivet

Fɪɢ. 2–16. — Possible types of failure if rivet hole is too close to edge of plate.

as shown in Fig. 2–16b, or a combination of both. Such failures are unlikely to occur if the distance from the edge of the plate to the center of the rivet is $1\frac{3}{4}$ to 2 times the diameter of the rivet. In the problems we shall assume that this distance is great enough to prevent this type of failure.

2–4. Strength of a Complex Butt Joint

The maximum safe load that can be transmitted by a complex joint is limited by the capacity of the rivets to transmit load, or by the tearing resistance of the plates. The procedure and reasoning are explained in the following problem.

ILLUSTRATIVE PROBLEM

211. A repeating section 7 in. long of a triple-riveted butt joint of the pressure type is illustrated in Fig. 2–17. The rivet hole diameter is $d = \frac{3}{4}$ in., the thickness of the main plates is $t = \frac{1}{2}$ in., the thickness of each cover plate is $t' = \frac{5}{16}$ in. The allowable stresses in shear, bearing, and tension are respectively $S_s = 8800$ psi, $S_b = 19{,}000$ psi, and $S_t = 11{,}000$ psi. Determine the strength of a repeating section, the efficiency of the joint, and the maximum internal pressure that may be carried in a 5-ft-diameter boiler for which this joint is the longitudinal seam.

Solution: The calculations are divided into two steps: (1) preliminary calculations to determine the load that can be transmitted by one rivet in shear or bearing, and (2) calculations to determine possible methods of failure. In these computations, if allowable stresses are used, the result will determine the safe working load; on the other hand, if ultimate stresses are used, the result will be the ultimate load which may then be divided by a suitable factor of safety to determine the safe working load.

Preliminary Calculations: To single shear one rivet:

$$P_s = \frac{\pi\, d^2}{4}\, S_s = \frac{\pi}{4}\left(\frac{3}{4}\right)^2 (8800) = 3890\,\text{lb}$$

To double shear one rivet:

$$P_s = 2(3890) = 7780 \text{ lb}$$

To crush one rivet in main plate:

$$P_b = (dt)S_b = \tfrac{3}{4}(\tfrac{1}{2})(19{,}000) = 7130 \text{ lb}$$

To crush one rivet in one cover plate:

$$P_b' = (dt')S_b = \tfrac{3}{4}(\tfrac{5}{16})(19{,}000) = 4460 \text{ lb}$$

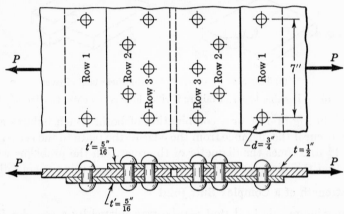

FIG. 2–17.

Possible Methods of Failure: Generally, there are only two basic methods of failure. These are determined by (*a*) capacity of the rivets to transmit load, and (*b*) the tearing resistance of the plates.

(*a*) *Rivet Capacity.* The strength of the single rivet in row 1 in a repeating section is determined by the lowest value of the load that will single shear the rivet, crush it in the main plate, or crush it in one cover plate. On the basis of the values derived from the preliminary calculations, this value is 3890 lb.

The strength of each of the two rivets in row 2 depends on the lowest value required to double shear the rivet, crush it in the main plate, or crush it in both cover plates. The preliminary calculations show this value to be 7130 lb per rivet, or 14,260 lb for both rivets in row 2.

Each of the two rivets in a repeating section in row 3 transmits the load between the main plate and the cover plates in the same manner as those in row 2, and hence the strength of the two rivets in row 3 is also 14,260 lb.

The total rivet capacity equals the sum of the rivet strengths in all rows:

$$P_r = 3890 + 14{,}260 + 14{,}260 = 32{,}410 \text{ lb} \qquad (a)$$

(*b*) *Tearing Capacity.* The external load applied to the joint acts directly to tear the main plate at row 1, and a failure would be similar to that shown in Fig. 2–14. The load that will tear the main plate at row 1 is given by

$$P_1 = (p - d)t\, S_t = (7 - \tfrac{3}{4})(\tfrac{1}{2})(11{,}000) = 34{,}400 \text{ lb} \qquad (b)$$

The external load applied to the joint does not act directly to tear the main plate at row 2, because part of the load is absorbed or transmitted by the rivet in row 1 from the main plate to the cover plate. Hence, if the main plate is to tear at row 2, the external load must be the sum of the tearing resistance of the main plate at row 2, plus the load transmitted by the rivet in row 1 from the main plate to the cover plate. This statement is illustrated by the free-body diagram in Fig. 2–18 and is further clarified by Fig. 2–19, which shows how the failure may actually occur.

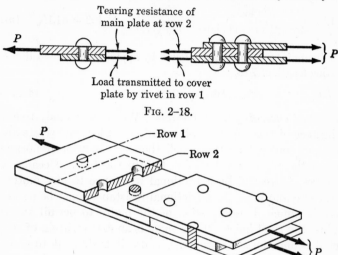

Tearing resistance of
main plate at row 2

Load transmitted to cover
plate by rivet in row 1

Fig. 2–18.

Fig. 2–19. — Failure by shear of rivet in Row 1 plus tear of main plate in Row 2.

The load transmitted by the rivet in row 1 is the first term on the right-hand side of Eq. (a), and is the value of the rivet strength in row 1. The external load to tear the main plate at row 2 must include this value; it is given by

$$P_2 = (p - 2\,d)t\,S_t + \text{rivet strength in row 1}$$
$$= (7 - 2 \times \tfrac{3}{4})(\tfrac{1}{2})(11{,}000) + 3890$$
$$= 30{,}200 + 3890 = 34{,}090 \text{ lb} \qquad (c)$$

Similarly, the external load required to tear the main plate at row 3 must include the rivet resistance in rows 1 and 2, or

$$P_3 = (7 - 2 \times \tfrac{3}{4})(\tfrac{1}{2})(11{,}000) + 3890 + 14{,}260 = 48{,}350 \text{ lb} \qquad (d)$$

It is obvious now that this computation need not be made, because, since the tearing resistance of the main plates at rows 2 and 3 is equal, it gives a larger value than that of Eq. (c). However, it illustrates the procedure to be used when a greater number of rivet holes in row 3 than row 2 reduces the tearing resistance of row 3 below that of row 2.

At row 3, the tearing of the *cover plates* is resisted only by the tensile strength of the cover plates at that row (see Fig. 2–18) and is given by

$$P_c = (7 - 2 \times \tfrac{3}{4})(2 \times \tfrac{5}{16})(11{,}000) = 37{,}900 \text{ lb}$$

The safe load is the lowest value of these several possible methods of failure. Its value is

$$P = 32,410 \text{ lb}$$

and failure occurs by shearing of the rivet in row 1 and crushing of the main plate in rows 2 and 3.

The efficiency is

$$\text{eff.} = \frac{\text{safe load}}{\text{strength of solid plate}} = \frac{32,410}{7(\frac{1}{2})(11,000)} \times 100 = 84.1\% \quad Ans.$$

The maximum internal pressure is found by applying the safe load of 32,410 lb in a repeating length of 7 in.

$$[2\,P = p\,DL] \qquad\qquad 2(32,410) = p(5 \times 12)(7) \qquad\qquad p = 149.5\,\text{psi} \quad Ans.$$

Observations Concerning Riveted Joints. We are now ready to appreciate the significance of the following observations. Since the rivets are driven when hot and contract as they cool, there are developed normal forces which press the plates of the joint tightly together. Because of these normal forces, there will be a frictional resistance to any motion of the plates past one another. This frictional resistance must be overcome before there is sufficient deformation of the plates to permit the rivets to bear against the rivet holes. Thus there is an extra margin of strength in the riveted connection. However, because it is difficult to estimate accurately this frictional resistance, it is not considered when computing the strength of a riveted connection.

It is assumed further that each rivet, when driven, expands to fill the rivet hole completely. Only when this is true will all the rivets transmit the load simultaneously. If some of the rivets fill the holes only partially, these rivets will not begin to bear against the plates until there has been sufficient deformation in the remaining rivets and/or plates to take up the slack in the rivet holes.

Because of these and other reasons, an *exact* analysis of a riveted connection cannot be made. The procedures used here for boiler joints (and those described later for structural joints) give usable values determined by comparatively simple methods.

PROBLEMS

Unless otherwise stated, assume the allowable stresses in the following problems to be $S_s = 8800$; $S_b = 19,000$; and $S_t = 11,000$ psi.

212. The longitudinal joint of a boiler having $\frac{3}{4}$-in. plates has a strength of 120,000 lb in a pitch length of 16 in. The efficiency of the girth joint is 45% and the allowable tensile stress is 11,000 psi. Determine the maximum diameter of the boiler if it is designed to operate at a pressure of 200 psi. $\qquad$ *Ans.* $D = 74.2$ in.

213. A double-riveted lap joint forms the girth seam of a boiler 5 ft in diameter. Pitch of the rivets is $3\frac{1}{2}$ in., diameter of rivet hole is $\frac{3}{4}$ in., thickness of plate is $\frac{1}{2}$ in. Find the strength of a repeating section, the efficiency, and maximum internal pressure.

214. The longitudinal seam of a boiler is a triple-riveted lap joint, with the pitch in the outer rows equal to $5\frac{1}{2}$ in. and that in the middle row equal to $2\frac{3}{4}$ in. Diameter of rivet hole is $\frac{7}{8}$ in.; the thickness of plate is $\frac{3}{8}$ in. Determine the strength of a repeating section and the efficiency.

215. The dimensions of a double-riveted butt joint like that in Fig. 2–12b are: diameter of rivet hole, $\frac{7}{8}$ in.; long pitch, 5 in.; short pitch, $2\frac{1}{2}$ in.; thickness of main plate, $\frac{1}{2}$ in., and of cover plates, $\frac{3}{8}$ in. Compute the strength of a repeating section and the efficiency.

216. If the joint described in Prob. 215 were of the pressure type, determine the strength of a repeating section and the efficiency.

Ans. $P = 21,930$ lb; 79.7% efficient

217. If the joint described in Prob. 215 were of the pressure type with cover plates each $\frac{5}{16}$ in. thick, determine the method of failure and the efficiency.

Ans.   Failure occurs by crushing of the upper cover plate and tearing at the inner row of the lower cover plate; efficiency = 78.3%

218. In a double-riveted butt joint of the pressure type, the thickness of the main plates is $\frac{9}{16}$ in., that of the shorter upper cover plate is $\frac{1}{4}$ in., that of the longer lower cover plate is $\frac{3}{8}$ in. Diameter of rivet holes is $\frac{3}{4}$ in., long pitch is $4\frac{1}{4}$ in., short pitch is $2\frac{1}{8}$ in. Compute the strength of a repeating section. *Ans.* $P = 18,470$ lb.

219. A triple-riveted butt joint like that in Fig. 2–12c has a long pitch of $8\frac{1}{4}$ in. and a short pitch of $4\frac{1}{8}$ in. Diameter of rivet hole, $1\frac{3}{16}$ in.; thickness of main plate, $\frac{3}{4}$ in., and of each cover plate, $\frac{1}{2}$ in. Find the strength of a repeating section and the efficiency.   *Ans.*   Efficiency = 85.5%

220. A quadruple-riveted joint similar to that in Fig. 2–12d has a long pitch of 16 in.; diameter of rivet hole is $1\frac{5}{16}$ in., thickness of main plate is $\frac{1}{2}$ in., thickness of each cover plate is $\frac{7}{16}$ in. Determine the strength of a repeating section and the efficiency.   *Ans.*   Efficiency = 94.1%

221. A quadruple-riveted butt joint like that in Fig. 2–12d has a long pitch of $16\frac{1}{2}$ in.; diameter of rivet hole is $1\frac{3}{16}$ in., thickness of main plate is $\frac{3}{4}$ in., and of each cover plate, $\frac{1}{2}$ in. Compute the strength of a repeating section, using a factor of safety of 4, based on the ultimate stresses of $S_s = 42,000$ in single shear and $S_s = 78,000$ in double shear, $S_b = 95,000$, and $S_t = 58,000$ psi. If this joint is the longitudinal seam of a boiler carrying an internal pressure of 250 psi, and the girth joint is 42% efficient, what is the maximum allowable boiler diameter?

2–5. Stresses in Riveted Joints

Sometimes it is necessary to investigate a joint and determine the stresses caused by a given loading. The usual assumption is that each rivet carries its proportional share of the applied load. This assumes that each rivet is loaded in the same way. Since this is not true for a butt joint of the pressure type, the procedure must be varied slightly, as is illustrated in the problem that follows.

It will be observed that the method used in the problem closely parallels that used in determining the strength of a joint, except that, since shear and bearing stresses are not specified, average values for them must first be computed.

ILLUSTRATIVE PROBLEM

222. A load of 36,000 lb acts on the repeating section of the triple-riveted butt joint in Fig. 2–20. Length of section = 8 in., diameter of rivet hole, $\frac{7}{8}$ in.; thickness of main plate, $\frac{1}{2}$ in., and of each cover plate, $\frac{3}{8}$ in. Compute the shearing, bearing, and tensile stresses developed in the joint.

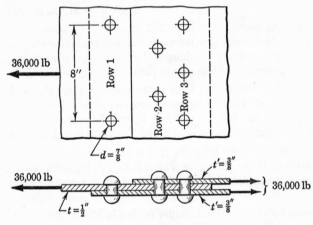

FIG. 2–20.

Solution: Assuming that all the rivets resist shear simultaneously, the total shearing area is that of one rivet in single shear and of four rivets in double shear, or a total of 9 shearing areas. The average shearing stress therefore is

$$S_s = \frac{P}{A_s} = \frac{36,000}{9\left(\dfrac{\pi}{4}\right)\left(\dfrac{7}{8}\right)^2} = 6650 \text{ psi}$$

To develop this stress, the shearing load on the rivet in row 1 must be 4000 lb.

The minimum area resisting bearing is determined by the minimum plate thickness at the various rows. It is the sum of the projected area behind one rivet in the cover plate at row 1 and that behind 4 rivets in the main plate at rows 2 and 3, or a total bearing area of $A_b = \frac{7}{8} \times \frac{3}{8} + 4(\frac{7}{8} \times \frac{1}{2}) = 2.08$ sq in. The average bearing stress is therefore

$$S_b = \frac{P}{A_b} = \frac{36,000}{2.08} = 17,300 \text{ psi}$$

To develop this stress, the bearing load on the rivet in row 1 must be $17,300(\frac{7}{8} \times \frac{3}{8}) = 5680$ lb. Since this value is larger than the shearing capacity of 4000 lb at row 1, the logical procedure might be to assume that the bearing stress developed in the main plate at rows 2 and 3 is caused by the remainder of the external load, i.e., $36,000 - 4000 = 32,000$ lb. This gives an average bearing stress at rows 2 and 3 of

$$S_b = \frac{P}{A} = \frac{32,000}{4(\frac{7}{8} \times \frac{1}{2})} = 18,300 \text{ psi}$$

This procedure, however, is not justified by the highly indeterminate manner in which the load actually is distributed along the joint.

The tensile stress in the main plate at row 1 is caused by the entire load acting across the net section of the plate:

$$S_t = \frac{P}{(p - d)t} = \frac{36,000}{(8 - \frac{7}{8})(\frac{1}{2})} = 10,100 \text{ psi}$$

The external load reduced by the amount already transmitted to the cover plate by the rivet in row 1 acts across the net section of the main plate at row 2. The tensile stress at row 2 therefore is

$$S_t = \frac{P}{(p - 2 d)t} = \frac{36,000 - 4000}{(8 - 2 \times \frac{7}{8})(\frac{1}{2})} = 10,240 \text{ psi}$$

The tensile stress in the main plate at row 3 need not be computed, because the net load there is still further decreased by the load transmitted by the rivets of row 2, and the net tensile area at row 3 is the same as that of row 2.

At row 3 in the cover plates, it is assumed that the total load acts across the net area of both cover plates, producing an average tensile stress there of

$$S_t = \frac{P}{(p - 2 d)(2 t')} = \frac{36,000}{(8 - 2 \times \frac{7}{8})(2 \times \frac{3}{8})} = 7680 \text{ psi}$$

PROBLEMS

Compute the maximum shearing, bearing, and tensile stresses developed in the following riveted joints under the action of the indicated loads.

223. Double-riveted lap joint of Prob. 213: Load = 2000 lb per inch of length.

224. Double-riveted butt joint of Prob. 215: Load = 4000 lb per inch of length.
Ans. $S_s = 5550$ psi; $S_b = 15,230$ psi; $S_t = 9700$ psi

225. Triple-riveted lap joint of Prob. 214: Load on a repeating section = 16,500 lb.

226. Double-riveted butt joint of Prob. 216: Load on a repeating section = 20,000 lb.

227. Triple-riveted butt joint of Prob. 219: Load on a repeating section = 50,000 lb.   *Ans.* $S_s = 5010$ psi; $S_b = 12,030$ psi; $S_t = 9890$ psi

228. Quadruple-riveted joint of Prob. 220: Load on a repeating section = 80,000 lb.   *Ans.* $S_s = 6100$ psi; $S_b = 16,060$ psi; $S_t = 11,000$ psi

2-6.   Structural Riveted Joints

Structural riveted joints differ in several ways from those for pressure vessels. The most important differences are as follows: (1) Each rivet is assumed to carry its proportional share of the applied load, and (2) the diameter of the rivet hole is taken as $\frac{1}{8}$ in. larger than the diameter of the undriven rivet.

For condition (1) to be true, it is necessary that the applied load pass through the centroid of the rivet group (see page 5). Condition (2) results from the fact that the parts to be joined are punched separately, the diameter of the punched hole being $\frac{1}{16}$ in. larger than the rivet diameter. Another $\frac{1}{16}$ in. is added to compensate for the probable damage done to the metal around the hole by punching. For shearing and bearing calculations, however, the diameter of the undriven rivet is used, because the rivet holes in plates that are punched separately are unlikely to match perfectly, and consequently the cross-section of the rivet will be less than that of the rivet hole.

ILLUSTRATIVE PROBLEMS

229. Using the structural method of assuming all rivets to carry a proportional share of the load, compute the tensile stress in the main plate at row 3 of the quadruple-riveted butt connection shown in Fig. 2–21. The connection transmits a

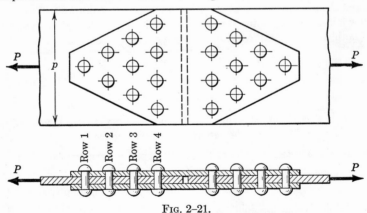

FIG. 2–21.

load $P = 80,000$ lb across a plate width $p = 10$ in. Also compute the width of the cover or strap plates at row 2 if the tensile stress is not to exceed 16,000 psi. Rivet diameter is $\frac{3}{4}$ in.; thickness of main plate is $\frac{1}{2}$ in., and of each cover plate, $\frac{5}{16}$ in.

Solution: Fig. 2–21 shows the entire connection; there is no repeating pattern of rivets as in a boiler joint. As there are 10 rivets to carry the load, each rivet may be assumed to carry $\frac{1}{10}$ of the load. Since the single rivet in row 1 transmits $\frac{1}{10}$ of the load to the cover plates, and the two rivets in row 2 transmit $\frac{2}{10}$ of the load, $\frac{7}{10}$ of the load are left to tear the main plate at row 3. This is shown in the free-body diagram of a section between rows 2 and 3 in Fig. 2–22. Thus we obtain

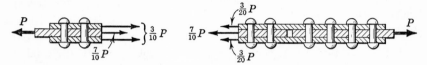

Fig. 2–22. — Free-body diagram of section between Rows 2 and 3.

for the tensile stress in the main plate at row 3, where 3 rivet holes reduce the net section (note that the rivet hole diameter = rivet diameter + $\frac{1}{8}$ in.),

$$[P = AS = (p - 3\,d)t\,S_t] \qquad \tfrac{7}{10}(80{,}000) = (10 - 3 \times \tfrac{7}{8})(\tfrac{1}{2})S_t$$

$$S_t = 15{,}200 \text{ psi} \quad Ans.$$

Fig. 2–22 also shows that the cover plates at row 2 are subject to $\frac{3}{10}$ of the applied load. Hence, the width of these cover plates required to develop the maximum tensile stress permitted is

$$[P = AS = (p - 2\,d)(2\,t')S_t] \qquad \tfrac{3}{10}(80{,}000) = (p - 2 \times \tfrac{7}{8})(2 \times \tfrac{5}{16})(16{,}000)$$

whence

$$p = 4.15 \text{ in.} \quad Ans.$$

230. Fig. 2–23 shows an 18 WF 70 beam riveted to a 24 WF 100 girder by two $4 \times 3\frac{1}{2} \times \frac{3}{8}$ in. angles with $\frac{3}{4}$-in.-diameter rivets. For the shop-driven rivets that

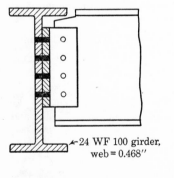
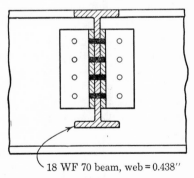

←24 WF 100 girder, web = 0.468″

18 WF 70 beam, web = 0.438″

Fig. 2–23. — Strength of beam and girder connection.

attach the angles to the beam, assume $S_s = 12{,}000$ psi and $S_b = 25{,}000$ psi. For the field-driven rivets (riveted on the job), assume $S_s = 10{,}000$ psi and $S_b = 20{,}000$ psi. The web of the girder is 0.468 in. thick and that of the beam is 0.438 in. thick. Determine the allowable end reaction.

Solution: At the girder, the shearing resistance is that of 8 field-driven rivets in single shear; hence we have

$$[P = AS] \qquad P = 8\left(\frac{\pi}{4}\right)\left(\frac{3}{4}\right)^2(10,000) = 35,400\,\text{lb}$$

The bearing resistance at the girder depends on the minimum thickness of the connection, which in this case is the $\frac{3}{8}$-in. thickness of the clip angle. We obtain for 8 field-driven rivets in bearing:

$$[P = AS] \qquad P = 8(\tfrac{3}{4})(\tfrac{3}{8})(20,000) = 45,000\,\text{lb}$$

At the beam, there are 4 shop-driven rivets in double shear, giving a total of 8 single-shear areas. With an allowable stress of 12,000 psi, this makes the shear resistance greater here than at the girder.

The bearing resistance at the beam depends on the web thickness of the beam. Since this is smaller than the combined thickness of the two clip angles, for the 4 rivets in bearing, we obtain,

$$[P = AS] \qquad P = 4(\tfrac{3}{4})(0.438)(25,000) = 32,900\,\text{lb}$$

The safe beam reaction is the smallest of the above figures, or 32,900 lb; it is limited by the bearing of the shop-driven rivets against the web of the 18-in. beam.

PROBLEMS

231. Determine the safe load on the butt connection in Fig. 2–21 if the allowable stresses are $S_s = 10,000$, $S_t = 16,000$, and $S_b = 20,000$ psi. Use $\frac{3}{4}$-in. rivets, plate width $p = 11$ in., thickness of main plate $= \frac{1}{2}$ in. and of each strap plate $= \frac{3}{8}$ in.
Ans. $P = 75,000$ lb

232. In the joint in Illus. Prob. 229, if the rivet at row 1 is omitted, determine the maximum stresses in shear, bearing, and tension in the main plate. Also compute the minimum width of the strap plates at rows 2 and 3 if the tensile stress is limited to 16,000 psi.

233. Omitting row 4 of the butt connection shown in Fig. 2–21, compute the safe load and efficiency if the allowable stresses are $S_s = 13,500$, $S_t = 18,000$, and $S_b = 27,000$ psi. Use $1\frac{5}{16}$-in. rivets, plate width $p = 8$ in., thickness of main plate $= \frac{1}{2}$ in. and of each strap plate $= \frac{3}{8}$ in.

234. Two plates are joined by four rivets 1 in. in diameter, as shown. Find the allowable load P if the working stresses are $S_s = 12,000$, $S_t = 15,000$, and $S_b = 20,000$ psi.
Ans. $P = 34,400$ lb

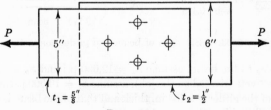

PROB. 234.

235. An 18 WF 96 beam having a web thickness of 0.512 in. is riveted to a 24 WF 100 girder by a connection similar to that in Fig. 2–23. Using $\frac{3}{4}$-in.-diameter rivets, compute the allowable load on the connection. For all rivets, assume $S_s = 15,000$ psi and $S_b = 32,000$ psi.

236. Fig. *b* shows the detail of the riveted connection at *B* of the roof truss in Fig. *a*. How many $\frac{3}{4}$-in.-diameter rivets are required to fasten member *BC* to the gusset plate? Member *BE?* Allowable stresses are $S_s = 10,000$ psi and $S_b = 20,000$ psi.   *Ans.*   For *BC*, 4 rivets; for *BE*, 3 rivets

237. In Prob. 236, compute the required number of rivets if the rivet diameter is $\frac{7}{8}$ in., all other data remaining unchanged.
Ans.   For *BC*, 3 rivets; for *BE*, 2 rivets

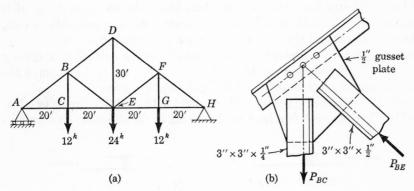

(a)   (b)

PROB. 236 and 237.

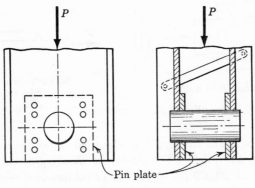

Pin plate

PROB. 238.

238. One end of a three-hinged arch consists of two 15-in. 33.9-lb channels latticed together. The total end reaction is $P = 99$ tons, which is transmitted to a 4-in.-diameter steel pin by means of bearing on the webs of the channels and on a "pin plate" riveted to each channel as shown. If the bearing stress is not to exceed 27,000 psi, what is the required thickness of each pin plate? What is the shearing stress in the eight $\frac{7}{8}$-in.-diameter rivets joining the pin plates to the channel webs?

Ans. $t = 0.517$ in.; $S_s = 11,600$ psi

2–7. Welded Connections

The reliability of welded connections has increased to the point where they are used extensively to supplement or replace riveted connections in structural and machine design. It is frequently more economical to fabricate a member by welding simple component parts together than to use a complicated casting.

Welding is a method of joining metals by fusion. By means of heat from either an electric arc or an oxyacetylene torch, the metal at the joint is melted and fuses with additional metal from a welding rod. When cool, the weld metal and the base metal form a continuous and almost homogeneous joint. To protect the weld from excessive oxidation, a heavily coated welding rod is used which releases an inert gas that envelopes the arc stream; this technique is called the *shielded arc process*.

The two principal types of welds are butt welds and fillet welds (see Fig. 2–24). The strength of a butt weld is equal to the allowable stress multi-

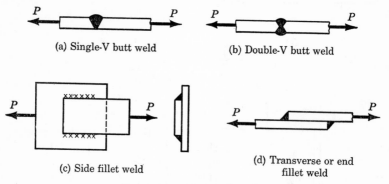

(a) Single-V butt weld   (b) Double-V butt weld

(c) Side fillet weld   (d) Transverse or end fillet weld

FIG. 2–24. — Types of welds.

plied by the product of the length of the weld times the thickness of the thinner plate of the joint. The American Welding Society specifies allowable stresses of 20,000 psi in tension or compression and 13,600 psi in shear.

The strength of side or transverse fillet welds is assumed to be determined by the shearing resistance of the throat of the weld. In the 45° fillet weld in Fig. 2–25, with leg equal to t, the shearing area through the throat is the length L of the weld times the throat depth, or $A = L t \sin 45° = L(0.707\ t)$.

Using the allowable shearing stress S_s of 13,600 psi specified by the American Welding Society, the strength of the weld is

$$P = AS_s = L(0.707\ t)(13,600) = 9600\ t\ L.$$

Usually, however, the strength of a fillet weld is expressed as the strength per linear inch of weld; successive values are as follows:

Size of Fillet	Strength per Inch
$\frac{1}{8}$ in.	1200 lb
$\frac{3}{16}$ in.	1800 lb
$\frac{1}{4}$ in.	2400 lb
$\frac{5}{16}$ in.	3000 lb
$\frac{3}{8}$ in.	3600 lb
$\frac{7}{16}$ in.	4200 lb
$\frac{1}{2}$ in.	4800 lb

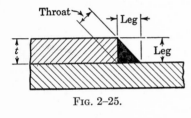

Fig. 2-25.

As a rule, special precautions are necessary to insure that the leg of a fillet weld actually is equal to the thickness of the plate. As a result, the maximum size of a fillet weld at the square edge of a plate is limited to $\frac{1}{16}$ in. less than the plate thickness; a weld at the rounded edges of flanges or the toe of an angle may be three-fourths the thickness of the edge. These specifications are illustrated in Fig. 2-26.

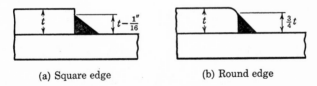

(a) Square edge   (b) Round edge

Fig. 2-26. — Maximum size of fillets.

ILLUSTRATIVE PROBLEM

239. A 4 x 4 x $\frac{3}{8}$ angle is to be welded to a gusset plate. The angle carries a load of 42,000 lb applied along its centroidal axis. (*a*) Determine the lengths of side fillet welds required at the heel and toe of the angle. The weld at the heel is to be the same size as the maximum permissible weld at the toe. (*b*) Determine the lengths of the side fillet welds if a transverse fillet weld is added at the end of the angle.

Solution: Part a. Fig. 2-27 shows the forces that keep the angle in equilibrium. P_1 and P_2 are the resisting forces exerted by the welds at the heel and toe respectively. They are assumed to act along the edges of the angle. Taking moments about a center on the line of action of P_2, we obtain

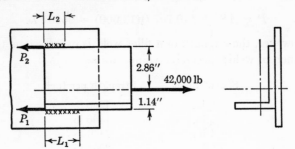

FIG. 2-27.

$[\Sigma M_{P_2} = 0]$ $\qquad$ $4\,P_1 = 42,000\,(2.86)$ $\qquad$ $P_1 = 30,000\,\text{lb}$

With respect to a moment center on the line of action of P_1, we have

$[\Sigma M_{P_1} = 0]$ $\qquad$ $4\,P_2 = 42,000\,(1.14)$ $\qquad$ $P_2 = 12,000\,\text{lb}$

The maximum size of the fillet weld for a rounded edge at the toe of an angle is three-fourths of the thickness, or $\frac{3}{4} \times \frac{3}{8} = \frac{9}{32}$ in. The strength per inch of this size of weld is $F = 9600\,t = 9600 \times \frac{9}{32} = 2700$ lb/in. Hence the required lengths of weld are

$$\left[L = \frac{P}{F}\right] \qquad\qquad L_1 = \frac{30,000}{2700} = 11.1\,\text{in.}$$

and

$$L_2 = \frac{12,000}{2700} = 4.44\,\text{in.}$$

These values should be increased by $\frac{1}{4}$ in. to provide for starting and stopping the weld.

Part b: For the square edge at the end of the angle, the specifications limit the maximum size of the transverse fillet weld to $\frac{1}{16}$ in. less than the thickness of $\frac{3}{8}$ in., that is, to $\frac{5}{16}$ in. This size of weld has a strength per inch of 3000 lb; hence a 4-in. length will sustain a load of 12,000 lb acting at the center of the weld as shown in Fig. 2–28.

Taking moments first about a center on the line of action of P_2 and then about a center on the line of action of P_1, we obtain

$[\Sigma M_{P_2} = 0]$ $\qquad$ $4\,P_1 + 12,000\,(2) = 42,000\,(2.86)$ $\qquad$ $P_1 = 24,000\,\text{lb}$

$[\Sigma M_{P_1} = 0]$ $\qquad$ $4\,P_2 + 12,000\,(2) = 42,000\,(1.14)$ $\qquad$ $P_2 = 6000\,\text{lb}$

Using a $\frac{9}{32}$-in. side fillet weld with a strength of 2700 lb/in., we obtain the following lengths at the heel and toe respectively:

$$\left[L = \frac{P}{F} \right] \qquad L_1 = \frac{24,000}{2700} = 8.90 \text{ in.}$$

$$L_2 = \frac{6000}{2700} = 2.22 \text{ in.}$$

A larger weld may be used at the heel if it is necessary to reduce the overlap to less than 8.90 in.

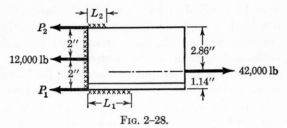

FIG. 2–28.

PROBLEMS

240. A plate 5 in. wide and $\frac{1}{2}$ in. thick is lapped over and welded to a gusset plate. Determine the minimum length of $\frac{5}{16}$-in. side fillet weld that will be necessary if the plate is stressed to 18,000 psi.

241. Solve Prob. 240 if a $\frac{5}{16}$-in. transverse fillet weld is used across the back of the plate, in addition to the side fillet welds.   *Ans.*   5 in. on each side

242. A $5 \times 3\frac{1}{2} \times \frac{1}{2}$ angle is to be welded to a gusset plate with the 5-in. leg in contact with the plate. If the angle carries a load of 60,000 lb applied along its centroidal axis, what lengths of $\frac{5}{16}$-in. side fillet welds will be required along the toe and heel of the angle?

243. Solve Prob. 242, using a $\frac{1}{2}$-in. weld at the heel of the angle and the maximum permissible size at the toe.   *Ans.*   5.53 in. and 8.35 in.

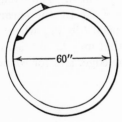

PROB. 244.

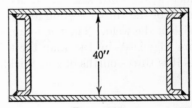

PROB. 245.

244. A $\frac{1}{2}$-in. plate is lapped over and secured, as shown, by transverse fillet welds on the inside and outside to form a penstock of 60-in. diameter. Determine the safe internal pressure, assuming allowable stresses of $S_t = 20,000$ psi for the plate and $S_s = 13,000$ psi through the throat of the welds. Use the maximum size of welds permitted.   *Ans.* $p = 268$ psi

245. A tank is fabricated by welding two caps, as shown, to the ends of a cylinder 40 in. in diameter. If the caps and cylinder are $\frac{1}{2}$ in. thick, determine the safe internal pressure that will not exceed a shearing stress of 14,000 psi in the throat of the maximum size of fillet weld around the entire circumference. What tangential stress does this pressure cause in the cylinder?   *Ans.* $S_t = 17,350$ psi

SUMMARY

The stresses in thin-walled cylinders created by internal pressure are most readily obtained by applying the conditions of equilibrium to a free-body diagram of either a longitudinal or a transverse section, depending on whether tangential or longitudinal stress is desired.

There are two classes of riveted joints: those used for boilers and those used in structures. In the former, the diameter of the rivet hole determines the diameter used for shearing and bearing calculations; in the latter, the actual rivet diameter is used for shearing and bearing, the rivet hole being assumed to be $\frac{1}{8}$ in. larger.

Further differences between these two types of riveted joints are given by the methods used to compute their strength. For boiler joints, it is preferable to begin with the strength of a single rivet in shear and bearing, and, depending upon the conditions in each row of rivets, compute the governing load per rivet in each row. The sum of these governing loads is the total rivet strength. The tensile strength of the main plate in any row is assumed to be increased by the strength of the rivets in the rows between that row and the externally applied load. In structural joints, all the rivets are assumed to carry their proportional share of the load. In either type of joint, the effect of frictional resistance is neglected.

The length of welds is determined by computing the resisting forces required to satisfy the conditions of static equilibrium, and then dividing the resisting load by the strength of the weld in lb per inch. The strength of fillet welds, both side and transverse, is determined by the shearing strength of the throat section and is specified as $9600\,t$ lb/in., where t is the size of the weld. The maximum size of weld that may be applied to a square edge is $\frac{1}{16}$ in. less than the thickness of the edge, and for rounded edges it is three-fourths of this thickness.

Chapter III
Torsion

3-1. Introduction and Assumptions

In this chapter we shall consider the derivation and application of the twisting or torsion problem only in connection with circular shafts. The twisting of noncircular shafts is so complex that we will only state the formulas that are used.

Torsion is our introduction to the problems of variable stress. Although the theory of these problems is complex, its application consists of little more than substituting given values in the formulas soon to be derived, and is fairly simple.

The general technique used in all cases of nonuniform stress distribution is outlined in these steps:

1. From a study of the elastic deformations produced by a specified load, plus the application of Hooke's law, determine the relations between stresses that are compatible with the deformations. Such relations are known as the *equations of compatibility*.

2. By applying the conditions of equilibrium to a free-body diagram of a portion of the body, obtain additional relations between the stresses. These relations, resulting from considering the equilibrium between externally applied loads and the internal resisting forces over an exploratory section, are called the *equations of equilibrium*.

3. Be sure that the solution of the equations in steps 1 and 2 is consistent with the loading conditions at the surface of the body. This is known as *satisfying the boundary conditions*.

In the theory of elasticity, it is shown that a solution satisfying these three steps is unique; i.e., it is the only possible solution.

In deriving the torsion formulas, we make the following assumptions. These assumptions may be proved mathematically, and some may be demonstrated experimentally. The first two apply only to shafts of circular section.

1. Circular sections remain circular.

2. Plane sections remain plane and do not warp.

3. Straight radial lines in the section remain straight.

4. Shaft is loaded by twisting couples in planes that are perpendicular to the axis of the shaft.

5. Stresses do not exceed the proportional limit.

3–2. Derivation of Torsion Formulas

Fig. 3–1 shows two views of a solid circular shaft. If a torque T is applied at the ends of the shaft, a fiber AB on the outside surface, which is originally straight, will be twisted into a helix AC as the shaft is twisted through the angle θ. This helix is formed as follows:

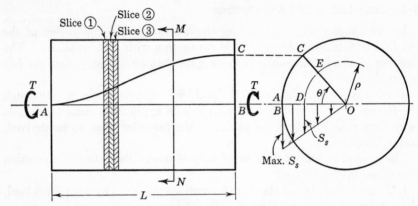

FIG. 3–1. — Deformation of circular shaft.

Imagine the shaft to consist of innumerable thin slices, each of which is rigid and joined to adjacent slices by elastic fibers. Slice (2) will rotate past slice (1) until the elastic fibers joining them are deformed enough to create a resisting torque which balances the applied torque. When this happens, slices (1) and (2) will act as a rigid unit and transmit the torque to slice (3); this slice will rotate enough so that the elastic fibers joining it and slice (2) develop a resisting torque equal to the applied torque. This type of deformation proceeds throughout the length L of the shaft. The helix AC is the line joining the original reference line AB on these slices as they become infinitely thin. This description of the twisting action is idealized; for all such slices actually start rotating simultaneously relative to each other as soon as the torque is applied, the angle of rotation θ becoming larger as the applied torque is increased.

Consider now any internal fiber located a radial distance ρ from the axis of the shaft. From assumption 3 of Art. 3–1, the radius of such a fiber also rotates through the angle θ, causing a total shearing deformation δ_s equal to DE. The length of this deformation is the arc of a circle whose radius is ρ and which is subtended by the angle of θ radians; the length is given by

$$\delta_s = DE = \rho\theta \tag{a}$$

The unit deformation of this fiber is

$$\gamma = \frac{\delta_s}{L} = \frac{\rho\theta}{L} \tag{b}$$

The shearing stress at this typical fiber is determined from Hooke's law to be

$$S_s = G\gamma = \left(\frac{G\theta}{L}\right)\rho \tag{c}$$

Eq. (c) may be called the equation of compatibility, since the stresses expressed by it are compatible with the elastic deformations. Note that each of the terms in the parentheses in this equation is a constant which does not depend upon the particular internal fiber chosen for analysis; the product of these terms represents a constant. Therefore we conclude that the shearing stress at any internal fiber is determined by the product of a constant and a variable radial distance; i.e., *the stress distribution along any radius varies linearly with the distance from the axis of the shaft.* Fig. 3–1 illustrates the stress variation along the radius *OB;* the maximum stress occurs at the outside fiber and is denoted by max. S_s.

In line with the general procedure outlined in Art. 3–1, the shaft is divided into two segments by a cutting plane *MN.* Fig. 3–2 shows the free-body diagram of the left-hand portion.

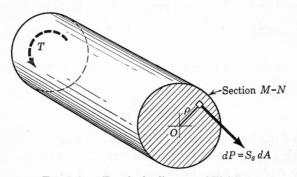

FIG. 3–2. — Free-body diagram of Fig. 3–1.

A differential area of section *M–N* at a radial distance ρ from the axis of the shaft carries the differential resisting load $dP = S_s\,dA$. By considering an area infinitesimally small, we may assume the stress to be uniform over such an area. Since the function of this resisting load dP is to produce resistance to the applied torque T, the load must be directed perpendicular to the radius ρ in order to produce the maximum effect. It is true, but difficult to prove here, that dP is directed perpendicular to ρ; nevertheless, we may take it as axiomatic that loads always distribute themselves as efficiently as possible. It is this variation of the principle of the conservation of energy that determines the direction of dP as perpendicular to ρ so that it produces maximum torsional resistance.

To satisfy the condition of static equilibrium, we apply $\Sigma M = 0$, or the fact that the applied torque T equals the resisting torque T_r. The resisting torque T_r is the sum of the resisting torques developed by all differential loads dP:

$$T = T_r = \int \rho \, dP = \int \rho \, (S_s \, dA)$$

Replacing S_s by its value from Eq. (c) gives

$$T = \frac{G\theta}{L} \int \rho^2 \, dA$$

or, since $\int \rho^2 \, dA = J$, the polar moment of inertia of the cross-section,

$$T = \frac{G\theta}{L} J$$

This is usually written,[1]

$$\theta = \frac{TL}{JG} \tag{3-1}$$

In order for θ to be in the proper units of radians, T must be in in.-lb and L in in.; J of course is in in.⁴, and G is in psi. If we wish to express θ in degrees, we multiply the right-hand member of Eq. (3–1) by the unit fraction, $\dfrac{180 \text{ degrees}}{\pi \text{ radians}} = 57.3$ degrees/radian.

By replacing the product $\dfrac{G\theta}{L}$ in Eq. (c) by its equivalent value $\dfrac{T}{J}$ from Eq. (3–1), we obtain

$$S_s = \frac{T\rho}{J} \tag{3-2}$$

This is called the torsion formula. The formula that determines the maximum shearing stress is a more common form of the torsion formula. It is obtained by replacing ρ by the radius r of the shaft:

$$\textbf{Max. } S_s = \frac{Tr}{J} \tag{3-2a}$$

Note that since Hooke's law was used in deriving these equations, the stresses must not exceed the shearing proportional limit;[2] also, these for-

---

[1] Note the similarity of Eq. (3–1) and the equation for linear deformation $\delta = \dfrac{PL}{AE}$. This similarity will make the two equations easier to remember.

[2] Eq. (3–2a) is sometimes used to determine the shearing stress at rupture. Although the proportional limit is exceeded, the fictitious shearing stress so obtained is called the *torsional modulus of rupture*. It is used to compare the ultimate strengths of specimens of various materials and diameters.

mulas are applicable only to circular shafts, either solid or hollow.[3]

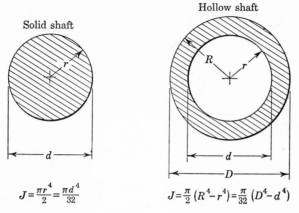

FIG. 3–3. — Polar moments of inertia.

The values of polar moments of inertia for circular shafts are given in Fig. 3–3. Using these values, we obtain the following modifications of the torsion formula:

Solid shaft: **Max. S_s** $= \dfrac{2\,T}{\pi r^3} = \dfrac{16\,T}{\pi\,d^3}$ **(3–2b)**

Hollow shaft: **Max. S_s** $= \dfrac{2\,TR}{\pi(R^4-r^4)} = \dfrac{16\,T\,D}{\pi(D^4-d^4)}$ **(3–2c)**

In practical applications, the shaft is used to transmit power. A power-torque relation is obtained from the fact that the work W done by a torque T in N revolutions is

$$W = T(2\,\pi N) \text{ in.-lb}$$

If N is expressed in revolutions per minute (rpm) the power is

$$P = 2\,\pi TN \text{ in.-lb/min}$$

This is usually converted to horsepower by multiplying by the unit fraction, $\dfrac{1 \text{ hp}}{(33{,}000 \times 12) \text{ in.-lb/min}}$. Thus we obtain

[3] A satisfactory formula for determining the maximum shearing stress in rectangular shafts is

$$S_s = \frac{T}{ab^2}\left(3 + 1.8\,\frac{b}{a}\right)$$

where a is the long side and b the short side of the rectangular section.

$$\text{hp} = \frac{2\,\pi TN}{33,000 \times 12}$$

By multiplying the constants and rearranging the terms, we can write this as

$$T = 63,000\,\frac{hp}{N} \tag{3-3}$$

This value of T in in.-lb may be used in Eq. (3-2) to obtain the maximum shearing stress, and in Eq. (3-1) to determine the angle of twist.

ILLUSTRATIVE PROBLEMS

301. A solid shaft in a certain rolling mill transmits 30 hp at 100 rpm. Find the diameter of the shaft so as not to exceed a shearing stress of 6000 psi and an angle of twist of more than 5.73° in a length of 10 ft. $G = 12 \times 10^6$ psi.

Solution: This problem illustrates a design that must possess sufficient strength as well as rigidity. We start by applying Eq. (3-3) to determine the torque.

$$\left[T = 63,000\,\frac{hp}{N}\right] \qquad T = (63,000)\,\frac{30}{100} = 18,900 \text{ in.-lb}$$

To satisfy the condition of strength, we apply the torsion formula, Eq. (3-2b).

$$\left[S_s = \frac{16\,T}{\pi d^3}\right] \qquad 6000 = \frac{16(18,900)}{\pi d^3}$$

from which

$$d^3 = 16.05 \quad \text{and} \quad d = 2.52 \text{ in.}$$

We next apply the angle of twist relation, Eq. (3-1), to determine the diameter necessary to satisfy the requirement of rigidity. In degrees, this is

$$\theta = \frac{TL}{JG} \times 57.3 \quad \text{or} \quad J = \frac{TL}{\theta G} \times 57.3$$

whence

$$\frac{\pi d^4}{32} = \frac{18,900(10 \times 12)(57.3)}{(5.73)(12 \times 10^6)}$$

From this

$$d^4 = 19.25 \quad \text{and} \quad d = 2.09 \text{ in.}$$

The larger diameter, $d = 2.52$ in., will satisfy both strength and rigidity.

302. Two solid shafts of different materials are rigidly fastened together and attached to rigid supports as shown in Fig. 3-4. The aluminum segment is 3 in. in diameter, and $G_a = 4 \times 10^6$ psi. The steel segment has a diameter of 2 in. and $G_s = 12 \times 10^6$ psi. The torque, $T = 10,000$ in.-lb, is applied at the junction of the two segments. Compute the maximum shearing stress developed in the assembly.

Solution: This problem is statically indeterminate in that we do not know how the applied torque is apportioned to each segment. From statics, we have

$[\Sigma M = 0]$ $\qquad\qquad T_s + T_a = T = 10{,}000$ $\qquad\qquad$ (a)

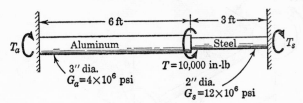

FIG. 3–4. — Statically indeterminate composite shaft.

Another relation between T_s and T_a is obtained from the condition that each segment has the same angular deformation, so that $\theta_s = \theta_a$. Applying Eq. (3–1) gives

$$\left[\left(\frac{TL}{JG}\right)_s = \left(\frac{TL}{JG}\right)_a\right]$$
$$\frac{T_s(3)}{\dfrac{\pi(2)^4}{32}(12 \times 10^6)} = \frac{T_a(6)}{\dfrac{\pi(3)^4}{32}(4 \times 10^6)}$$

from which

$$T_s = \frac{96}{81} T_a \qquad\qquad (b)$$

Solving Eqs. (a) and (b), we obtain

$$T_a = 4570 \text{ in.-lb} \quad\text{and}\quad T_s = 5430 \text{ in.-lb}$$

Applying the torsion formula, we find the stresses to be

$$\left[S_s = \frac{16\,T}{\pi d^3}\right]$$
$$(S_s)_a = \frac{16(4570)}{\pi(3)^3} = 843 \text{ psi} \quad Ans.$$
$$(S_s)_s = \frac{16(5430)}{\pi(2)^3} = 3460 \text{ psi} \quad Ans.$$

303. A shaft 2 in. in diameter is loaded by torques applied to gears fastened to it as indicated in Fig. 3–5. If $G = 12 \times 10^6$ psi, compute the relative angle of twist in degrees between gears A and C.

Solution: A vertical line through each gear being taken as a reference line, the angular deformations of gears A and C relative to B are indicated on gears A and C respectively as $\theta_{A/B}$ and $\theta_{C/B}$. Projecting these deformations on gear B shows that the relative twist between gears A and C, $\theta_{A/C}$, is the difference between $\theta_{A/B}$ and $\theta_{C/B}$. Therefore, applying Eq. (3–1) gives,

$$\theta_{A/C} = \theta_{A/B} - \theta_{C/B} = \left(\frac{TL}{JG}\right)_{AB} - \left(\frac{TL}{JG}\right)_{CB}$$

$$= \frac{(500 \times 12)(6 \times 12)(57.3)}{\dfrac{\pi(2)^4}{32}(12 \times 10^6)} - \frac{(300 \times 12)(4 \times 12)(57.3)}{\dfrac{\pi(2)^4}{32}(12 \times 10^6)}$$

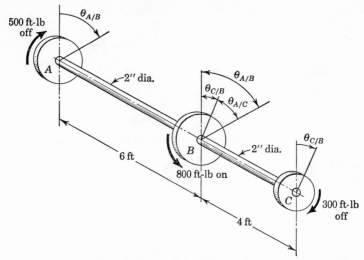

FIG. 3–5. — Angular deformations.

This is written more conveniently as

$$\theta_{A/C} = \frac{(12)(12)(57.3)}{\dfrac{\pi(2)^4}{32}(12 \times 10^6)} [(500)(6) - (300)(4)] = 0.789° \quad Ans.$$

PROBLEMS

304. What is the minimum diameter of a solid shaft that will not twist through more than $3°$ in a 10-ft length when subjected to a torque of 100,000 in.-lb? $G = 12 \times 10^6$ psi. $\qquad Ans.\quad d = 3.74$ in.

305. A solid shaft 12 ft long is stressed to 8000 psi when twisted through $8°$. If $G = 12 \times 10^6$ psi, compute the shaft diameter. What hp may be transmitted at 1200 rpm? $\qquad Ans.\quad d = 1.376$ in.

306. A marine propeller shaft is to transmit 5000 hp at 126 rpm without exceeding a shearing stress of 6000 psi or twisting through more than $1°$ in a length of 20 diameters. Compute the proper diameter if $G = 12 \times 10^6$ psi.

307. Show that a hollow circular shaft whose inner diameter is half the outer diameter has a torsional strength equal to $\frac{15}{16}$ of that of a solid shaft of the same outside diameter.

308. Determine the maximum torque that may be applied to a hollow circular shaft 5 in. outside diameter and 3 in. inside diameter, without exceeding a shearing stress of 8000 psi and a twist of $\frac{1}{12}$ degree per ft. Assume $G = 12 \times 10^6$ psi.

309. A stepped steel shaft consists of a hollow shaft 6 ft long, with an outside diameter of 3 in. and an inside diameter of $2\frac{1}{2}$ in., rigidly attached to a solid shaft 4 ft long and $2\frac{1}{2}$ in. in diameter. Determine the maximum torque that may be applied

without exceeding a shearing stress of 10,000 psi and a twist of 1.5° in the 10-ft
length. Assume $G = 12 \times 10^6$ psi.   *Ans.* $T = 10,480$ in.-lb

310. In the compound shaft described in Illus. Prob. 302 and Fig. 3–4, compute
the torque that may be applied without exceeding a shearing stress of 10,000 psi in
the steel and 6000 psi in the aluminum.

311. The compound shaft shown is attached to rigid supports. Segment AB is
of aluminum, for which $S_s \leq 4000$ psi and
$G = 4 \times 10^6$ psi. Segment BC is of steel,
for which $S_s \leq 12,000$ psi and $G = 12 \times$
10^6 psi. If $a = 4$ ft, $b = 6$ ft, and $T =$
10,000 ft-lb, find the diameters at which

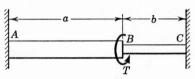

PROB. 311 and 312.

each material will be simultaneously stressed to its limit.
                                    Ans. $d_a = 2.40$ in.; $d_s = 3.60$ in.

312. A compound shaft is attached to rigid supports. If AB is a solid bronze
shaft 3 in. in diameter with maximum $S_s = 10,000$ psi and $G = 6 \times 10^6$ psi, and if
BC is a solid steel shaft 2 in. in diameter with maximum $S_s = 12,000$ psi and $G =$
12×10^6 psi, compute the ratio of lengths $\dfrac{b}{a}$ so that each shaft is stressed to its limit.

What torque T is required?   *Ans.* $\dfrac{b}{a} = \dfrac{10}{9}$; $T = 71,870$ in.-lb

313. A shaft loaded as indicated rotates at 1890 rpm. If $G = 12 \times 10^6$ psi, find
the maximum shear stress and the angle of twist of gear A relative to gear C.
                            Ans.   Max. $S_s = 5080$ psi; $\theta = 7.52°$

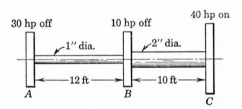

PROB. 313 and 314.

314. Solve Prob. 313 if the shaft rotates at 525 rpm, with 20 hp taken off at A,
30 hp removed at C, and 50 hp applied at B.

315. A torque T is applied, as shown, to a solid shaft with built-in ends. Prove
that the resisting torques at the walls

are $T_1 = \dfrac{Tb}{L}$ and $T_2 = \dfrac{Ta}{L}$. How would

these values be changed if the shaft

were hollow?

PROB. 315.

316. A shaft 4 in. in diameter and 12 ft long, with built-in ends, is subjected to one clockwise torque of 4000 ft-lb applied at 3 ft from the left end, and to another clockwise torque of 6000 ft-lb applied at 4 ft from the right end. Compute the shearing stress developed in each segment of the shaft. *Hint:* Use the results of Prob. 315 and apply superposition.

317. A hollow aluminum shaft of 3 in. outer diameter and 2 in. inner diameter is slipped over a solid steel shaft 2 in. in diameter and of the same length as the hollow shaft. The two are then fastened rigidly together at their ends. Determine the maximum shearing stress developed in each material by a torque of 2500 ft-lb. $G_a = 4 \times 10^6$ psi; $G_s = 12 \times 10^6$ psi.   *Ans.* $(S_s)_a = 4050$ psi; $(S_s)_s = 8110$ psi

318. A shaft composed of segments AC, CD, and DB is fastened to rigid supports as shown. For steel, $G = 12 \times 10^6$ psi; for aluminum, $G = 4 \times 10^6$ psi. Compute the maximum shearing stress developed in each segment. Are the results valid?   *Ans.* $T_A = 6470$ in.-lb; $T_B = 11,530$ in.-lb; $(S_s)_{al} = 3520$ psi

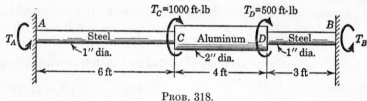

PROB. 318.

3–3. Flanged Bolt Couplings

A commonly used connection between two shafts is a flanged bolt coupling. It consists of flanges rigidly attached to the ends of the shafts and bolted together, as in Fig. 3–6. The torque is transmitted by the shearing force P created in the bolts.

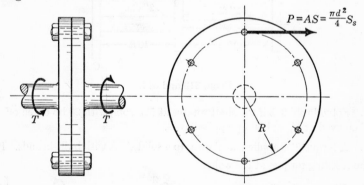

FIG. 3–6. — Flanged bolt coupling.

Assuming that the stress is uniformly distributed, the load in any bolt is given by the simple stress equation $P = AS$ and equals $\dfrac{\pi d^2}{4} S_s$. It acts through the center of the bolt and tangent to the bolt circle. The torque resistance of one bolt is PR, where R is the radius of the bolt circle. Therefore, for any number of bolts, n, the torque capacity of the coupling is expressed by

$$T = PRn = \frac{\pi d^2}{4} S_s Rn \qquad (3\text{–}4)$$

Occasionally a coupling has two concentric rows of bolts, as in Fig. 3–7. The load on any bolt in the outer row being denoted by P_1, and that on any bolt in the inner row by P_2, the torque capacity of the coupling is

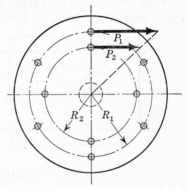

$$T = P_1R_1n_1 + P_2R_2n_2 \qquad (3\text{–}5)$$

The relation between P_1 and P_2 is determined from the fact that the comparatively rigid flanges cause deformations in the bolts that are proportional to their radial distances from the shaft axis. Consequently, remembering that loads are proportional to their deformations, we obtain

FIG. 3–7. — Coupling with two concentric bolt circles.

$$\frac{P_1}{R_1} = \frac{P_2}{R_2} \qquad (3\text{–}6)$$

From Eq. (3–6), P_2 may be expressed in terms of the maximum bolt load P_1 (equal to $\frac{\pi d^2}{4} S_s$), whence Eq. (3–5) determines the torque capacity. A similar procedure may be used for three or more concentric bolt circles. As we shall see in the next article, this situation occurs in eccentrically loaded riveted connections.

PROBLEMS

319. A flanged bolt coupling consists of eight $\frac{3}{4}$-in.-diameter bolts spaced evenly around a bolt circle 10 in. in diameter. Determine the torque capacity of the coupling if the allowable shearing stress in the bolts is 8000 psi.

Ans. $T = 11{,}700$ ft-lb

320. A flanged bolt coupling is used to connect a solid shaft 3 in. in diameter to a hollow shaft of $3\frac{1}{2}$ in. O.D. and 3 in. I.D. How many $\frac{1}{2}$-in. bolts must be used on an 8-in. diameter bolt circle so that the shearing stress will not exceed 8000 psi anywhere in the assembly?

321. A flanged bolt coupling consists of six $\frac{1}{2}$-in. bolts on a bolt circle 12 in. in diameter, and four $\frac{1}{2}$-in. bolts on a concentric bolt circle 9 in. in diameter, as shown in Fig. 3–7. What torque may be applied without exceeding a shearing stress of 8000 psi in the bolts?   Ans. $T = 6470$ ft-lb

3–4. Eccentrically Loaded Riveted Connections

Occasionally it is impossible to load a riveted connection so that the load passes through the centroid of the rivet group. Such a condition is called *eccentric loading;* the load is not distributed equally over all the rivets (see Fig. 3–8a). However, by adding a pair of equal, oppositely directed, and

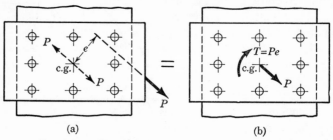

(a)   (b)

FIG. 3–8. — Eccentrically loaded riveted connection.

collinear forces of magnitude P (shown dashed) at the centroid of the rivet group, the applied eccentric load P is replaced by a central load P and the torsional couple $T = P\,e$, as shown in Fig. 3–8b.

The effect of the central load P is resisted equally by the direct load $P_d = \dfrac{P}{n}$ acting on each of the n rivets, as shown in Fig. 3–9a. The torsional couple T is resisted by torsional loads P_t (Fig. 3–9b), which act perpendicular to the radius ρ from the centroid of the rivet group and vary directly with the distance of the rivets from the centroid. To determine the torsional load on any rivet, we may consider that the connection is equivalent to a flanged coupling consisting of three concentric circles of rivets, and use the method outlined in Art. 3–3. The resultant load on any rivet is the vector sum of the direct and torsional loads on that rivet, and appears as shown in Fig. 3–9c.

A better method of determining the torsional load is to apply the torsion formula $S_s = \dfrac{T\rho}{J}$. If S_s represents the shearing stress at the center of any rivet and ρ is its radial distance from the centroid of the rivet group, J may be expressed as

$$J = \Sigma A \rho^2 \qquad (a)$$

Since all the rivets have the same area A, and since ρ^2 may be expressed in terms of the x and y coordinates of any rivet so that $\rho^2 = x^2 + y^2$ (see Fig. 3–9b), we may rewrite Eq. (a) as

$$J = A(\Sigma x^2 + \Sigma y^2) \qquad (b)$$

whence the torsion formula becomes

$$S_s = \frac{T\rho}{A(\Sigma x^2 + \Sigma y^2)} \qquad (c)$$

Transposing A to the left side of this equation determines the torsional load P_t on any rivet from $P_t = AS_s$, so we finally obtain

$$\boldsymbol{P_t} = \frac{T\rho}{\Sigma x^2 + \Sigma y^2} \qquad \textbf{(3–7)}$$

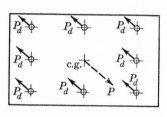

(a) Equal direct rivet loads

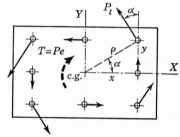

(b) Distribution of torsional loads

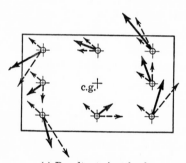

(c) Resultant rivet loads

Fig. 3–9. — Analysis of eccentrically loaded connection.

The resultant load on a typical rivet is obtained as the vector sum of P_d and P_t. See Fig. 3–9c. This vector addition is easily performed analytically by resolving P_d and P_t into x and y components. The components P_{d_x} and P_{d_y} of the direct load are constant for all rivets. The components of the torsional load P_t are obtained by observing from Fig. 3–9b that the angle α between the radius ρ and the X axis equals the angle between P_t and the Y axis; hence

$$P_{t_x} = P_t \sin \alpha = P_t \frac{y}{\rho}$$

and

$$P_{t_y} = P_t \cos \alpha = P_t \frac{x}{\rho}$$

since $\sin \alpha = \dfrac{y}{\rho}$ and $\cos \alpha = \dfrac{x}{\rho}.$ Replacing P_t in these relations by its value from Eq. (3–7), we obtain

$$\left.\begin{array}{l} P_{t_x} = \dfrac{T}{\Sigma x^2 + \Sigma y^2} \cdot y \\[4mm] P_{t_y} = \dfrac{T}{\Sigma x^2 + \Sigma y^2} \cdot x \end{array}\right\} \tag{3–8}$$

The maximum load on any rivet occurs when P_{d_x} and maximum P_{t_x}, as well as P_{d_y} and maximum P_{t_y}, are additive, as at the upper right corner; whence the resultant rivet load is found from

$$P_r = \sqrt{(P_{d_x} + P_{t_x})^2 + (P_{d_y} + P_{t_y})^2} \tag{3–9}$$

The use of these equations is illustrated in the following example.

ILLUSTRATIVE PROBLEM

322. On the connection of 12 rivets shown in Fig. 3–10, the load $P = 48,000$ lb passes through the center of rivet C and has a slope of 4 to 3. Determine the resultant load on the most heavily loaded rivet.

Solution: The effect of the applied load is equivalent to an equal central load acting through the centroid of the rivet group plus a torsional couple equal to the moment of P about the centroid of the rivet group. Replacing P by its components $P_x = 28,800$ lb and $P_y = 38,400$ lb, and noting that the moment of P is equal to the moment sum of its components, we find that the torsional couple is

$$T = 38,400(4.5) = 172,800 \text{ in.-lb}$$

Before applying Eq. (3–8) we compute the value of Σx^2 and Σy^2. There are six rivets whose x coordinate is 1.5 in. and six rivets whose x coordinate is 4.5 in. Also there are eight rivets whose y coordinate is 4 in. Therefore,

$$\Sigma x^2 + \Sigma y^2 = [6(1.5)^2 + 6(4.5)^2] + 8(4)^2 = 263$$

Applying Eq. (3–8) gives the maximum components of the torsional load as

$$\left[P_{t_x} = \frac{T}{\Sigma x^2 + \Sigma y^2} \cdot y\right] \qquad P_{t_x} = \frac{172,800}{263}(4) = 2620 \text{ lb}$$

$$\left[P_{t_y} = \frac{T}{\Sigma x^2 + \Sigma y^2} \cdot x\right] \qquad P_{t_y} = \frac{172,800}{263}(4.5) = 2950 \text{ lb}$$

The x and y components of the direct load on any rivet are found by dividing the x and y components of the applied load by the number of rivets. Thus

$$P_{d_x} = \frac{P_x}{n} = \frac{28,800}{12} = 2400 \text{ lb}$$

and

$$P_{d_y} = \frac{P_y}{n} = \frac{38,400}{12} = 3200 \text{ lb}$$

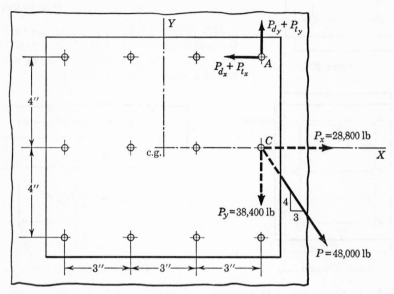

FIG. 3–10.

The most heavily loaded rivet is at A, where the maximum components of the direct and torsional loads are additive as shown. Applying Eq. (3–9), we have,

$$P_r = \sqrt{(P_{d_x} + P_{t_x})^2 + (P_{d_y} + P_{t_y})^2}$$

$$= \sqrt{(2400 + 2620)^2 + (3200 + 2950)^2} = 7950 \text{ lb} \quad Ans.$$

PROBLEMS

323. Compute the resultant load on the least loaded rivet in Prob. 322.

324. A gusset plate is riveted to a larger plate by means of four $\frac{3}{4}$-in. rivets arranged and loaded as shown. Determine the maximum and minimum shear stress developed in the rivets.   *Ans.* Max. $S_s = 5300$ psi; min. $S_s = 3670$ psi

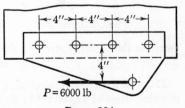

PROB. 324.

325. If the maximum load permitted on any single rivet in the given connection is

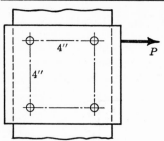

Prob. 325.

5000 lb, compute the safe value of P.

Ans. $P = 12{,}650$ lb

326.   For the eccentrically loaded rivet group shown, compute P so that there will be a maximum rivet load of 6000 lb.

Ans. $P = 18{,}800$ lb

327.   Rivets $\frac{15}{16}$ in. in diameter are used in the connection in Prob. 326. If $P = 21{,}000$ lb, what thickness of plate is required so as not to exceed a bearing stress of 20,000 psi?

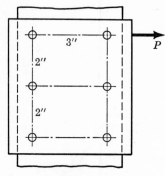

Prob. 326 and 327.

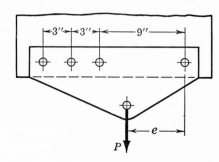

Prob. 328, 329, and 330.

328.   In the gusset plate connection shown, if $e = 6$ in. and $P = 12{,}000$ lb, determine the shearing stress in the most heavily loaded of the four $\frac{3}{4}$-in. rivets.

Ans. $S_s = 12{,}600$ psi

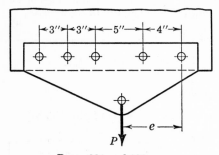

Prob. 331 and 332.

329.   If $P = 10{,}000$ lb applied as shown, what min. value of e will cause a maximum shearing stress of 12,000 psi in the worst loaded of the four $\frac{3}{4}$-in. rivets?   Ans. $e = 5.06$ in.

330.   In the connection shown, what value of P will cause a maximum shearing stress of 13,500 psi in the $\frac{3}{4}$-in. rivets if $e = 5$ in.?   Ans. $P = 11{,}150$ lb

331.   In the gusset plate connection shown, if $e = 6$ in. and $P = 20{,}000$ lb, compute the shearing stress in the worst and least loaded of the five $\frac{7}{8}$-in. rivets.

Ans.   Max. $S_s = 10{,}300$ psi; min. $S_s = 3460$ psi

332.   In the given connection, if $P = 20{,}000$ lb, what min. value of e will cause a shearing stress of 12,000 psi in the most heavily loaded of the five $\frac{7}{8}$-in. rivets?

Ans. $e = 5.07$ in.

3–5. Helical Springs

The close-coiled helical spring in Fig. 3–11 is elongated by an axial load
P. The spring is composed of a wire or round rod of diameter *d* wound into
a helix of mean radius *R*. The helix angle is small, so that any coil of the
spring may be considered as lying approximately in a plane perpendicular
to the axis of the spring.

To determine the stresses produced by *P*, we
follow the general procedure of passing an exploratory cutting plane *m–n* through any typical section
as shown, and then determining the resisting forces
required for equilibrium. We then analyze the
stress distribution that creates these resisting
forces.

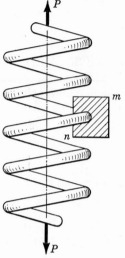

Fig. 3–12*a* shows the free-body diagram of the
upper half of the spring. To balance the applied
axial load *P*, the exposed shaded cross-section of the
spring must provide the resistance P_r equal to *P*.
The free body is now in equilibrium as far as a
vertical and horizontal summation of forces is concerned. To complete equilibrium, however, a moment summation must also equal zero. It is evident that *P* and P_r, being equal, opposite, and
parallel, create a couple of magnitude *PR* which
can be balanced only by an opposite couple. This

FIG. 3–11. — Helical
spring.

resisting couple is created by a torsional shearing stress distributed over
the cross-section of the spring; it is represented by $T = PR$.

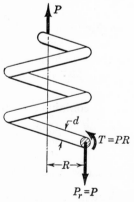

(a) Free-body diagram

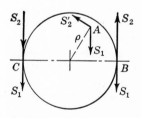

(b) Magnified view of
spring cross-section *m-n*

FIG. 3–12. — Analysis of helical spring.

The magnified view of the cross-section in Fig. 3–12b shows the stress distribution that created the resisting forces. Two types of shearing stress are produced: (1) direct shearing stresses like S_1, uniformly distributed over the spring section and creating the resisting load P_r that passes through the centroid of the section, and (2) variable torsional shearing stresses like S_2, caused by the twisting couple $T = PR$. The torsional stresses S_2 vary in magnitude with their radial distance from the centroid, and are directed perpendicular to the radius, as at A. The resultant shearing stress is the vector sum of the direct and torsional shearing stresses. At B, the stresses are oppositely directed, and the resultant stress is the difference between S_2 and S_1. At the inside fiber C, however, the two stresses are collinear and in the same sense; their sum produces the maximum stress in the section. The maximum stress always occurs at the inside element of the spring wire. Is there any position on the diameter BC at which the shearing stress is zero? If so, how can you locate it?

To summarize the above discussion, the maximum shearing stress occurs at the inside element and is given by the sum of the direct shearing stress $S_1 = \dfrac{P}{A}$ and the maximum value of the torsional shearing stress $S_2 = \dfrac{Tr}{J}$, or

$$S_s = S_1 + S_2 = \frac{4\,P}{\pi d^2} + \frac{16(PR)}{\pi d^3}$$

This may be written

$$S_s = \frac{16\,PR}{\pi d^3}\left(1 + \frac{d}{4\,R}\right) \tag{3–10}$$

Examination of Eq. (3–10) shows that the ratio $\dfrac{d}{4\,R}$ is small for a spring composed of a wire of relatively small diameter wound on a spring with a large radius; this indicates that in such cases the maximum stress is caused primarily by torsion of the spring wire. On the other hand, heavy coil springs, such as are used on railroad cars, are made of wire with a relatively large diameter d in comparison with R, the mean radius of the spring; in these springs the effect of direct shearing stress is 14% or more of the total stress and cannot be disregarded.

It should be noted that the above discussion contains an error because the torsion formula, derived for use with straight bars, was applied to a curved bar. This error is of significance in heavy springs and is explained in Fig. 3–13. In the straight bar in Fig. 3–13a, torsion produces the same shearing deformation δ_s on fibers AB and CD. The shearing strain, $\gamma = \dfrac{\delta_s}{L}$, is the same at B and D, since the elements AB and CD have the same original length. A different situation, however, exists in the curved bar in Fig. 3–13b. Although fibers AB and CD undergo the same shearing deformation, the shearing strain at B on the inside element is greater than at D on the outside element because of the shorter initial length of AB. Therefore, since stress is proportional to strain, the shearing stress on the inner fibers of a curved bar is greater than on the outer fibers. This fact

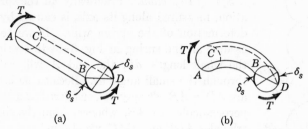

(a)   (b)

Fig. 3–13. — Torsion of straight and of curved segments.

is not taken into account in Eq. (3–10). Of course, the importance of this error depends upon how greatly elements AB and CD differ in original length. Evidently this difference depends on how sharply curved the spring wire is, i.e., upon the ratio of d to R. A. M. Wahl has developed the following formula that takes account of the initial curvature of the spring wire:[4]

$$\text{Max. } S_s = \frac{16\,PR}{\pi d^3}\left(\frac{4\,m-1}{4\,m-4}+\frac{0.615}{m}\right) \tag{3–11}$$

where $m = \dfrac{2\,R}{d} = \dfrac{D}{d}$, the ratio of the mean diameter of the spring to the diameter of the spring wire. In light springs, where the ratio m is large, the first term in the parentheses approaches unity. Compare with Eq. (3–10) which may be rewritten in the following form:

$$\text{Max. } S_s = \frac{16\,PR}{\pi d^3}\left(1+\frac{0.5}{m}\right) \tag{3–10a}$$

For heavy springs which are sharply curved and in which m is not so large, Eq. (3–11) emphasizes and corrects the error in Eq. (3–10).

Factors 0.5 and 0.615 differ in Eqs. (3–10a) and (3–11) largely because the direct shearing stress is not actually distributed uniformly over the cross-section. We shall see later (page 156), when discussing horizontal shearing stress in beams, that, for a circular cross-section, the maximum shearing stress produced is approximately $\frac{4}{3}$ times the average shearing

[4] See A. M. Wahl, "Stresses in Heavy Closely Coiled Helical Springs," Trans. A.S.M.E., Vol. 51, paper No. APM–51–17.

stress and varies from 1.23 at the outside edges to 1.38 at the center. The factor 0.615 in Eq. (3–11) results from multiplying 0.5 by 1.23.

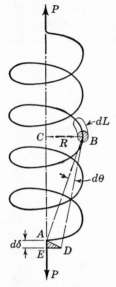

Note that springs are made of special steels and bronzes in which the allowable shearing stresses range from 30,000 to 120,000 psi.

Spring Deflection. Practically all the spring elongation, measured along its axis, is caused by torsional deformation of the spring wire. If we temporarily assume all the spring in Fig. 3–14 to be rigid except the small length dL, the end A will rotate to D through the small angle $d\theta$. Because $d\theta$ is small, the arc $AD = AB \cdot d\theta$ may be considered as a straight line perpendicular to AB, whence, from the similarity of triangles ADE and BAC, we obtain

$$\frac{AE}{AD} = \frac{BC}{AB}$$

or

$$\frac{d\delta}{AB \cdot d\theta} = \frac{R}{AB}$$

whence

$$d\delta = R \, d\theta \qquad (a)$$

Fig. 3–14. — Deflection of helical spring.

Applying Eq. (3–1), we may replace $d\theta$ by its equivalent value in terms of the torque and length:

$$d\delta = R \frac{(PR) \, dL}{JG} \qquad (b)$$

which is integrated to give the total elongation contributed by all elements of the spring:

$$\delta = \frac{PR^2 L}{JG} \qquad (c)$$

Replacing L by $2 \pi R n$, which is the length of n coils of radius R, and J by $\dfrac{\pi d^4}{32}$, we obtain

$$\delta = \frac{64 \, PR^3 n}{d^4 G} \qquad (3\text{–}12)$$

This expression for spring deflection neglects the deformation caused by direct shear:

$$\delta' = \frac{PL}{A_s G} = \frac{P(2 \pi R n)}{\dfrac{\pi d^2}{4} G} = \frac{8 \, PRn}{d^2 G} \qquad (3\text{–}13)$$

This latter deformation, however, is generally negligible compared to the value of δ given by Eq. (3–12) and consequently is usually ignored. Eq. (3–12) is also used to compute the deflection in compression springs provided the coils are not spaced so closely that they touch when the load is applied.

ILLUSTRATIVE PROBLEM

333. A weight $W = 150$ lb drops from rest through a height $h = 18$ in. before striking the steel spring shown in Fig. 3–15. The steel rod supporting the spring is 100 ft long and $\frac{1}{4}$-in. in diameter. The spring, which has a mean diameter of 4 in., consists of 8 turns of wire $\frac{3}{4}$ in. in diameter. Compute the maximum stress and deformation produced in the spring and in the rod. Assume $E = 30 \times 10^6$ psi and $G = 12 \times 10^6$ psi. Neglect the mass of the spring and of the rod.

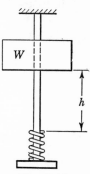

Fig. 3–15.

Solution: This problem illustrates the effect of dynamic loading. We use the work-energy method (see any standard text on engineering mechanics) in which the equivalent spring constant k of the assembly is given by

$$\frac{1}{k} = \frac{1}{k_1} + \frac{1}{k_2} = \frac{k_1 + k_2}{k_1 k_2} \tag{a}$$

where k_1 is the modulus of the spring and k_2 is the spring constant of the rod.

Since the spring constant is defined as the load that produces unit deformation of the spring, we obtain from Eq. (3–12):

$$k_1 = \frac{P}{\delta} = \frac{d^4 G}{64\, R^3 n} = \frac{(\frac{3}{4})^4 (12 \times 10^6)}{64 (2)^3 (8)} = 926 \text{ lb/in.}$$

For the steel rod, the spring constant is found from Eq. (1–6) to be

$$k_2 = \frac{P}{\delta} = \frac{AE}{L} = \frac{\frac{\pi}{4} \left(\frac{1}{4}\right)^2 (30 \times 10^6)}{100 \times 12} = 1230 \text{ lb/in.}$$

Substituting these values in Eq. (a), we obtain the equivalent spring constant

$$k = \frac{(926)(1230)}{926 + 1230} = 528 \text{ lb/in.}$$

The weight W has zero velocity when first dropped and zero velocity when the equivalent spring is deflected through δ in. Equating the resultant work on W to the zero change in kinetic energy, we have

$$[W(h + \delta) - \tfrac{1}{2} k \delta^2 = 0] \qquad\qquad 150(18 + \delta) - \tfrac{1}{2}(528)\delta^2 = 0$$
$$\delta^2 - 0.568\, \delta - 10.22 = 0$$
$$\delta = 3.49 \text{ in.}$$

The dynamic load that produces this deflection of the equivalent spring is

$[P = k\delta]$ $\qquad P = 528(3.49) = 1840 \text{ lb}$

Comparing the dynamic and the static load shows that the dynamic effect increases the stresses by $\dfrac{1840}{150}$, or 12.3 times.

The shearing stress in the spring is found from Eq. (3–11), with

$$m = \frac{2R}{d} = \frac{2(2)}{\frac{3}{4}} = 5.3$$

$$S_s = \frac{16\,PR}{\pi d^3}\left(\frac{4m-1}{4m-4} + \frac{0.615}{m}\right) = \frac{16(1840)(2)}{\pi(\frac{3}{4})^3}\left(\frac{21.3-1}{21.3-4} + \frac{0.615}{5.33}\right) = 56{,}700 \text{ psi}$$

If Eq. (3–10) had been used to compute the shearing stress, the result would have been 48,600 psi.

The tensile stress in the rod is

$$S = \frac{P}{A} = \frac{1840}{\dfrac{\pi}{4}\left(\dfrac{1}{4}\right)^2} = 37{,}500 \text{ psi}$$

The spring deflection is

$$\delta_1 = \frac{P}{k_1} = \frac{1840}{926} = 1.985 \text{ in.}$$

and the extension of the rod is

$$\delta_2 = \frac{P}{k_2} = \frac{1840}{1230} = 1.497 \text{ in.}$$

Query: Should the sum of the two deflections have any relation to the deflection of the equivalent spring? Does this provide any check?

PROBLEMS

334. Determine the maximum stress and elongation in a helical spring composed of 20 turns of $\frac{3}{4}$-in. wire with a mean diameter of 7 in. when the spring is supporting a load of 300 lb. $G = 12 \times 10^6$ psi. Use Eq. (3–11).

335. What is the maximum elongation of the spring in Prob. 334 if the spring is made of phosphor bronze, with $G = 6 \times 10^6$ psi and max. $S_s = 20{,}000$ psi? Use Eq. (3–11).

336. A helical spring is made by wrapping wire 1 in. in diameter around a forming cylinder 4 in. in diameter. Compute the number of turns required to permit a stretch of 2 in. without exceeding a shearing stress of 10,000 psi. $G = 12 \times 10^6$ psi. Use Eq. (3–10). *Ans.* $n = 33.6$ turns

337. A helical spring made of wire $\frac{3}{4}$ in. in diameter has a mean diameter of 6 in. and 20 turns. What is the maximum stress developed by a deflection of 1 in.? $G = 12 \times 10^6$ psi. Use Eq. (3–11). *Ans.* $S_s = 4720$ psi

338. A clutch is activated by six helical springs symmetrically spaced. Each spring consists of 16 turns of steel wire $\frac{1}{4}$ in. in diameter; the outside diameter of the spring is 3 in. Determine the load exerted against the clutch plate by a contraction of $1\frac{1}{2}$ in. in the springs. What is the shearing stress in the springs? $G = 12 \times 10^6$ psi. Use Eq. (3–10).

339. A helical spring has a mean diameter of 4 in. and is made of 20 turns of wire $\frac{1}{2}$ in. in diameter. What is the maximum shearing stress when the spring is stretched $\frac{3}{4}$ in.? $G = 12 \times 10^6$ psi. Use Eq. (3–11).   *Ans.* $S_s = 5300$ psi

340. Two steel springs arranged in series as shown support a load P. The upper spring has 16 turns of wire $\frac{3}{8}$ in. in diameter on a mean radius of 2 in. The lower spring consists of 12 turns of $\frac{1}{4}$-in.-diameter wire on a mean radius of $1\frac{3}{4}$ in. If the stress in either spring must not exceed 40,000 psi, compute P and the total elongation of the assembly. $G = 12 \times 10^6$ psi. Use Eq. (3–11). Compute the equivalent spring constant as discussed in Illus. Prob. 333.

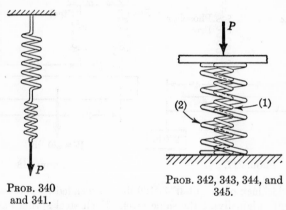

PROB. 340
and 341.

PROB. 342, 343, 344, and
345.

341. Solve Prob. 340 if the lower spring is made of phosphor bronze for which max. $S_s = 30,000$ psi and $G = 6 \times 10^6$ psi, all other data remaining unchanged.

342. A load P is supported by two concentric steel springs arranged as shown. The inner spring consists of 18 turns of wire $\frac{1}{2}$ in. in diameter on a mean diameter of 4 in.; the outer spring has 24 turns of $\frac{3}{4}$-in. wire on a mean diameter of 6 in. Compute the maximum load P that will not exceed a stress of 20,000 psi in either spring. Use Eq. (3–10).   *Ans.* $P = 491$ lb

343. If the inner spring in Prob. 342 is made of phosphor bronze, with $G = 6 \times 10^6$ psi, compute the shearing stress in each spring from a load $P = 600$ lb. All other data remain unchanged. Use Eq. (3–11).

344. Two concentric steel springs arranged as shown support a load $P = 600$ lb. The inner spring (1) is made of 18 turns of wire $\frac{3}{8}$ in. in diameter and has a mean diameter of 3 in. The outer spring (2) is composed of 20 turns of wire $\frac{5}{8}$ in. in diameter on a mean diameter of 5 in. $G = 12 \times 10^6$ psi. Compute the deflection and maximum stress. Use Eq. (3–11).   *Ans.* $\delta = 3.93$ in.; $S_s = 41,300$ psi

345. Using the data in Prob. 344, determine the maximum load P that can be supported without exceeding a shearing stress of 30,000 psi in either spring. What deflection is produced? Use Eq. (3–11). *Ans.* $P = 435$ lb; $\delta = 2.85$ in.

346. A weight W of 100 lb is dropped from rest through a height of 2 ft on a helical spring having a mean diameter of 4 in. and composed of 12 turns of wire $\frac{1}{2}$ in. in diameter. Compute the maximum stress and deformation produced in the spring. $G = 12 \times 10^6$ psi. Use Eq. (3–10).

347. A rigid bar, hinged at one end, is supported by two springs as shown. The bronze spring has 20 turns of $\frac{1}{4}$-in. wire, $R = 3$ in., $G = 6 \times 10^6$ psi. The steel spring has 15 turns of $\frac{1}{4}$-in. wire, $R = 3$ in., $G = 12 \times 10^6$ psi. Compute the load supported by each spring. *Ans.* $P_s = 240$ lb

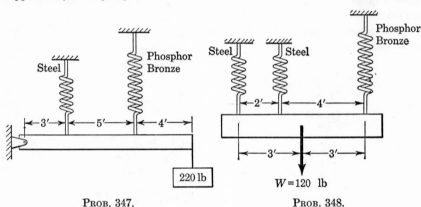

PROB. 347. PROB. 348.

348. A rigid block of weight $W = 120$ lb is suspended by three springs whose lower ends were originally at the same level. Each steel spring has 24 turns of wire $\frac{1}{4}$ in. in diameter on a mean diameter of 3 in., and $G = 12 \times 10^6$ psi. The bronze spring has 40 turns of $\frac{3}{8}$-in. wire on a mean diameter of 4 in., and $G = 6 \times 10^6$ psi. Compute the maximum shearing stress in each spring. Use Eq. (3–10).

SUMMARY

The discussion of torsion in this chapter is limited to circular sections, solid or hollow. The shearing stress varies directly with the radial distance from the center of the cross-section and is expressed by

$$S_s = \frac{T\rho}{J} \tag{3-2}$$

The maximum shearing stress in solid shafts of diameter d becomes

$$S_s = \frac{16\,T}{\pi d^3} \tag{3-2b}$$

In hollow shafts of external diameter D and internal diameter d, it is

$$S_s = \frac{16\,TD}{\pi\,(D^4 - d^4)} \tag{3-2c}$$

The angular deformation in a length L is expressed in radians by

$$\theta = \frac{TL}{JG} \tag{3-1}$$

which is converted to degrees by multiplying by $\dfrac{180}{\pi} = 57.3$. Eq. (3–1) is useful not only in determining angular deformations, but also as a basis for solving statically indeterminate problems in torsion.

A convenient relation between torque in in.-lb and horsepower transmitted by a shaft rotating at N rpm is

$$T = 63{,}000\,\frac{hp}{N} \tag{3-3}$$

The study of flanged bolt couplings (Art. 3–3) served to introduce the more general problem of eccentrically loaded riveted connections (Art. 3–4). If the eccentric load is replaced by a central load P and a torsional couple $T = Pe$, the resultant load on any rivet is the vector sum of the direct rivet load $P_d = \dfrac{P}{n}$ (n being the number of rivets) and a torsional rivet load P_t expressed by

$$P_t = \frac{T\rho}{\Sigma x^2 + \Sigma y^2} \tag{3-7}$$

However, the resultant rivet load P_r is more conveniently determined by combining the components of the direct rivet load and the torsional load. The components P_{d_x} and P_{d_y} are constant for all rivets, and the components of the torsional load are given by

and

$$\left. \begin{aligned} P_{t_x} &= \frac{Ty}{\Sigma x^2 + \Sigma y^2} \\[2mm] P_{t_y} &= \frac{Tx}{\Sigma x^2 + \Sigma y^2} \end{aligned} \right\} \tag{3-8}$$

The maximum rivet load is found from

$$P_r = \sqrt{(P_{d_x} + P_{t_x})^2 + (P_{d_y} + P_{t_y})^2} \tag{3-9}$$

In close-coiled helical springs (Art. 3–5) the maximum shearing stress is expressed fairly accurately by

$$S_s = \frac{16\,PR}{\pi d^3}\left(1 + \frac{d}{4\,R}\right)$$ (3–10)

and more exactly by

$$S_s = \frac{16\,PR}{\pi d^3}\left(\frac{4\,m - 1}{4\,m - 4} + \frac{0.615}{m}\right)$$ (3–11)

where $m = \dfrac{2\,R}{d}$.

The elongation of the spring generally neglects the effect of direct shearing deformation and is given by

$$\delta = \frac{64\,PR^3 n}{d^4 G}$$ (3–12)

Chapter IV
Shear and Moment in Beams

4–1. Introduction

The basic problem in strength of materials is to determine the relations between the stresses and deformations caused by loads applied to any structure. In axial or torsional loadings, we had little trouble in applying the stress and deformation relations, because in the majority of cases the loading either remains constant over the entire structure or is distributed in definite amounts to the component parts.

The study of bending loads, however, is complicated by the fact that the loading effects vary from section to section of the beam. These loading effects take the form of a vertical shearing force and a bending moment, sometimes referred to as *shear* and *moment*. These terms will be defined in the next article. It will be shown in Chapter V that two kinds of stress act over the transverse section of a beam: (*1*) a bending stress, which varies directly with the bending moment, and (*2*) a shearing stress, which varies directly with the vertical shear. As a preliminary to the study of stresses in beams, therefore, this chapter is concerned with the variation in vertical shear and bending moment in beams subjected to various combinations of loadings under different conditions of support, particularly the determination of the maximum values of shear and moment. Beam deflections will be discussed in Chapter VI.

Methods of supporting some types of beams are shown in Fig. 4–1. A simple beam is supported by a hinged reaction at one end and a roller support at the other, but is not otherwise restrained. A cantilever beam is supported at one end only, with suitable restraint to prevent rotation of that end. An overhanging beam is supported by a hinge and a roller reaction, with either or both ends extending beyond the supports. These beams are all statically determinate; their reactions can be determined directly from the equations of static equilibrium.

Other methods of supporting beams are shown in Fig. 4–2. The propped beam, the fixed-ended or restrained beam, and the continuous beam each has at least one more reactive element than is absolutely necessary to support it. Such beams are statically indeterminate; the presence of excess supports requires the use of additional equations obtained from considering the elastic deformations of the beam. Their solution is discussed in Chapters VII and VIII.

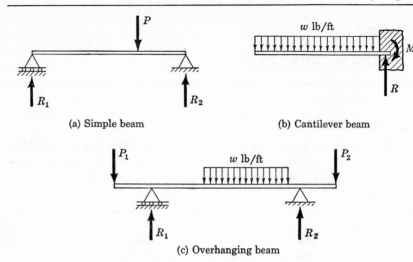

(a) Simple beam   (b) Cantilever beam

(c) Overhanging beam

FIG. 4–1. — Statically determinate beams.

A *concentrated load* is one that acts over so small a distance that it can be assumed to act at a point, as in Fig. 4–1a. In contrast, a *distributed load* acts over a considerable length of the beam. It may be distributed uniformly over the entire length, as in Fig. 4–1b, or over part of the length, as in Fig. 4–1c. Distributed loads may also be uniformly varying or non-uniform. In a uniformly varying or triangular load, the intensity of load-

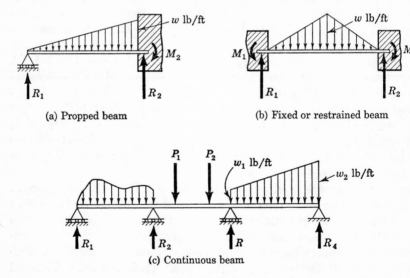

(a) Propped beam   (b) Fixed or restrained beam

(c) Continuous beam

FIG. 4–2. — Statically indeterminate beams.

ing increases or decreases at a constant rate, as in Fig. 4–2a and 4–2b; this condition might result from water pressure acting on the face of a dam or from the dumping of a pile of sand. The trapezoidal loading in the right segment of Fig. 4–2c is a combination of a uniform and a uniformly varying load. The loading may also be nonuniform, as in the left segment of Fig. 4–2c; this may result from the haphazard piling of sand bags.

4–2. Shear and Moment

Fig. 4–3a shows a simple beam that carries a concentrated load P and is held in equilibrium by the reactions R_1 and R_2. For the time being, neglect

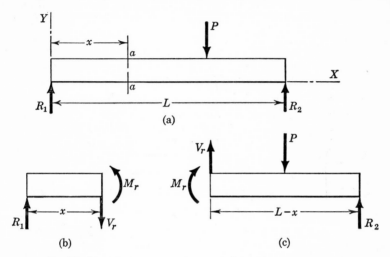

Fɪɢ. 4–3. — Equilibrium of segments to left and right of any exploratory section a–a.

the weight of the beam itself and consider only the effect of the load P. Assume that a cutting plane a–a at a distance x from R_1 divides the beam into two segments. The free-body diagram of the left segment in Fig. 4–3b shows that the externally applied load is R_1. To maintain equilibrium in this segment of the beam, the fibers in the exploratory section a–a must supply the resisting forces necessary to satisfy the conditions of static equilibrium. In this case, the external load is vertical, so the condition $\Sigma X = 0$ (the X axis is horizontal) is automatically satisfied.

To satisfy $\Sigma Y = 0$, the vertical unbalance caused by R_1 requires the fibers in section a–a to create a resisting force. This is shown as V_r, and is called the resisting shearing force. For the loading shown, V_r is numerically equal to R_1; but if additional loads had been applied between R_1 and section a–a (as in Figs. 4–5 and 4–6), the net vertical unbalance (which is equal but oppositely directed to the resisting shearing force) would be found from the summation of their vertical components. We define this net vertical unbalance as the shearing force in the beam. It is denoted by V and may be determined from the summation of the vertical components[1] of the external loads acting on either side of the section. However, for the reason given in the footnote on page 96, it is simpler to restrict this summation to the loads that act on the segment to the *left* of the section. This definition of shearing force (sometimes called vertical shear or just shear) may be expressed mathematically as

$$V = (\Sigma Y)_L \tag{4-1}$$

the subscript L emphasizing that the vertical summation includes only the external loads acting on the beam segment to the left of the section being considered.

The resisting shear V_r set up by the fibers in any section is always equal but oppositely directed to the shearing force V. In computing V, upward-acting forces or loads are considered as positive. This rule of sign produces the effect shown in Fig. 4-4, in which a positive shearing force tends to move the left segment upward with respect to the right, and vice versa.

Positive shear   Negative shear

FIG. 4-4. — Relative movements corresponding to signs of shearing force.

For complete equilibrium of the free-body diagram in Fig. 4-3b, the summation of moments must also balance. In this discussion, R_1 and V_r are equal, thereby producing a couple M that is equal to $R_1 x$ and is called the *bending moment*, because it tends to bend the beam. The fibers in the exploratory section must create a numerically equal resisting moment, M_r, that acts as shown.[2] In most beams, the free-body diagram carries a number of loads, as shown in Fig. 4-5; hence a more complete definition of bending moment is necessary.

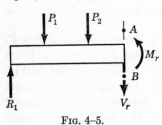

FIG. 4-5.

Definition of Bending Moment. Bending moment is defined as the summation of moments about the centroidal axis of any selected section of all the loads acting either to the left or to the right side of the section, and is expressed mathematically as

[1] The beam is assumed to be horizontal. With the beam in any other position, the shearing force is computed from the summation of the components perpendicular to the beam.

[2] Art. 4-3 shows that the bending moment, and hence the resisting moment, is always a couple.

$$M = (\Sigma M)_L = (\Sigma M)_R \qquad\qquad (4\text{--}2)$$

the subscript L indicating that the bending moment is computed in terms of the loads acting to the left of the section, and the subscript R referring to loads to the right of the section.

Why the centroidal axis of the exploratory section must be chosen as the axis of bending moment may not be clear at this point; however, the reason is explained in Art. 5–2 (page 127). Actually, in Fig. 4–5 where the loads are perpendicular to the beam, the axis of bending moment may be at point A, or B, or anywhere in the exploratory section, without changing the moment arms of the applied loads. But if the applied loads are inclined to the beam as shown in Fig. 4–6, the moment arms of the applied loads are unspecified unless the moment axis is at a definite location in the exploratory section. Such inclined loads cause combined axial and bending effects which are discussed in Art. 9–2.

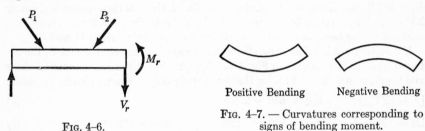

Fig. 4–6.

Positive Bending   Negative Bending

Fig. 4–7. — Curvatures corresponding to signs of bending moment.

Sign of Bending Moment. To many engineers, bending moment is positive if it produces bending of the beam concave upward, as in Fig. 4–7. We prefer to use an equivalent convention which states that *upward-acting external forces cause positive bending moments with respect to any section; downward forces cause negative bending moments.* In so far as the left segment of a beam is concerned (Fig. 4–3*b*), this is equivalent to taking clockwise moments about the bending axis as positive, as indicated by the moment sense of R_1. With respect to the right segment of a beam (Fig. 4–3*c*), this convention means that the moment sense of the upward reaction R_2 is positive in a counterclockwise direction. This convention has the advantage of permitting bending moment to be computed, without any confusion in sign, in terms of the forces to either the left or the right of a section, depending on which requires the least arithmetical work. We never need think about whether a moment is clockwise or counterclockwise; upward-acting forces always cause positive bending moments regardless of whether they act to the left or the right of the exploratory section.

The definitions of vertical shear and bending moment may be summarized mathematically as

$$V = (\Sigma Y)_L \qquad\qquad\qquad (4\text{–}1)$$

$$M = (\Sigma M)_L = (\Sigma M)_R \qquad\qquad (4\text{–}2)$$

in which positive effects are produced by upward forces and negative effects by downward forces. This rule of sign[3] will be used exclusively hereafter, and it will be further extended to give a positive sign to any quantity or expression in which such adjectives as "up," "above," etc., are used, and vice versa for negative signs. Remember that the subscripts L and R refer to the beam segment lying respectively to the left and right of the exploratory section.

ILLUSTRATIVE PROBLEM

401. Write shear and moment equations for the beam loaded as shown in Fig. 4–10, and sketch the shear and moment diagrams.

Solution: Begin by computing the reactions. Applying $\Sigma M_{R_2} = 0$ gives $R_1 = 630$ lb, and $\Sigma M_{R_1} = 0$ yields $R_2 = 670$ lb. A check of these values is given by $\Sigma Y = 0$. The sections in the beam at which the loading conditions change are called *change of load points* and are designated by the letters A, B, C, and D.

If a section a–a is taken through the beam anywhere between A and B, the external loads on it appear as in Fig. 4–8. Applying the definitions of vertical shear and bending moment, and noting that they apply only to external loads, we obtain

$$[V = (\Sigma Y)_L] \qquad V_{AB} = 630 - 200\,x \qquad\qquad (a)$$

$$[M = (\Sigma M)_L] \qquad M_{AB} = 630\,x - (200\,x)\,\frac{x}{2} = 630\,x - 100\,x^2 \qquad (b)$$

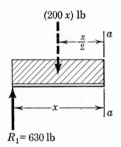

FIG. 4–8.

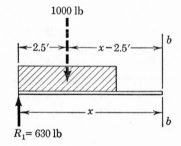

FIG. 4–9.

These equations are valid only for values of x between 0 and 5, i.e., between points A and B. To obtain shear and moment equations between B and C, assume another exploratory section b–b taken anywhere between B and C. Note that the location of section b–b is still defined in terms of x as measured from the left end of the beam, although x now ranges between the limits of 5 and 10. The effects of the

---

[3] To avoid conflict with this rule, it is necessary to compute vertical shear in terms of the forces lying to the left of the exploratory section. If the forces to the *right* of the section were used, it would be necessary to take downward forces as positive so as to agree with the sign convention shown in Fig. 4–4.

external forces on this section are determined by applying the definitions of shear and moment to Fig. 4–9.

$$[V = (\Sigma Y)_L] \qquad V_{BC} = 630 - 1000 = -370 \qquad\qquad (c)$$

$$[M = (\Sigma M)_L] \qquad M_{BC} = 630\,x - 1000(x - 2.5) = -370\,x + 2500 \qquad (d)$$

The shear and moment equations for segment CD are obtained similarly by passing a section c–c anywhere between C and D. The external loads acting on the

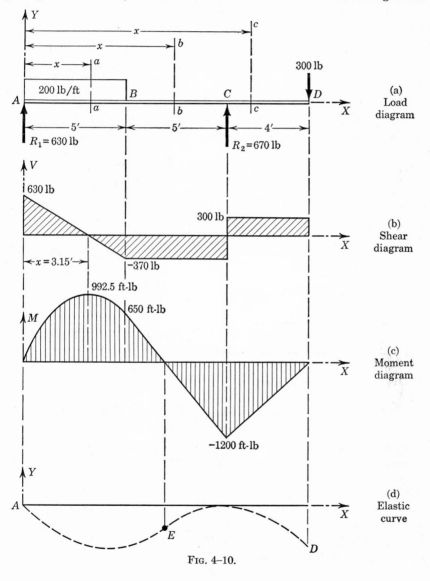

FIG. 4–10.

beam to the left of this section are shown in Fig. 4–11, whence we obtain

$$[V = (\Sigma Y)_L] \qquad V_{CD} = 630 - 1000 + 670 = +300 \qquad (e)$$

$$[M = (\Sigma M)_L]$$
$$M_{CD} = 630\,x - 1000(x - 2.5) + 670(x - 10) = 300\,x - 4200 \qquad (f)$$

A simpler method of obtaining M_{CD} is to consider the forces lying to the right of section c–c as shown in Fig. 4–12, from which, noting that downward forces produce negative bending moment, we also obtain

$$[M = (\Sigma M)_R] \qquad M_{CD} = -300(14 - x) = 300\,x - 4200 \qquad (f')$$

Summarizing, we have computed V by considering only the external forces lying to the *left* of any exploratory section, whereas M may be computed by taking moments about the exploratory section caused by the external loads which lie *either* to the left or to the right of the section. We have been careful to assign plus signs to V and M caused by upward-acting loads, and minus signs to V and M caused by downward-acting loads. We shall be consistent in assigning a plus sign to any upward quantity and a minus sign to any quantity associated with the word "down" or its equivalent.

Note further that Figs. 4–8, 4–9, 4–11, and 4–12 have been used only for explanation; you will soon learn to visualize such diagrams directly from the original ·beam loading.

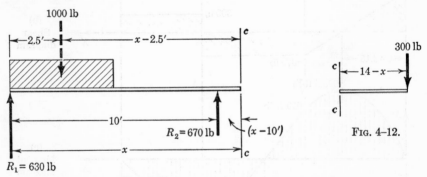

Fig. 4–11.

Fig. 4–12.

Shear and Moment Diagrams. Shear and moment diagrams are merely the graphical visualization of the shear and moment equations plotted on V–x and M–x axes, usually located below the loading diagram, as in parts (b) and (c) of Fig. 4–10.

The discontinuities in the shear diagram (Fig. 4–10b) are joined by vertical lines drawn up or down to represent the abrupt changes in shear caused respectively by upward or downward concentrated loads. Art. 4–4 (page 112) shows why this is correct. A final point to be observed at this time is that the highest and lowest points on the moment diagram (Fig. 4–10c) always correspond to sections of zero shear. This observation is also discussed in Art. 4–4, but it should be noted now that the value of x making M_{AB} maximum can be found by differentiating M_{AB} with respect to x and equating the result to zero. This result will be the shear equation V_{AB}. Thus we see that maximum moment corresponds to the section of zero shear.

Shear and moment at change of load points can be computed by substituting appropriate values of x in the V and M equations (a) to (f), but it is simpler and more direct to compute these numerical values by applying the fundamental definitions of V and M to specific sections. For example, the section of zero shear between A and B occurs because the weight of x feet of load applied at 200 lb per ft must balance the vertical shear of 630 lb at A. Hence we have

$$630 = 200\, x \quad \text{or} \quad x = 3.15 \text{ ft}$$

The moment at this section of zero shear is computed by taking moments of the forces to the left of the section. These forces consist of the upward reaction $R_1 = 630$ lb and the downward load of 630 lb caused by the length of the uniformly distributed load necessary to cause zero shear. From the definition of bending moment, we obtain

$$[M = (\Sigma M)_L] \quad \text{at } x = 3.15,\ M = (630)(3.15) - 630\left(\frac{3.15}{2}\right) = 992.5 \text{ ft-lb}$$

A final point of interest is brought out in Fig. 4–10d, showing the shape taken by the beam under the given loading, assuming the beam to be quite flexible. The beam between A and E is concave up, and between E and D it is concave down. Since anything associated with up has a positive sign, it is not surprising that the moment diagram has positive values corresponding to the region AE, while for the portion ED, where the beam is concave down, the moment diagram has negative values. Sketching the shape of the beam therefore provides a check of the sign of bending moment.

At point E, where the beam changes its shape from concave up to concave down, we have what is called a *point of inflection;* it corresponds to the section of zero bending moment. Its position may be calculated by setting Eq. (d) equal to zero, which yields

$$[M_{BC} = 0] \qquad - 370\, x + 2500 = 0, \quad x = 6.76 \text{ ft}$$

ILLUSTRATIVE PROBLEM

402. Write the shear and moment equations for the cantilever beam carrying the uniformly varying load and concentrated load shown in Fig. 4–13. Also sketch the shear and moment diagrams.

Solution: Shear and moment calculations for a cantilever beam are simplified by drawing the load diagram with the restraining wall at the right end. Drawing dia-

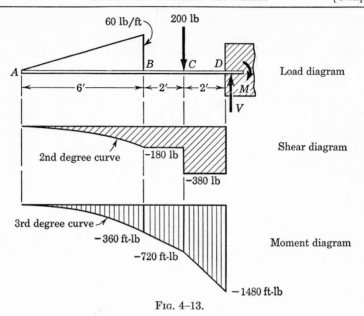

Fig. 4–13.

grams similar to Figs. 4–8 or 4–9 where necessary, we find the shear and moment equations between each change of load position by applying Eqs. (4–1) and (4–2). For the region AB, in which x varies from 0 to 6, we have (see Fig. 4–14),

$$[V = (\Sigma Y)_L] \qquad V_{AB} = -5\,x^2$$

$$[M = (\Sigma M)_L] \qquad M_{AB} = -5\,x^2\left(\frac{x}{3}\right) = -\frac{5}{3}\,x^3$$

After passing B, the resultant weight of the triangular load is constant at a value of $\frac{1}{2}(60)(6) = 180$ lb acting through the centroid of the triangular load diagram at 4 ft from A. For the region BC, in which x varies between 6 and 8, we therefore obtain (see Fig. 4–15),

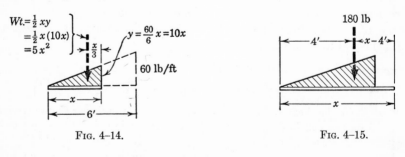

Fig. 4–14.   Fig. 4–15.

$$[V = (\Sigma Y)_L] \qquad V_{BC} = -180$$

$$[M = (\Sigma M)_L] \qquad M_{BC} = -180(x - 4) = -180\,x + 720$$

For a section between C and D (Fig. 4–16) in which x varies from 8 to 10, we obtain

$[V = (\Sigma Y)_L]$ $V_{CD} = -180 - 200 = -380$

$[M = (\Sigma M)_L]$ $M_{CD} = -180(x-4) - 200(x-8) = -380\,x + 2320$

The shear and moment equations are graphed as shown in the shear and moment diagrams in Fig. 4–13. At the wall D, the diagrams return to zero by means of the shear and moment reactions exerted by the wall. Observe that the maximum shear and the maximum bending moment always occur at the restrained end of a cantilever beam. Note also that the moment equation M_{CD} is not necessary in computing the bending moment at D; this is found by a direct application of Eq. (4–2):

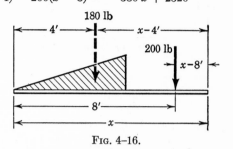

FIG. 4–16.

$$M = (\Sigma M)_L = -180(6) - 200(2) = -1480 \text{ ft-lb}$$

PROBLEMS

Write shear and moment equations for the beams in the following problems. Also draw shear and moment diagrams, specifying values at all change of loading positions and at all points of zero shear. Neglect the weight of the beam itself.

403. Beam loaded as shown.
Ans. $V_{BC} = 300 - 50\,x$; $M_{BC} = 300\,x - 25\,x^2 + 1600$; Max. $M = 2500$ ft-lb

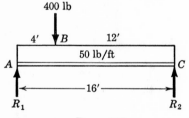

PROB. 403.

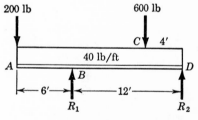

PROB. 404.

404. Beam loaded as shown.   *Ans.* $M_{BC} = 840\,x - 20\,x^2 - 6240$

405. Beam loaded as shown.   *Ans.* Max. $M = 6250$ ft-lb

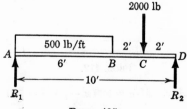

PROB. 405.

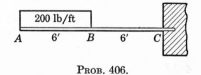

PROB. 406.

406. Beam loaded as shown.

407. Beam loaded as shown.　　　*Ans.* $M_{BC} = 200\,x - 50\,x^2 - 800$

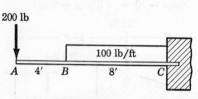

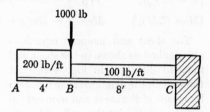

Prob. 407.　　　　　　　　　　　　Prob. 408.

408. Beam loaded as shown.

409. Beam loaded as shown.　　*Ans.* $M_{CD} = 1700\,x - 14{,}800$

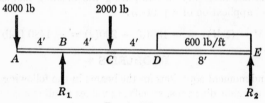

Prob. 409.

410. Beam loaded as shown.

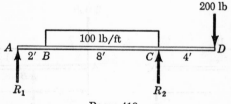

Prob. 410.

411. Beam loaded as shown.　　*Ans.* $M_{BC} = 1120\,x - 100\,x^2 - 1600$

412. Beam loaded as shown.

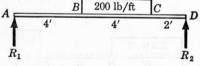

Prob. 411.

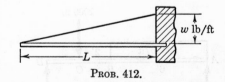

Prob. 412.

413. Beam loaded as shown.　　*Ans.* $M_{BC} = 980\,x - 80\,x^2 - 560$

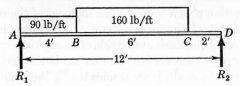

PROB. 413.

4–3. Interpretation of Vertical Shear and Bending Moment

The beam in Fig. 4–17a carries a uniformly distributed load as well as concentrated loads. The external effects of the loads acting to the left of section b–b are shown separately in parts (b), (c), and (d). In each of these figures, the effect of the applied load has been transferred to the exploratory section by adding a pair of equal but oppositely directed forces at that section which, as shown in the right side of the figures, reduce to

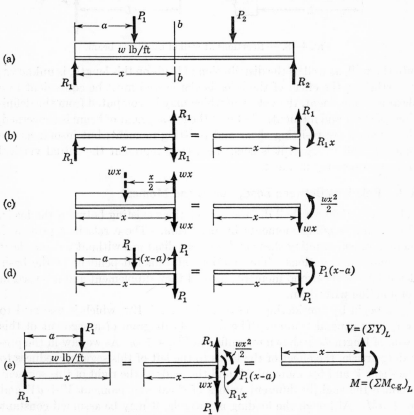

FIG. 4–17. — Shear and moment are resultant effects of loads acting to one side of exploratory section.

a force at that section plus a couple. The moment of the couple is equal to the bending moment of the load. Hence, as is shown in the composite figure (e), the effect of the loads at one side of an exploratory section reduces to a system of forces whose vertical summation is the vertical shear and a system of couples whose algebraic summation is the bending moment.

We may therefore conclude that the resultant effect of the forces at one side of an exploratory section reduces to a single force and a couple which are respectively the vertical shear and the bending moment at that section.

One application of this concept of vertical shear and bending moment is shown in the cantilever beam in Fig. 4–18. The length of beam extending

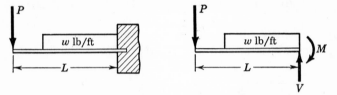

Fig. 4–18. — Reactions at wall of cantilever beam.

into the wall, as well as the distribution of loads on this length, is unknown; nevertheless, the effect of these loads at the wall must be equivalent to a shear and a moment, the values of which may be computed from the definitions of shear and moment. As far as the left segment of beam is concerned, these values are resisting shear and resisting moment; but insofar as the right or built-in segment is concerned, they represent the actual vertical shear and bending moment.

4–4. Relations Between Load, Shear, and Moment

In this article we shall discuss the relations existing between the loads, shears, and bending moments in any beam. These relations provide a method of constructing shear and moment diagrams without writing shear and moment equations. The relations are not independent of the basic definitions of shear and moment; instead they supplement and are used in conjunction with them.

We begin by considering the beam in Fig. 4–19a, which is assumed to carry any general loading. The free-body diagram of a segment of this beam of length dx is shown magnified in Fig. 4–19b. As we saw in the preceding article, the effect of the loads to the left of this segment reduces to the shear V and the moment M, and the loads to the right of this segment produce the slightly different values of shear and moment $V + dV$ and $M + dM$. Although the loading is variable, it may be assumed constant at the intensity of w lb/ft over the small length dx, thereby producing the upward load $w\,dx$ which completes the free-body diagram.

Applying the conditions of static equilibrium to Fig. 4–19*b*, a summation of vertical forces yields

$$[\Sigma Y = 0] \qquad V + w\,dx - (V + dV) = 0$$

which reduces to

$$dV = w\,dx \qquad (a)$$

From a moment summation about point *B* we have

$$[\Sigma M_B = 0] \qquad M + V\,dx + (w\,dx)\frac{dx}{2} - (M + dM) = 0$$

The third term in this equation is the square of a differential that is negligible in comparison with the other terms; hence the equation reduces to

$$dM = V\,dx \qquad (b)$$

Integrating Eq. (*a*), we obtain

$$\int_{V_1}^{V_2} dV = \int_{x_1}^{x_2} w\,dx$$

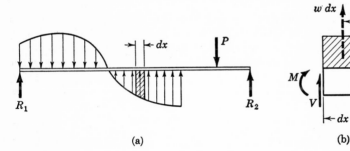

FIG. 4–19.

in which the limits are the shear V_1 at position x_1 and the shear V_2 at position x_2. The left-hand term is easily integrable; it reduces to $V_2 - V_1$ and represents the change in shearing force between sections x_2 and x_1. We denote this change in shear as ΔV. In the right-hand term the product $w\,dx$ represents the area of an element of the load diagram like that shown shaded in Fig. 4–19*a*. Hence the definite integral $\int_{x_1}^{x_2} w\,dx$, which means the summation of such terms, represents the area under the load diagram between positions x_1 and x_2. Therefore the integration of Eq. (*a*) yields

$$V_2 - V_1 = \Delta V = (\text{Area})_{load} \qquad (4\text{–}3)$$

Similarly the integration of Eq. (*b*) gives

$$\int_{M_1}^{M_2} dM = \int_{x_1}^{x_2} V \, dx$$

This reduces to

$$M_2 - M_1 = \Delta M = (\text{Area})_{shear} \qquad (4\text{--}4)$$

inasmuch as the product $V \, dx$ in the right-hand integral represents the area of an element under the shear diagram. Therefore the integral itself is equivalent to the area under the shear diagram between positions x_1 and x_2. Expressed in words, Eq. (4–4) shows that the change in bending moment ΔM between any two sections is equal to the area of the shear diagram for this interval.

Positive shearing forces are plotted upward from the X axis; hence positive shear areas are those which lie above the X axis and represent increases in the bending moment. The load diagram, however, is usually drawn with the loads on top of the beam because this is their natural position; as a consequence, the area of such downward-acting loads is considered negative and represents *decreases* in the shearing force.

Eqs. (4–3) and (4–4) provide a convenient means of computing the changes in shear and moment and also the numerical values of shear and moment at any section, as will be demonstrated in the illustrative examples below. Of almost equal importance are the following variations of Eqs. (*a*) and (*b*) which enable us to sketch the shapes of the shear and moment diagrams.

$$w = \frac{dV}{dx} = \text{slope of shear diagram} \qquad (4\text{--}5)$$

$$V = \frac{dM}{dx} = \text{slope of moment diagram} \qquad (4\text{--}6)$$

As an application of these principles, consider the simply supported beam carrying the variable loading shown in Fig. 4–20*a*. Since positive slopes are directed up to the right and negative slopes are directed down to the right, i.e.,

$$+ \text{ slope } = \nearrow$$

$$- \text{ slope } = \searrow$$

we observe from Eq. (4–5) that the shear diagram in Fig. 4–20*b* must slope continuously down to the right. The inclination varies directly with the corresponding ordinate of the load diagram, being steepest where the load ordinate is maximum, and horizontal (or of zero slope) at the ends where the intensity of loading is zero.

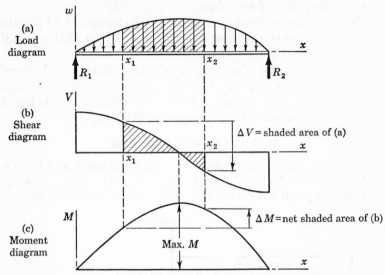

FIG. 4–20. — Relations between load, shear, and moment diagrams.

Similarly, by means of Eq. (4–6), the slope and shape of the moment diagram in Fig. 4–20c are determined by the corresponding ordinates of the shear diagram which, being positive but decreasing in magnitude for the left portion, determine that the moment diagram slopes continuously up to the right with decreasing inclination. The slope becomes zero where the shear ordinate is zero. Note also that after the shear ordinates change sign and become increasingly larger negatively, the moment diagram slopes correspondingly more steeply down to the right. These conditions establish a maximum moment at the ordinate of zero shear.

The changes in shear (ΔV) and moment (ΔM) defined by Eqs. (4–3) and (4–4) are indicated in Figs. 4–20b and 4–20c. The shaded negative area of the load diagram determines ΔV to be negative or directed downward; in the shear diagram, the excess of positive over negative area in the region between x_1 and x_2 determines the positive change in moment ΔM, which is therefore directed upward.

A summary of the principles presented here and in Art. 4–2 suggests the following procedure for the construction of shear and moment diagrams:

1. Compute the reactions.

2. Compute values of shear at the change of load points, using either $V = (\Sigma Y)_L$ or $\Delta V = (\text{Area})_{load}$.

3. Sketch the shear diagram, determining the shape from Eq. (4–5); i.e., the intensity of the load ordinate equals the slope at the corresponding ordinate of the shear diagram.

4. Locate the points of zero shear.

5. Compute values of bending moment at the change of load points and at the points of zero shear, using either $M = (\Sigma M)_L = (\Sigma M)_R$ or $\Delta M = (\text{Area})_{shear}$, whichever is more convenient.

6. Sketch the moment diagram through the ordinates of the bending moments computed in step 5. The shape of the diagram is determined from Eq. (4–6); i.e., the intensity of the shear ordinate equals the slope at the corresponding ordinate of the moment diagram.

ILLUSTRATIVE PROBLEMS

414. Using the semigraphical method described in this article, sketch shear and moment diagrams for the beam shown in Fig. 4–21, computing the values at all change of loading points and the maximum shear and maximum moment.

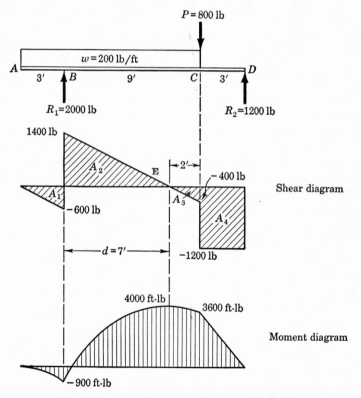

FIG. 4–21. — Load, shear, and moment diagrams.

Solution: The reactions are determined by equating to zero a moment summation about R_2 and then about R_1; this yields respectively $R_1 = 2000$ lb and $R_2 = 1200$ lb.

We next determine the values of vertical shear at the change of load positions. At A, the shear is zero. At the left of B, applying $V = (\Sigma Y)_L$ gives the shear as -600 lb caused by the downward resultant of the distributed load of 200 lb/ft applied for 3 ft. The same result may be obtained with Eq. (4–3), which indicates that the change in shear between A and B caused by the downward or negative uniformly distributed load is equal to the area of the load diagram in this interval, i.e., $\Delta V = -200 \times 3 = -600$ lb. Hence the shear ordinate to the left of B has decreased 600 lb from the zero shear ordinate at A, to yield a net value of -600 lb. The concentrated load reaction at B causes the shear at B to increase abruptly by 2000 lb to a net positive shear ordinate of 1400 lb at the right of B.

Between B and C, the area of the load diagram is $-200 \times 9 = -1800$, which by Eq. (4–3) represents the change in shear between B and C. The net shear ordinate at the left of C is therefore $V_C = V_B + \Delta V = 1400 - 1800 = -400$ lb. At C, the concentrated load of 800 lb changes the shear ordinate to -1200 lb at the right of C. The shear ordinate stays constant at this value between C and D, since there is no load in this interval; at D, the upward reaction of 1200 lb reduces the shear ordinate to zero.

The shape of the diagram connecting these shear ordinates is determined from Eq. (4–5), which shows that the slope is equal to the corresponding ordinates of the load diagram. Thus between A and B, the load intensity is constant and downward (or negative); hence the slope of the shear diagram in this interval is constant and down to the right. Similarly, between B and C, the load intensity is constant and negative; therefore the slope of the shear diagram here also is constant and down to the right. The slopes in the intervals AB and BC are parallel because they are each equal to the same load intensity. Finally between C and D, the intensity of loading is zero and the corresponding slope of the shear diagram is zero (a horizontal line).

We may conclude therefore that the shear diagram consists of straight horizontal lines for intervals in which the load intensity is zero, and of straight inclined lines for intervals of uniform load intensity.

The shear diagram passes through zero at B, where $x = 3$ ft, and also at E. The position of E is determined from the fact that the shear at the right of B is 1400 lb which is reduced to zero in the interval BE at the rate of 200 lb/ft. Hence $BE = d = \frac{1400}{200} = 7$ ft.

As a preliminary to computing the bending moments, we determine the areas of the shear diagram marked A_1, A_2, A_3, and A_4.

$$A_1 = \tfrac{1}{2}(3)(-600) = -900 \text{ ft-lb}$$
$$A_2 = \tfrac{1}{2}(7)(1400) = +4900 \text{ ft-lb}$$
$$A_3 = \tfrac{1}{2}(2)(-400) = -400 \text{ ft-lb}$$
$$A_4 = 3(-1200) = -3600 \text{ ft-lb}$$

According to Eq. (4–4), the change in bending moment between any two sections equals the corresponding area of the shear diagram; hence, since the bending moment is zero at A (there are no loads to the left of A to cause a bending moment), the bending moment at B is given by A_1, or $M_B = -900$ ft-lb.

Similarly, the bending moment at E is

$$M_E = M_B + \Delta M = A_1 + A_2 = -900 + 4900 = +4000 \text{ ft-lb}$$

The bending moment at C can also be computed as the sum of the areas A_1, A_2, and A_3, giving $M_C = 3600$ ft-lb; but small errors arising from neglecting sufficient significant figures in computing these areas may cause a cumulative error. Hence at sections near the right end of the beam, it is usually preferable to use the shear area to the right of such sections, or to apply the basic definition $M = (\Sigma M)_R$; whence in terms of the loads acting to the right of C we find $M_C = 1200 \times 3 = 3600$ ft-lb. The correlation between this result and the area A_4 is evident if we observe that A_4 represents the amount by which the moment at C changes to become zero at D; i.e.,

$$M_D = M_C + \Delta M = M_C + A_4$$

or

$$0 = M_C - 3600 \quad \text{and} \quad M_C = 3600 \text{ ft-lb}$$

Whenever the change in bending moment between the ends of a beam is zero, as in this problem, the net area under the shear diagram is also zero; in other words, there must be as much positive as there is negative shear area. This provides a useful check on the accuracy of all intermediate values of bending moments computed from the area of a shear diagram.

After these bending moments are plotted as ordinates, the shape of the moment diagram connecting them is determined from Eq. (4–6); i.e., the intensity of the shear ordinate equals the slope at the corresponding ordinate of the moment diagram. Thus as the shear ordinates between A and B change linearly from zero to -600 lb, the slopes at corresponding ordinates of the moment diagram change from horizontal or zero slope at A to increasingly steeper negative slopes as we pass from A to B, thereby producing a second-degree curve concave downward, as shown. In other words, the tangents to the moment curve have increasingly steeper slopes directed downward to the right.

The sudden change in shear at B from -600 lb to 1400 lb causes the moment curve there to slope abruptly upward to the right; it becomes less steep, and eventually horizontal, as we move from B to E, because the corresponding positive shear ordinates decrease uniformly to zero. From E to C, however, the slope is again increasingly steeper and directed downward to the right as the corresponding shear ordinates change their sign to negative.

At C, the shear ordinate changes abruptly from -400 lb to -1200 lb, at which it remains until D. The slope of the moment diagram is correspondingly abruptly steeper and constant, resulting in the straight line.

From the above discussion, it is apparent that an abrupt change in shear creates an abrupt change in the slope of the moment curve as at C, and that if the shear changes sign abruptly, there is a cusp in the moment diagram as at B. Also, where the shear diagram is constant because only concentrated loads are involved, as in the region CD, the moment diagram consists of straight lines, whereas for an interval in which the shear diagram varies uniformly because of a uniformly distributed load, the moment diagram is a parabolic arc with a vertical axis of symmetry at the section of zero shear, as at E.

415. Without writing shear or moment equations, sketch shear and moment diagrams for the beam in Fig. 4–22, and compute values at all change of loading points and the values of maximum shear and maximum moment.

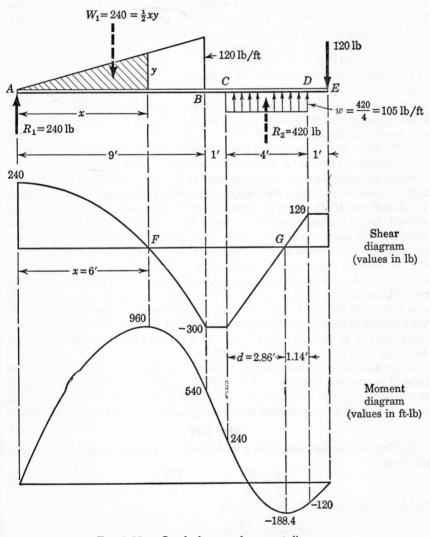

Fig. 4–22. — Load, shear, and moment diagrams.

Solution: We begin by computing the reactions. Replacing the uniformly distributed reaction between C and D by its resultant R_2 and equating moments about R_1 to zero, we then set moments about R_2 equal to zero, whence $R_1 = 240$ lb and $R_2 = 420$ lb. Dividing R_2 by the length of 4 ft over which it is assumed to be uniformly distributed gives the upward intensity of this reaction as 105 lb per ft.

The shear diagram starts with an abrupt change in shear of 240 lb caused by the reaction R_1. Applying $\Delta V = (\text{Area})_{load}$ between A and B, the change in shear is equal to the area of the triangular load diagram, $\frac{1}{2} \times 9 \times (- 120) = - 540$ lb; this reduces the vertical shear at B to $- 300$ lb. The shape of the shear diagram from A to B is determined from Eq. (4–5), which shows that the shape must vary from zero slope to increasingly steeper negative slopes corresponding to the increasingly greater downward intensity of the loading.

Between B and C, the intensity of loading is zero; hence, from Eq. (4–5), the slope of the corresponding portion of the shear diagram is zero, i.e., horizontal.

From C to D, the loading is at a constant upward rate of 105 lb per ft, creating a positive change of shear of 420 lb equal to the area of the load diagram in this interval, and a constant upward slope of the shear diagram as shown. This shear change of $+ 420$ lb added to the shear of $- 300$ lb at C produces the shear of $+ 120$ lb at D. From D to E, the loading is zero, which means that the slope is horizontal. The concentrated load of 120 lb at E reduces the shear abruptly to zero.

Before we locate the positions of zero shear at F and G on the shear diagram, consider the effect of narrowing the distance over which the reaction R_2 is distributed. If points C and D are moved an equal amount toward each other, this narrowing will not change the magnitude or position of R_2. However, a reduction in the distance CD will increase the intensity at which R_2 is distributed and cause a corresponding increase in the slope of the shear diagram in the narrowed interval CD. For the extreme case in which the reaction is distributed over an infinitesimal width — i.e., becomes a concentrated force — the intensity of loading is infinitely upward, and the corresponding slope of the shear diagram is vertically upward, as is the case at the reaction R_1. Similarly for a concentrated downward load at E, the intensity of loading is infinitely downward, and the corresponding slope of the shear diagram is vertically downward. This explains why a concentrated load causes an abrupt change in the vertical shear.

Let us now locate the sections of zero shear. The vertical shear of 240 lb at A is reduced to zero at F by the weight W_1 of the load diagram (shown shaded) applied over the interval AF. Evidently the magnitude of W_1 is also 240 lb and is equal to the area $\frac{1}{2}xy$, where y denotes the intensity of loading at the section F. Hence

$$240 = \tfrac{1}{2} xy \qquad (a)$$

Another relation between x and y is obtained from similar triangles in the load diagram:

$$\frac{y}{x} = \frac{120}{9} \quad \text{or} \quad y = \frac{120}{9} x \qquad (b)$$

which is substituted in Eq. (*a*) to obtain

$$240 = \frac{1}{2} x \cdot \frac{120}{9} x$$

from which

$$x^2 = \frac{240(18)}{120} = 36 \quad \text{and} \quad x = 6 \text{ ft}$$

The section of zero shear at G is found from the fact that the upward reaction applied over the interval CG must total 300 lb in order to reduce the shear of -300 lb at C to zero at G. Since the reaction is distributed at 105 lb per ft,

$$300 = 105\,d \quad \text{or} \quad d = 2.86 \text{ ft}$$

or, in terms of x measured from the left end of the beam,

$$x = 10 + d = 12.86 \text{ ft}$$

Bending Moment. The moment at F where $x = 6$ ft is found by applying the definition of bending moment.[4] Note that the shaded part of the triangular load applied between A and F totals 240 lb and acts at the centroid of the triangular area, i.e., at $\frac{1}{3}$ of 6 ft from F. Thus we obtain

$$[M = (\Sigma M)_L] \qquad M_F = 240(6) - 240(\tfrac{6}{3}) = 960 \text{ ft-lb}$$

Similarly, the moment at B where $x = 9$ ft is found to be

$$[M = (\Sigma M)_L] \qquad M_B = 240(9) - 540(\tfrac{9}{3}) = 540 \text{ ft-lb}$$

The moment at C can also be computed from this basic definition but, whenever the shear diagram consists of straight lines (either horizontal or inclined), it is usually simpler to apply Eq. (4–4); i.e., the change in bending moment between any two sections equals the corresponding area of the shear diagram. For example, between B and C, the area of the shear diagram is a rectangle and equals $\Delta M = -300 \times 1 = -300$ ft-lb. Hence, if the bending moment changes by -300 ft-lb between B and C, the bending moment at C is

$$[M_C = M_B + \Delta M] \qquad M_C = 540 - 300 = 240 \text{ ft-lb}$$

The bending moment at D is found from the fact that the area of the shear diagram between D and E equals $120 \times 1 = 120$ ft-lb. Since this change in moment is positive, it follows that to produce zero moment at the free end E, the moment at D must be -120 ft-lb.

Similarly, the area of the shear diagram between G and D equals $\frac{1}{2} \times 120 \times 1.14 = 68.4$ ft-lb. Since this is a positive increase in bending moment, the moment at G must be smaller by this amount than the moment at D, or

$$M_G = -120 - 68.4 = -188.4 \text{ ft-lb}$$

[4] It is better not to use Eq. (4–4) when the shear diagram is curved, since then the areas under the diagram are not too easily computed, especially in the interval FB. The computation of such areas is discussed in Chap. VI, especially on page 182 and in Fig. 6–10. For the present, when the shear diagram is curved, as over the region AB, compute the bending moment by applying $(\Sigma M)_L$ or $(\Sigma M)_R$ rather than using the area of the shear diagram.

Sketching the bent beam, as in Fig. 4–10d of Prob. 401, shows it to be concave downward at G and D, which is further verification of the negative bending moment signs at these sections.

Shape of the Moment Diagram. After plotting the values of the bending moment, we consider next the shape of the moment curve connecting these points. Applying Eq. (4–6), we notice that since the shear ordinates are positive and decrease to zero as we move from A to F, the moment curve has correspondingly positive slopes (i.e., directed upward to the right) that decrease to zero slope at F.

Between F and B, the vertical shear is increasingly negative, and hence the corresponding slopes of the moment curve become increasingly steeper downward to the right until the steepest slope is reached at section B. Between B and C, the shear stays constant; therefore the slope of the moment curve is constant, being represented by the straight line that joins sections B and C.

Between sections C and G, the shear is negative, becoming zero at G; hence the slope of the moment curve is negative and gradually reduces to zero (i.e., horizontal) at G. Similarly the increasing positive shear between G and D results in an increasingly positive slope (directed upward to the right) up to D. Between D and E the slope remains constant because the vertical shear is constant between D and E.

The moment curve between C and D is a symmetric parabola with its vertex at G, because at equal distances to either side of G the shear is numerically equal but of opposite sign, thereby producing equal slopes oppositely directed. The moment curve between A and F, however, is *not* symmetric about F because the shear ordinates do not have equal values at equal distances on either side of F; here the moment curve is actually a third-degree parabola.

PROBLEMS

Without writing shear or moment equations, draw shear and moment diagrams for the beams specified in the following problems. Give numerical values at all change of loading positions and at all points of zero shear. (Problems 403 to 413 may also be solved by the semigraphical method of this article.)

416. Beam loaded as shown.　　　　*Ans.* Maximum $M = 3530$ ft-lb

417. Beam loaded as shown.

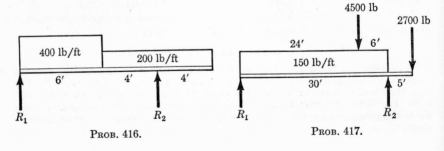

PROB. 416.　　　　　　　　　　PROB. 417.

418. Beam loaded as shown.   *Ans.* Maximum $M = 5000$ ft-lb

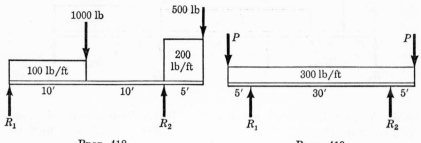

PROB. 418.   PROB. 419.

419. In the overhanging beam shown, determine P so that the moments over the supports equal the moment at midspan.

420. A total distributed load of 30,000 lb is supported by a uniformly distributed reaction as shown.

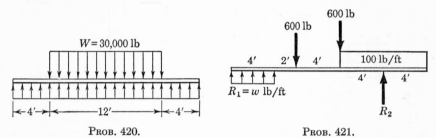

PROB. 420.   PROB. 421.

421. Beam loaded as shown.   *Ans.* Maximum $M = 2400$ ft-lb

422. A beam loaded as shown consists of two segments joined by a frictionless hinge at which the bending moment is zero.   *Ans.* Max. $M = -\ 12{,}000$ ft-lb

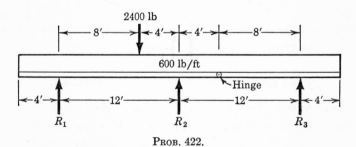

PROB. 422.

423. A beam carrying the given loads is composed of three segments. It is supported on four reactions and joined by two frictionless hinges at which the bending moments are zero.   *Ans.* Max. $M = -\ 2400$ ft-lb

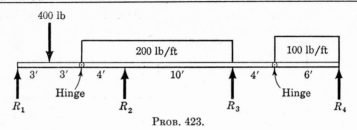

PROB. 423.

424. A frame $ABCD$, with rigid corners at B and C, supports the given uniformly distributed load.   *Ans.* Max. $M = - 6400$ ft-lb

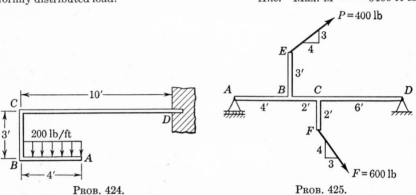

PROB. 424.   PROB. 425.

425. A beam $ABCD$ is supported by a roller at A and a hinge at D. It is subjected to the given loads which act at the ends of the vertical members BE and CF. These vertical members are rigidly attached to the beam at B and C.

Ans. Max. $M = 1800$ ft-lb

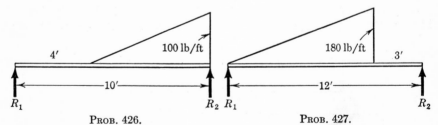

PROB. 426.   PROB. 427.

426. Beam loaded as shown.   *Ans.* Max. $M = 346$ ft-lb

427. Beam loaded as shown.   *Ans.* Max. $M = 1720$ ft-lb at $x = 6.37$ ft

428. Beam loaded as shown.   *Ans.* Max. $M = \dfrac{wL^2}{9\sqrt{3}} = \dfrac{2\,WL}{9\sqrt{3}}$ at $x = \dfrac{L}{\sqrt{3}}$

429. Beam loaded as shown.   *Ans.* Max. $M = \dfrac{wL^2}{12}$

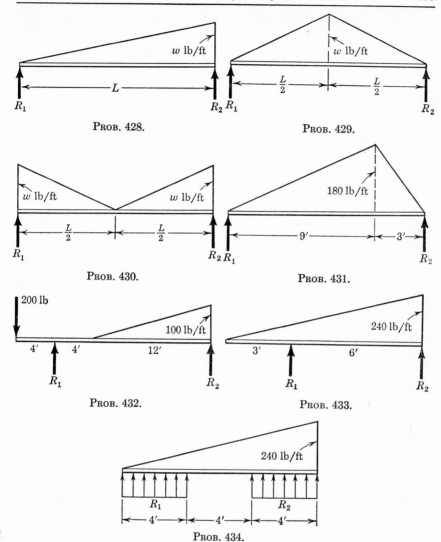

PROB. 428.

PROB. 429.

PROB. 430.

PROB. 431.

PROB. 432.

PROB. 433.

PROB. 434.

430. Beam loaded as shown.   *Ans.* Max. $M = \dfrac{wL^2}{24}$

431. Beam loaded as shown.   *Ans.* Max. $M = 2010$ ft-lb at $x = 6.7$ ft

432. Beam loaded as shown.   *Ans.* Max. $M = 924$ ft-lb

433. Beam loaded as shown.

434. A uniformly varying load is supported on two uniformly distributed reactions as shown.   *Ans.* Max. $V = 280$ lb; max. $M = 720$ ft-lb

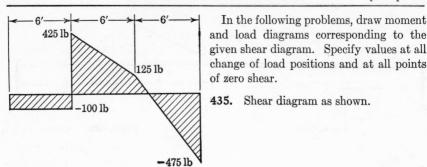

In the following problems, draw moment and load diagrams corresponding to the given shear diagram. Specify values at all change of load positions and at all points of zero shear.

435. Shear diagram as shown.

Prob. 435.

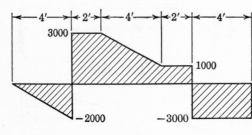

436. Shear diagram as shown.
Ans. Max. $M = 12{,}000$ ft-lb

Prob. 436.

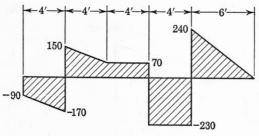

437. Shear diagram as shown.

Prob. 437.

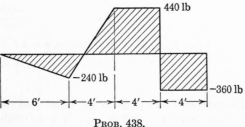

438. Shear diagram as shown.
Ans. Max. positive moment $= 1440$ ft-lb at $x = 14$ ft; max. negative moment $= -890$ ft-lb at $x = 7.41$ ft

Prob. 438.

4–5. Moving Loads

A truck or other vehicle rolling across a beam or girder constitutes a system of concentrated loads at fixed distances from one another. For beams carrying only concentrated loads, the maximum bending moment occurs under one of the loads. Therefore, the problem here is to determine the bending moment under each load when each load is in a position to cause a maximum moment to occur under it. The largest of these various values is the maximum moment that governs the design of the beam.

In Fig. 4–23, P_1, P_2, P_3, and P_4 represent a system of loads at fixed distances a, b, and c from one another; the loads move as a unit across the sim-

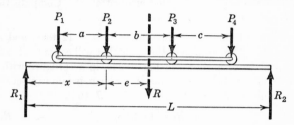

Fig. 4–23. — Moving loads.

ply supported beam with span L. Let us locate the position of P_2 when the bending moment under this load is maximum. Denoting the resultant of the loads on the span by R and its position from P_2 by e, the value of the left reaction is $R_1 = \dfrac{R}{L}(L - e - x)$. The bending moment under P_2 is then

$$[M = (\Sigma M)_L] \qquad M_2 = \frac{R}{L}(L - e - x)(x) - P_1 a$$

To compute the value of x which will give maximum M_2, we set the derivative of M_2 with respect to x equal to zero:

$$\frac{dM_2}{dx} = \frac{R}{L}(L - e - 2x) = 0$$

from which

$$x = \frac{L}{2} - \frac{e}{2} \qquad\qquad (4\text{--}7)$$

This value of x is independent of the number of loads to the left of P_2, since the derivative of all terms of the form $P_1 a$ with respect to x will be zero.

Eq. (4–7) may be expressed in terms of the following rule: *The bending moment under a particular load is a maximum when the center of the beam is midway between that load and the resultant of all loads then on the span.* With this rule we locate the position of each load when the moment at that load is a maximum, and compute the value of each such maximum moment.

The maximum shearing force occurs at, and is equal to, the maximum reaction. The maximum reaction for a group of moving loads on a span occurs either at the left reaction when the leftmost load is over that reaction, or at the right reaction when the rightmost load is over it. In other words, the maximum reaction is the reaction to which the resultant load is nearest.

ILLUSTRATIVE PROBLEM

439. A truck and trailer combination having the axle loads shown in Fig. 4–24a rolls across the simply supported span of 40 ft. Compute the maximum bending moment and the maximum shearing force.

Solution: The resultant of the three loads is $R = 12$ tons, and is located as shown in Fig. 4–24a. The position of the loads that will cause the bending moment to be maximum under A is shown in Fig. 4–24b, in accordance with the rule expressed by Eq. (4–7), that the center line of the beam is midway between A and R. Taking moments about R_2 equal to zero, we find R_1 to be

$$[\Sigma M_{R_2} = 0] \qquad\qquad 40\,R_1 = 12(12.5) \qquad\qquad R_1 = 3.75\,\text{tons}$$

whence the bending moment at A is

$$[M = (\Sigma M)_L] \qquad\qquad M_A = 3.75(12.5) = 46.9\,\text{ton-ft}$$

We next consider Fig. 4–24c, where the loads are so located that the center line of the beam is midway between B and R. Setting moments about R_2 equal to zero, the value of R_1 for this position of the loads is

$$[\Sigma M_{R_2} = 0] \qquad\qquad 40\,R_1 = 12(15.5) \qquad\qquad R_1 = 4.65\,\text{tons}$$

whence the bending moment at B is

$$[M = (\Sigma M)_L] \qquad\qquad M_B = 4.65(15.5) - 2(6) = 60.1\,\text{ton-ft}$$

If we now position the loads so that the center line of the beam is midway between C and R, in order to have the bending moment a maximum under C, we find that load A comes off the span, which is contrary to the assumption that all three loads are on the span. This indicates the possibility of a maximum bending moment under C when only loads B and C are on the span.

When only loads B and C are on the span, their resultant is $R' = 10$ tons at 8 ft from C. This position of the loads to cause maximum bending moment under C is shown in Fig. 4–24d, in which the center line of the beam is midway between R' and C. Setting moments about R_1 equal to zero, we find R_2 for this condition to be

$$[\Sigma M_{R_1} = 0] \qquad\qquad 40\,R_2 = 10(16) \qquad\qquad R_2 = 4\,\text{tons}$$

whence the bending moment at C is computed to be

$$[M = (\Sigma M)_R] \qquad\qquad M_C = 4(16) = 64.0\,\text{ton-ft}$$

It is left as an exercise for the reader to show that the maximum bending moments under *A* and *B*, when only loads *A* and *B* are on the span, are respectively 48.6

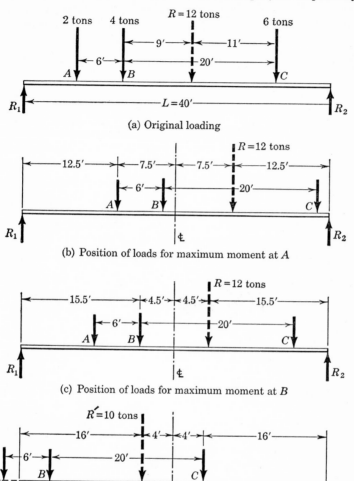

(a) Original loading

(b) Position of loads for maximum moment at *A*

(c) Position of loads for maximum moment at *B*

(d) Position of loads for maximum moment at *C*
with only *B* and *C* on span

Fig. 4–24. — Moving loads.

ton-ft and 54.1 ton-ft, while with only *C* on the span, the maximum moment occurs with *C* at midspan and equals 60.0 ton-ft.

A comparison of the above results shows that the most dangerous bending moment is 64.0 ton-ft, occurring under *C* when only loads *B* and *C* are on the span.

Maximum Shearing Force. If all three loads are on the span, the resultant load R is 11 ft from R_2 when C is over R_2 and is 15 ft from R_1, with A over R_1. Evidently the maximum reaction, and consequently the maximum shearing force, is at R_2, since it is nearer the resultant load. By setting moments about R_1 equal to zero, the value of R_2 is found to be

$$[\Sigma M_{R_1} = 0] \qquad 40\,R_2 = 12(40 - 11) \qquad R_2 = \text{Max. } V = 8.7 \text{ tons}$$

We must also investigate the possibility of the maximum shearing force occurring when only loads B and C are on the span. The maximum reaction in this case will be at R_1, when B is over R_1 and the resultant load $R' = 10$ tons is 12 ft from R_1. Its value will be $R_1 = \frac{10}{40}(40 - 12) = 7$ tons. The condition when only A and B are on the span need not be checked, because their resultant load of 6 tons is less than the reaction $R_2 = 8.7$ tons found above.

PROBLEMS

440. A truck with axle loads of 4 tons and 6 tons on a wheel base of 12 ft rolls across a 20-ft span. Compute the maximum bending moment and the maximum shearing force.   *Ans.* Max. $M = 30.0$ ton-ft; max. $V = 7.6$ tons

441. Repeat Prob. 440 with axle loads of 5 tons and 10 tons on a wheel base of 15 ft crossing a 30-ft span.

442. A tractor weighing 2400 lb, with a wheel base of 10 ft, carries 1800 lb of its load on the rear wheels. Compute the maximum moment and maximum shear when crossing a 14-ft span.   *Ans.* Max. $M = 6300$ ft-lb; max. $V = 1970$ lb

443. Three equal wheel loads of 2 tons each, separated by 4 ft between each load, roll as a unit across a 24-ft span. Determine the maximum moment and maximum shear.

444. Three wheel loads roll as a unit across a 34-ft span. The loads are $W_1 = 1200$ lb and $W_2 = 2400$ lb separated by 6 ft, and $W_3 = 1800$ lb at 16 ft from W_2. Determine the maximum moment and maximum shear in the beam.   *Ans.* Max. $M = 28,500$ ft-lb; max. $V = 3810$ lb

445. A truck and trailer combination crossing a 30-ft span has axle loads of 2 tons, 4 tons, and 6 tons separated respectively by distances of 6 ft and 15 ft. Compute the maximum moment and maximum shear developed in the span.

SUMMARY

The fundamental definitions of shear and bending moment are expressed by

$$V = (\Sigma Y)_L \tag{4-1}$$

and

$$M = (\Sigma M)_L = (\Sigma M)_R \tag{4-2}$$

in which upward-acting forces or loads cause positive effects. The shearing force V should be computed only in terms of the forces to the left of the section being considered; the bending moment M may be computed in terms of the forces to either the left or the right of the section, depending on which requires less arithmetical work.

Relations between load, shear, and moment are given by

$$w = \frac{dV}{dx} \tag{4-5}$$

and

$$V = \frac{dM}{dx} \tag{4-6}$$

These relations are amplified in Art. 4–4 to provide a semigraphical method of computing shear and moment which supplements Eqs. (4–1) and (4–2). We obtain

$$V_2 - V_1 = \Delta V = (\text{Area})_{load} \tag{4-3}$$

and

$$M_2 - M_1 = \Delta M = (\text{Area})_{shear} \tag{4-4}$$

which provide alternate methods of computing shear and moment. The relations (4–5) and (4–6), expressed in the form,

Intensity of load = corresponding slope of shear diagram

and

Intensity of shear = corresponding slope of moment diagram

enable us to sketch the proper shapes of the shear and moment diagrams rapidly and correctly.

When systems of wheel loads move as a unit across a beam, the bending moment is a maximum under one of the loads. To determine the position of the loads when the moment is maximum under a particular load, the system of loads must be in such a position that the center line of the span is midway between that load and the resultant of all the loads then on the span. With the loads in this position, the reactions are computed and Eq. (4–2) applied to compute the bending moment in the beam under the particular load.

Chapter V

Stresses in Beams

5–1. Introduction

In this chapter we derive the relations between the bending moment and the flexure stresses it causes, and between the vertical shear and the shearing stresses. In deriving these relations, the following assumptions are made:

1. Plane sections of the beam, originally plane, remain plane.
2. The material of the beam is homogeneous and obeys Hooke's law.
3. The moduli of elasticity for tension and compression are equal.
4. The beam is initially straight and of constant cross-section.

The application and limits of these assumptions will be discussed in succeeding articles as the reason for them becomes apparent.

5–2. Derivation of Flexure Formula

The stresses caused by the bending moment are known as bending or *flexure stresses*, and the relation between these stresses and the bending moment is expressed by the *flexure formula*. The derivation of this relation follows the procedure developed in deriving the torsion formula (see Art. 3–2); i.e., the elastic deformations plus Hooke's law determine the manner of stress variation, after which the conditions of equilibrium then establish the relation between stress and load.

Fig. 5–1a shows two adjacent sections ab and cd separated by the distance dx. Because of the bending caused by load P, sections ab and cd rotate relative to each other by the amount $d\theta$ as shown in Fig. 5–1b, but remain straight and undistorted, in accordance with assumption 1 of the preceding article.

Fiber ac at the top is shortened, and fiber bd at the bottom is lengthened. Somewhere between them is located fiber ef, whose length is unchanged. Drawing the line $c'd'$ through f parallel to ab shows that fiber ac is shortened an amount cc' and is in compression, and that fiber bd is lengthened by an amount $d'd$ and is in tension.

The plane containing fibers like ef is called the *neutral surface*, because such fibers remain unchanged in length and hence carry no stress. It will be shown shortly that this neutral surface contains the centroids of all transverse sections.

124

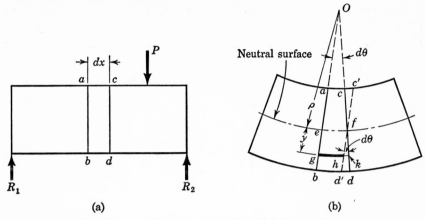

Fig. 5–1. — Deformations.

Consider now the deformation of a typical fiber *gh* located *y* units from the neutral surface. Its elongation *hk* is the arc of a circle of radius *y* subtended by the angle $d\theta$ and is given by

$$\delta = hk = y\, d\theta$$

The strain is found by dividing the deformation by the original length *ef* of the fiber:

$$\epsilon = \frac{\delta}{L} = \frac{y\, d\theta}{ef}$$

If we denote the radius of curvature of the neutral surface by ρ, the curved length *ef* is equal to $\rho\, d\theta$; whence the strain becomes

$$\epsilon = \frac{y\, d\theta}{\rho\, d\theta} = \frac{y}{\rho}$$

Assuming that the material is homogeneous and obeys Hooke's law (assumption 2), the stress in fiber *gh* is given by

$$S = E\epsilon = \left(\frac{E}{\rho}\right) y \qquad\qquad (a)$$

Eq. (*a*) indicates that the stress in any fiber varies directly with its location *y* from the neutral surface, since it is assumed that the modulus of elasticity *E* is equal in tension and compression (assumption 3) and the radius of curvature ρ of the neutral surface is independent of the location *y* of the fiber. However, the stresses must not exceed the proportional limit, for this would invalidate Hooke's law on which this stress variation is based.

To complete the derivation of the flexure formula, we apply the conditions of equilibrium. In our discussion of vertical shear and bending moment, we saw that the equations of equilibrium require that the forces over

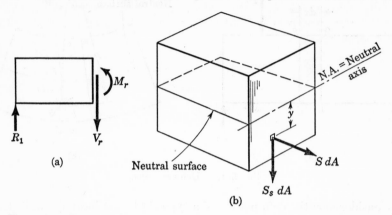

FIG. 5–2. — Forces acting upon any element of the cross-section of a beam.

any exploratory section satisfy the conditions $\Sigma X = 0$, $V = V_r$, and $M = M_r$. The pictorial sketch[1] (Fig. 5–2) shows the forces that act over the cross-section of a typical element of the exploratory section. The line of intersection between the neutral surface and the transverse section of the beam is called the *neutral axis*, abbreviated *N.A.*

To satisfy the condition that a horizontal summation of forces is zero, we must have

$$[\Sigma X = 0] \qquad\qquad \int S \, dA = 0$$

By replacing S with its value as given by Eq. (a), this becomes

$$\frac{E}{\rho} \int y \, dA = 0$$

The constant ratio $\dfrac{E}{\rho}$ is written outside the integral sign. Since $y \, dA$ is the moment of the differential area dA about the neutral axis, the integral $\int y \, dA$ is the total moment of area. Hence

$$\frac{E}{\rho} A\bar{y} = 0$$

However, since only $\bar{y}$ in this relation can be zero, we conclude that the distance from the neutral axis (which is the reference axis) to the centroid

[1] The cross-section is drawn as rectangular only for ease of representation; it may have any shape.

of the cross-sectional area must be zero; i.e., *the neutral axis must contain the centroid of the cross-sectional area.*

The condition that $\Sigma Y = 0$ resulting in $V = V_r$ leads to the shear stress formula, the derivation of which is postponed until later (Art. 5–7). It should be observed here that the resisting shear V_r is the summation of all the shearing forces $S_s\, dA$, i.e., $V_r = \int S_s\, dA$.

To satisfy the condition that the bending moment is balanced by the resisting moment, i.e., $M = M_r$, the resisting moment about the neutral axis of a typical element is $y(S\, dA)$. Hence for all elements in the cross-section,

$$M = \int y(S\, dA)$$

which, by replacing S by $\dfrac{E}{\rho}\, y$ from Eq. (*a*), becomes

$$M = \frac{E}{\rho} \int y^2\, dA$$

Since $\int y^2\, dA$ is defined as I, the moment of inertia[2] of the area about a reference axis which here is the neutral axis (equivalent to the centroidal axis), we finally obtain

$$M = \frac{EI}{\rho} \tag{b}$$

Observe now that it was necessary in Art. 4–2 to specify the centroidal axis of the exploratory section as the axis about which bending moment is computed in order to obtain a common axis for computing and equating M and M_r.

The usual form of writing Eq. (*b*) is

$$\frac{1}{\rho} = \frac{M}{EI} \tag{5–1}$$

which we shall use in Arts. 6–2 and 6–3 as the basis for determining deflections in beams. Because curvature is equal to the reciprocal of the radius of curvature, Eq. (5–1) indicates that curvature is directly proportional to bending moment, an observation which we have already used (page 99) in checking the sign of bending moment with the shape of the deflected beam — positive curvature, which is concave upward, correlating with positive bending moment, and vice versa.

Equating the ratio $\dfrac{E}{\rho}$ from Eq. (5–1) with its value from Eq. (*a*), we have

$$\frac{E}{\rho} = \frac{M}{I} = \frac{S}{y}$$

[2] A complete discussion of moment of inertia is given in Appendix A.

which leads directly to the flexure formula[3]

$$S = \frac{My}{I} \qquad (5\text{-}2)$$

This formula indicates that the flexure stress in any section varies directly with the distance of the section from the neutral axis. In a more common form of the flexure formula y is replaced by the distance c, which is defined as the distance from the neutral axis to the remotest element. With this change, the maximum flexure stress in any section is given by

$$\textbf{Max. } S = \frac{Mc}{I} \qquad (5\text{-}2a)$$

If $\dfrac{I}{c}$ is called the *section modulus* and denoted by Z, another common variation of the flexure formula is

$$\textbf{Max. } S = \frac{M}{I/c} = \frac{M}{Z} \qquad (5\text{-}2b)$$

This variation is useful for beams of constant cross-section, as it shows that maximum flexure stress occurs at the section of maximum bending moment. Various values of section modulus for common cross-sections are listed in Table V–1.

An interesting analysis, similar to that we shall use later in analyzing reinforced concrete beams (Art. 10–4), is to consider the variation in flexure stress over a rectangular cross-section, as shown in Fig. 5–3.

Because the horizontal summation of forces over a section must be zero, the total compressive force C in the upper half of the cross-section is equal to the total tensile force T in the lower half. Thus the resisting moment M_r consists of the couple composed of the equal, oppositely directed forces C and T. The value of each of these forces is equal to the product of the average stress multiplied by the area. Therefore, since the average stress in a linear stress distribution is one-half the maximum stress,

$$T = C = (S_{ave})(\text{Area}) = \left(\frac{1}{2}S\right)\left(b\,\frac{h}{2}\right)$$

The forces C and T act through the centroid of the triangular load distribution at a distance k from $N.A.$ Since $k = \dfrac{2}{3}c = \dfrac{2}{3}\left(\dfrac{h}{2}\right)$, the moment

[3] Note the similarity between the torsion formula $S_s = \dfrac{T\rho}{J}$ and the flexure formula $S = \dfrac{My}{I}$. This similarity not only makes them easy to remember, but indicates that the units of T and M are the same; they both are in in.-lb.

TABLE V-1. Section Moduli

CROSS-SECTION	DIMENSIONS	SECTION MODULUS
Rectangle	N.A. b, h	$\dfrac{bh^2}{6}$
Solid Circle	N.A. r, d	$\dfrac{\pi r^3}{4} = \dfrac{\pi d^3}{32}$
Tube	R, r N.A.	$\dfrac{\pi}{4R}(R^4 - r^4)$
Triangle	$c = \frac{2}{3}h$ h N.A. b	$\dfrac{bh^2}{24}$

arm of the resisting couple is $e = 2k = \frac{2}{3}h$. Equating bending moment to resisting moment, we have

$$M = M_r = Ce = Te$$

$$M = \left(\frac{1}{2}S\right)\left(b\,\frac{h}{2}\right)\left(\frac{2}{3}h\right) = S\,\frac{bh^2}{6}$$

which agrees with Eq. (5–2b) for a rectangular section.

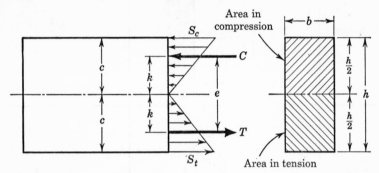

FIG. 5–3. — Resisting moment is equivalent to the couple created by the resultant compressive and tensile forces.

Modulus of Rupture. Eq. (5–2a) may be used to compute the flexure stress in a beam loaded to rupture in a testing machine. Because the proportional limit of the material is then exceeded, the stress determined in this manner is not a true stress; nevertheless, the fictitious stress so obtained is called the modulus of rupture. It is used to compare the ultimate strengths of beams of various sizes and materials.

ILLUSTRATIVE PROBLEMS

501. A beam 6 in. wide by 10 in. deep supports the loads shown in Fig. 5–4. Determine the maximum flexural stress.

Solution: We start by computing the maximum bending moment. The shear diagram shows that zero shear occurs at $x = 6$ ft. Using the area of this diagram to compute the bending moment, we have at $x = 6$ ft,

$$[\Delta M = (\text{Area})_V] \qquad \text{Max. } M = \left(\frac{2800 + 400}{2}\right)(6) = 9600 \text{ ft-lb}$$

It is unnecessary to draw the moment diagram.

We now apply the flexure formula. The bending moment is multiplied by 12 to convert it into in.-lb. From Table V–1 we find that the section modulus is $Z = \dfrac{bh^2}{6}$, so

$$\left[S = \frac{M}{Z} = \frac{6M}{bh^2}\right] \qquad \text{Max. } S = \frac{6(9600 \times 12)}{6(10)^2} = 1152 \text{ psi} \quad Ans.$$

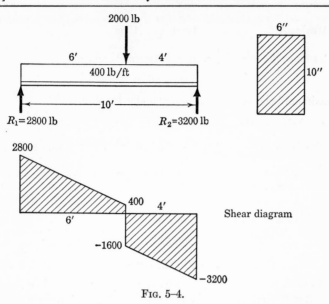

FIG. 5–4.

502. A timber beam 4 in. wide by 12 in. high and 20 ft long carries the loading shown in Fig. 5–5. If the maximum flexure stress is 1200 psi, for what maximum value of w will the shear be zero under P, and what is the value of P?

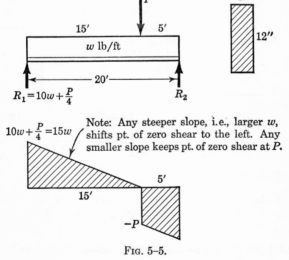

Note: Any steeper slope, i.e., larger w, shifts pt. of zero shear to the left. Any smaller slope keeps pt. of zero shear at P.

FIG. 5–5.

Solution: To satisfy the given conditions, the shear diagram must appear as shown. The maximum value of w to reduce the shear to zero at P is determined from Eq. (4–3).

$[\Delta V = (\text{Area})_{Load}]$ $10\,w + \dfrac{P}{4} = 15\,w$

which determines the following relation between P and w:

$$P = 20\,w \tag{a}$$

The maximum bending moment occurs under P and is

$[\Delta M = (\text{Area})_V]$ Max. $M = \frac{1}{2}(15)(15\,w) = 112.5\,w$ ft-lb

Converting bending moment to in.-lb and applying the flexure formula, we obtain

$$\left[M = S\frac{I}{c} = S\frac{bh^2}{6}\right] \qquad (112.5\,w)(12) = 1200\,\frac{(4)(12)^2}{6}$$

$$w = 85.3\ \text{lb/ft} \quad \textbf{Ans.}$$

whence from relation (a), the value of P is

$$P = 20\,w = 20(85.3) = 1706\ \text{lb} \quad \textbf{Ans.}$$

PROBLEMS

503. A cantilever beam 3 in. wide by 8 in. deep and 10 ft long carries a load varying uniformly from zero at the free end to 1000 lb/ft at the wall. Compute the type and magnitude of stress in a fiber 2 in. below the $N.A.$ in a section 6 ft from the free end.   *Ans.* $S = 675$ psi

504. Do Prob. 503 if the loading varies from 1000 lb/ft at the free end to zero at the wall.   *Ans.* $S = 2700$ psi

505. A beam 2 in. wide by 6 in. deep is loaded as shown. Compute the type and magnitude of stress in a fiber 2 in. below the $N.A.$ in a section 6 ft from the left end of the beam. Also find the maximum stress.

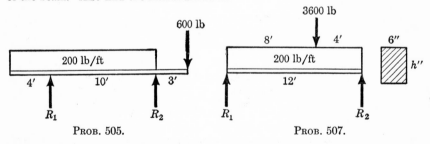

PROB. 505.   PROB. 507.

506. A high-strength steel band saw $\frac{3}{4}$ in. wide by $\frac{1}{32}$ in. thick runs over pulleys 18 in. in diameter. What maximum flexural stress is developed? $E = 30 \times 10^6$ psi.   *Ans.* $S = 52,000$ psi

507. What depth h will cause a maximum stress of 1200 psi in the given beam?

508. A rectangular timber beam b in. wide and 10 in. deep supports the loads shown. What must be the width of the beam if the stress is not to exceed 1200 psi?   *Ans.* $b = 6.78$ in.

509. A timber beam 6 in. wide by 12 in. deep supports the loads shown. Determine the maximum stress developed in the beam.   *Ans.* $S = 412$ psi

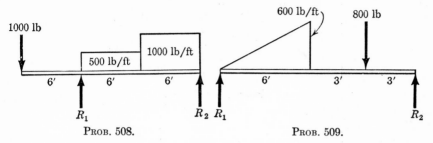

PROB. 508.   PROB. 509.

510. A simply supported beam 16 ft long is composed of two 10-in. 25-lb channels riveted back to back. What uniformly distributed load can be carried, in addition to the weight of the beam, without exceeding a flexural stress of 18,000 psi if (*a*) the webs are vertical? (*b*) the webs are horizontal?
Ans. (*a*) $w = 1650$ lb/ft; (*b*) $w = 152$ lb/ft

511. In a butt joint, a $\frac{3}{4}$-in. rivet secures $\frac{3}{8}$-in. cover plates to a $\frac{1}{2}$-in. main plate as shown. Assuming the loads are uniformly distributed along the rivet, determine the maximum flexural stress in the rivet.   *Ans.* $S = 30,200$ psi

512. A square timber beam used as a railroad tie is supported by a uniformly distributed reaction and carries two uniformly distributed loads each totaling 10 kips applied as shown. Determine the size of the section if the maximum stress is 1600 psi.

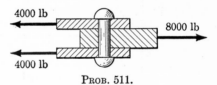

PROB. 511.

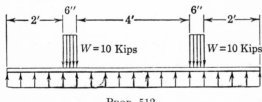

PROB. 512.

513. A 12-in. 31.8-lb I beam ($Z = 36.0$ in.³) is simply supported at the ends. It supports a central concentrated load of 12,000 lb and a uniformly distributed load of 1000 lb/ft, including the weight of the beam. Compute the maximum length of the beam so that the flexural stress will not exceed 18,000 psi.   *Ans.* $L = 12.0$ ft

514. A box beam is composed of four planks, each 2 in. by 8 in., securely spiked together to form the given section. Show that $I_{N.A.} = 981.3$ in.⁴ If $w = 200$ lb/ft, find P to cause a maximum flexural stress of 1200 psi.   *Ans.* $P = 4930$ lb

515. Solve Prob. 514 if $w = 700$ lb/ft.   *Ans.* $P = 1740$ lb

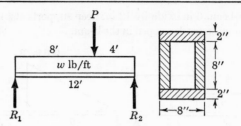

PROB. 514 and 515.

5-3. Economic Sections

In a beam having a rectangular or circular cross-section, the fibers near the neutral axis are understressed compared with those at the top or bottom. The fact that a large portion of the cross-section is thus understressed makes it inefficient for resisting flexure.

The flexure formula, $M = \dfrac{SI}{c}$, shows that if the area of a beam of rectangular section (Fig. 5–6a) could be rearranged so as to keep the same overall depth, but have the shape shown in Fig. 5–6b, the moment of inertia

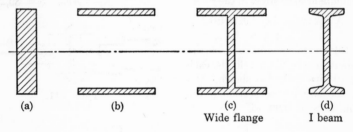

(a)   (b)   (c)   (d)

Wide flange   I beam

FIG. 5–6.

would be greatly increased, resulting in a greater resisting moment. Physically the increase in resisting moment is due to more fibers being located at a greater distance from the $N.A.$, for such fibers carry a greater stress and have a larger moment arm about the $N.A.$ to resist the applied bending moment. However, the section in Fig. 5–6b is not practicable; the two parts of it would collapse together. It is necessary to use some of the area to fix these parts in place relative to each other, as in Fig. 5–6c. We shall see later (page 159) that this web area transmits practically all the vertical shear, and we shall learn how to compute its dimensions.

Fig. 5–6c represents a wide flanged beam (symbolized as WF). This is one of the most efficient structural shapes manufactured because it not only provides great flexural strength with minimum weight of material, but is highly efficient when used as a column (see Chapter XI). Another structural shape is the I beam in Fig. 5–6d; it preceded the WF beam and, because it is not as efficient, has been largely replaced by the WF beam. Properties of both these sections are given in Appendix B. A beam of either type is specified by stating its over-all depth and weight per foot. The designation 24 WF 100, for example, indicates a wide flange beam having an over-all depth of 24 in. and weighing 100 lb per ft. The structural tables give the exact dimensions and other properties of the cross-sectional area, such as moment of inertia (I), section modulus (Z), and radius of gyration (k) for each principal axis of the section.

In selecting a structural section to be used as a beam, it is almost obvious that the resisting moment $M_r = \dfrac{SI}{c} = SZ$ must be equal to or greater than the applied bending moment M. This may be expressed as

$$Z \geqq \frac{M}{S} \tag{a}$$

Eq. (a) indicates that a beam must be selected whose section modulus is equal to or greater than the ratio of bending moment to allowable stress. The illustrative example below will demonstrate the necessary procedure and cautions.

Lateral Deflection of Beams. The compression flanges of beams tend to buckle horizontally sideways if the beam is too long. This buckling is a column effect, and will be discussed in Chap. XI. When this lateral deflection is prevented by the floor system, or by the compression flanges being braced with tie rods spaced at proper intervals, the full allowable stresses may be used. Otherwise, the stresses should be reduced. This reduction is accomplished in the specifications of the American Institute of Steel Construction in the following manner:

$$\left. \begin{array}{l} \text{For } \dfrac{Ld}{bt} < 600, \text{ use } S_c = 20{,}000 \text{ psi} \\[2em] \text{For } \dfrac{Ld}{bt} > 600, \text{ use } S_c = \dfrac{12{,}000{,}000}{\dfrac{Ld}{bt}} \end{array} \right\} \tag{5–3}$$

Here L is the unbraced length, d the depth of the beam, b the breadth and t the thickness of the compression flange; all dimensions are in inches. For convenience, the values of $\dfrac{d}{bt}$ are listed in Table V–2 on page 138.

ILLUSTRATIVE PROBLEM

516. What is the lightest WF beam that will support the load shown in Fig. 5–7 without exceeding a flexural stress of 18,000 psi?

Solution: We begin by computing the reactions and sketching the shear diagram. The maximum moment occurs under the load and equals $3000 \times 15 = 45,000$ ft-lb. Applying Eq. (*a*), we have

$$\left[Z \geqq \frac{M}{S} \right] \qquad\qquad Z \geqq \frac{45,000(12)}{18,000} = 30 \text{ in.}^3$$

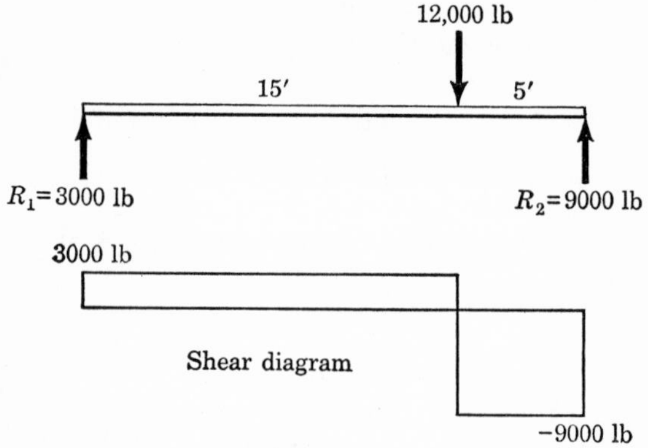

FIG. 5–7. — Live load. (Applied load exclusive of weight of beam.)

Referring to the table of properties of WF beams (page 448) and starting at the bottom, we find that the first beam whose section modulus is more than 30 in.³ is 8 WF 35, with $Z = 31.1$ in.³ In the 10-in. group we find a 10 WF 29 beam with $Z = 30.8$ in.³, which is also satisfactory as well as being lighter. The 12-in. group lists a 12 WF 27 beam with $Z = 34.1$ in.³; this is the best one, because the lightest suitable beam in the next (14-in.) group weighs more than 27 lb per ft.

The student may wonder why more than one size of beam is manufactured with approximately the same section modulus. The explanation is that although the lightest beam is the cheapest on the basis of weight alone, frequently headroom clearances require a beam of less depth than the lightest one.

The selection of the beam is not complete until a check calculation is made that includes the weight of the beam.[4] The beam's resisting moment M_B must be equal to or greater than the sum of the live load moment M_L caused by the applied loads and the dead load moment M_D caused by the dead weight of the beam:

$$M_B \geqq M_L + M_D$$

[4] Frequently the steel beam is haunched, i.e., encased in concrete for fireproofing or to form part of a concrete floor. The concrete may be assumed to extend at least 2 in. beyond the dimensions of the beam. For example, a 12 WF 40 beam with a depth of 12 in. and a flange width of 8 in. will be encased in concrete having over-all dimensions of 16 in. by 12 in. Computed at 150 lb/ft³, the haunch adds an extra load of approximately 290 lb/ft which should be included in the weight of the steel beam. In subsequent problems, however, the weight of the haunch should be neglected unless otherwise stated. In actual practice, its weight is usually included in an estimate of the dead loads.

Dividing each term of this equation by the stress S gives

$$\frac{M_B}{S} \geq \frac{M_L}{S} + \frac{M_D}{S}$$

whence, replacing $\dfrac{M}{S}$ by section modulus Z, we obtain the governing equation for design:

$$Z_B \geq Z_L + Z_D$$

The weight of the beam in this example is not sufficient to change the location of the maximum moment resulting from the combined live and dead loads. Hence we

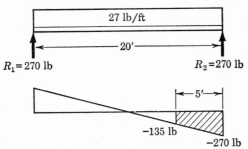

FIG. 5–8. — Dead load. (Due to weight of beam.)

compute the dead load moment M_D at $x = 15$ ft (Fig. 5–8). From the definition of bending moment, $M = (\Sigma M)_R$, we have

$$M_D = 270(5) - (27 \times 5)(\tfrac{5}{2}) = 1013 \text{ ft-lb}$$

or, from the shaded area of the shear diagram,

$$M_D = \frac{(270 + 135)}{2} (5) = 1013 \text{ ft-lb}$$

Therefore, the section modulus required to support the dead weight of the beam is

$$\left[Z_D = \frac{M_D}{S} \right] \qquad\qquad Z_D = \frac{1013(12)}{18,000} = 0.677 \text{ in.}^3$$

Applying the governing equation,

$$[Z_B \geq Z_L + Z_D] \qquad\qquad 34.1 > 30 + 0.677$$

we see that the 12 WF 27 beam is satisfactory.

The lightest I beam available in stock sizes that will support the given loading is a 12 I 31.8 with $Z = 36.0$ in.^{3} The I beam is 4.8 lb heavier per foot than the WF beam, which indicates one reason for the latter's popularity.

After you have used the tables of properties of structural shapes several times to select the proper size of a beam and are thoroughly familiar with them, you may find it convenient to use Table V–2. This table enables you to select rapidly the lightest shape of beam to support any required section modulus. In addition to section modulus and shape, the table lists the weight of a concrete haunch in lb/ft, and the product $\dfrac{d}{bt}$ for checking lateral deflection when necessary. The table is a modification of a similar table prepared by the American Institute of Steel Construction, which lists in descending order the section modulus not only of the lightest but of *all* shapes used as beams. Table V–2 includes, however, only WF beams, light or B beams, I beams, and channels (C).

To use Table V–2, in the column headed "Section Modulus," find the value equal to or next larger than the section modulus required. The beam size opposite this

TABLE V–2. Beam Economy

Section Modulus	Shape	Haunch (lb/ft)	$\dfrac{d}{bt}$	Section Modulus	Shape	Haunch (lb/ft)	$\dfrac{d}{bt}$
1105.1	36 WF 300	1160	1.31	107.8	18 WF 60	360	3.48
1031.2	36 WF 280	1160	1.40	98.2	18 WF 55	360	3.82
951.1	36 WF 260	1160	1.52	89.0	18 WF 50	360	4.22
892.5	36 WF 245	1160	1.62	80.7	16 WF 50	320	3.66
835.5	36 WF 230	1160	1.73	72.4	16 WF 45	320	4.07
740.6	33 WF 220	1020	1.65	64.4	16 WF 40	320	4.54
669.6	33 WF 200	1020	1.82	56.3	16 WF 36	320	5.30
663.6	36 WF 194	870	2.39	48.5	14 WF 34	280	4.58
621.2	36 WF 182	870	2.55	41.8	14 WF 30	280	5.37
579.1	36 WF 170	870	2.73	34.1	12 WF 27	250	4.50
541.0	36 WF 160	870	2.94	26.4	10 WF 25	210	4.08
502.9	36 WF 150	870	3.19				
446.8	33 WF 141	770	3.01				
404.8	33 WF 130	770	3.36	25.3	12 B 22	190	7.2
354.6	30 WF 124	670	3.08	21.5	10 WF 21	210	5.07
327.9	30 WF 116	670	3.36	21.4	12 B 19	190	8.7
299.2	30 WF 108	670	3.74	18.8	10 B 19	170	6.5
266.3	27 WF 102	600	3.27	17.5	12 B 16.5	190	11.2
248.9	24 WF 100	620	2.58	14.8	12 B 14	190	13.4
242.8	27 WF 94	600	3.61	10.5	10 B 11.5	170	12.3
220.9	24 WF 94	500	3.07	8.1	8 C 11.5	130	—
196.3	24 WF 84	500	3.47	7.8	8 B 10	150	9.8
175.4	24 WF 76	500	3.90	6.0	7 C 9.8	110	—
150.7	21 WF 73	420	3.46	5.1	6 B 8.5	130	7.7
139.9	21 WF 68	420	3.73	4.3	6 C 8.2	100	—
126.4	21 WF 62	420	4.15	3.0	5 C 6.7	90	—

Note: Unless suitable provision is made for lateral bracing, the beams below the heavy horizontal line have such narrow flanges that they must be checked with Eq. (5–3) for stress reduction. It may then be necessary to use the tables in Appendix B to select a slightly heavier but wider flanged section.

value is the lightest beam that can be used. After you have selected the beam, check for increase in section modulus caused by the weight of the beam or haunch, or both, unless otherwise instructed. *Do not attempt to use Table V–2 until you thoroughly understand the tables of properties of structural shapes.*

PROBLEMS

In the following problems, neglect the effect of lateral deflection and the weight of a haunch unless otherwise instructed. Do not fail to consider the weight of the beam itself.

517. A beam simply supported at the ends of a 30-ft span carries a uniformly distributed load of 1000 lb/ft over its entire length. What is the lightest beam section that will not exceed a stress of 18,000 psi if braced at the third points?

518. Solve Prob. 517 if the distributed load is increased to 2000 lb/ft and applied only over the middle half of the beam.   *Ans.*   21 WF 62

519. A concentrated load of 10,000 lb is applied at the center of a simply supported beam 30 ft long. (*a*) Using an allowable stress of 20,000 psi, select the lightest suitable section. (*b*) Considering the effect of lateral deflection, at what points should the beam selected be braced to permit using $S = 20,000$ psi? (*c*) What is the actual maximum stress in the selected beam?

Ans.   (*a*) 14 WF 34; (*b*) at the third points; (*c*) $S = 19,500$ psi

520. Solve Prob. 519 and include the weight of the concrete haunch.

521. A simply supported beam 24 ft long carries a uniformly distributed load of 1000 lb/ft over its entire length, and a concentrated load of 6000 lb at 8 ft from the left end. If the allowable stress is 18,000 psi, select the lightest beam section that will carry the loads. What is the actual maximum stress in the selected beam?

522. Solve Prob. 521 if the weight of the concrete haunch is included.

Ans.   18 WF 50; $S = 17,080$ psi

5–4. Floor Framing

Probably the commonest structural use of beams is to provide support for the floors and frameworks of buildings. Fig. 5–9 illustrates a typical detail in a home. The subfloor is supported by floor joists (called floor beams in steel construction). The floor joists are assumed to act as simply supported beams. They are supported by heavier beams called girders, which in turn are supported by columns that transmit the loads to the foundation.

The floor load is specified as p lb per sq ft (psf) and varies from 50 psf for homes to as high as 500 psf for industrial buildings. If the floor joists are L ft long and spaced a ft apart on centers, each joist is assumed to support the loading on an area a ft by L ft, shown shaded in the figure. The loading on a typical floor joist therefore is the uniformly distributed load

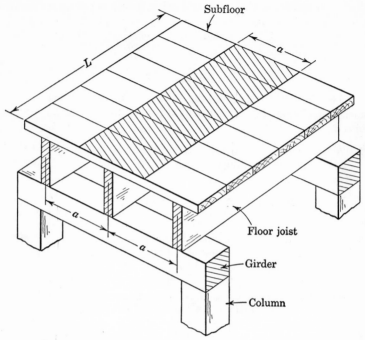

FIG. 5 -9. — Floor framing.

shown in Fig. 5–10. The total weight W equals the load p psf acting over the area aL. This may be divided by the length L to give a loading per ft of $w = pa$ lb/ft.

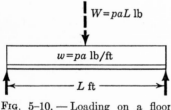

FIG. 5–10. — Loading on a floor joist.

In steel construction, the same general plan is followed except that the floor beams are usually riveted to the webs of the girders as shown in Fig. 2–23 (page 57).   The figures in the illustrative problem represent a small building and show how to construct the loading diagrams for the various beams.

ILLUSTRATIVE PROBLEM

523. Determine the loading diagrams for beams B–1, G–1, B–2, and G–2 for the building whose partial floor plan is shown in Fig. 5–11. The loading for each bay is as indicated.

Solution: Beams supporting only floor loads are designated B–1, B–2, etc. Beams that support the reactions of floor beams are called girders and are denoted by G–1, G–2, etc. At beam B–1, the loading is 100 psf uniformly distributed over a length of 15 ft and a width of 6 ft, resulting in the loading diagram shown in Fig. 5–12.

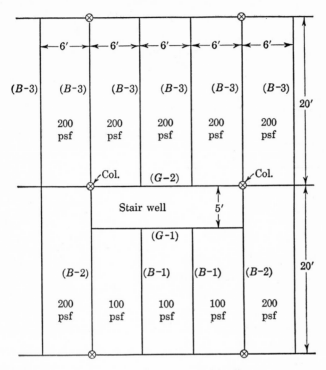

Fig. 5–11. — Floor plan and loading.

Beam G–1 is a girder used to support one end of beams B–1 and framed into beams B–2. It is loaded by the end reactions of beams B–1, as in Fig. 5–13.

Beam B–2 supports the end reaction of beam G–1, as well as half the loadings in the bays adjacent to it. Its loading diagram therefore appears as shown in Fig. 5–14. For the first 5 ft, beam B–2 supports a total load of 200 psf over a floor area 3 ft by 5 ft, equivalent to 3000 lb applied at 600 lb/ft. The reaction of beam G–1 is shown as a concentrated load of 4500 lb. For the rest of the

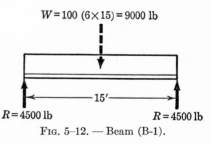

Fig. 5–12. — Beam (B-1).

beam, the loading is 900 lb/ft computed as the sum of the loadings per foot extending for 3 ft into the 200-psf bay and the 100-psf bay.

The girder beam G–2 is loaded by the reactions of beams B–3 only as shown in Fig. 5–15. Verify that the reaction of beam B–3 is 12,000 lb.

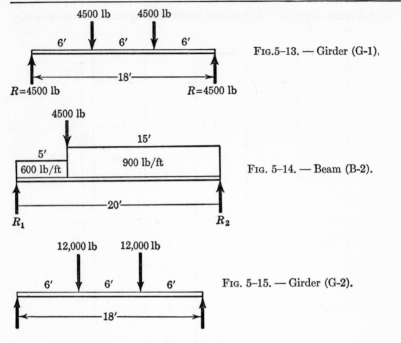

FIG.5–13. — Girder (G-1),

FIG. 5–14. — Beam (B-2).

FIG. 5–15. — Girder (G-2).

PROBLEMS

524. Floor joists 2 in. wide by 8 in. high, simply supported on a 12-ft span, carry a floor loaded at 100 psf. Compute the center-line spacing between joists to develop $S_f = 1200$ psi. *Ans.* 14.2 in.

525. Timbers 10 in. by 10 in., spaced 4 ft apart on centers, are driven into the ground and act as cantilever beams to back up the sheet piling of a coffer dam. What is the maximum safe height of water behind the dam if $w = 62.5$ lb/ft³ and $S_f = 1200$ psi? *Ans.* $h = 7.37$ ft

526. Timbers 6 in. wide by 10 in. deep and 12 ft long, supported at top and bottom, back up a dam restraining water 9 ft deep. (*a*) Compute the center-line spacing of the timbers to cause $S_f = 1200$ psi. (*b*) Will this spacing be safe if the maximum $S_f = 1600$ psi and the water reaches its maximum depth of 12 ft? *Ans.* (*a*) 31.6 in.

527. A portion of the floor plan of a certain building is shown. The total loading (including live and dead loads) in each bay is as shown. Select the lightest suitable WF beams if $S_f = 18,000$ psi.

528. A portion of the floor plan for a factory is shown. The total floor load (including live and dead loads) is 180 psf everywhere except on the 6-ft light well to the right of the load-bearing partition that forms the wall of a setback. The flooring consists of precast concrete slabs, which are available in widths up to $6\frac{1}{2}$ ft. Compute the center-line spacing of 12 B 19 beams in the right-hand portion if (*a*) they are braced by tie rods at the midpoints and if (*b*) they are braced at the third points. Use Eq. (5–3).   *Ans.*   (*a*) 2.42 ft; (*b*) 3.63 ft

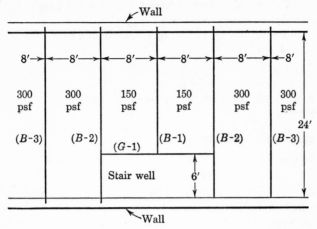

PROB. 527.

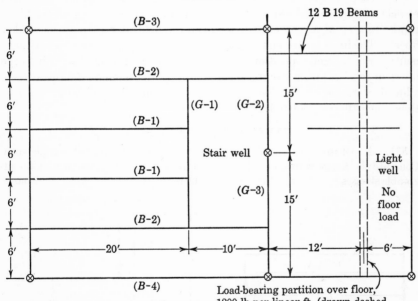

PROB. 528, 529, and 530.

529. In Prob. 528, if $S_f = 20{,}000$ psi (*a*) determine the size of the lightest WF sections for beams B–1, G–1, B–2, B–3, and B–4 if the effect of lateral deflection is ignored. (*b*) How would these beam selections be modified if lateral deflection is prevented by tie rods spaced 10 ft apart where necessary? (*c*) What beams would be selected, considering the effect of lateral deflection but providing no bracing? Use Eq. (5–3).

    Ans. (*a*) B–1 — 12 WF 27; G–1 — 14 WF 30; B–2 — 18 WF 60; B–3 — 16 WF 50; B–4 — 14 WF 30

530. Assuming that girders G–2 and G–3 carry the reactions of beams B–2, and that the reaction of the right portion (which includes the light well) is considered as a uniformly distributed load, select WF sections of least weight, using $S_f = 20,000$ psi.   *Ans.* 16 WF 45

5–5. Unsymmetrical Beams

All the beams discussed so far have been symmetrical with respect to the neutral axis. Because flexure stresses vary directly with distance from the neutral axis — which is the centroidal axis — such beam sections are desirable for materials that are equally strong in tension and compression. However, for materials relatively weak in tension and strong in compression, such as cast iron, it is desirable to use beams that are unsymmetrical with respect to the neutral axis. With such a cross-section, the stronger fibers can be located at a greater distance from the neutral axis than the weaker fibers. The ideal treatment for such materials is to locate the centroidal or neutral axis in such a position that the ratio of the distances from it to the fibers in tension and in compression is exactly the same as the ratio of the allowable stresses in tension and in compression. The allowable stresses thus reach their permitted values simultaneously.

ILLUSTRATIVE PROBLEMS

531. A cast-iron beam carries a uniformly distributed load on a simple span. Compute the flange width *b* of the inverted T section (Fig. 5–16) so that the allowable stresses $S_t = 5000$ psi and $S_c = 12,000$ psi reach their limits simultaneously.

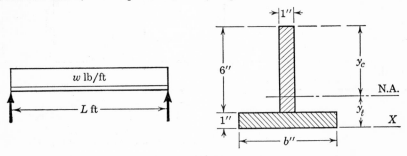

FIG. 5–16.

Solution: The beam is bent concave upward so that the uppermost fibers are in compression and the lowermost fibers are in tension. As discussed in Art. 5–2, flexure stresses vary directly with their distance from the neutral axis. Therefore to cause S_t and S_c to reach their limits simultaneously, we must have

$$\left[\frac{y_t}{y_c} = \frac{S_t}{S_c}\right] \qquad\qquad \frac{y_t}{y_c} = \frac{5000}{12,000}$$

or

$$y_c = \tfrac{12}{5}\, y_t \qquad\qquad\qquad (a)$$

Fig. 5–16 shows that another relation between y_t and y_c is

$$y_t + y_c = 7 \qquad\qquad\qquad (b)$$

so that, using relation (*a*), we obtain

$$y_t + \tfrac{12}{5}y_t = 7$$

from which

$$y_t = 2.06 \text{ in.}$$

Now consider the T section to consist of the two shaded rectangles. Since the neutral axis coincides with the centroidal axis, we take moments of areas with respect to an X axis through the base of the flange and obtain

$$[A\bar{y} = \Sigma ay] \qquad (6 \times 1 + b \times 1)y_t = (6 \times 1)(3 + 1) + (b \times 1)(\tfrac{1}{2})$$

In this is substituted the value $y_t = 2.06$, which gives

$$b = 7.46 \text{ in.} \quad Ans.$$

532. Compute the maximum tensile and compressive stresses developed in the beam that is loaded and has the cross-sectional properties as shown in Fig. 5–17.

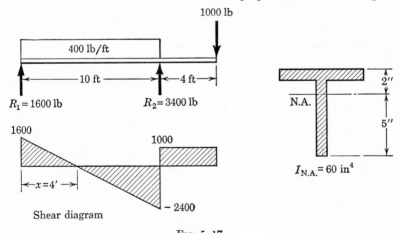

Fig. 5–17.

Solution: Sections of zero shear are at $x = 4$ ft and $x = 10$ ft. The bending moments at these sections are $M_4 = 3200$ ft-lb and $M_{10} = -4000$ ft-lb. Check these values.

The positive moment at $x = 4$ ft indicates curvature concave upward (see Art. 4–2); hence the upper fibers are in compression and the lower fibers are in tension. Applying Eq. (5–2) shows the flexure stresses to be

$$\left[S = \frac{My}{I} \right] \qquad S_c = \frac{(3200 \times 12)(2)}{60} = 1280 \, \text{psi}$$

$$S_t = \frac{(3200 \times 12)(5)}{60} = 3200 \, \text{psi}$$

At $x = 10$ ft, the negative bending moment is interpreted as curvature concave downward; so the upper fibers are in tension and the lower ones are in compression. Having thus interpreted the sign of the bending moment, the numerical value of the bending moment is substituted in Eq. (5–2) and yields the following flexure stresses:

$$\left[S = \frac{My}{I} \right] \qquad S_t = \frac{(4000 \times 12)(2)}{60} = 1600 \, \text{psi}$$

$$S_c = \frac{(4000 \times 12)(5)}{60} = 4000 \, \text{psi}$$

Hence the maximum tensile stress is 3200 psi, occurring at $x = 4$ ft, and the maximum compressive stress is 4000 psi, occurring at $x = 10$ ft. In an unsymmetrical section having a reversal in curvature, the maximum stresses need not both occur at the section of maximum bending moment. The stresses at each section of zero shear must be investigated.

533. The overhanging beam in Fig. 5–18 is made of cast iron, for which the allowable stresses are $S_t = 6000$ psi and $S_c = 15,000$ psi. If the properties of the cross-section are as shown, determine the maximum uniformly distributed load that can be supported.

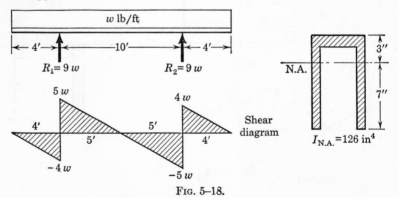

Fig. 5–18.

Solution: At $x = 4$ ft, the bending moment is $- 8\,w$ ft-lb, the negative sign indicating tension in the upper fibers. Using Eq. (5–2), we find that the safe resisting moments in tension and compression are:

$$\left[M_r = \frac{SI}{y} \right] \qquad M_t = \frac{6000(126)}{3} = 252{,}000 \text{ in.-lb}$$

$$M_c = \frac{15{,}000(126)}{7} = 270{,}000 \text{ in.-lb}$$

Evidently tension governs, since the safe resisting moment is the lower value. Equating this to the bending moment converted to in.-lb, we have

$$[M = M_r] \qquad\qquad (8\,w)(12) = 252{,}000 \qquad\qquad w = 2630 \text{ lb/ft}$$

Before concluding that this is the safe load, we must also investigate the other section of zero shear. At $x = 9$ ft, $M = 4.5\,w$ ft-lb. Although this is lower than the moment at $x = 4$ ft, the curvature is reversed, being concave upward and placing the upper fibers in compression and the lower ones in tension. From Eq. (5–2) the safe resisting moment is

$$\left[M_r = \frac{SI}{y} \right] \qquad M_c = \frac{15{,}000(126)}{3} = 630{,}000 \text{ in.-lb}$$

$$M_t = \frac{6000(126)}{7} = 108{,}000 \text{ in.-lb}$$

Equating the lower resisting moment to the bending moment expressed in in.-lb, we obtain

$$[M = M_r] \qquad\qquad (4.5\,w)(12) = 108{,}000 \qquad\qquad w = 2000 \text{ lb/ft}$$

The maximum safe load is the lower of the values obtained at $x = 4$ ft and $x = 9$ ft, i.e., 2000 lb/ft. Show that inverting the beam section will reduce the allowable load to 1125 lb/ft. Why is it unnecessary to investigate the section of zero shear at $x = 14$ ft?

PROBLEMS

534. Determine the maximum tensile and compressive stresses developed in the given overhanging beam. The cross-section is an inverted T having the properties shown.   *Ans.* $S_c = 10{,}800$ psi; $S_t = 7200$ psi

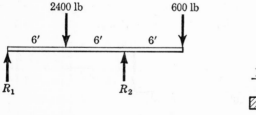
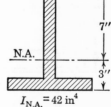

$I_{\text{N.A.}} = 42 \text{ in}^4$

PROB. 534.

535. Compute the maximum concentrated load that can be applied at the free end of a 10-ft cantilever beam if $S_t \leq 6000$ psi and $S_c \leq 14{,}000$ psi. The T section has the properties shown.   *Ans.* $P = 934$ lb

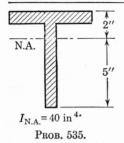

$I_{\text{N.A.}} = 40 \text{ in}^{4.}$

PROB. 535.

536. Three equal concentrated loads are carried on a cast-iron beam as shown. If $S_t \leqq 4000$ psi and $S_c \leqq$ 12,000 psi, compute the allowable load P.

537. Two angles 5 in. by 3 in. by $\frac{1}{2}$ in. are riveted back to back and used with the long legs vertical to form the cross-section of a beam 12 ft. long. The beam is simply supported and carries three equal concentrated loads P applied at the midpoint and at each quarter point. What value of P will develop a flexure stress of 18,000 psi?

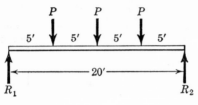

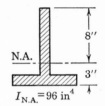

$I_{\text{N.A.}} = 96 \text{ in}^4$

PROB. 536.

538. A beam carries a concentrated load W and a total uniformly distributed load of $4\,W$ as shown. What safe value of W can be applied if $S_c \leqq 14,000$ psi and $S_t \leqq 9000$ psi? Can a greater load be applied if the section is inverted? Explain.

Ans. $W = 2810$ lb

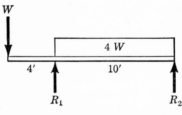

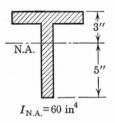

$I_{\text{N.A.}} = 60 \text{ in}^4$

PROB. 538

539. A cast-iron beam carries the loads shown. If $S_t \leqq 3000$ psi and $S_c \leqq$ 12,000 psi, compute the permissible limits of the overhang. *Ans.* $x = 7$ ft to 8 ft

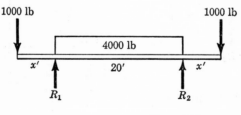

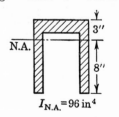

$I_{\text{N.A.}} = 96 \text{ in}^4$

PROB. 539.

540. A cast-iron beam 20 ft long and supported as shown carries a uniformly distributed load of w lb/ft (including its own weight). Allowable stresses are

$S_t \leq 5000$ psi and $S_c \leq 12,000$ psi. (*a*) Find the safe value of w if $x = 4$ ft. (*b*) Find the values of x and w so that w is a maximum.

Ans. (*a*) $w = 312$ lb/ft; (*b*) $x = 3.54$ ft; $w = 399$ lb/ft

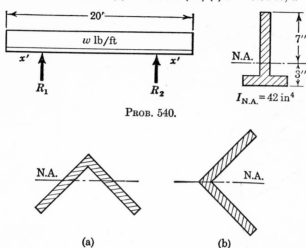

PROB. 540.

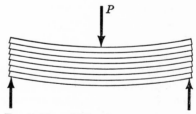

(a)   (b)

PROB. 541.

541. A simply supported beam 12 ft long carries a uniformly distributed load over its right half. The beam is a steel angle 6 in. by 6 in. by 1 in. Using $S = 18,000$ psi, determine the safe total load if the cross-section is in position (*a*). In position (*b*). Neglect the weight of the beam and assume that the load acts through the flexural center so that bending occurs without twisting (see Art. 12–7).

5–6. Analysis of Flexure Action

If a beam were composed of many thin layers placed on each other, bending would produce the effect shown in Fig. 5–19. The separate layers would slide past each other and the total strength of the beam would be the sum of the strengths of the various layers. Such a built-up beam would be considerably weaker than a solid beam of equivalent dimensions. For a demonstration of this, flex a pack of playing cards between the fingers, holding them rather loosely so that the cards can slide past one another as they are bent. Then grip the ends of them tightly, so that they cannot slip — thus approximating a solid section — and try to flex them. You will discover that considerably more effort is required.

FIG. 5–19. — Sliding between layers of a built-up beam.

Fig. 5–20a will aid in understanding this action. The figure is a pictorial representation of the flexural stress distribution over the portion to the left of the exploratory section m–n of the solid beam in Fig. 5–20b.

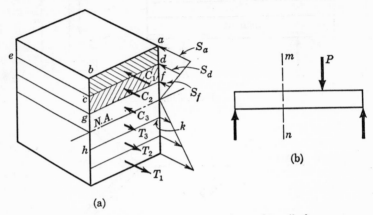

(a)   (b)

FIG. 5–20. — Distribution of compressive and tensile forces.

If we add the horizontal forces acting over the entire depth of the section, the compressive forces will exactly balance the tensile forces, as is required by the equilibrium condition $\Sigma X = 0$ (Art. 5–2). However, if we take a summation of horizontal forces over a partial depth of the section, say from the top elements a–b to those at c–d, the total compressive force C_1 over the area $abcd$ (equal to the area $abcd$ multiplied by the average of the stresses S_a and S_d) can be balanced only by a shear resistance developed at the horizontal layer dce. Such shear resistance is available in a solid beam but not in a built-up beam of unconnected layers.

If we extend the summation of horizontal forces down to layer fg, the resultant compressive force is increased by C_2, which is the average of the stresses S_d and S_f multiplied by the area $cdfg$. Thus a larger shear resistance must be developed over the horizontal layer at fg than at dce. Of course, the total compressive force C_1 plus C_2 acting over the area $abgf$ may also be computed as the average of the stresses S_a and S_f multiplied by the area $abgf$. However, the first method indicates the decreasing magnitude of the increase in the total compressive force as we descend by equal intervals from the top; i.e., although the total compressive force increases as we descend by equal intervals from the top, it does so by smaller increments.

This analysis shows that the maximum unbalanced horizontal force exists at the neutral axis. This unbalanced force decreases gradually to zero as the effects of layers below the neutral axis are included. This is so because the horizontal effect of the compressive forces is increasingly offset by the neutralizing effect of the tensile forces, until finally complete balance is attained and $\Sigma X = 0$ over the entire section.

This analysis also indicates that layers equidistant from the neutral axis, such as fg and hk, are subject to the same net horizontal unbalance, because in adding the horizontal forces from the top to these layers the equal compressive forces C_3 and T_3 cancel out. We conclude that equal shear resistances are developed at layers fg and hk. However, this requires that the areas from the neutral axis to the equidistant layers be symmetrical with respect to the neutral axis. The conclusion would not hold, for example, if the beam section were a triangle with its base horizontal.

PROBLEMS

542. A beam is composed of 6 planks, each 4 in. wide and 1 in. thick, piled loosely on each other to an over-all dimension of 4 in. wide by 6 in. high. (*a*) Compare the strength of such a beam with that of a solid beam of equal over-all dimensions. (*b*) What would be the ratio if the built-up beam consisted of 12 planks each 4 in. wide by $\frac{1}{2}$ in. thick?   *Ans.*   (*a*) 1 to 6; (*b*) 1 to 12

543. The WF beam shown is strengthened by riveting two cover plates 8 in. by 1 in. to the top and bottom flanges. If the maximum flexure stress is 18,000 psi, compute the total force (*a*) in each cover plate and (*b*) in each flange. Neglect the weakening effect of the rivet holes.   *Ans.*   (*a*) 136,000 lb; (*b*) 120,000 lb

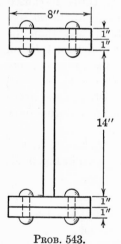

PROB. 543.

544. A T section has the dimensions given. Show that the neutral axis is 3 in. below the top and that $I_{N.A.}$ = 166.7 in.[4] If the tensile stress at the bottom of the flange is 1000 psi, calculate (*a*) the total tensile force in the flange and (*b*) the total compressive force in the cross-section. Also compute (*c*) the moment of the total compressive force and (*d*) the moment of the total tensile force about the N.A. (*e*) How does the sum of (*c*) and (*d*) compare with the total applied bending moment as computed from the flexure formula?

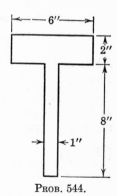

PROB. 544.

Ans.   (*a*) 24,000 lb; (*b*) 24,500 lb; (*c*) $M_c = 114,333$ in.-lb; (*d*) $M_t = 52,333$ in.-lb

5–7. Derivation of Formula for Horizontal Shearing Stress

Consider two adjacent sections (1) and (2) in a beam separated by the distance dx, as shown in Fig. 5–21, and let the shaded part between them be isolated as a free body. Fig. 5–22 is a pictorial representation of this part, the beam from which it is taken being shown in dashed outline.

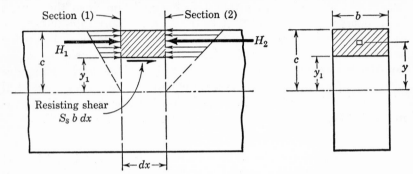

FIG. 5–21.

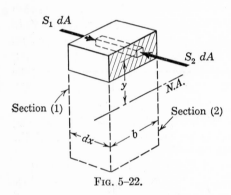

FIG. 5–22.

Assume the bending moment at section (2) to be larger than that at section (1), thus causing larger flexural stresses on section (2) than on section (1). Therefore, the resultant horizontal thrust H_2 caused by the compressive forces on section (2) will be greater than the resultant horizontal thrust H_1 on section (1). This difference between H_2 and H_1 can be balanced only by the resisting shear force $S_s b\, dx$ acting on the bottom face of the free body, since no external force acts on the top or side faces of the free body.

Since $H_2 - H_1$ is the summation of the differences in thrusts $S_2\, dA$ and $S_1\, dA$ on the ends of all elements contained in the part shown in Fig. 5–22, a horizontal summation of forces gives

$$[\Sigma H = 0] \qquad S_s b\, dx = H_2 - H_1$$

$$= \int_{y_1}^{c} S_2\, dA - \int_{y_1}^{c} S_1\, dA$$

whence, replacing the flexural stress S by its equivalent $\dfrac{My}{I}$, we obtain

$$S_s b\, dx = \frac{M_2}{I}\int_{y_1}^{c} y\, dA - \frac{M_1}{I}\int_{y_1}^{c} y\, dA = \frac{M_2 - M_1}{I}\int_{y_1}^{c} y\, dA$$

$M_2 - M_1$ represents the differential change in bending moment dM in the distance dx; hence the above relation is rewritten as

$$S_s = \frac{dM}{Ib\,dx}\int_{y_1}^{c} y\,dA$$

From Art. 4–4 we recall that $\dfrac{dM}{dx} = V$, the vertical shear; so we obtain for the horizontal shearing stress,

$$S_s = \frac{V}{Ib}\int_{y_1}^{c} y\,dA = \frac{V}{Ib}A'\bar{y} = \frac{V}{Ib}Q \qquad (5\text{–}4)$$

We have replaced the integral $\displaystyle\int_{y_1}^{c} y\,dA$, which means the sum of the moments of the differential areas dA about the neutral axis, by its equivalent $A'\bar{y}$, where A' is the partial area of the section above the layer at which the shearing stress is being computed, and $\bar{y}$ is the moment arm of this area with respect to the neutral axis. A' is the shaded area in the end view of Fig. 5–21. A variation of the product $A'\bar{y}$ is the symbol Q, which frequently is used to represent the static moment of area.

Relation Between Horizontal and Vertical Shearing Stresses. Most students are surprised to find the term *vertical shear* (V) appearing in the formula for horizontal shearing stress (S_{s_h}). However, as we shall show presently, a horizontal shearing stress is always accompanied by an equal vertical shearing stress. It is this vertical shearing stress S_{s_v}, shown in Fig. 5–23, that forms the resisting vertical shear $V_r = \int S_s\,dA$ which balances the vertical shear V. Since it is not feasible to determine S_{s_v} directly, we have resorted to deriving the numerically equal value of S_{s_h}.

To prove the equivalence of S_{s_h} and S_{s_v}, consider their effect on a freebody diagram of a typical element of Fig. 5–23. A pictorial view of this element is shown in Fig. 5–24a; a front view, in Fig. 5–24b. For equilibrium of this element, the shearing stress S_{s_h} on the bottom face requires an equal balancing shearing stress on the top face. The forces causing these shearing stresses (Fig. 5–24c) form a counterclockwise couple, which requires a clockwise

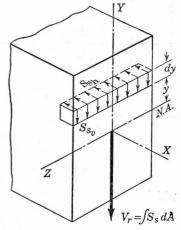

Fig. 5–23. — Horizontal and vertical shearing stresses.

couple to ensure balance. The forces of this clockwise couple induce the shearing stresses S_{s_v} on the vertical faces of the element as shown.

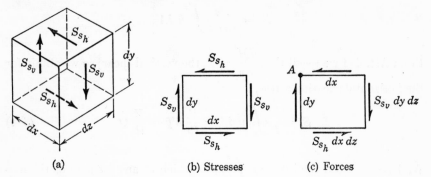

(a)   (b) Stresses   (c) Forces

FIG. 5–24. — Shearing stresses on a typical element.

By taking moments about an axis through A (Fig. 5–24c), we obtain

$$[\Sigma M_A = 0] \qquad (S_{s_h}\, dx\, dz)\, dy - (S_{s_v}\, dy\, dz)\, dx = 0$$

from which the constant product $dx\, dy\, dz$ is canceled to yield

$$S_{s_h} = S_{s_v} \tag{5-5}$$

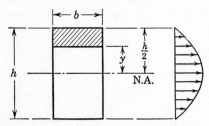

FIG. 5–25. — Shearing stress is distributed parabolically across a rectangular section.

We conclude therefore that a shearing stress acting on one face of an element is always accompanied by a numerically equal shearing stress acting on a perpendicular face.

Application to Rectangular Section. The distribution of shearing stresses in a rectangular section can be obtained by applying Eq. (5–4) to Fig. 5–25. For a layer at a distance y from the neutral axis, we have

$$S_s = \frac{V}{Ib} A' \bar{y} = \frac{V}{Ib}\left[b\left(\frac{h}{2} - y\right)\right]\left[y + \frac{1}{2}\left(\frac{h}{2} - y\right)\right]$$

which reduces to

$$S_s = \frac{V}{2I}\left(\frac{h^2}{4} - y^2\right)$$

This shows that the shearing stress is distributed parabolically across the depth of the section.

The maximum shearing stress occurs at the neutral axis, and is found by substituting the dimensions of the rectangle in Eq. (5–4), as follows:

$$S_s = \frac{V}{Ib}A'\bar{y} = \frac{V}{\dfrac{bh^3}{12}\cdot b}\left(\frac{bh}{2}\right)\left(\frac{h}{4}\right)$$

which reduces to

$$\text{Max } S_s = \frac{3}{2}\frac{V}{bh} = \frac{3}{2}\frac{V}{A} \tag{5–6}$$

This indicates that the maximum shearing stress in a rectangular section is 50% greater than the average shear stress.

Assumptions and Limitations of Formula.   We have assumed, without saying so implicitly, that the shearing stress is uniform across the width of the cross-section. Although this assumption does not hold rigorously, it is sufficiently accurate for sections in which the flexure forces are evenly distributed over a horizontal layer.

This condition is present in a rectangular section and in the WF section shown in Fig. 5–26a, where the flexure forces on the vertical strips, both

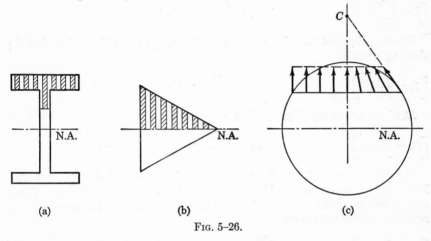

(a)   (b)   (c)

Fɪɢ. 5–26.

shaded and unshaded, are evenly distributed across any horizontal layer. But this condition does not exist in the triangular section in Fig. 5–26b, where the shearing stress is maximum at the left edge of the neutral axis diminishing to zero at the right edge. Even here, however, Eq. (5–4) can be used to compute the *average* value of shearing stress across any layer. Another exception is a circular cross-section (Fig. 5–26c). It can be shown that the stress at the edge of any layer must be tangent to the surface, as in the right half of the figure; but the direction of shearing stresses at interior points is unknown, although they are assumed to pass through a common center *C* as shown. The vertical components of these shearing stresses are usually assumed to be uniform across any layer, as in the left half of the figure, and are computed by means of Eq. (5–4). With this assumption, the maximum shearing stress across the neutral axis is $\dfrac{4}{3}\dfrac{P}{\pi r^2}$. A more elaborate study[5] shows that the shearing stress actually varies at the neutral axis from $1.23\dfrac{P}{\pi r^2}$ at the edges to $1.38\dfrac{P}{\pi r^2}$ at the center.

ILLUSTRATIVE PROBLEMS

545. A simply supported beam 4 in. wide, 6 in. deep, and 16 ft long carries a uniformly distributed load of 300 lb/ft. (a) Compute the shearing stress developed at horizontal layers 1 in. apart from top to bottom of a section 2 ft from the left end. (b) Compute the maximum shearing stress developed in the beam.

Solution: Part a. As shown on the shear diagram (Fig. 5–27a), the definition of vertical shear $V = (\Sigma Y)_L$ gives $V = 1800$ lb at $x = 2$ ft.

The moment of inertia about the neutral axis is

$$\left[I = \frac{bh^3}{12}\right] \qquad I_{N.A.} = \frac{4(6)^3}{12} = 72 \text{ in.}^4$$

Applying Eq. (5–4) to a layer 1 in. from the top (Fig. 5–27b), we find that the shearing stress is

$$\left[S_s = \frac{V}{Ib}A'\bar{y}\right] \qquad S_s = \frac{1800}{72(4)}(4 \times 1)(2.5) = 62.5 \text{ psi}$$

At 2 in. from the top (Fig. 5–27c), the shearing stress is

$$\left[S_s = \frac{V}{Ib}A'\bar{y}\right] \qquad S_s = \frac{1800}{72(4)}(4 \times 2)(2) = 100 \text{ psi}$$

The shearing stress at 2 in. from the top can also be computed from Fig. 5–27d, in which the area A' is resolved into two strips 1 in. thick. Since a moment of area equals the sum of the moments of area of its parts (i.e., $A'\bar{y} = \Sigma ay$), an identical result is obtained as follows:

$$\left[S_s = \frac{V}{Ib}\Sigma ay\right] \qquad S_s = \frac{1800}{72(4)}[(4 \times 1)(2.5) + (4 \times 1)(1.5)] = 100 \text{ psi}$$

Although this computation is admittedly more complex than the preceding, it indicates the procedure to be followed when the area A' is more complex, as in the case of a WF beam.

At the neutral axis, or at 3 in. from the top (Fig. 5–27e), the shearing stress is

$$\left[S_s = \frac{V}{Ib}A'\bar{y}\right] \qquad S_s = \frac{1800}{72(4)}(4 \times 3)(1.5) = 112.5 \text{ psi}$$

If desired, Eq. (5–6) may be used. As noted on page 155, this equation determines the maximum shearing stress on any rectangular section.

[5] See Timoshenko, *Theory of Elasticity*, McGraw-Hill, p. 290.

$$\left[S_s = \frac{3}{2}\frac{V}{bh}\right] \qquad S_s = \frac{3}{2}\frac{1800}{(4)(6)} = 112.5\,\text{psi}$$

The shearing stresses at the 4-in. layer and the 5-in. layer are determined similarly to be 100 psi and 62.5 psi respectively.

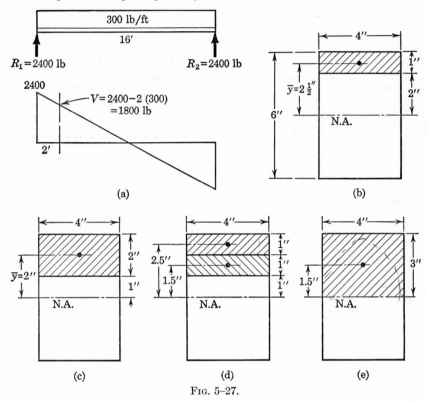

Fig. 5–27.

Notice that equal values of S_s are obtained at layers equidistant from the *N.A.* in any beam symmetrical about the neutral axis. Physically, this is true because the compressive and tensile flexure forces between these layers cancel each other, as was said on page 151. Analytically, it is true because the neutral axis is the centroidal axis, and hence the moment of area $A'\bar{y}$ computed for a partial area A' located above the *N.A.* equals that for a symmetrically placed area below the *N.A.* Further, since the total moment of area is zero with respect to a centroidal axis, it follows that the moment of area about the *N.A.* of the area above any layer equals that of the area below that layer. Stated differently, in computing $A'\bar{y}$ we may use either the area above or that below any layer, depending upon which is easier to use.

Part b. The maximum shearing stress occurs at the neutral axis of the section of maximum shear. The shear diagram shows that maximum shear occurs at either end, and hence from Eq. (5–6) the maximum shearing stress is

$$\left[S_s = \frac{3}{2} \frac{V}{A} \right]$$ Max. $S_s = \frac{3}{2} \cdot \frac{2400}{(4)(6)} = 150\,\text{psi}$ *Ans.*

546. A beam has the WF section shown in Fig. 5–28a. At a section where the vertical shear is $V = 16{,}000$ lb, compute (a) the maximum shearing stress and (b) the shearing stress at the junction of the flange and the web. (c) Plot the shearing stress distribution in the web and determine the percentage of shear carried by the web alone.

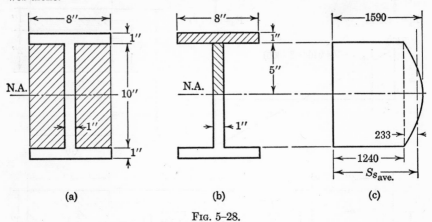

(a)   (b)   (c)

FIG. 5–28.

Solution: The moment of inertia is found by resolving the section into a large rectangle from which is subtracted the two shaded rectangles. We obtain

$$\left[I = \Sigma I = \Sigma \frac{bh^3}{12} \right]$$ $I_{N.A.} = \dfrac{8(12)^3}{12} - 2\left[\dfrac{3.5(10)^3}{12} \right] = 568\,\text{in.}^4$

The maximum shearing stress occurs at the neutral axis. In applying Eq. (5–4), compute $A'\bar{y}$ as the sum of the moments of area of the rectangles shaded in Fig. 5–28b.

$$\left[S_s = \frac{V}{Ib} A'\bar{y} \right]$$ Max. $S_s = \dfrac{16{,}000}{568(1)}\left[(8 \times 1)(5.5) + (5 \times 1)(2.5) \right] = 1590\,\text{psi}$

At the junction of the web and flange, the shearing stress is

$$\left[S_s = \frac{V}{Ib} A'\bar{y} \right]$$ $S_s = \dfrac{16{,}000}{568 \times 1}\,(8 \times 1)(5.5) = 1240\,\text{psi}$

These stresses vary parabolically from top to bottom of the web, as shown in Fig. 5–28c. The average height of the parabolic segment is $\frac{2}{3}$ of $(1590 - 1240)$, or 233 psi. The average shear stress in the web therefore is

$$S_{s_{ave}} = 1240 + 233 = 1473\,\text{psi}$$

The shearing force in the web is

$[P = AS_{ave}]$ $V_{web} = (10 \times 1)(1473) = 14{,}730 \text{ lb}$

whence the percentage of shear carried by the web alone is

$$\% \, V_{web} = \frac{14{,}730}{16{,}000} \times 100 = 92.2\%$$

This shows that the flanges are almost ineffective in resisting the vertical shear. If it is assumed that the total vertical shear is carried by the web alone, the average shearing stress in the web will be very close to the maximum shearing stress as computed from Eq. (5–4). Thus

$$\left[S_s = \frac{V}{A_{web}} \right] \qquad S_s = \frac{16{,}000}{10 \times 1} = 1600 \text{ psi}$$

This is very close to the computed maximum, 1590 psi.

This method gives results that closely approximate the actual maximum S_s. In most design specifications or codes, however, the height of the web is not taken as the distance between flanges, but is assumed to be the total depth of the beam. This procedure is not as accurate as the method given above, but lower allowable shearing stresses are usually specified in order to compensate.

PROBLEMS

547. A timber beam 6 in. wide by 12 in. high is subjected to a vertical shear $V = 5760 \text{ lb}$. Compute the shearing stress developed at layers 1 in. apart from top to bottom of the section.

548. Show that the shearing stress developed at the neutral axis of a circular beam is $S_s = \dfrac{4}{3} \dfrac{V}{\pi r^2}$. Assume that the shearing stress is uniformly distributed across the neutral axis.

549. A simply supported wooden beam L ft long and 2 in. wide by 6 in. high carries a uniformly distributed load of w lb/ft. Compute L in ft to develop $S_f = 1200 \text{ psi}$ and $S_s = 100 \text{ psi}$ simultaneously.

550. A rectangular beam b in. wide by h in. high carries a central concentrated load P on a simply supported span of L ft. Express the maximum S_s in terms of the maximum S_f.

$\qquad\qquad\qquad\qquad\qquad\qquad\qquad$ *Ans.* $S_s = \dfrac{hS_f}{24\,L}$

551. A laminated beam is composed of 5 planks, each 2 in. by 4 in., glued together to form a section 4 in. wide by 10 in. high. If the allowable strength of the glue is 60 psi, what maximum flexure stress may be developed when supporting a uniformly distributed load on a 12-ft simple span? *Ans.* $S_f = 900 \text{ psi}$

552. The cross-section of a wooden beam is an isosceles triangle, with vertex uppermost, of altitude $h = 6$ in. and base $b = 6$ in. Determine the shearing stress at 1-in. intervals from top to bottom, at a section where the vertical shear $V = 2160 \text{ lb}$. Also show that the maximum S_s is $\dfrac{3V}{bh}$ located at the midpoint of the altitude.

$\qquad\qquad$ *Ans.* At 1 in. from top, $S_s = 100 \text{ psi}$; at 2 in., $S_s = 160 \text{ psi}$

553. Determine the maximum and minimum S_s in the web of the WF section given if $V = 138,000$ lb. Also compute the per cent of vertical shear carried only by the web of the beam.   *Ans.*   Min. $S_s = 11,000$ psi; max. $S_s = 13,500$ psi; 91.7%

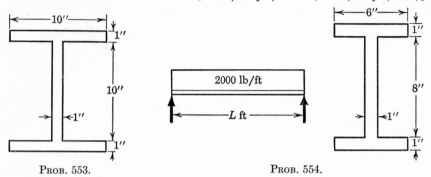

PROB. 553.   PROB. 554.

554. Determine the length of the given beam that will develop a maximum $S_s = 3000$ psi. What maximum flexural stress is developed?   *Ans.* $L = 24.6$ ft

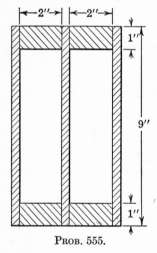

PROB. 555.

555. A plywood beam is built up of $\frac{3}{16}$-in. strips separated by blocks, as shown. What shearing force V will set up a maximum shearing stress of 200 psi?

5–8. Design for Flexure and Shear

In this article we consider the determination of load capacity or the size of beam section that will satisfy allowable stresses in both flexure and shear. No principles are required beyond those already developed.

In heavily loaded short beams, the design is usually governed by the shearing stress (which varies with V); but in longer beams, the flexure stress generally governs, because the bending moment varies with both load and length of beam. Shearing is more important in timber beams than in steel beams, because of the low shearing strength of wood.

ILLUSTRATIVE PROBLEMS

556. A rectangular beam carries a distributed load of w lb/ft on a simply supported span of L ft. Determine the critical length at which the shearing stress S_s and the flexure stress S reach their allowable values simultaneously.

Solution: As shown in Fig. 5–29, max. $V = \dfrac{W}{2}$, where W is the total distributed load. The maximum load as limited by the allowable shearing stress is determined from Eq. (5–6).

$$\left[\text{Max. } S_s = \frac{3}{2}\frac{V}{bh}\right] \qquad\qquad S_s = \frac{3}{2}\cdot\frac{W/2}{bh} \qquad\qquad W = \frac{4}{3}bh\,S_s$$

Note that W is independent of the length.

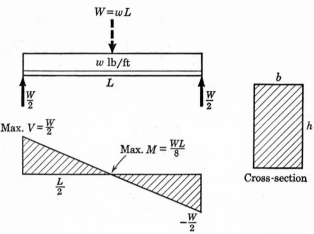

FIG. 5–29.

At the point of zero shear, the maximum bending moment, computed from the area of the shear diagram, is $M = \dfrac{1}{2}\left(\dfrac{W}{2}\right)\left(\dfrac{L}{2}\right) = \dfrac{WL}{8}$ ft-lb. Substituting this value in the flexure formula, Eq. (5–2a), we obtain

$$\left[M = \frac{SI}{c} = \frac{S\,bh^2}{6}\right] \qquad\qquad \left(\frac{WL}{8}\right)(12) = \frac{S\,bh^2}{6}$$

Replacing W by its value in terms of the shear stress, we have

$$\left(\frac{4}{3}bh\,S_s\right)\left(\frac{L}{8}\right)(12) = \frac{S\,bh^2}{6}$$

which reduces to

$$L = \frac{Sh}{12\,S_s}$$

Here L is in ft, but h is in inches. For values larger than this critical length, flexure governs the design; for shorter values, shear governs.

557. A box beam supports the loads shown in Fig. 5–30. Compute the maximum value of P that will not exceed a flexural stress $S = 1000$ psi or a shearing stress $S_s = 100$ psi.

Solution: We start by computing I for the net section, which is the difference between two rectangles. Hence

$$I = \Sigma\frac{bh^3}{12} = \frac{8(10)^3}{12} - \frac{6(8)^3}{12} = 411 \text{ in.}^4$$

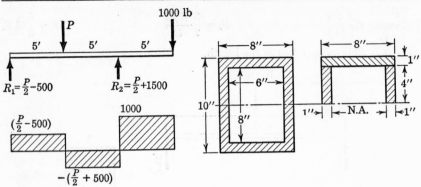

FIG. 5–30.

Determining the reactions from statics gives the shear diagram the values shown.

In terms of P, the maximum V is $-\left(\dfrac{P}{2} + 500\right)$. Representing the area of the cross-section above the $N.A.$, where S_s is a maximum, by the three rectangles shown, we substitute the absolute value of max. V in Eq. (5–4) to obtain

$$\left[S_s = \frac{V}{Ib}A'\bar{y}\right] \qquad 100 = \frac{\dfrac{P}{2} + 500}{411(2)}\left[(8 \times 1)(4.5) + 2(4 \times 1)\left(\frac{4}{2}\right)\right]$$

$$P = 2160 \,\text{lb}$$

The maximum moment in terms of P is at $x = 5$ ft and has the value $M = \left(\dfrac{P}{2} - 500\right)(5) = 2.5\,P - 2500$ ft-lb. Applying the flexure formula, we have

$$\left[M = \frac{SI}{c}\right] \qquad (2.5\,P - 2500)(12) = \frac{1000(411)}{5} \qquad P = 3740\,\text{lb}$$

The safe load is the smaller of the above values, namely, $P = 2160$ lb.

PROBLEMS

558. A maximum shearing stress of 120 psi is caused by a uniformly distributed load applied over the entire length of a simply supported beam 8 ft long. If the beam is rectangular in section, 8 in. wide by 10 in. high, compute the maximum flexural stress.

559. A wooden beam 4 in. wide and h in. high carries a uniformly distributed load of 600 lb/ft on a simply supported span 8 ft long. Find the proper height of the beam if $S \leqq 1000$ psi and $S_s \leqq 120$ psi.

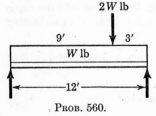

PROB. 560.

560. A rectangular beam 6 in. wide by 8 in. high supports a total distributed load of W lb and a concentrated load of $2\,W$ lb applied as shown. If $S \leqq 1500$ psi and $S_s \leqq 160$ psi, determine the maximum value of W.   *Ans.* $W = 1420$ lb

561. A distributed load of w lb/ft is applied over part of a box beam as shown. Determine the maximum value of w if $S \leq 1000$ psi and $S_s \leq 120$ psi.

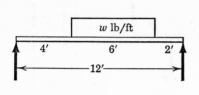
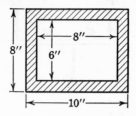

Prob. 561.

562. Three planks 8 in. by 1 in. are spiked together to form a beam that supports a distributed load as shown. If $S_s \leq 400$ psi and $S \leq 1600$ psi, at what length will these stresses reach their allowable values simultaneously?

Ans. $L = 11.7$ ft

563. A built-up timber beam having the cross-section given is used to support a concentrated load P on a simply supported span 30 ft long. Determine P and its location to cause a flexural stress of 1200 psi and a shearing stress of 100 psi simultaneously.

Ans. $P = 1637$ lb at 11.25 ft from one end

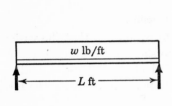
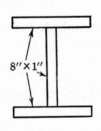
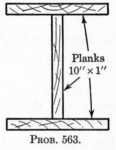

Prob. 562.   Prob. 563.

564. The distributed load shown is supported by a box beam having the same cross-section as that in Prob. 557. Determine the maximum value of w that will not exceed a flexural stress of 2000 psi or a shearing stress of 120 psi.

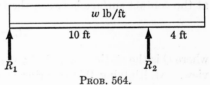

Prob. 564.

565. A T beam supports the three concentrated loads shown. Prove that the $N.A.$ is 3.50 in. above the bottom and that $I_{N.A.} = 97.0$ in.^{4} Then use these values to determine the maximum value of P that will not exceed allowable stresses in tension of 4000 psi, in compression of 10,000 psi, or in shear of 600 psi.

Ans. $P = 1470$ lb

566. A box beam carries two concentrated loads W and a total distributed load of 6 W as shown. Determine the maximum value of W if $S \leq 1200$ psi and $S_s \leq 100$ psi.

Ans. $W = 315$ lb

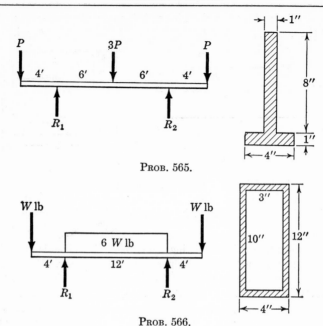

PROB. 565.

PROB. 566.

5–9. Spacing of Rivets or Bolts in Built-up Beams

In our analysis of flexure action (Art. 5–6) we showed that the various elements composing a built-up beam tend to slide past one another. We shall now consider the size and spacing of rivets or bolts in a built-up beam to resist this sliding action. The first step is to calculate the force to be resisted by such rivets.

Fig. 5–31 shows a beam composed of three planks bolted together by two rows of bolts spaced e inches apart. Eq. (5–4) gives the shearing stress at the contact surface between the two upper planks as

$$S_s = \frac{V}{Ib} Q$$

where Q is the static moment about the $N.A.$ of the shaded area in the end view. Multiplying this shearing stress by the shaded area eb in the top view gives the force F to be resisted in a length e:

$$F = S_s(eb) = \frac{V}{Ib} Q(eb) = \frac{Ve}{I} Q$$

Neglecting friction, this force is resisted by the shearing or bearing strength R of the bolts, whichever is smaller. Equating R to F gives

$$R = \frac{Ve}{I} Q \qquad\qquad (5\text{--}7)$$

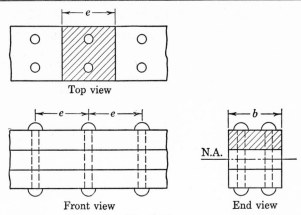

Top view

Front view   End view

Fig. 5–31.

If the vertical shear varies in a beam, V is the average vertical shear in the interval e; but it is usually taken as the maximum V in this interval, especially in built-up steel girders where the length of the interval is taken as a panel length equal to the depth of the girder. In this case, Eq. (5–7) gives the rivet pitch in each panel length.

ILLUSTRATIVE PROBLEM

567. A plate and angle girder is fabricated by attaching the short legs of angles 5 by $3\frac{1}{2}$ by $\frac{1}{2}$ in. to a web plate $43\frac{1}{2}$ in. by $\frac{3}{8}$ in. to form a section 44 in. deep, as shown in Fig. 5–32. The moment of inertia[6] about the N.A. is $I = 9705$ in.[4] At a section where V = 100,000 lb, determine the spacing between $\frac{3}{4}$-in. rivets that fasten the angles to the web plate. Use $S_s = 15,000$ psi; in bearing, use $S_b = 32,000$ psi for rivets in single shear and $S_b = 40,000$ psi for rivets in double shear.

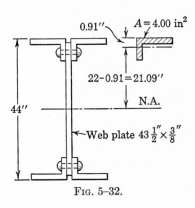

Fig. 5–32.

Solution: The static moment of area about the N.A. of two flange angles is

$$Q = 2(4.00)(21.09) = 168.7 \text{ in.}^3$$

The shearing resistance of a $\frac{3}{4}$-in. rivet in double shear is

$$R_s = (A_s S_s)(2) = \frac{\pi}{4}\left(\frac{3}{4}\right)^2 (15,000)(2) = 13,300 \text{ lb}$$

---

[6] The latest recommendations of the A.I.S.C. call for no deduction for rivet holes in computing I, provided that the rivet hole area does not exceed 15% of the gross flange area. If it does, only the area in excess of 15% need be considered in modifying I to deduct for rivet holes.

The bearing resistance against the web plate is

$$R_b = (dt)S_b = \tfrac{3}{4}(\tfrac{3}{8})(40,000) = 11,250 \text{ lb}$$

Using the lower of these values in Eq. (5–7), we get the required rivet pitch

$$e = \frac{RI}{VQ} = \frac{11,250(9705)}{100,000(168.7)} = 6.48 \text{ in.}$$

PROBLEMS

568. A concentrated load P is carried at the center of a simply supported span 10 ft long. The beam is built up of three planks 3 in. by 8 in., arranged as shown and secured by $\tfrac{1}{2}$-in. bolts spaced 8 in. apart. Determine the maximum value of P that will not exceed $S_s = 12,000$ psi in the bolts or $S_s = 200$ psi in the beam.

Ans. $P = 7220$ lb

569. A box beam, built up as shown, is secured by screws, each capable of withstanding a shearing force of 400 lb. Determine their pitch if the beam is loaded so as to cause a maximum horizontal shearing stress of 120 psi.

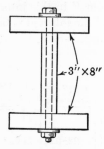

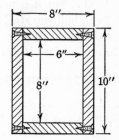

PROB. 568.   PROB. 569.

570. Three planks 3 in. by 4 in., secured by bolts spaced 1 ft apart, are used to support a concentrated load P at the center of a simply supported span 12 ft long. If P causes a maximum flexural stress of 1200 psi, determine the bolt diameters, assuming that the shear between the planks is transmitted by friction only. The bolts are tightened to a tension of 18,000 psi and the coefficient of friction between the planks is 0.20.   *Ans.* $d = 0.752$ in.

571. A plate and angle girder is fabricated by riveting the short legs of 5 by $3\tfrac{1}{2}$ by $\tfrac{1}{2}$ angles to a web plate $35\tfrac{1}{2}$ in. by $\tfrac{3}{8}$ in. to form a section 36 in. deep, similar to that in Fig. 5–32. Cover plates, each 12 in. by $\tfrac{1}{2}$ in., are then riveted to the flange angles, making the over-all height 37 in. The moment of inertia of the entire section about the $N.A.$ is 10,084 in.[4] Using the allowable stresses specified in Illus. Prob. 567, determine the rivet pitch for $\tfrac{7}{8}$-in. rivets at a section where $V = 100,000$ lb.   *Ans.* $e = 5.35$ in.

572. Two 12-in. 20.7-lb channels are riveted together, as shown, by pairs of $\tfrac{3}{4}$-in. rivets spaced 8 in. apart along the length of the beam. What maximum vertical shear V can be applied to the section using the stresses given in Prob. 567?

573. A beam is formed by riveting together two 8 WF 17 sections, as shown. It is used to support a uniformly distributed load of 1000 lb/ft on a simply supported 24-ft span. Compute the maximum flexural stress and the pitch between rivets having a shearing strength of 6000 lb each. *Ans. S* = 25,300 psi; *e* = 13.65 in.

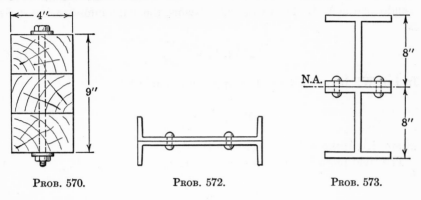

PROB. 570. PROB. 572. PROB. 573.

SUMMARY

For homogeneous beams, originally straight, carrying transverse loads in the plane of symmetry, the bending moment creates flexural stresses expressed by

$$S = \frac{My}{I} \tag{5-2}$$

The flexural stresses vary directly with their distance y from the neutral axis, which coincides with the centroidal axis of the cross-section.

Maximum flexural stresses occur at the section of maximum bending moment at the extreme fibers of the section. The distance from the *N.A.* to the extreme fibers being denoted by c, the flexure formula becomes

$$\text{Max. } S = \frac{Mc}{I} = \frac{M}{Z} \tag{5-2a, b}$$

in which $Z = \dfrac{I}{c}$ represents the section modulus of the beam. For geometric shapes, values of Z are tabulated in Table V–1 (page 129); for structural shapes, the values are given in Appendix B. In selecting beams on the basis of least weight, Table V–2 (page 138) is convenient. Allowable stresses in beams laterally unsupported, especially in light or B beams having relatively narrow flanges, should be checked by Eq. 5–3 (page 135).

The vertical shear sets up numerically equal shearing stresses on longitudinal and transverse sections (Eq. 5–5, page 154), which are determined from

$$S_s = \frac{V}{Ib} A'\bar{y} = \frac{V}{Ib} Q \tag{5-4}$$

in which A' is the partial area of the cross-section above a line drawn through the point at which the shearing stress is desired. $Q = A'\bar{y}$ is the static moment about the $N.A.$ of this area (or of the area below this line).

Maximum shearing stresses occur at the section of maximum V and usually at the $N.A.$ For rectangular beams, the maximum shearing stress is

$$\text{Max. } S_s = \frac{3}{2}\frac{V}{bh} \qquad\qquad (5\text{-}6)$$

In I or WF beams, a very close approximation is

$$\text{Max. } S_s = \frac{V}{A_{web}}$$

where A_{web} is the web area between the flanges.

The rivet pitch in built-up beams is given by

$$e = \frac{RI}{VQ} \qquad\qquad (5\text{-}7)$$

where R is the rivet resistance in the pitch length e, I is the moment of inertia of the gross section about the $N.A.$, V is the maximum vertical shear in the interval e, and Q is the moment of area about the $N.A.$ of the elements whose sliding is resisted by the rivets.

Chapter VI

Beam Deflections

===

6-1. Introduction

  In this chapter we consider the rigidity of beams. Frequently, the design of a beam is determined by its rigidity rather than by its strength. For example, in designing metalworking equipment for precision work, such as lathes, milling machines, grinders, etc., the deformations must be kept below the permissible tolerances of the work being machined. Again, floor beams carrying plastered ceilings beneath them are usually restricted to a maximum deflection of 1/360 of their length in order to avoid cracks in the plaster. The most important reason for studying beam deflections is to obtain equations with which, in combination with the conditions of static equilibrium, statically indeterminate beams can be analysed. (See Chaps. VII and VIII.)

  Several methods are available for determining beam deflections. Although based on the same principle, they differ in technique and in the amount of computation involved. We shall consider first the oldest method, the double-integration method. Another method, the area-moment method, is thought to be the most direct of any. After a preliminary discussion (Art. 6-4), it will be found to be not only simple, but extremely rapid to apply. A variation of it, which we will take up in Art. 8-7, is also rapid and easy to use.

  Other methods are the conjugate beam method and the method of superposition. The conjugate beam method is a variation of the area-moment method, but differs from it in technique. The method of superposition is not an independent method; it uses the deflection formulas for certain fundamental types of loadings to obtain results for loadings that consist of combinations of these fundamental types.

6-2. Double-Integration Method

  The edge view of the neutral surface of a deflected beam is called the *elastic curve* of the beam. It is shown greatly exaggerated in Fig. 6-1. This article shows how to determine the equation of this curve, i.e., how to determine the vertical displacement y of any point in terms of its x coordinate.

  Select the left end of the beam as the origin of an X axis directed along the original undeflected position of the beam, and a Y axis directed positive upward. The deflections are assumed to be so small that there is no appreciable difference between the original length of the beam and the projection of its deflected length. Consequently, the elastic curve is very flat and its slope at any point is very small. The value of the slope, $\tan \theta = \dfrac{dy}{dx}$, may therefore with only small error be set equal to θ; hence

$$\theta = \frac{dy}{dx} \qquad (a)$$

and

$$\frac{d\theta}{dx} = \frac{d^2y}{dx^2} \qquad (b)$$

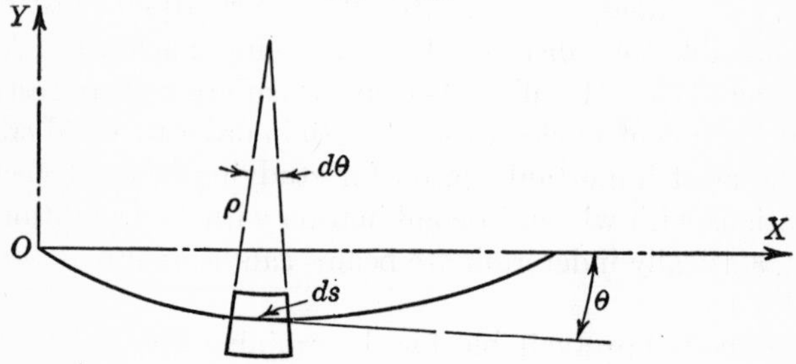

FIG. 6–1. — Elastic curve.

If we now consider the variation in θ in a differential length ds caused by bending in the beam, it is evident that

$$ds = \rho\, d\theta \qquad (c)$$

where ρ is the radius of curvature over the arc length ds. Because the elastic curve is very flat, ds is practically equivalent to dx; so from Eq. (c) and (b) we obtain

$$\frac{1}{\rho} = \frac{d\theta}{ds} \approx \frac{d\theta}{dx} \quad \text{or} \quad \frac{1}{\rho} = \frac{d^2y}{dx^2} \qquad (d)$$

In deriving the flexure formula in Art. 5–2, we obtained on page 127 the relation

$$\frac{1}{\rho} = \frac{M}{EI} \qquad (5\text{–}1)$$

Equating the values of $\dfrac{1}{\rho}$ from Eqs. (d) and $(5\text{–}1)$, we have

$$EI\frac{d^2y}{dx^2} = M \qquad (6\text{–}1)$$

This is known as the differential equation of the elastic curve of a beam. The product EI, called the *flexural rigidity* of the beam, is usually constant along the beam.

The approximations we have made do not seriously invalidate Eq. (6–1), for if we replace $\dfrac{1}{\rho}$ by its exact value as found in any calculus text, we have, from Eq. (5–1)

$$\frac{\dfrac{d^2y}{dx^2}}{\left[1 + \left(\dfrac{dy}{dx}\right)^2\right]^{\frac{3}{2}}} = \frac{M}{EI}$$

Since $\dfrac{dy}{dx}$ is very small, its square is negligible compared with unity, and hence we obtain

$$\frac{d^2y}{dx^2} = \frac{M}{EI}$$

which is the same as Eq. (6–1).

If Eq. (6–1) is now integrated, assuming EI constant, we obtain

$$EI\frac{dy}{dx} = \int M\,dx + C_1 \tag{6–2}$$

This is the slope equation specifying the slope or value of $\dfrac{dy}{dx}$ at any point.

Note that here M represents the moment equation expressed in terms of x, and C_1 is a constant to be evaluated from the given conditions of loading.

We now integrate Eq. (6–2) to obtain

$$EIy = \iint M\,dx\,dx + C_1x + C_2 \tag{6–3}$$

This is the required deflection equation of the elastic curve specifying the value of y for any value of x. C_2 is another constant of integration which must be evaluated from the given conditions of the beam and its loading.

If the loading conditions change along the beam, a moment equation must be written between each change of load point, and the above procedure must be repeated for each portion of the beam between change of load points.

ILLUSTRATIVE PROBLEMS

601. A concentrated load of 60 lb is supported as shown in Fig. 6–2. Determine the equations of the elastic curve between each change of load point, and the maximum deflection in the beam.

Solution: Using the method discussed in Art. 4–2, we first write the bending moment equations between the change of load points. These are $M_{AB} = 20\,x$ and $M_{BC} = 20\,x - 60(x - 6)$, which may be simplified to $M'_{BC} = 360 - 40\,x$, valid respectively for values of x between 0 and 6 and between 6 and 9 ft. In the double-integration method, it is preferable to use the equation M_{BC} rather than its simplified form M'_{BC} because, as we shall see on page 173, this simplifies the determination of the constants of integration.

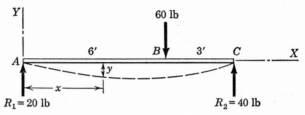

FIG. 6–2.

We now apply the differential equation of the elastic curve (Eq. 6–1) to segments AB and BC, arranging the computations as shown below. Two successive integrations give the slope and deflection equations for each beam segment and introduce four constants of integration.

Segment AB $(0 \leqq x \leqq 6)$	Segment BC $(6 \leqq x \leqq 9)$
(a) $EI \dfrac{d^2y}{dx^2} = M_{AB} = 20\,x$	(d) $EI \dfrac{d^2y}{dx^2} = M_{BC} = 20\,x - 60(x - 6)$
(b) $EI \dfrac{dy}{dx} = 10\,x^2 + C_1$	(e) $EI \dfrac{dy}{dx} = 10\,x^2 - 30(x - 6)^2 + C_3$
(c) $EIy = \tfrac{10}{3}\,x^3 + C_1 x + C_2$	(f) $EIy = \tfrac{10}{3}\,x^3 - 10(x - 6)^3 + C_3 x + C_4$

To evaluate the four constants of integration in these equations, we apply the following boundary conditions:

1. At A, where $x = 0$, the deflection $y = 0$. Substituting these values in Eq. (c), we find that $C_2 = 0$.

2. At B, where $x = 6$, the slope as defined from Eq. (b) must equal that given by Eq. (e) since the deflection curve is smooth and continuous. Equating the right sides of these equations at the value $x = 6$, we find that $C_1 = C_3$.

3. Also at B, the deflection given by Eqs. (c) and (f) must be equal. Since we now know that $C_1 = C_3$, substituting $x = 6$ and equating the right sides of these equations yields $C_4 = 0$.

4. Of the four constants of integration, we now have $C_2 = C_4 = 0$, and $C_1 = C_3$. The value of C_1 (or of C_3) is determined from the condition of zero deflection at the right support, where for $x = 9$, $y = 0$. Hence, substituting these values in Eq. (f) and replacing C_3 by its equivalent C_1, we have

$$0 = \tfrac{10}{3}(9)^3 - 10(9 - 6)^3 + 9\,C_1 \quad \text{or} \quad C_1 = -240$$

Having thus evaluated the constants of integration, we have complete slope and deflection equations:

Segment AB $(0 \leq x \leq 6)$	Segment BC $(6 \leq x \leq 9)$
(b') $EI \dfrac{dy}{dx} = 10\,x^2 - 240$	(e') $EI \dfrac{dy}{dx} = 10\,x^2 - 30(x - 6)^2 - 240$
	$\qquad = -20\,x^2 + 360\,x - 1320$
(c') $EIy = \frac{10}{3}\,x^3 - 240\,x$	(f') $EIy = \frac{10}{3}\,x^3 - 10(x - 6)^3 - 240\,x$
	$\qquad = -\frac{20}{3}\,x^3 + 180\,x^2 - 1320\,x + 2160$

Before applying these results to determine the maximum deflection, let us examine the use of $M'_{BC} = 360 - 40\,x$ instead of $M_{BC} = 20\,x - 60(x - 6)$ in Eq. (d) above. With this change, Eqs. (e) and (f) become respectively $EI \dfrac{dy}{dx} = -20\,x^2 + 360\,x + C'_3$ and $EIy = -\frac{20}{3}\,x^3 + 180\,x^2 + C'_3\,x + C'_4$. Applying the above four boundary conditions, we find from condition 2 that $C_1 - C'_3 = 1080$. Substituting this difference in condition 3 gives C'_4 as 2160. With C'_4 known, condition 4 may be used to find $C'_3 = -1320$; this value is substituted in the difference $C_1 - C'_3 = 1080$ obtained from condition 2 to yield $C_1 = -240$. Placing the values of C'_3 and C'_4 in the above equations finally gives Eqs. (e') and (f') as tabulated above, but only after considerable numerical computation. Hence it is simpler to start with the unexpanded form of the moment equation (i.e., M_{BC}), then solve for the constants of integration, and finally expand or simplify as in Eqs. (e') and (f').

Continuing the solution, we assume that the maximum deflection will occur in the segment AB. Its location may be found by differentiating Eq. (c') with respect to x and setting the derivative equal to zero, or, what amounts to the same thing, setting the slope equation (b') equal to zero and solving for the point of zero slope. We obtain

$$10\,x^2 - 240 = 0 \quad \text{or} \quad x = 4.9 \text{ ft}$$

Since this value of x is valid for the segment AB, our assumption that the maximum deflection occurs in this region is confirmed. Hence, to determine the maximum deflection, we substitute $x = 4.9$ in Eq. (c'):

$$\text{Max. } EIy = -785 \text{ lb-ft}^3$$

The negative value obtained indicates that the deflection y is downward from the X axis. Frequently only the magnitude of the deflection, without regard to sign, is desired; this is denoted by δ, the use of y being reserved to indicate a directed value of deflection.

The unit of the product EIy is lb-ft.^{3} This follows from integrating Eq. (6–1) twice. With M in units of lb-ft, the first integration gives lb-ft^2 as the unit of the slope equation. A second integration results in lb-ft^3 as the unit of the deflection equation. Until we are ready to compute the numerical value of deflection, it is convenient to keep the unit of length in feet so that the numerical values will be small. When substituting numerical values of E in psi, and I in in.^{4}, it is necessary only to multiply the value of EIy expressed in lb-ft^3 by the unit fraction 1728 in.^{3}/ft^3

in order to obtain y in inches. For example, if $E = 1.5 \times 10^6$ psi and $I = 30$ in.^{4}, the value of y in inches is

$$(1.5 \times 10^6)(30)y = -785(1728)$$

whence

$$y = -0.0301 \text{ in.}$$

602. Determine the deflection equation of a cantilever beam supporting a uniformly distributed load of w lb/ft over its length L, as shown in Fig. 6–3.

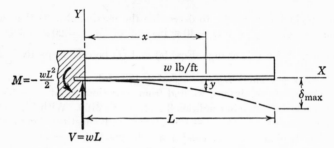

FIG. 6–3.

Solution: Selecting axes with their origin at the wall, we determine the bending moment at any section distant x from the wall:

$$M = (\Sigma M)_L = wLx - \frac{wL^2}{2} - \frac{wx^2}{2}$$

whence the differential equation of the elastic curve becomes

$$EI \frac{d^2y}{dx^2} = M = wLx - \frac{wL^2}{2} - \frac{wx^2}{2} \qquad (a)$$

Integrating Eq. (a), we obtain the slope equation:

$$EI \frac{dy}{dx} = \frac{wLx^2}{2} - \frac{wL^2x}{2} - \frac{wx^3}{6} + C_1 \qquad (b)$$

However, the slope $\frac{dy}{dx}$ is zero at $x = 0$, so $C_1 = 0$. We may now integrate the slope equation (with $C_1 = 0$) and obtain the deflection equation:

$$EIy = \frac{wLx^3}{6} - \frac{wL^2x^2}{4} - \frac{wx^4}{24} + C_2 \qquad (c)$$

Here $y = 0$ at $x = 0$, so C_2 is also zero. The maximum numerical deflection δ, occurring at $x = L$, is found by substitution in Eq. (c):

$$\delta_{max} = \frac{wL^4}{8\,EI} \qquad (d)$$

The double-integration method was simple to apply here because the origin of the axes was selected at the perfectly restrained wall where the zero slope and zero deflection made the constants of integration zero.

603.   Determine the maximum deflection in a simply supported beam carrying a central concentrated load P, as shown in Fig. 6–4.

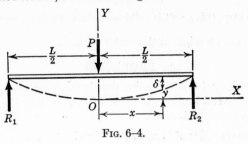

FIG. 6–4.

Solution: By choosing the origin of the axes at the center of the beam on the elastic curve, the slope is zero because of symmetry and the deflection is also zero; this duplicates the conditions at the fixed end of a cantilever beam.   Hence, as in Problem 602, the constants of integration will reduce to zero.

Just to the right of P, the bending moment and vertical shear are respectively $\dfrac{PL}{4}$ and $-\dfrac{P}{2}$.   Hence the moment equation at any section distant x from the indicated origin of axes is

$$M = (\Sigma M)_L = \frac{PL}{4} - \frac{Px}{2}$$

and the differential equation of the elastic curve is

$$EI\frac{d^2y}{dx^2} = M = \frac{PL}{4} - \frac{Px}{2} \tag{a}$$

Integration determines the following slope equation:

$$EI\frac{dy}{dx} = \frac{PLx}{4} - \frac{Px^2}{4} + C_1 \tag{b}$$

Because of symmetry, the slope $\dfrac{dy}{dx}$ is zero at $x = 0$, so $C_1 = 0$.   Integrating Eq. (*b*)

with $C_1 = 0$ gives the deflection equation

$$EIy = \frac{PLx^2}{8} - \frac{Px^3}{12} + C_2 \tag{c}$$

Since the origin of axes is on the elastic curve, $y = 0$ at $x = 0$, so C_2 also equals zero. With respect to the given axes, the maximum deflection occurs at R_2 and is directed upward from the X axis.   Substituting $x = \dfrac{L}{2}$, we obtain

$$EIy = \frac{PL}{8} \cdot \left(\frac{L}{2}\right)^2 - \frac{P}{12}\left(\frac{L}{2}\right)^3 = \frac{PL^3}{48}$$

The deflection δ at any intermediate point is obtained as the difference between this value and values from Eq. (*c*), or

$$EI\delta = \frac{PL^3}{48} - \frac{PLx^2}{8} + \frac{Px^3}{12}$$

Because of symmetry, this result is valid for values of x between 0 and $\dfrac{L}{2}$ measured to the left or right of an origin at the center of the beam.

PROBLEMS

Additional problems for solution by the double-integration method may be selected from the several loadings in Table VI-2, page 212; Probs. 626, 638, 642, 645, 648, 650, 651 may also be used.

604. Compute the value of max. EIy for the given beam.

Ans. Max. $EIy = -233$ lb-ft³ at $x = 3.88$ ft

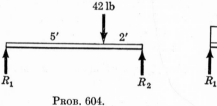

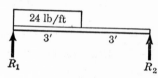

PROB. 604.   PROB. 605.

605. Compute the value of EIy at midspan for the given loading. *Hint:* Select the origin at the right end with x positive leftward. *Ans.* $EIy = -202.5$ lb-ft³

606. Determine the maximum value of EIy for the given cantilever beam. Take the origin at the wall.

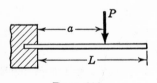

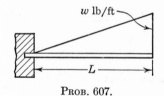

PROB. 606.   PROB. 607.

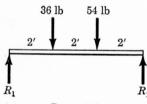

PROB. 608.

607. Find the equation of the elastic curve for the cantilever beam carrying a load that varies from zero at the wall to w lb/ft at the free end. Take the origin at the wall.

608. Find the midspan value of EIy for the given beam.   *Ans.* $EIy = -345$ lb-ft³

609. Determine the absolute value of the maximum deflection δ in a simply supported beam of length L carrying a uniformly distributed load of w lb/ft applied over the entire length.   *Ans.* $\delta = \dfrac{5}{384}\dfrac{wL^4}{EI} = \dfrac{5}{384}\dfrac{WL^3}{EI}$

6–3. Theorems of Area-Moment Method

A useful and simple method of determining slopes and deflections in beams involves the area of the moment diagram and also the moment of that area — the *area-moment method*. We shall discuss first the two basic theorems of the method; then, after showing how to compute the area and moment of area of the moment diagram, we shall apply the method to several types of problems.

Fig. 6–5a shows a simple beam that supports any type of loading. The elastic curve is the edge view of the neutral surface and is shown, with greatly exaggerated deflections, in Fig. 6–5b; the moment diagram is assumed to be as in Fig. 6–5c.

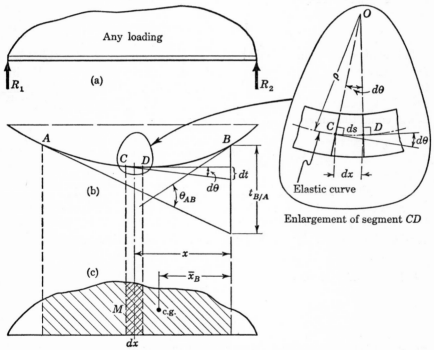

FIG. 6–5. — Area-moment theorems.

As we saw in the derivation of the flexure formula, Art. (5–2), two adjacent plane sections of an originally straight beam will rotate through the angle $d\theta$ relative to each other. This is demonstrated in the enlarged detail of Fig. 6–5b, in which it is also apparent that the arc distance ds measured along the elastic curve between these two sections equals $\rho\,d\theta$ where ρ is the radius of curvature of the elastic curve at the given position. From Eq. (5–1) we have

$$\frac{1}{\rho} = \frac{M}{EI}$$

and since $ds = \rho \, d\theta$, we now write

$$\frac{1}{\rho} = \frac{M}{EI} = \frac{d\theta}{ds}$$

or

$$d\theta = \frac{M}{EI} \, ds \qquad\qquad (a)$$

In most practical cases the elastic curve is so flat that no serious error is made in assuming the length ds to equal its projection dx. With this assumption,[1] we obtain

$$d\theta = \frac{M}{EI} \, dx \qquad\qquad (b)$$

It is evident that tangents drawn to the elastic curve at C and D in Fig. 6–5b are separated by the same angle $d\theta$ by which sections OC and OD (in the enlarged detail) rotate relative to each other. Hence the change in slope between tangents drawn to the elastic curve at any two points A and B will equal the sum of such small angles:

$$\theta_{AB} = \int_{\theta_A}^{\theta_B} d\theta = \frac{1}{EI} \int_{x_A}^{x_B} M \, dx \qquad\qquad (c)$$

The product EI is called *flexural rigidity*. Note that we have tacitly assumed that E and I remain constant throughout the length of the beam; this is usually the case. If they vary, however, they cannot be written outside the integral sign, and the manner of their variation with x must be known.

[1] ρ is expressed mathematically as

$$\frac{1}{\rho} = \frac{\dfrac{d^2y}{dx^2}}{\left[1 + \left(\dfrac{dy}{dx}\right)^2\right]^{3/2}}$$

The right-hand member of this equation is practically equivalent to $\dfrac{d^2y}{dx^2}$ if the slope $\dfrac{dy}{dx}$ is small, as it usually is. Hence

$$\frac{1}{\rho} = \frac{d^2y}{dx^2} = \frac{d}{dx}\left(\frac{dy}{dx}\right) = \frac{d}{dx}(\tan\theta)$$

and since, for small angles, $\tan\theta = \theta$ in radians, we finally obtain

$$\frac{1}{\rho} = \frac{d\theta}{dx} = \frac{M}{EI}$$

which agrees with Eq. (b).

Note also in Fig. 6–5*b* that the distance from *B* on the elastic curve (measured perpendicular to the original position of the beam) that will intersect a tangent drawn to this curve at any other point *A* is the sum of the intercepts *dt* created by tangents to the curve at adjacent points. Each of these intercepts may be considered as the arc of a circle of radius *x* subtended by the angle *dθ*:

$$dt = x \, d\theta$$

Hence

$$t_{B/A} = \int dt = \int x \, d\theta$$

Replacing *dθ* by the value in Eq. (*b*), we obtain

$$t_{B/A} = \frac{1}{EI} \int_{x_A}^{x_B} x \, (M \, dx) \tag{d}$$

The length $t_{B/A}$ is known as the deviation of *B* from a tangent drawn at *A*, or as the tangential deviation of *B* with respect to *A*. The subscript indicates that the deviation is measured from *B* relative to a reference tangent drawn at *A*. Fig. 6–6 illustrates the difference between the devia-

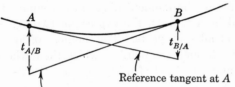

FIG. 6–6. — Inequality of $t_{A/B}$ and $t_{B/A}$.

tion $t_{B/A}$ of *B* from a reference tangent at *A*, and the deviation $t_{A/B}$ of *A* from a reference tangent at *B*. In general, such deviations are unequal.

The geometric significance of Eqs. (*c*) and (*d*) gives rise to the two basic theorems of the area-moment method. From the moment diagram in Fig. 6–5*c* we see that *M dx* is the area of the shaded element located a distance *x* from the ordinate through *B*. Since $\int M \, dx$ means a summation of such elements, we obtain

$$\theta_{AB} = \frac{1}{EI} (\text{Area})_{AB} \tag{6-4}$$

This is the algebraic expression of Theorem I, which is stated as follows:

Theorem I: **The change in slope between tangents drawn to the elastic curve at any two points *A* and *B* is equal to the product of $\dfrac{1}{EI}$ multiplied by the area of the moment diagram between these two points.**

Fig. 6–5c shows that the expression $x\ (M\ dx)$ which appears under the integral sign in Eq. (d) is the moment of area of the shaded element about the ordinate at B. Hence the geometric significance of the integral $\int x\ (M\ dx)$ is that the integral is equivalent to the moment of area about the ordinate at B of that part of the moment diagram between A and B. Thus we obtain the algebraic form of Theorem II

$$t_{B/A} = \frac{1}{EI}\ (\text{Area})_{AB} \cdot \bar{x}_B \qquad (6\text{–}5)$$

This is stated more formally as:

Theorem II: **The deviation of any point B relative to a tangent drawn to the elastic curve at any other point A, in a direction perpendicular to the original position of the beam, is equal to the product of $\dfrac{1}{EI}$ multiplied by the moment of area about B of that part of the moment diagram between points A and B.**

In the above theorems, $(\text{Area})_{AB}$ is the area of the moment diagram between points A and B, and $\bar{x}_B$ is the moment arm of this area measured from B. When the area of the moment diagram is composed of several parts (this is explained in Art. 6–4), the expression $(\text{Area})_{AB} \cdot \bar{x}_B$ includes the moment of area of all such parts. The moment of area is always taken about an ordinate through the point at which the deviation is being computed. An automatic method of using the correct axis for moments is to give $\bar{x}$ the same subscript, e.g., B, (meaning that moment arms are to be measured from this point) as appears in the numerator of the subscript to t (i.e., B/A).

One rule of sign is very important: The deviation at any point is *positive* if the point lies above the reference tangent from which the deviation is measured, and *negative* if the point lies below the reference tangent. Positive and negative deviations are shown in Fig. 6–7. Conversely, a computed

(a) Positive deviation; B located   (b) Negative deviation; B located
above reference tangent   below reference tangent

FIG. 6–7. — Signs of deviations.

positive value for deviation means that the point must lie above the reference tangent.

Another rule of sign that concerns slopes is shown in Fig. 6–8. A positive value for the change in slope θ_{AB} means that the tangent at the rightmost point B is measured in a counterclockwise direction from the tangent at the leftmost point, and vice versa.

(a) Positive change of slope; θ_{AB} is counterclockwise from left tangent

(b) Negative change of slope; θ_{AB} is clockwise from left tangent

Fig. 6–8. — Signs of change of slope.

6–4. Moment Diagrams by Parts

In order to apply the theorems of the area-moment method, we should be able to compute easily and accurately the area under any part of a moment diagram, and the moment of such an area about any axis. A method of doing this from calculus is to integrate the two expressions $\int M\,dx$ and $\int x\,(M\,dx)$ between proper limits, noting that the bending moment M must be expressed as a function of x.

Our purpose here, however, is to discuss a method of dividing moment diagrams into parts whose areas and centroids are known; this permits simple numerical calculations to replace integrations.   The first step is to learn how to draw moment effects of each separate loading (hereafter called *moment diagram by parts*) instead of a *conventional* moment diagram.

The construction of moment diagrams by parts depends on two basic principles:

1. The resultant bending moment at any section caused by any load system is the algebraic sum of the bending moments at that section caused by each load acting separately.   This statement is expressed algebraically by

$$M = (\Sigma M)_L = (\Sigma M)_R \qquad (4\text{–}2)$$

where $(\Sigma M)_L$ indicates the sum of the moments caused by all the forces to the left of the section, and $(\Sigma M)_R$ is the sum of the moments caused by all the forces to the right of the section.

2. The moment effect of any single specified loading is always some variation of the general equation

$$y = kx^n \qquad (a)$$

The graph of this equation is shown in Fig. 6–9.   The shaded area and the location of its centroid are easily shown by calculus to be

$$\text{Area} = \frac{1}{n+1}\,bh \qquad (b)$$

$$\bar{x} = \frac{1}{n+2} \cdot b \qquad\qquad (c)$$

where b is the base and h is the height.

In computing the area under the curve between positions like A and B in Fig. 6–10, Eqs. (b) and (c) refer to the shaded area between the curve,

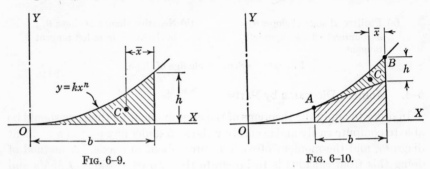

FIG. 6–9.   FIG. 6–10.

the *ordinate* at B and the *tangent* at A. To this area must be added, of course, the shaded trapezoidal area between the tangent and the X axis.

Table VI–1 demonstrates the truth of the second basic principle stated above, viz., that the moment effect of any load is some variation of the equation $y = kx^n$. This table gives data on four cantilever beams, each loaded differently with increasingly complex loads.

Note that a cantilever loaded by a couple C has a moment equation of the type $y = kx^n$ in which $k = -C$ and n is zero; viz., $M = -Cx^0$. In other words, a couple type of loading produces a moment equation of zero degree. Similarly, a concentrated load produces a moment equation of the first degree; a uniform load produces a moment equation of the second degree, etc.

In the column headed "Area," the area of the moment diagram is expressed in terms of a factor multiplied by the general base distance b and the maximum height h of the moment diagram. The position of the centroid of each moment diagram from the maximum ordinate of the diagram is defined as a factor of the base distance. These factors or coefficients, which increase very simply, are obtained from Eqs. (b) and (c) by assigning to n the value of the degree of each equation, i.e., $n = 0$, $n = 1$, $n = 2$, etc.

An example will illustrate how Table VI–1 is used to draw moment diagrams by parts. The simple beam in Fig. 6–11 is 9 ft long and supports a uniformly distributed load of 30 lb/ft over the right 6 ft of the span.

At any section a–a between A and B, the moment effect defined by $M = (\Sigma M)_L$ is caused only by R_1. Also, at any section b–b between B and C, the moment effect will be due to R_1 and to the portion of the uniformly

TABLE VI-1. Cantilever Loadings

TYPE OF LOADING	CANTILEVER BEAM	MOMENT EQUATION (Moment at Any Section x)	DEGREE OF MOMENT EQUATION	MOMENT DIAGRAM	AREA	$\bar{x}$
Couple		$M = -C$	Zero (i.e., $M = -Cx^0$)	$b=L$, $h=-C$	$\frac{1}{1} \cdot bh$	$\frac{1}{2}b$
Concentrated		$M = -Px$	1st	$b=L$, $h=-PL$	$\frac{1}{2}bh$	$\frac{1}{3}b$
Uniformly Distributed		$M = -\frac{w}{2}x^2$	2nd	$b=L$, $h=-\frac{wL^2}{2}$	$\frac{1}{3}bh$	$\frac{1}{4}b$
Uniformly Varying		$M = -\frac{w}{6L}x^3$	3rd	$b=L$, $h=-\frac{wL^2}{6}$	$\frac{1}{4}bh$	$\frac{1}{5}b$

distributed load included between B and $b-b$. Note that defining the bending moment in terms of the forces to the left of the section means that the uniformly distributed load has no moment effect on segment AB. Actually, the moment effect of R_1 at any section of the beam is equivalent to the cantilever loading at (a), whereas the moment effect of the uniform loading on any section of the beam is equivalent to the cantilever loading at (b).

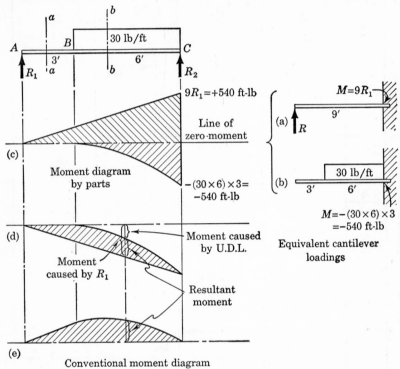

FIG. 6–11. — Moment diagram by parts.

By referring to Table VI–1, we may plot the moment diagrams of beams (a) and (b) on a common base line (the line of zero moment), as shown at (c) in the figure. That the algebraic sum of the shaded areas of (c) will yield the resultant or conventional moment diagram is evident from the fact that the moment at any section of the original beam is equal to the sum of the moments at that section caused by the individual loads (basic principle 1 above). Hence, if the triangular area is revolved about the line of zero moment as an axis, we obtain diagram (d). The shaded area of diagram (d) is evidently equal to the area of the conventional moment diagram (e) obtained by plotting the resultant moment at any section as ordinates to a horizontal base line.

Hence the conventional moment diagram may be replaced by an equivalent moment diagram constructed of parts whose areas and centroids can be easily computed from the data in Table VI–1.

ILLUSTRATIVE PROBLEMS

610. Compute the area under the moment diagram of the beam shown in Fig. 6–12a, and the moment of this area about the right end.

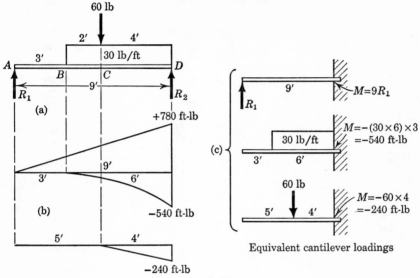

Fig. 6–12.

Solution: If the conventional bending moment at any section of the beam is computed from $M = (\Sigma M)_L$, it is evident from this article that the conventional bending moment will be the algebraic sum of the bending moments (at the same section) of the three cantilever loadings shown in Fig. 6–12c. The moment diagrams of these cantilever loadings are shown in Fig. 6–12b. This procedure is called drawing moment diagrams by parts from left to right.

It is convenient to represent the M diagram of the uniform load and of the concentrated load by separate diagrams; the M diagram of the reaction R_1 may be plotted on the base line used for the uniform load. Since the conventional bending moment at D must be zero (no loads act to the right of D to cause bending moment), the reaction R_1 need not be computed, because its moment at D (equal to $9 R_1$) must balance the sum of the bending moments at D caused by the loads.

Using the principle that the total area is the sum of its parts, and noting that each area is the product of a coefficient listed in Table VI–1 multiplied by the dimensions of the circumscribing rectangle, we obtain

$[(\text{Area})_{AD} = \Sigma(\text{areas})]$

$$(\text{Area})_{AD} = \tfrac{1}{2} \times 780 \times 9 - \tfrac{1}{3} \times 540 \times 6 - \tfrac{1}{2} \times 240 \times 4$$
$$= 1950 \text{ lb-ft}^2 \quad Ans.$$

Similarly, the moment of the area of the conventional moment diagram is the sum of the moments of area of its parts. Hence the moment of area about the right end (point D) is given by

$$[(\text{Area})_{AD} \cdot \bar{x}_D = \Sigma ax]$$

$$(\text{Area})_{AD} \cdot \bar{x}_D = \left(\frac{780 \times 9}{2}\right)\left(\frac{1}{3} \times 9\right) - \left(\frac{540 \times 6}{3}\right)\left(\frac{1}{4} \times 6\right) - \left(\frac{240 \times 4}{2}\right)\left(\frac{1}{3} \times 4\right)$$

$$= 10{,}530 - 1620 - 640 = 8270 \text{ lb-ft}^3 \quad Ans.$$

The symbol $\bar{x}_D$ means that moment arms are to be measured from D. From Theorem II of the area-moment method (Eq. 6–5), this result represents the product $EIt_{D/A}$ where $t_{D/A}$ is the deviation of D from a tangent drawn to the elastic curve at A.

611. For the beam shown in Fig. 6–13a, compute the moment of area of the moment diagram about the right end.

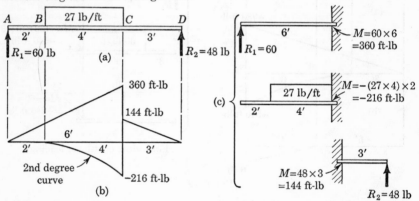

Equivalent cantilever loadings

Fig. 6–13.

Solution: The moment diagram by parts is constructed by applying the definition $M = (\Sigma M)_L$ to segments AB and BC and the definition $M = (\Sigma M)_R$ to segment CD. The equivalent cantilever loadings are shown in Fig. 6–13c. The moment at C in terms of the forces to the left of C is $360 - 216 = 144$ ft-lb, which checks the moment at C expressed in terms of the forces acting to the right of C.

It is simpler to compute the conventional bending moment for an exploratory section in segment CD by taking moments of forces to the right of the section rather than to the left. Computing bending moment by applying either $M = (\Sigma M)_L$ or $M = (\Sigma M)_R$ generally indicates the simplest method of drawing the M diagram by parts.

The moment of the area of the M diagram about D equals the sum of the moments of area of its parts:

$$[(\text{Area})_{AD} \cdot \bar{x}_D = \Sigma ax]$$

$$(\text{Area})_{AD} \cdot \bar{x}_D = \left(\frac{360 \times 6}{2}\right)\left(3 + \frac{1}{3} \times 6\right) \qquad \text{[Equation continued on p. 187]}$$

$$+ \left(\frac{144 \times 3}{2}\right)\left(\frac{2}{3} \times 3\right) - \left(\frac{216 \times 4}{3}\right)\left(3 + \frac{1}{4} \times 4\right)$$

$$= 5400 + 432 - 1152 = 4680 \text{ lb-ft}^3 \quad Ans.$$

What value of EIt does this result represent?

612. For the beam shown in Fig. 6–14*a*, compute the moment of area of the moment diagram between A and C about C.

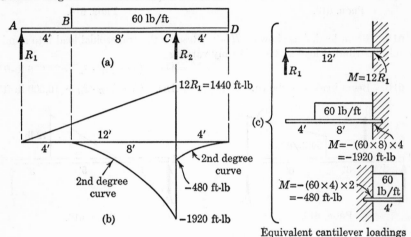

FIG. 6–14.

Solution: At any section between A and C, the conventional bending moment is computed more easily by applying $M = (\Sigma M)_L$, whereas between C and D it is simpler to apply $M = (\Sigma M)_R$. The moment diagram by parts shown in Fig. 6–14*b* is therefore constructed by combining the cantilever loadings in Fig. 6–14*c*.

In this problem, the value of the reactions need not be computed. The moment at C caused by R_1 is found from the fact that the bending moment at C of all forces to the left of C must equal the bending moment of all forces to the right of C, which is in accord with the fundamental definition $M = (\Sigma M)_L = (\Sigma M)_R$. In other words, $12 R_1 - 1920 = -480$; hence $12 R_1 = 1920 - 480 = 1440$ ft-lb.

We obtain the moment of area of the M diagram between A and C about C by applying

$$[(\text{Area})_{AC} \cdot \bar{x}_C = \Sigma ax]$$

$$(\text{Area})_{AC} \cdot \bar{x}_C = \left(\frac{1440 \times 12}{2}\right)\left(\frac{12}{3}\right) - \left(\frac{1920 \times 8}{3}\right)\left(\frac{8}{4}\right)$$

$$= 34,560 - 10,240 = 24,220 \text{ lb-ft}^3 \quad Ans.$$

PROBLEMS

For each of the beams in the following problems, compute the moment of area of the M diagram between the reactions about both the left and the right reaction.

613. Beam loaded as shown.   *Ans.* $(\text{Area})_{AB} \cdot \bar{x}_A = 2688$ lb-ft³

614. Beam loaded as shown.

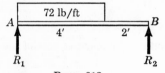

PROB. 613.

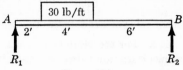

PROB. 614.

615. Beam loaded as shown. *Hint:* Resolve the trapezoidal load into a uniformly distributed load and a uniformly varying load.

Ans. $(\text{Area})_{AB} \cdot \bar{x}_B = 21,006$ lb-ft³

616. Beam loaded as shown.   *Ans.* $(\text{Area})_{AB} \cdot \bar{x}_B = 16,500$ lb-ft³

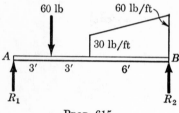

PROB. 615.

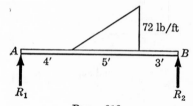

PROB. 616.

617. Beam loaded as shown. From the result $(\text{Area})_{AB} \cdot \bar{x}_A$ and Fig. 6–7, is the tangent drawn to the elastic curve at B directed up or down to the right?

618. Beam loaded as shown. From the result $(\text{Area})_{AB} \cdot \bar{x}_A$ and Fig. 6–7, is the tangent drawn to the elastic curve at B directed up or down to the right?

Ans. $(\text{Area})_{AB} \cdot \bar{x}_A = -23,450$ lb-ft³; $(\text{Area})_{AB} \cdot \bar{x}_B = +2600$ lb-ft³

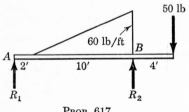

PROB. 617.

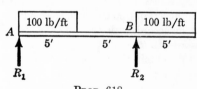

PROB. 618.

6–5. Deflection of Cantilever Beams

It will be recalled that the tangential deviation at any point is the distance from the point on the elastic curve to a tangent drawn to the curve at some other point (Art. 6–3 and Fig. 6–5). As a consequence, the tangential deviation is generally not equal to the deflection. In cantilever beams, however, the wall is usually assumed to be perfectly fixed, and

hence the tangent drawn to the elastic
curve at the wall will be horizontal, as
in Fig. 6–15. Therefore, if the tangential deviation at A is measured from
a tangent drawn at B, the deviation
$t_{A/B}$ will equal the deflection y.

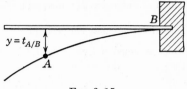

Fig. 6–15.

Several examples will illustrate how
area-moment principles are used to determine slope and deflection in
cantilever beams. Other types of beams are considered later.

ILLUSTRATIVE PROBLEMS

619. The cantilever beam in Fig. 6–16 is made of wood. It is 2 in. wide by 6 in.
deep, and $E = 1.5 \times 10^6$ psi. Compute the maximum deflection in inches, and the
maximum slope in degrees.

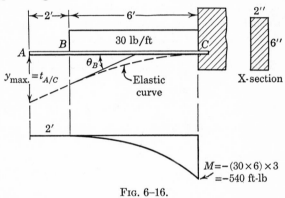

Fig. 6–16.

Solution: A tangent to the elastic curve at C is horizontal; hence the maximum
deflection, which evidently occurs at A, is $t_{A/C}$.

The moment diagram is a second-degree curve extending from B to C. Applying
Theorem II of the area-moment method, we obtain

$$\left[t_{A/C} = \frac{1}{EI} \, (\text{Area})_{AC} \cdot \bar{x}_A \right] \qquad y = \frac{1}{EI} \left(\frac{-540 \times 6}{3} \right)\left(2 + \frac{3}{4} \times 6 \right)$$

whence

$$EIy = -7020 \text{ lb-ft}^3 \tag{a}$$

The negative sign indicates the deflection y is directed downward from the
reference tangent drawn at C.

If dimensional values of E, I, and y are substituted in the above result, the left-
hand member will be

$$EIy = \frac{\text{lb}}{\text{in.}^2} \times \text{in.}^4 \times \text{in.} = \text{lb-in.}^3 \tag{b}$$

which is dimensionally unequal to lb-ft³. However, in Eq. (a) the right-hand member in lb-ft³ is easily converted to lb-in.³ by multiplying by the unit fraction $\dfrac{1728 \text{ in.}^3}{\text{ft}^3}$, which dimensionally cancels ft³ from the right-hand member of Eq. (a) and makes the equation dimensionally homogeneous. It is usually simpler to work in feet and convert to inches by multiplying by 1728 rather than use inches throughout the computations.

Since $I = \dfrac{bh^3}{12}$, we substitute numerical values for E and I in Eq. (a) and obtain

$$EI\delta = 7020 \times 1728 \text{ lb-in.}^3$$

$$1.5 \times 10^6 \times \frac{2 \times (6)^3}{12} \times \delta = 7020 \times 1728$$

$$\delta = 0.225 \text{ in.} \quad Ans.$$

δ represents the *magnitude* of the deflection which here is evidently downward.

The slope θ at B (and also at A, since the elastic curve between A and B is a straight line) is equal to the change in slope between the horizontal tangent at C and the tangent at B. Applying Theorem I, we obtain

$$\theta_B = \theta_{BC} = \frac{1}{EI} (\text{Area})_{BC} = \frac{1}{EI} \left(\frac{-540 \times 6}{3} \right)$$

or

$$EI\theta_B = -1080 \text{ lb-ft}^2 \tag{c}$$

Fig. 6–8 shows that the minus sign means that the right-hand tangent at C should be located at a clockwise angle from the left-hand tangent at B. Hence the elastic curve at B slopes up to the right, as shown. Substituting numerical values of E and I in Eq. (c) and multiplying the right side by 144 (why?), we obtain

$$(1.5 \times 10^6) \left(\frac{2 \times 6^3}{12} \right) \theta_B = 1080 \times 144$$

whence

$$\theta_B = 0.00288 \text{ radians} = 0.165 \text{ degrees}$$

620. For the cantilever beam in Fig. 6–17, it is assumed that $E = 1,728,000$ psi, $I = 15.6$ in.⁴ What value of P will cause a 1-in. deflection at the free end?

Solution: The moment diagram by parts is drawn as shown. Evidently the deflection δ at A is numerically equal to the deviation of A from a tangent drawn at C. Since the deviation at A is negative because A lies below the tangent, we have from Theorem II,

$$t_{A/C} = \frac{1}{EI} (\text{Area})_{AC} \cdot \bar{x}_A$$

$$-\delta = \frac{1}{EI} \left[\left(\frac{-6P \times 6}{2} \right) \left(4 + \frac{2}{3} \times 6 \right) + \left(\frac{-900 \times 10}{2} \right) \left(\frac{2}{3} \times 10 \right) \right]$$

whence

$$EI\delta = (144P + 30,000) \text{ lb-ft}^3$$

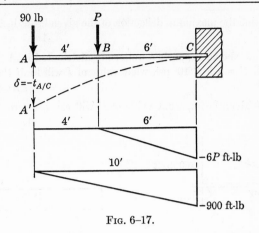

FIG. 6–17.

Substituting numerical values for E, I, and δ, and dividing the left-hand member by 1728 to make the equation dimensionally homogeneous, we obtain

$$\frac{1{,}728{,}000 \times 15.6 \times 1}{1728} = 144\,P + 30{,}000$$

$$15{,}600 = 144\,P + 30{,}000$$

$$P = -\,100\,\text{lb} \quad Ans.$$

The minus value of P indicates that the direction of P must be reversed to that originally assumed; i.e., P must act upward.

PROBLEMS

621. For the cantilever beam shown, $E = 1.5 \times 10^6$ psi, and the free end deflection is 1 in. Determine P.   *Ans.* $P = 44$ lb

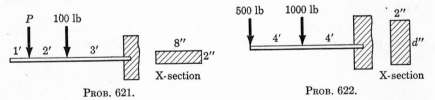

PROB. 621.   PROB. 622.

622. For the beam shown, find the depth of the rectangular section so as not to exceed a maximum deflection of $\frac{1}{2}$ in. $E = 1.5 \times 10^6$ psi. *Ans.* $d = 12.4$ in.

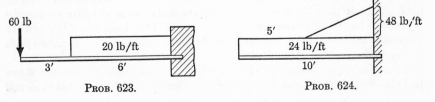

PROB. 623.   PROB. 624.

623. Determine the maximum deflection of the given beam if $E = 2 \times 10^6$ psi, and $I = 20$ in.^{4} *Ans.* max. $\delta = 0.862$ in.

624. The beam shown supports a uniformly distributed load plus a uniformly varying load. If $E = 1.5 \times 10^6$ psi, what value of I will limit the maximum deflection to 1 in.?   *Ans.* $I = 37.2$ in.^{4}

625. For the given beam, what value of P will cause a zero deflection at A? At B?   *Ans.* (a) $P = 43.4$ lb

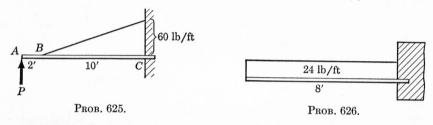

PROB. 625.   PROB. 626.

626. For the beam shown, determine the value of EIy at 4 ft from the wall.   *Ans.* $EIy = -4352$ lb-ft^3

6–6. More Complex Cantilever Loadings

Although no new theory is involved, this article discusses certain techniques of drawing moment diagrams by parts that simplify calculations. This is especially true for cantilevers carrying more complex loadings or when the deflection is desired at some intermediate point. These techniques are developed in the following examples.

ILLUSTRATIVE PROBLEMS

627. Determine the deflection at any section of a cantilever beam L ft long carrying a uniformly distributed load of w lb/ft.

Solution: In Fig. 6–18a, at a section x ft from the wall, the deviation of B from a tangent drawn to the elastic curve at C is evidently equal to the deflection y. Hence

$$t_{B/C} = \frac{1}{EI} (\text{Area})_{BC} \cdot \bar{x}_B = y \tag{a}$$

If the moment diagram is drawn in terms of forces to the left of any section, as in Fig. 6–18b, it is evident that the shaded area between B and C is *not* of a type covered in Table VI–1. Although the moment of this area may be computed by resolving it into the three parts indicated by the dashed lines, or by considering the moment to be the difference between the moment of the total area DGH and the moment of the area DEF, it is simpler to redraw the M diagram so as to obtain parts similar to the areas in Table VI–1.

Expressing the moment at B in terms of the loads to the *right* of the section shows that the bending moment at B is due to the vertical shear and moment at C, as well as the load on BC. Fig. 6–18c represents the equivalent cantilever loadings and moment diagram when drawn by parts from right to left. Each part in Fig. 6–18c is of a type covered in Table VI–1. Hence, applying Eq. (a) by taking moments of these areas about B, we have

$$y = \frac{1}{EI}\left[\left(\frac{wLx}{2}\cdot x\right)\left(\frac{x}{3}\right) - \left(\frac{wL^2}{2}\cdot x\right)\left(\frac{x}{2}\right) - \left(\frac{1}{3}\cdot\frac{wx^2}{2}\cdot x\right)\left(\frac{x}{4}\right)\right]$$

which reduces to

$$y = -\frac{wx^2}{24\,EI}[6\,L^2 - 4\,Lx + x^2]\quad Ans.$$

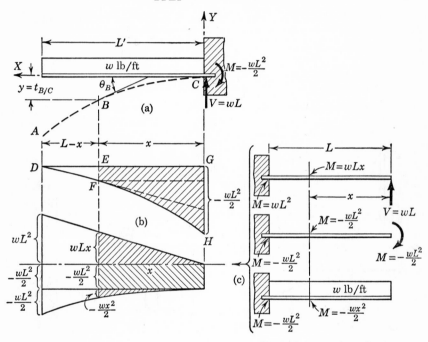

Equivalent cantilever loadings

Fig. 6–18.

The minus sign means that point B is below the tangent drawn to the elastic curve at C; i.e., the deflection y is directed downward. At the free end, where $x = L$, we obtain

$$\delta_{max} = \frac{wL^4}{8\,EI}$$

The slope θ at any point B is clearly equal to the change in slope θ_{BC} measured between tangents at B and C. Then, by Theorem I, we obtain

$$\theta_B = \theta_{BC} = \frac{1}{EI}(\text{Area})_{BC} = \frac{1}{EI}\left(\frac{wLx^2}{2} - \frac{wL^2x}{2} - \frac{wx^3}{6}\right)$$

At the free end A, where $x = L$,

$$\theta_A = -\frac{wL^3}{6\,EI}$$

According to Fig. 6–8, the minus sign indicates that the right-hand tangent at C makes a clockwise angle from the left-hand tangent at A; hence the slope at A is up to the right.

628. Compute the maximum value of EIy for the cantilever beam L ft long which carries a load varying uniformly from zero at the wall to w lb/ft at the free end.

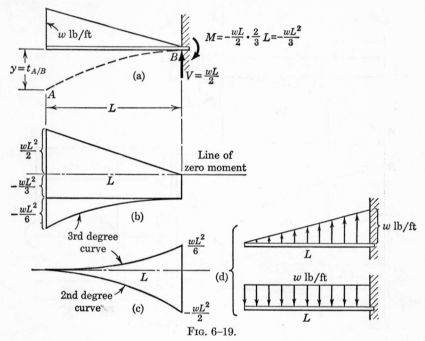

Fig. 6–19.

Solution: The elastic curve in Fig. 6–19a shows that the maximum deflection occurs at the free end A. It is numerically equal to $t_{A/B}$. Hence, from Theorem II,

$$y = t_{A/B} = \frac{1}{EI}\,(\text{Area})_{AB} \cdot \bar{x}_A \qquad (a)$$

The area of the M diagram is easily found from Fig. 6–19b, which is drawn by parts from right to left according to the procedure outlined in Prob. 627. Hence

$$y = \frac{1}{EI}\Big[\Big(\frac{1}{2}\cdot\frac{wL^2}{2}\cdot L\Big)\Big(\frac{L}{3}\Big) - \Big(\frac{wL^2}{3}\cdot L\Big)\Big(\frac{L}{2}\Big) - \Big(\frac{1}{4}\cdot\frac{wL^2}{6}\cdot L\Big)\Big(\frac{L}{5}\Big)\Big]$$

which reduces to

$$\text{Max. } EIy = -\frac{11}{120} wL^4 \quad Ans.$$

The minus sign indicates that the deflection is directed downward.

Another variation of drawing the M diagram is shown in Fig. 6–19c, which results from replacing the given load in Fig. 6–19a by those in Fig. 6–19d, i.e., superposing a downward uniformly distributed load and an upward uniformly varying load. Applying Eq. (a) to Fig. 6–19c yields

$$y = \frac{1}{EI}\left[\left(\frac{1}{4}\cdot\frac{wL^2}{6}\cdot L\right)\left(\frac{4}{5}L\right) - \left(\frac{1}{3}\cdot\frac{wL^2}{2}\cdot L\right)\left(\frac{3}{4}L\right)\right]$$

which also reduces to

$$\text{Max. } EIy = -\frac{11}{120} wL^4 \quad Ans.$$

629.   For the cantilever beam in Fig. 6–20a compute the value of EIy at A and B.

Solution: Fig. 6–20a shows that the deflection at A is $t_{A/C}$. From Theorem II we obtain

$$y = t_{A/C} = \frac{1}{EI} (\text{Area})_{AC} \cdot \bar{x}_A \tag{a}$$

Before applying Eq. (a), let us examine the various ways in which the M diagram by parts can be drawn so that the simplest diagram may be used. First, the M diagram in Fig. 6–20b, is drawn by expressing the bending moment at any section in terms of the loads to the right of the section in accordance with the basic definition $M = (\Sigma M)_R$. The equivalent cantilever loadings are also shown.

Second, the M diagram can also be drawn by expressing the bending moment between A and B by the definition $M = (\Sigma M)_L$, and that between B and C by $M = (\Sigma M)_R$. This results in the M diagram and equivalent cantilever loadings shown in Fig. 6–20c.

Third, still another method is to replace the given loading by superposing the loadings in Fig. 6–20d. This gives what is probably the simplest M diagram by parts.

Although identical results will be obtained by using any of the above M diagrams, we shall apply Eq. (a) to the third one (Fig. 6–20d). On taking the moment of area about A, we obtain

$$y = \frac{1}{EI}\left[\left(\frac{240 \times 4}{3}\right)\left(4 + \frac{3}{4}\times 4\right) - \left(\frac{960 \times 8}{3}\right)\left(\frac{3}{4}\times 8\right)\right]$$

which reduces to

$$EIy = +\,2240 - 15{,}360 = -\,13{,}120 \text{ lb-ft}^3 \quad Ans.$$

The deflection at B is determined by Theorem II:

$$y = t_{B/C} = \frac{1}{EI} (\text{Area})_{BC} \cdot \bar{x}_B \tag{b}$$

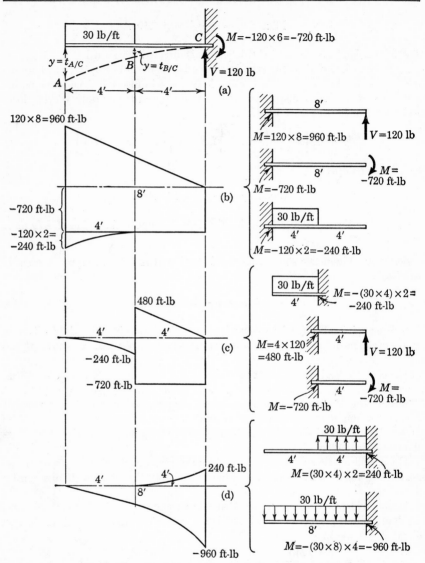

FIG. 6–20. — Variations of moment diagrams by parts.

Either of the M diagrams in parts (b) or (c) of Fig. 6–20 may be used, for they are identical for segment BC. Taking moments about B as indicated by Eq. (b), we obtain

$$y = \frac{1}{EI}\left[\left(\frac{480 \times 4}{2}\right)\left(\frac{4}{3}\right) - (720 \times 4)\left(\frac{4}{2}\right)\right]$$

Hence at B,

$$EIy = +\,1280 - 5760 = -\,4480 \text{ lb-ft}^3 \quad Ans.$$

PROBLEMS

630. Compute the maximum deflection for the given beam if $E = 1.5 \times 10^6$ psi and $I = 20$ in.[4]   *Ans.* $\delta = 0.534$ in.

631. Determine the maximum deflection for the beam shown.

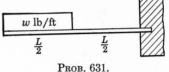

Ans. $\delta = \dfrac{41}{384} \dfrac{wL^4}{EI}$

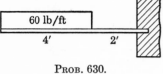

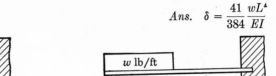

PROB. 630.   PROB. 631.

632. For the given beam, find the maximum EIy.

Ans. $EIy = -26{,}637$ lb-ft[3]

633. Compute the value of EIy at a section 7 ft from the wall of the given beam.

634. Find the maximum value of EIy for the given beam.

635. For the beam shown, determine the value of EIy at a section 3 ft from the wall.

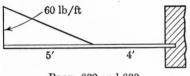

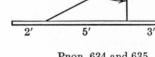

PROB. 632 and 633.   PROB. 634 and 635.

636. Compute the deflection at 6 ft from the wall for the given beam. Assume $E = 1.5 \times 10^6$ psi and $I = 100$ in.[4]   *Ans.* $\delta = 0.295$ in.

637. In the beam shown, what value of I will limit the maximum deflection to 0.50 in. if $E = 1.5 \times 10^6$ psi?   *Ans.* $I = 126.7$ in.[4]

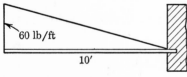

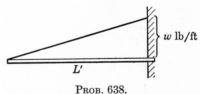

PROB. 636 and 637.   PROB. 638.

638. The beam shown has a load varying uniformly from zero at the free end to w lb/ft at the wall. Determine the slope and deflection at any section x ft from the wall.

Ans. $y = -\dfrac{1}{EI} \cdot \dfrac{wx^2}{120\,L} [10\,L^3 - 10\,L^2x + 5\,Lx^2 - x^3]$

6–7. Deflections of Simple Beams

Deflections in cantilever beams were simplified by the fact that the tangent to the elastic curve at the fixed end was known to be horizontal.

In simply supported beams, the position at which a tangent to the elastic curve will be horizontal is usually unknown, and therefore a different method must be used. This method may seem devious, but actually it is simple and rapid. It is illustrated by Fig. 6–21, which shows only the elastic curve of a simple beam. The loads and moment diagrams have been omitted for clarity.

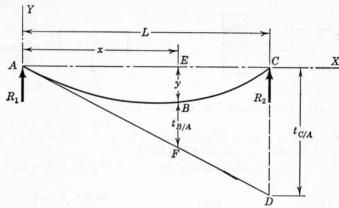

FIG. 6–21. — Geometry of area-moment method applied to simple beams.

The problem is to determine the value of the deflection y at some position B. If a tangent to the elastic curve is drawn at A, the deviation $t_{B/A}$ at B from this tangent is evidently *not* the required deflection y. However, the sum of y and $t_{B/A}$ constitutes the distance EF; and if both EF and $t_{B/A}$ were known, y could easily be found. Hence the distance EF must also be found. This is done by noting that the triangle AEF is similar to the triangle ACD, of which the leg CD equals the deviation $t_{C/A}$ of C from the reference tangent drawn at A.

The proper procedure to apply is obtained by reversing the steps of the above analysis into the following order:

1. Compute $t_{C/A}$, using the relation $t_{C/A} = \dfrac{1}{EI} (\text{Area})_{AC} \cdot \bar{x}_C$.

2. From the relations between similar triangles, determine EF in terms of $t_{C/A}$. We obtain $EF = \dfrac{x}{L} \cdot t_{C/A}$.

3. Compute $t_{B/A}$ from the relation $t_{B/A} = \dfrac{1}{EI} (\text{Area})_{BA} \cdot \bar{x}_B$.

4. Since EF is the sum of y and $t_{B/A}$, the value of y is given by $y = EF - t_{B/A}$.

As mentioned previously, this procedure may seem very long, but actually it is rapid. Several examples will demonstrate the method. Only simple loadings are used, since this concentrates attention upon basic ideas. For more complex loadings the basic method is unchanged, the more complicated M diagram by parts being constructed as indicated in Art. 6–4.

ILLUSTRATIVE PROBLEMS

639.   The simple beam in Fig. 6–22 supports a concentrated load of 60 lb at 6 ft from the left support.   Compute the value of EIy at B, which is 3 ft from the left support.

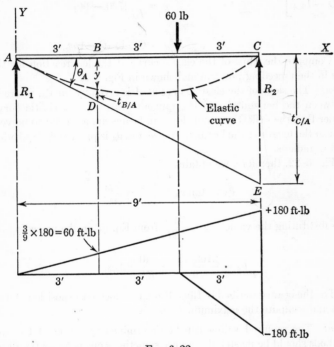

FIG. 6–22.

Solution: We begin by sketching the dashed outline of the elastic curve and drawing the M diagram by parts from left to right.   Following the procedure discussed above, we first obtain $t_{C/A}$.

$$t_{C/A} = \frac{1}{EI}\,(\text{Area})_{AC} \cdot \bar{x}_C$$

$$t_{C/A} = \frac{1}{EI}\left[\left(\frac{180 \times 9}{2}\right)\left(\frac{9}{3}\right) - \left(\frac{180 \times 3}{2}\right)\left(\frac{3}{3}\right)\right]$$

$$= \frac{1}{EI}\,[2430 - 270] = \frac{2160}{EI} \qquad\qquad (a)$$

Since triangle ABD is similar to triangle ACE,

$$BD = \frac{3}{9} \times t_{C/A} = \frac{1}{3} \times \frac{2160}{EI} = \frac{720}{EI} \qquad (b)$$

The deviation $t_{B/A}$ is next obtained from

$$\left[t_{B/A} = \frac{1}{EI} (\text{Area})_{BA} \cdot \bar{x}_B \right] \qquad t_{B/A} = \frac{1}{EI} \left[\left(\frac{60 \times 3}{2} \right) \left(\frac{3}{3} \right) \right] = \frac{90}{EI} \qquad (c)$$

Finally, the value of y is given by

$$\left[y = BD - t_{B/A} \right] \qquad\qquad y = \frac{1}{EI} [720 - 90]$$

or

$$EIy = 630 \text{ lb-ft}^3 \quad Ans.$$

640. Compute the slope of the elastic curve at the left reaction for the beam discussed in the preceding problem and shown in Fig. 6–22.

Solution: The slope of the elastic curve at A is given by $\tan \theta_A$, where θ_A is the angle between the horizontal and the tangent drawn to the elastic curve at A. (Remember that the deflections and slopes in beams are assumed to be very small compared to the length of the beam.) Hence, $\tan \theta_A$ is practically equivalent to θ_A expressed in radians.

From Fig. 6–22, therefore, we obtain

$$\theta_A \approx \tan \theta_A = \frac{CE}{AC} = \frac{t_{C/A}}{AC}$$

whence, substituting the value $t_{C/A} = \dfrac{2160}{EI}$ from Eq. (a) in the preceding problem, we have

$$\theta_A = \frac{2160/EI}{9} = \frac{240}{EI} \quad Ans.$$

641. For the beam described in Illus. Prob. 639, locate the position of maximum deflection and compute the maximum EIy.

Solution: The required values can be determined by either of two methods. Both methods should be mastered, because sometimes one is easier than the other.

Method I. We begin by computing the deflection at any position B located x ft from the left reaction. Using the technique applied in Illus. Prob. 639, we obtain from Fig. 6–23,

$$\left[t_{B/A} = \frac{1}{EI} (\text{Area})_{BA} \cdot \bar{x}_B \right] \qquad t_{B/A} = \frac{1}{EI} \left(\frac{20 \, x \cdot x}{2} \right) \cdot \frac{x}{3} = \frac{1}{EI} \cdot \frac{10 \, x^3}{3}$$

Using the value of $t_{C/A}$ given in Eq. (a) of that problem, we also have in Fig. 6–23,

$$\left[BD = \frac{x}{9} \cdot t_{C/A} \right] \qquad\qquad BD = \frac{x}{9} \cdot \frac{2160}{EI} = \frac{240 \, x}{EI}$$

The value of the deflection y is the difference between BD and $t_{B/A}$; this difference is positive. But y is downward or negative if the Y axis is positive upward, and

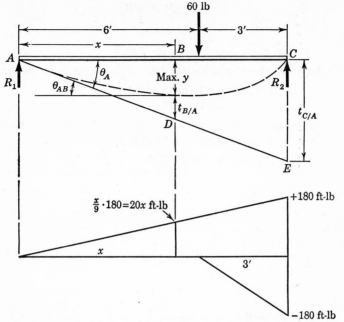

FIG. 6–23.

therefore a minus sign should precede this difference. When solving simple beams by the area-moment method, it is more convenient to eliminate the minus sign altogether (and the errors caused by forgetting to include it) by assuming the Y axis and deflections as positive downward. Hence, with the Y axis taken as positive downward, the value of y at any position (i.e., the equation of the elastic curve) is

$$[y = BD - t_{B/A}] \qquad\qquad y = \frac{1}{EI}\left[240\,x - \frac{10\,x^3}{3}\right]$$

or

$$EIy = 240\,x - \frac{10\,x^3}{3} \tag{a}$$

This is valid for any position between the left reaction and the load (i.e., between $x = 0$ and $x = 6$). The slope equation for this portion of the beam is found by differentiating the deflection equation, Eq. (a):

$$EI\,\frac{dy}{dx} = 240 - 10\,x^2 \tag{b}$$

From the principle of maxima and minima developed in calculus, setting the first derivative of Eq. (a) equal to zero will determine the position of maximum deflection. This is equivalent to setting Eq. (b) equal to zero, thus determining the position of zero slope in the beam. We obtain

$$240 - 10\,x^2 = 0$$

or

$$x^2 = 24$$
$$x = 4.9 \text{ ft} \quad Ans.$$

Substituting this value of x in Eq. (a) determines the maximum deflection.

$$\text{Max. } EIy = 240(4.9) - \tfrac{10}{3}(4.9)^3$$
$$= 1177 - 392 = 785 \text{ lb-ft}^3 \quad Ans.$$

It is instructive to compare the maximum value of EIy with the value of EIy at midspan. At midspan, $x = 4.5$, and substitution of this value of x in Eq. (a) gives

$$\text{Midspan } EIy = 240(4.5) - \tfrac{10}{3}(4.5)^3$$
$$= 1080 - 303 = 777 \text{ lb-ft}^3$$

This is about 1% less than the maximum value. This difference is so negligible in comparison with possible variations in the given data that for all practical purposes we may assume the midspan deflection to be equivalent to the actual maximum deflection. Indeed, it may be shown that, for a concentrated load located anywhere on a simple span, the maximum difference between midspan and maximum deflection is only 2.6%.

Method II. At the position of maximum deflection, the tangent to the elastic curve will be horizontal. As shown in Fig. 6–23, the change in slope between tangents at this position B and at A (i.e., θ_{AB}) is equal to the slope θ_A at A, since for small angles the radian measure and the tangent of the angle are practically equivalent, i.e., $\theta_A = \tan\theta_A$.

From Theorem I of the area-moment method, we obtain

$$\left[\theta_{AB} = \frac{1}{EI}\,(\text{Area})_{AB}\right] \qquad \theta_{AB} = \frac{1}{EI}\left[\frac{20\,x\cdot x}{2}\right] = \frac{10\,x^2}{EI}$$

which, on being equated to $\theta_A = \dfrac{240}{EI}$ obtained in Prob. 640, gives

$$\frac{10\,x^2}{EI} = \frac{240}{EI}$$
$$x^2 = 24$$
$$x = 4.9 \text{ ft} \quad Ans.$$

Computing the value of EIy at this position gives maximum $EIy = 785$ lb-ft³, as was shown in Method I.

If we successively differentiate the general deflection equation Eq. (a) obtained previously in Method I, we have

$$EIy = 240\,x - \frac{10\,x^3}{3} \tag{a}$$

$$EI\,\frac{dy}{dx} = 240 - 10\,x^2 \tag{b}$$

$$EI\,\frac{d^2y}{dx^2} = -20\,x \tag{c}$$

Since $R_1 = 20$ lb, the moment equation is $M = 20\,x$, and Eq. (c) may be rewritten

$EI \dfrac{d^2y}{dx^2} = -M$. Except for the minus sign, this is the differential equation of the

elastic curve developed from $\dfrac{1}{\rho} = \dfrac{M}{EI}$ in Art. 6–2, and used as the basis of the double-

integration method. The minus sign is present because in applying the area-moment method to simple beams we found it convenient to take downward deflections as positive, whereas in using the double-integration method we considered the Y axis and upward deflections as positive. Compare the results obtained here with those obtained previously with the double-integration solution of this problem on page 173.

PROBLEMS

Note that in the following problems the Y axis and deflections are considered as positive downward.

642. Compute the value of midspan EIy for the beam shown.

643. For the given beam, determine the value of midspan EIy.

$$Ans. \quad EIy = 182.25 \text{ lb-ft}^3$$

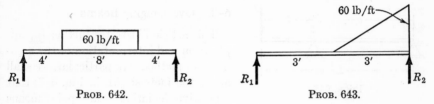

PROB. 642.   PROB. 643.

644. Determine the value of EIy under the 90-lb load.

$$Ans. \quad EIy = 2470 \text{ lb-ft}^3$$

645. Find the deflection equation for segment AB of the given beam.

$$Ans. \quad EIy = 512\,x - 32\,x^3 + 3\,x^4$$

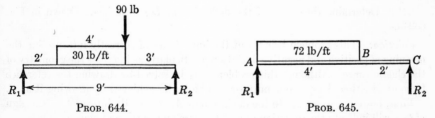

PROB. 644.   PROB. 645.

646. A simple beam supports a concentrated load P placed anywhere on the span, as shown. Measuring x from A, show that the deflection equation for the segment AB is

$$EIy = \frac{Pbx}{6L}[L^2 - b^2 - x^2]$$

and that if x is measured from C, the deflection equation for segment CB is

$$EIy = \frac{Pax}{6\,L}\,[L^2 - a^2 - x^2]$$

Also show that if $a > b$ the value of midspan EIy is

$$\text{Midspan } EIy = \frac{Pb}{48}\,(3\,L^2 - 4\,b^2)$$

647. Compute the value of midspan EIy for the beam shown.

Ans. $EIy = 4456$ lb-ft³

648. Determine the deflection and slope under the load P.

Ans. $y = \dfrac{PLb^2}{3\,EI}$, $\dfrac{dy}{dx} = \dfrac{Pb}{6\,EI}\,(2\,a + 3\,b)$

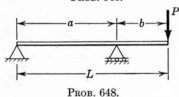

Prob. 646.

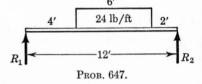

Prob. 647.

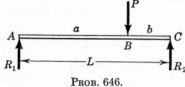

Prob. 648.

6–8. Overhanging Beams

This article illustrates further the application and interpretation of the area-moment method. In particular, we shall apply the facts shown in Fig. 6–7: that a positive deviation at any point means that the point lies above the reference tangent from which the deviation is measured, and conversely for a negative deviation. The following example illustrates some of the methods that can be used.

ILLUSTRATIVE PROBLEM

649. Determine the value of the deflection at D of the beam shown in Fig. 6–24a.

Solution: This problem brings out the importance of correctly interpreting the meaning of positive and negative deviation, particularly as it affects the geometry of the elastic curve. Although this problem may be solved by drawing the reference tangent at either A or C, our purpose will be better achieved by drawing it at C.

First, however, we compute the deviation at A. Correctly interpreting the sign of $t_{A/C}$ will indicate the direction in which the reference tangent slopes. Thus

$$t_{A/C} = \frac{1}{EI}\,(\text{Area})_{AC} \cdot \bar{x}_A$$

$$= \frac{1}{EI}\left[\left(\frac{780 \times 10}{2}\right)\left(\frac{2}{3} \times 10\right) - \left(\frac{900 \times 6}{2}\right)\left(4 + \frac{2}{3} \times 6\right)\right]$$

$$= \frac{1}{EI}\,[26{,}000 - 21{,}600] = \frac{4400}{EI}$$

The positive value of $t_{A/C}$ means that A on the elastic curve lies above the reference tangent at C. Hence the reference tangent at C slopes down to the left, as shown.

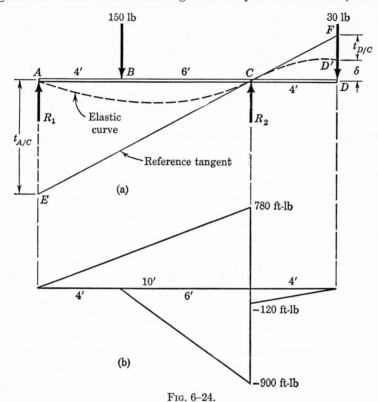

FIG. 6–24.

From the similar triangles ACE and CDF, we obtain

$$DF = \frac{4}{10} t_{A/C} = \frac{4}{10} \times \frac{4400}{EI} = \frac{1760}{EI}$$

The deviation of D from the reference tangent at C is

$$\left[t_{D/C} = \frac{1}{EI} (\text{Area})_{DC} \cdot \bar{x}_D \right] \qquad t_{D/C} = \frac{1}{EI}\left[-\left(\frac{120 \times 4}{2} \right) \frac{2}{3} \times 4 \right] = -\frac{640}{EI}$$

The minus sign for $t_{D/C}$ means that D' on the elastic curve is below the reference tangent. Also, since DF is numerically greater than the absolute magnitude of $t_{D/C}$, it is now apparent that D is deflected upward from its original position. Therefore, the elastic curve between C and D is sketched as shown.

The deflection δ is obtained from

$$\delta = DF - t_{D/C} = \frac{1760}{EI} - \frac{640}{EI} = \frac{1120}{EI} \quad Ans.$$

If the reference tangent had been drawn at A and the elastic curve had been assumed to have the shape shown in Fig. 6–25, we would have obtained the following results:

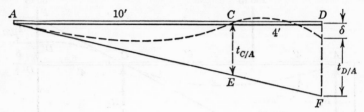

Fig. 6–25. — Elastic curve of Prob. 648 with reference tangent drawn at A.

$$t_{C/A} = \frac{1}{EI}(\text{Area})_{CA} \cdot \bar{x}_C$$

$$= \frac{1}{EI}\left[\left(\frac{780 \times 10}{2}\right)\frac{10}{3} - \left(\frac{900 \times 6}{2}\right)\frac{6}{3}\right] = \frac{7600}{EI}$$

$$t_{D/A} = \frac{1}{EI}(\text{Area})_{DA} \cdot \bar{x}_D$$

$$= \frac{1}{EI}\left[\left(\frac{780 \times 10}{2}\right)\left(4 + \frac{10}{3}\right) - \left(\frac{900 \times 6}{2}\right)\left(4 + \frac{6}{3}\right) - \left(\frac{120 \times 4}{2}\right)\frac{2}{3} \times 4\right]$$

$$= \frac{11{,}760}{EI}$$

The similar triangles ACE and ADF give

$$DF = \frac{14}{10} \times t_{C/A} = \frac{14}{10} \times \frac{7600}{EI} = \frac{10{,}640}{EI}$$

Finally, using the elastic curve sketched in Fig. 6–25, we obtain the deflection

$$\delta = DF - t_{D/A} = \frac{10{,}640 - 11{,}760}{EI} = -\frac{1120}{EI}$$

which, except for the minus sign, is that obtained previously. Here the minus sign indicates that the deflection at D is opposite to the direction sketched in Fig. 6–25; i.e., it is directed upward as before. This is checked by the fact that $t_{D/A}$ is numerically larger than DF.

One advantage of drawing the reference tangent at C rather than at A is the increase in slide rule accuracy obtained by working with smaller numerical quantities.

PROBLEMS

650. Determine $EI\delta$ at a section 8 ft from R_1.   *Ans.* $EI\delta = 1685$ lb-ft³

651. Compute the value of $EI\delta$ under the 40-lb load.

Ans. $EI\delta = 93.25$ lb-ft³

652. For the beam shown, determine the value of $EI\delta$ at B and D.

Ans. At B, $EI\delta = 6827$ lb-ft³

653. Determine the value of P that will cause a zero deflection under P.

$Ans.\quad P = 288$ lb

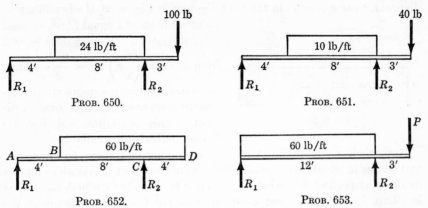

PROB. 650.

PROB. 651.

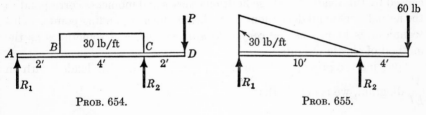

PROB. 652.

PROB. 653.

654. In the overhanging beam shown, (*a*) find P so that the tangent to the elastic curve at C will be horizontal. (*b*) What will be the value of $EI\delta$ at B?

$Ans.\quad$ (*a*) $P = 53.3$ lb

655. Compute the value of $EI\delta$ under the 60-lb load.

PROB. 654.

PROB. 655.

6–9. Conjugate-Beam Method

Successive differentiation of the deflection equation discloses the following relations:

$$EIy = \text{Deflection}$$

$$EI\frac{dy}{dx} = \text{Slope}$$

$$EI\frac{d^2y}{dx^2} = \text{Moment} = M$$

$$EI\frac{d^3y}{dx^3} = \text{Shear} = V = \frac{dM}{dx}$$

$$EI\frac{d^4y}{dx^4} = \text{Load} = \frac{dV}{dx} = \frac{d^2M}{dx^2}$$

It is evident that the relations among deflection, slope, and moment are the same as those among moment, shear, and load. This suggests that the area-moment method can be used to determine bending moment from the load diagram, just as deflection has been obtained from the moment diagram. For example, in the load diagram in Fig. 6–26, the bending moment at B should equal (Area of load diagram)$_{AB} \cdot \bar{x}_B$. That it does is seen

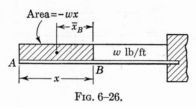

Area$=-wx$

w lb/ft

Fig. 6–26.

from $(-wx)\left(\dfrac{1}{2}x\right) = -\dfrac{wx^2}{2}.$ Thus we could apply area-moment principles to compute bending moment, although this is impractical because better methods are available.

Nevertheless, the similarity of relations among load, shear, and moment, and among moment, slope, and deflection suggests that the relations among moment, slope, and deflection can be found by using the methods developed in Chap. IV for computing shear and moment from load diagrams. We need merely assume that a beam is loaded, not with the actual loads, but with the $\dfrac{M}{EI}$ diagram corresponding to these loads. Treating this $\dfrac{M}{EI}$ diagram as a fictitious loading, we compute the shear and moment at any point caused by this loading. These fictitious shears and moments correspond to the actual slopes and deflections in the beam at corresponding points. This technique is known as the *conjugate-beam method*, and sometimes as the method of elastic weights.

Applying the principles of shear and moment to a beam loaded with an $\dfrac{M}{EI}$ diagram, we conclude that

    1. The actual slope = the fictitious shear   (6–6)
    2. The actual deflection = the fictitious moment   (6–7)

The method is really useful only for simply supported beams. For other beams, such as cantilevers or overhanging beams, artificial constraints must be applied; they are discussed later.

To evaluate the conjugate-beam method, let us compare it and the area-moment method when applied to a simple beam. Only in simply supported beams can the conjugate-beam method be applied directly without using artificial constraints.

Fig. 6–27a shows a simply supported beam carrying a distributed load of w lb/ft. The moment diagram for this loading (drawn by parts in Fig. 6–27b) is multiplied by $\dfrac{1}{EI}$ and used as the conjugate-beam loading shown simply supported on the span L in Fig. 6–27c. The reaction R_1 of this

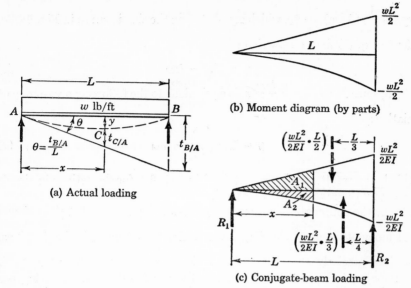

(b) Moment diagram (by parts)

(a) Actual loading

(c) Conjugate-beam loading

FIG. 6–27. — Comparison of conjugate-beam and area-moment methods.

conjugate beam is found by setting moments of the fictitious loads about B equal to zero. We obtain

$$[\Sigma M_B = 0] \qquad R_1 L = \left(\frac{wL^2}{2\,EI} \cdot \frac{L}{2}\right)\left(\frac{L}{3}\right) - \left(\frac{wL^2}{2\,EI} \cdot \frac{L}{3}\right)\left(\frac{L}{4}\right) \qquad (a)$$

The right-hand member of Eq. (a) will be recognized as $\dfrac{1}{EI}\,(\text{Area})_{AB} \cdot \bar{x}_B$,

that is, $t_{B/A}$. Obviously, solving for R_1 is equivalent to $\dfrac{t_{B/A}}{L}$, which is the ac-

tual slope at A; this fact is evident from the geometry of the elastic curve in Fig. 6–27a. Nevertheless, this is confirmation of rule 1 of the conjugate-beam method: The fictitious shear equals the actual slope at the corresponding point in the actual beam.

To obtain the deflection at any point on the actual beam, we apply the definition of bending moment to the conjugate loads:

$$\text{deflection } y = (\Sigma M)_L = R_1 x - A_1 \frac{x}{3} + A_2 \frac{x}{4}$$

$$= R_1 x - \left(A_1 \frac{x}{3} - A_2 \frac{x}{4}\right) \qquad (b)$$

However, in terms of the moment diagram in Fig. 6–27b $\left(A_1 \dfrac{x}{3} - A_2 \dfrac{x}{4}\right)$

equals $\dfrac{1}{EI}$ (Area)$_{AC} \cdot \bar{x}_C$, which equals $t_{C/A}$ on the elastic curve in Fig. 6–27a.
Hence Eq. (b) may be rewritten as

$$y = R_1 x - t_{C/A} \tag{c}$$

which, since $R_1 x = \theta x = \dfrac{t_{B/A}}{L} x$, is equivalent to the following area-moment
relation:

$$y = t_{B/A} \left(\frac{x}{L}\right) - t_{C/A} \tag{d}$$

This is the result previously obtained in Art. 6–7 for deflections in simple beams by the area-moment method.

Thus the conjugate-beam method, which computes the fictitious shears and moments of an $\dfrac{M}{EI}$ loading to determine actual slopes and deflections, involves precisely the same computations as the area-moment method. The conjugate-beam method also has the disadvantage of obscuring the physical significances of the computations. This disadvantage is even more pronounced when the method is used with cantilever and overhanging beams, where certain artificial constraints must be applied. Nevertheless, this method offers an occasional advantage in certain routine work, in that it permits direct application of the definitions of shear and moment to the fictitious loading to find slope and deflection without any need of an elastic curve.

Now for a word about the need for artificial constraints in certain cases. For the cantilever beam in Fig. 6–28a, the $\dfrac{M}{EI}$ diagram appears as in Fig. 6–28b. This diagram cannot be applied directly as a fictitious load to a cantilever with the wall at the right end C, because the fictitious shear and moment at B would be zero, whereas the actual slope and deflection at B are not zero. Therefore, the diagram of fictitious loads must be modified, as in Fig. 6–28c, so that the fictitious loading will correspond to the actual slope and deflection at the free end.

The reason for supplying artificial constraints when solving cantilever problems should now be clear. To produce an actual zero slope at C in the original cantilever, the fictitious shear must be zero at C; therefore

$$[V = (\Sigma Y)_L] \qquad\qquad 0 = V - A$$

From this we see that the fictitious shear of the conjugate beam at B must equal the area A of the $\dfrac{M}{EI}$ diagram. Also, to produce a zero fictitious moment at C, we must calculate the fictitious restraint M from

$$[M_C = (\Sigma M)_L] \qquad 0 = M + VL - A\frac{L}{4}$$

Only after the artificial constraints M and V have been found can the fictitious shear and moment (corresponding to actual slope and deflection) be computed. Hence cantilever problems can be solved more simply and more directly by the area-moment method.

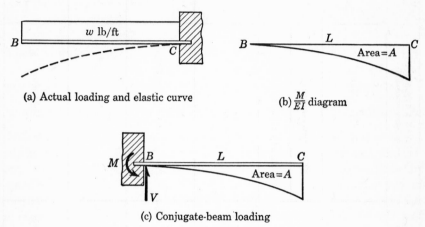

(a) Actual loading and elastic curve

(b) $\frac{M}{EI}$ diagram

(c) Conjugate-beam loading

FIG. 6–28. — Constraints required to solve cantilever beams by the conjugate-beam method.

PROBLEMS

Probs. 642 to 648 inclusive and cases 6 through 12 in Table VI–2 (page 212) may be assigned for solution by the conjugate-beam method.

6–10. Deflections by the Method of Superposition

In a supplementary method of determining slopes and deflections, the results of a few simple loadings are used to obtain those for more complicated loadings. This procedure, called the *method of superposition*, determines the slope or deflection at any point in a beam as the resultant of the slopes and deflections at that point caused by each of the loads acting separately. The only restriction on this method is that the effect produced by each load must be independent of that produced by the other loads; i.e., each separate load must not cause an excessive change in the original shape or length of the beam.

The technique of superposition is advantageous primarily for loadings that combine the types tabulated in Table VI–2. For partially distributed loads, either uniform or variable, the area-moment method is generally preferable.

TABLE VI-2. Summary of Beam Loadings

CASE NO.	TYPE OF LOAD	MAX. MOMENT	SLOPE AT END	DEFLECTION EQUATION (y is positive downward)	MAXIMUM DEFLECTION
1		$M = -PL$	$\theta = \dfrac{PL^2}{2EI}$	$EIy = \dfrac{Px^2}{6}(3L-x)$	$\delta = \dfrac{PL^3}{3EI}$
2		$M = -Pa$	$\theta = \dfrac{Pa^2}{2EI}$	$EIy = \dfrac{Px^2}{6}(3a-x)$ for $0<x<a$ $EIy = \dfrac{Pa^2}{6}(3x-a)$ for $a<x<L$	$\delta = \dfrac{Pa^2}{6EI}(3L-a)$
3	w lb/ft	$M = -\dfrac{wL^2}{2} = -\dfrac{WL}{2}$	$\theta = \dfrac{wL^3}{6EI} = \dfrac{WL^2}{6EI}$	$EIy = \dfrac{wx^2}{24}(6L^2 - 4Lx + x^2)$	$\delta = \dfrac{wL^4}{8EI} = \dfrac{WL^3}{8EI}$
4	w lb/ft	$M = -\dfrac{wL^2}{6} = -\dfrac{WL}{3}$	$\theta = \dfrac{wL^3}{24EI} = \dfrac{WL^2}{12EI}$	$EIy = \dfrac{wx^2}{120L}(10L^3 - 10L^2 x + 5Lx^2 - x^3)$	$\delta = \dfrac{wL^4}{30EI} = \dfrac{WL^3}{15EI}$
5		$M = -M$	$\theta = \dfrac{ML}{EI}$	$EIy = \dfrac{Mx^2}{2}$	$\delta = \dfrac{ML^2}{2EI}$
6		$M = \dfrac{PL}{4}$	$\theta_L = \theta_R = \dfrac{PL^2}{16EI}$	$EIy = \dfrac{Px}{12}\left(\dfrac{3}{4}L^2 - x^2\right)$ for $0<x<\dfrac{L}{2}$	$\delta = \dfrac{PL^3}{48EI}$

		M	θ	EIy	δ
7		$M=\dfrac{Pab}{L}$ at $x=a$	$\theta_L=\dfrac{Pb(L^2-b^2)}{6EIL}$ $\theta_R=\dfrac{Pa(L^2-a^2)}{6EIL}$	$EIy=\dfrac{Pbx}{6L}(L^2-x^2-b^2)$ for $0<x<a$ $EIy=\dfrac{Pb}{6L}\left[\dfrac{L}{b}(x-a)^3+(L^2-b^2)x-x^3\right]$ for $a<x<L$	$\delta=\dfrac{Pb(L^2-b^2)^{3/2}}{9\sqrt{3}\,EIL}$ at $x=\sqrt{\dfrac{L^2-b^2}{3}}$ (not max.) $\delta=\dfrac{Pb}{48EI}(3L^2-4b^2)$ At center (not max.) when $a>b$
8		$M=\dfrac{wL^2}{8}$ $=\dfrac{WL}{8}$	$\theta_L=\theta_R=\dfrac{wL^3}{24EI}$	$EIy=\dfrac{wx}{24}(L^3-2Lx^2+x^3)$	$\delta=\dfrac{5wL^4}{384EI}=\dfrac{5WL^3}{384EI}$
9		$M=\dfrac{wL^2}{9\sqrt{3}}$ $=\dfrac{2WL}{9\sqrt{3}}$	$\theta_L=\dfrac{7wL^3}{360EI}$ $\theta_R=\dfrac{8wL^3}{360EI}$	$EIy=\dfrac{wx}{360L}(7L^4-10L^2x^2+3x^4)$	$\delta=\dfrac{2.5wL^4}{384EI}=\dfrac{5WL^3}{384EI}$ at $x=0.519L$
10		$M=\dfrac{wL^2}{12}$ $=\dfrac{WL}{6}$	$\theta_L=\theta_R=\dfrac{5wL^3}{192EI}$	$EIy=\dfrac{wx}{960L}(25L^4-40L^2x^2+16x^4)$ for $0<x<\dfrac{L}{2}$	$\delta=\dfrac{wL^4}{120EI}=\dfrac{WL^3}{60EI}$
11		$M=M$	$\theta_L=\dfrac{ML}{6EI}$ $\theta_R=\dfrac{ML}{3EI}$	$EIy=\dfrac{MLx}{6}\left(1-\dfrac{x^2}{L^2}\right)$	$\delta=\dfrac{ML^2}{9\sqrt{3}EI}$ at $x=\dfrac{L}{\sqrt{3}}$ At center (not max.) $\delta=\dfrac{ML^2}{16EI}$
12		$M=M$	$\theta_L=\dfrac{ML}{3EI}$ $\theta_R=\dfrac{ML}{6EI}$	$EIy=\dfrac{Mx}{6L}(L-x)(2L-x)$	$\delta=\dfrac{ML^2}{9\sqrt{3}EI}$ at $x=\left(L-\dfrac{L}{\sqrt{3}}\right)$ At center (not max.) $\delta=\dfrac{ML^2}{16EI}$

Note: To compute deflection in inches, multiply by factor $(12)^3=1728$

To compute slope in radians, multiply by factor $(12)^2=144$

Units of terms in table are: P in lb; w in lb/ft; L in ft; E in lb/in²; I in in⁴; M in ft-lb

ILLUSTRATIVE PROBLEMS

656. Using the method of superposition, compute the midspan value of EIy for the beam carrying two concentrated loads, shown in Fig. 6–29a.

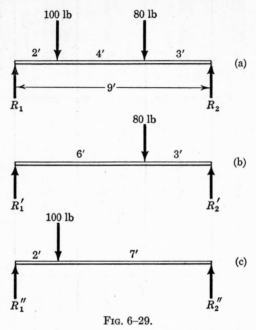

FIG. 6–29.

Solution: From case 7 of Table VI–2, the midspan deflection of an eccentrically placed concentrated load is $EIy = \dfrac{Pb}{48}(3\,L^2 - 4\,b^2)$, where b is the smaller of the two segments into which the beam is divided by the load. Resolving the given loading into those shown in (b) and (c) in Fig. 6–29, we find that the midspan deflection of (a) is equal to the sum of the midspan deflections of (b) and (c). Thus

$$EIy = \sum \frac{Pb}{48}(3\,L^2 - 4\,b^2)$$

$$= \frac{80(3)}{48}[3(9)^2 - 4(3)^2] + \frac{100(2)}{48}[3(9)^2 - 4(2)^2] = 1980 \text{ lb-ft}^3 \quad Ans.$$

657. A simply supported beam carries a uniformly distributed load over part of its length, as shown in Fig. 6–30. Compute the midspan value of EIy.

Solution: The continuous load may be considered as a series of concentrated elemental loads, each of $P = w\,dx = 60\,dx$ and located at a distance x from the end. At midspan, therefore, applying the result for case 7, we have

$$EIy = \sum \frac{Pb}{48}(3\,L^2 - 4\,b^2)$$

$$= \int_0^6 \frac{(60\,dx)(x)}{48} [3(12)^2 - 4\,x^2] + \int_4^6 \frac{(60\,dx)(x)}{48} [3(12)^2 - 4\,x^2]$$

$$= 8100 + 4100 = 12{,}200 \text{ lb-ft}^3$$

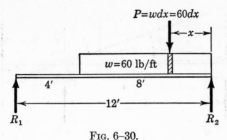

FIG. 6-30.

Two integrations are necessary — one from 0 to 6 for the right half of the beam, and the other from 4 to 6 for the left half. This is true because x, which replaces b, must be the length of the smaller segment into which P divides the beam.

If the given loading is divided into halves, and each half is replaced by its resultant of 240 lb acting as shown in Fig. 6-31, the sum of the midspan deflections of

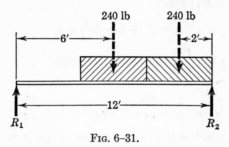

FIG. 6-31.

these loads will be a good approximation of the actual midspan deflection. Applying the result for case 7 gives

$$EIy = \frac{240(6)}{48} [3(144) - 4(36)] + \frac{240(2)}{48} [3(144) - 4(4)] = 12{,}800 \text{ lb-ft}^3$$

A closer approximation could be obtained by subdividing the given loading into three or more parts. However, even with only two subdivisions, the result is only about 5% larger than the correct value, 12,200 lb-ft.[3]

658. The overhanging beam in Fig. 6-32 carries a concentrated load P at its end. Determine the deflection under P.

Solution: The tangent to the elastic curve at R_2 is inclined at a small angle θ with the horizontal, but the figure shows it greatly exaggerated for convenience in representation. Imagine the original position of the beam to coincide with this tangent and to be clamped in this inclined position at R_2. Application of the loads

R_1 and P will produce the actual elastic curve. The deflections δ_1 and δ_2 produced by these loads are similar to those in case 1.

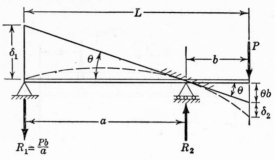

FIG. 6–32.

From the geometry of the elastic curve, we have

$$\delta_1 = \theta a; \qquad \text{hence } \theta = \frac{\delta_1}{a}$$

Therefore the deflection at P is

$$y = \theta b + \delta_2 = \delta_1 \frac{b}{a} + \delta_2$$

whence, substituting $\delta = \dfrac{PL^3}{3 EI}$ from case 1, we obtain

$$y = \frac{\dfrac{Pb}{a}(a^3)}{3 EI} \cdot \frac{b}{a} + \frac{Pb^3}{3 EI} = \frac{Pb^2}{3 EI}[a + b] = \frac{Pb^2 L}{3 EI} \quad Ans.$$

Actually δ_1 and δ_2 are deviations from a tangent drawn at R_2, and this procedure duplicates that described in Illus. Prob. 649. The difference is that here we used a formula from Table VI–2 instead of computing deviations by using a moment diagram.

Alternate Solution: The rotation of the beam at the support R_2 may also be found by dividing the beam in Fig. 6–32 into the two parts shown in Fig. 6–33. The action of the overhang upon the portion between the supports is replaced by a shear force P and a moment $M = Pb$. The shear force is transmitted directly to the reaction R_2, whence the couple produces the effect of case 11. The rotation of the beam at R_2 is given by $\theta = \dfrac{ML}{3 EI} = \dfrac{(Pb)a}{3 EI}$.

The deflection at the end of the overhang may now be found as for a cantilever beam (case 1) built in with an initial inclination θ. The total deflection is

$$y = \theta b + \delta_2 = \frac{Pba}{3 EI} \cdot b + \frac{Pb^3}{3 EI}$$

which, as before, reduces to

$$y = \frac{Pb^2}{3\,EI}\,(a + b) = \frac{Pb^2L}{3\,EI}$$

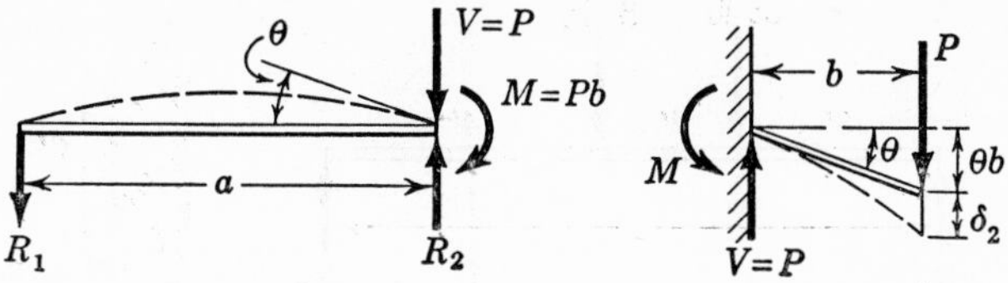

FIG. 6–33.

The deflection equation for any point between the supports, as found from case 11, is

$$y = \frac{Pbax}{6\,EI}\left(1 - \frac{x^2}{a^2}\right)$$

and, in terms of x measured from R_2, the deflection equation for the overhanging portion is

$$y = \frac{Pba}{3\,EI}\,x + \frac{Px^2}{6\,EI}\,(3\,b - x)$$

659. Two cantilever beams, having the same cross-section and made of the same material, jointly support a distributed load of w lb/ft, as shown in Fig. 6–34. Determine the pressure P at the roller between them.

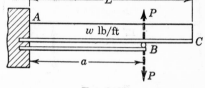

FIG. 6–34.

Solution: The pressure P may be determined by the condition that at B both cantilevers have the same deflection. The deflection at B for the lower cantilever is found from case 1 to be

$$y = \frac{Pa^3}{3\,EI}$$

The upper cantilever is loaded with a combination of cases 3 and 2, the resultant deflection at B being

$$y = \frac{wa^2}{24\,EI}\,(6\,L^2 + a^2 - 4\,La) - \frac{Pa^3}{3\,EI}$$

Equating these deflections gives, for P,

$$P = \frac{w}{16a}\,(6\,L^2 + a^2 - 4\,La)$$

PROBLEMS

In solving the following problems, use Table VI–2.

660. Determine the proper depth of the beam to support the given loads without exceeding a midspan deflection of 0.01 in. or a flexural stress of 1000 psi. Assume $E = 1.5 \times 10^6$ psi. $Ans.$ $d = 9.57$ in.

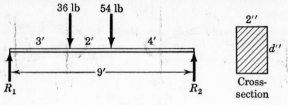

PROB. 660.

661. For the beam described in Prob. 647 (page 204), divide the distributed load into three equal parts, and replace each part by its resultant of 48 lb. Compute the midspan deflection of these three concentrated loads and compare with the answer to Prob. 647.

662. Solve Prob. 622 (page 191) by the method of superposition.

663. Solve Prob. 623 (page 192) by the method of superposition.

664. Use the method of superposition to solve the cantilever loading in Prob. 631 (page 197).

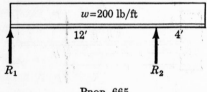

PROB. 665.

665. For the given overhanging beam, determine the value of $EI\delta$ (a) at the overhanging end, and (b) midway between the supports.

$Ans.$ (a) $EI\delta = 25,600$ lb-ft³ up

666. A 24-ft beam, simply supported at 4 ft from each end, carries a uniformly distributed load of 72 lb/ft over its entire length. Compute the value of $EI\delta$ at the middle and at the ends.

$Ans.$ At center, $EI\delta = 43,000$ lb-ft³ down; at ends, $EI\delta = 28,400$ lb-ft³ up

667. Two timber beams, each 3 in. wide by 6 in. high, are mounted at right angles and in contact with each other at their midpoints. The upper beam A is

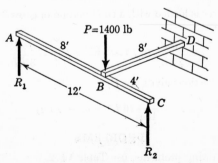

PROB. 668.

simply supported on an 8-ft span; the lower beam B is simply supported on a 10-ft span. At their cross-over point, they jointly support a load $P = 1300$ lb. Determine the load carried by each beam, and the maximum flexure stress developed in the assembly.

668. A cantilever beam BD rests on a simple beam AC, as shown. Both beams are of the same material and cross-section. If they jointly carry a load $P = 1400$ lb, compute the load supported by each beam.

$Ans.$ $P_{AC} = 1200$ lb; $P_{BD} = 200$ lb

SUMMARY

Starting with the relation $\dfrac{1}{\rho} = \dfrac{M}{EI}$ developed in Art. 5–2, two separate methods of determining slopes and deflections are discussed. The first one, the double-integration method, is primarily mathematical. Before the deflection at a particular point can be found, complete slope and deflection equations must be determined; sometimes extensive computation is required to evaluate the constants of integration. When used for cases in which the slope and deflection are known initially to be zero, as at a perfectly fixed end, the double-integration method provides a simple way of determining the slope and deflection equations.

The area-moment method is generally more direct than the double-integration method, especially when the deflection at a particular position is desired. Depending as it does upon the geometry of the elastic curve, it emphasizes the physical significance of the computations. The two basic theorems of the area-moment method, developed in Art. 6–3, are summarized by

$$\theta_{AB} = \frac{1}{EI}(\text{Area})_{AB} \tag{6–4}$$

and

$$t_{B/A} = \frac{1}{EI}(\text{Area})_{BA} \cdot \bar{x}_B \tag{6–5}$$

The tangential deviation at any point is positive if that point lies above the reference tangent from which the deviation is measured; the converse is true for negative deviation. A positive value for the change in slope means that the tangent at the right point is rotated in a counterclockwise direction relative to the tangent at the left point.

The use of the area-moment theorems requires that the area and the moment of area of bending-moment diagrams be readily calculated. Therefore, beginning in Art. 6–4, and discussed more fully in succeeding articles, there is developed a method of drawing moment diagrams by parts (i.e., in terms of equivalent cantilever loadings), which is equivalent to, and replaces, the conventional moment diagram.

Deflections in cantilever beams (Arts. 6–5 and 6–6) are determined from the fact that the deflection at any point is equal to the deviation of that point from a reference tangent drawn at the fixed end.

The deflections in simple and overhanging beams are determined by using a reference tangent to the elastic curve drawn at one reaction. The complete procedure is outlined in the four steps on page 198.

The conjugate-beam method (Art. 6–9) shows how the definitions of shear and moment may be applied to a fictitious loading (in terms of the $\frac{M}{EI}$ diagram of the original loading) to determine the slope and deflection at any point.

When beam loadings are combinations of the types listed in Table VI–2, deflections and slopes are obtained most easily by superposing the results listed there. See Art. 6–10 for further details.

Chapter VII

Restrained Beams

7-1. Introduction

Our study of simple stresses and torsion has shown that statically indeterminate problems require relations between the elastic deformations in addition to the equations of static equilibrium. Similarly, for our present study of indeterminate beams, additional relations must be found from the geometry of the elastic curves of the beams. Such relations are obtained from our study of the deflections in statically determinate beams.

Two techniques are discussed: (1) the method of superposition, which uses the general solutions in Table VI–2, and (2) the area-moment method, which deals directly with the shape of the elastic curve. As we shall see, sometimes the deflection at a particular position is required, sometimes a relation between the slopes at two positions, sometimes a combination of these concepts.

7-2. Propped Beams

A cantilever beam is supported by two reactive elements, the shear V and the moment M at the wall, as shown in Fig. 7-1. Since these values

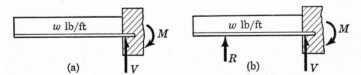

Fig. 7-1. — Determinate and indeterminate beams.

are readily computed from $\Sigma Y = 0$ and $\Sigma M = 0$, the cantilever beam is statically determinate. Propping up the beam at some other position, as in Fig. 7–1b, introduces an additional reaction, but does not increase the equations of static equilibrium, so the beam has one redundant support.

In other words, if any arbitrary value is assumed for R, values of V and M may be computed that will satisfy the equations of static equilibrium. Determination of the correct combination of R, V, and M therefore requires a condition in addition to those found from static equilibrium. Usually the most convenient condition is that the deflection under R is either zero

221

or some known value. Another condition sometimes used, generally in the method of superposition, is that the slope at the wall is zero.

ILLUSTRATIVE PROBLEMS

701. Fig. 7–2 shows a cantilever beam carrying a uniformly distributed load of w lb per ft. The beam is propped up at the free end by an unyielding support. Compute the reactions, and sketch the shear and moment diagrams.

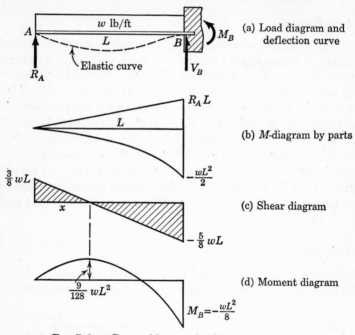

(a) Load diagram and deflection curve

(b) M-diagram by parts

(c) Shear diagram

(d) Moment diagram

Fig. 7–2. — Propped beam solved by area-moment.

Solution: The wall is assumed to provide absolute resistance to rotation of the beam, so that at B (Fig. 7–2a) a tangent to the elastic curve is horizontal and passes through A. Therefore, the deviation of A from the tangent at B is zero. Expressing this in terms of the moment diagram by parts shown in Fig. 7–2b, we obtain

$$[EIt_{A/B} = (\text{Area})_{AB} \cdot \bar{x}_A = 0] \qquad \frac{(L)(R_A L)}{2}\left(\frac{2}{3}L\right) - \frac{(L)}{3}\left(\frac{wL^2}{2}\right)\left(\frac{3}{4}L\right) = 0$$

or

$$R_A = \tfrac{3}{8}\,wL$$

A vertical summation of forces determines V at the wall.

$$[\Sigma Y = 0] \qquad\qquad R_A + V - wL = 0$$

whence, substituting the value of R_A, we obtain

$$V = wL - \tfrac{3}{8}\,wL = \tfrac{5}{8}\,wL$$

From the definition of bending moment at B, which is equivalent to $\Sigma M_B = 0$ but simpler to apply, we obtain

$$[M = (\Sigma M)_L] \qquad M_B = R_A L - \frac{wL^2}{2} = \left(\frac{3}{8} wL\right)(L) - \frac{wL^2}{2} \qquad M_B = -\frac{wL^2}{8}$$

The shear diagram being drawn as in Fig. 7–2c, the location of zero shear is determined from

$$[V = (\Sigma Y)_L = 0] \qquad \frac{3}{8} wL - wx = 0 \qquad x = \frac{3}{8} L$$

whence the maximum positive moment is

$$[\Delta M = (\text{Area})_V] \qquad M = \frac{1}{2}(\frac{3}{8} wL)(\frac{3}{8} L) = \frac{9}{128} wL^2$$

The moment diagram in Fig. 7–2d shows that the most dangerous moment is at the wall.

702. Using the method of superposition, solve for the reactive elements of the propped beam in Fig. 7–3a by two methods: (1) First consider R_B the redundant support; (2) consider M_C the redundant constraint.

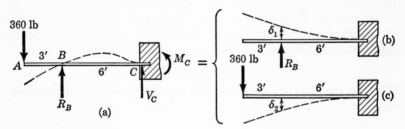

Fig. 7–3. — Propped beam solved by superposition.

Solution: Method I. The given beam may be duplicated by superposing the loadings shown in Fig. 7–3b and 7–3c, so that the deflection at B is zero; i.e., $\delta_1 = \delta_2$. Applying the results of case 1 in Table VI–2, we have

$$\frac{R_B(6)^3}{3 EI} = \frac{360(6)^2}{6 EI} [(3)(9) - 6]$$

from which

$$R_B = 630 \text{ lb}$$

From the definition of bending moment, the moment at C is

$$[M = (\Sigma M)_L] \qquad M_C = 630(6) - 360(9) = 540 \text{ ft-lb}$$

Method II. By removing the constraint M_C, the simple beam loading in Fig. 7–4a is obtained. By superposing on this the bending produced in Fig. 7–4b, the original loading will be obtained, provided that $\theta_2' + \theta_2'' = 0$.

The action between the supports in Fig. 7–4a is the same as that in case 12, Table VI–2, in which the overhanging load is replaced by a couple $M = -(360)(3)$ ft-lb. The loading in Fig. 7–4b is that in case 11, Table VI–2. Hence

$[\theta_2' + \theta_2'' = 0]$

$$\frac{-(360 \times 3)(6)}{6\,EI} + \frac{M_C(6)}{3\,EI} = 0$$

from which, as before,

$$M_C = 540 \text{ ft-lb}$$

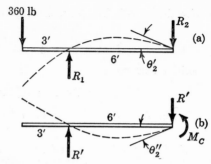

FIG. 7–4. — Alternate combination of Fig. 7–3(a).

From statics, we find that $R_1 = 540$ lb and $R' = 90$ lb. From this, since $R_B = R_1 + R'$, we obtain $R_B = 630$ lb, which agrees with the value previously obtained.

The resultant deflection at any point is obtained by combining the deflections at that point caused by the separate loadings.

PROBLEMS

703. For the propped beam shown, find R and draw the shear and moment diagrams.

$$Ans. \quad R = \frac{wb^3}{8\,L^3}(4\,L - b)$$

704. Determine the reaction R and sketch the shear and moment diagrams for the given propped beam. $Ans. \quad R = 28.5$ kips

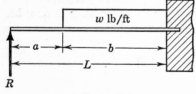

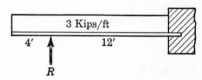

PROB. 703.   PROB. 704.

705. For the propped beam shown, compute the values of midspan $EI\delta$ and the maximum $EI\delta$.

$$Ans. \quad \text{Midspan } EI\delta = \frac{wL^4}{192}; \text{max. } EI\delta = \frac{wL^4}{185}$$

706. Compute the reaction R and sketch shear and moment diagrams for the propped beam shown.

$$Ans. \quad R = \frac{wL}{10}$$

707. For the propped beam shown, determine the reaction R and sketch the shear and moment diagrams.

708. The propped beam shown is 3 in. wide by 8 in. high. Determine the maximum safe value of P without exceeding a flexural stress of 1000 psi or a shearing stress of 120 psi. If $E = 1.5 \times 10^6$ psi, what deflection does this load cause at P?

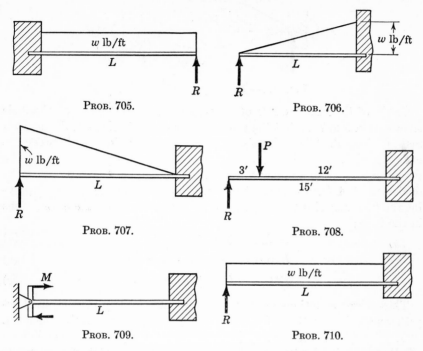

PROB. 705.   PROB. 706.

PROB. 707.   PROB. 708.

PROB. 709.   PROB. 710.

709. A couple M is applied at the propped end of the beam shown. Compute R at the propped end, and the wall moment.

$$Ans.\quad R = \frac{3\,M}{2\,L}$$

710. The beam shown is only partially restrained at the wall, so that, after the uniformly distributed load is applied, the slope there is $\dfrac{wL^3}{72\,EI}$ upward to the right. If the supports remain at the same level, determine R.

711. In Prob. 710, compute R if, in addition to the given conditions, R settles $\frac{1}{4}$ in. Assume a timber beam 2 in. wide by 6 in. high and 12 ft long, for which $E = 1.5 \times 10^6$ psi. $Ans.\quad R = 5w - 13.58$

7–3. Restrained Beams. General Loading

A beam restrained at both ends, as in Fig. 7–5, has four reactive elements. Unless otherwise specified, it will be assumed that the supports are at the same level. Because only two equations of static equilibrium are available, namely, $\Sigma Y = 0$ and $\Sigma M = 0$, the beam has two redundant supports. It is usually best to consider that the redundant supports are the shear and moment at the same wall, i.e., V_A and M_A; but sometimes, as discussed in Art. 7–5, the two end moments are taken as the redundancies.

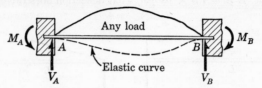

FIG. 7–5. — Perfectly restrained beam.

Study of the elastic curve of a beam perfectly restrained at the ends shows, as in Fig. 7–5, that the tangents to the elastic curve at the ends remain horizontal. Therefore, since there is no change in slope between the ends, $\theta_{AB} = 0$. In addition, if the ends A and B are at the same level, the deviation at B from a tangent drawn at A is zero; i.e. $t_{B/A} = 0$. Also, the deviation at A from a tangent drawn at B is zero, or $t_{A/B} = 0$. Applying the theorems of the area-moment method, we may put these conditions in the form:

$$EI\theta_{AB} = (\text{Area})_{AB} = 0 \qquad (a)$$

$$EIt_{B/A} = (\text{Area})_{BA} \cdot \bar{x}_B = 0 \qquad (b)$$

$$EIt_{A/B} = (\text{Area})_{AB} \cdot \bar{x}_A = 0 \qquad (c)$$

These three equations are not independent; any two may be used together with the equations of statics to determine the four reactive elements. As a rule, it is best to use Eq. (a) and either Eq. (b) or (c), depending on whether it is simpler to compute the moment of area of a particular moment diagram about the right or the left end. Which to choose will be apparent in the following illustrative problem.

ILLUSTRATIVE PROBLEMS

712. A beam 12 ft long and perfectly restrained at the ends carries a uniformly distributed load over part of its length, as shown in Fig. 7–6a. Compute the end shears and end moments.

Solution: We begin by drawing the moment diagram by parts from left to right, as in Fig. 7–6b. The moment at A is shown acting in a positive or clockwise direction, whereas we know from the downward curvature of the elastic curve that this moment is actually negative or counterclockwise. By making this deliberate error in the direction of the vector quantity M_A, our solution will determine not only the correct numerical value of M_A but also its correct negative sign.

The elastic curve in Fig. 7–6a shows that the change in slope between tangents drawn at A and B is zero. Applying the first theorem of area-moment, we obtain

$$[EI\theta_{AB} = (\text{Area})_{AB} = 0] \qquad \frac{12(12\,V_A)}{2} + 12\,M_A - \frac{9(2430)}{3} = 0 \qquad (a)$$

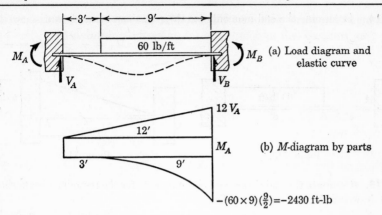

FIG. 7–6. — Restrained beam.

The deviation of B from a tangent drawn at A being zero, we obtain from the second theorem of area-moment:

$$[EIt_{B/A} = (\text{Area})_{BA} \cdot \bar{x}_B = 0]$$

$$\frac{12(12\,V_A)}{2}\left(\frac{12}{3}\right) + 12\,M_A\left(\frac{12}{2}\right) - \frac{9(2430)}{3}\left(\frac{9}{4}\right) = 0 \qquad (b)$$

Solving Eqs. (a) and (b) simultaneously yields

$$V_A = 190 \text{ lb} \quad \text{and} \quad M_A = -531 \text{ ft-lb} \quad Ans.$$

The negative sign for M_A indicates that the direction of M_A was incorrectly assumed. It actually is a negative moment, and there should now be no confusion as to sign in its subsequent use.

The deviation at A from a tangent drawn at B is also zero, so that we could have used $EIt_{A/B} = (\text{Area})_{AB} \cdot \bar{x}_A = 0$. A glance at the moment diagram (Fig. 7–6b) shows that it is simpler in this problem to take moments of area about B rather than about A. For this reason, we used $EIt_{B/A} = 0$ rather than $EIt_{A/B} = 0$.

A vertical summation of forces determines V_B.

$$[\Sigma Y = 0] \qquad V_B + 190 - 540 = 0 \qquad V_B = 350 \text{ lb} \qquad Ans.$$

We can now determine M_B from the condition $\Sigma M_B = 0$, but a simpler method is to apply the definition of bending moment:

$$[M = (\Sigma M)_L] \qquad M_B = 12\,V_A + M_A - 2430$$

$$= 12(190) - 531 - 2430 = -681 \text{ ft-lb} \quad Ans.$$

PROBLEMS

713. For the restrained beam shown, compute the end shears and end moments and sketch the shear and moment diagrams.

$$Ans. \quad V_A = 142.3 \text{ lb}; \quad M_A = -427 \text{ ft-lb}$$

714. Determine the end moments for the restrained beam shown.

$$Ans. \quad M_A = -\frac{wL^2}{30}; \; M_B = -\frac{wL^2}{20}$$

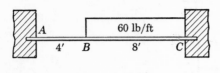

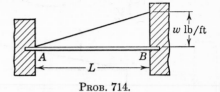

PROB. 713.   PROB. 714.

715. Compute the end shears and end moments for the restrained beam shown, and draw the shear and moment diagrams.

$$Ans. \quad V_A = 69.4 \text{ lb}; \; M_A = -208 \text{ ft-lb}$$

716. Solve for the end moments in the restrained beam shown.

$$Ans. \quad M_A = -\frac{Pab^2}{L^2}; \; M_C = -\frac{Pa^2b}{L^2}$$

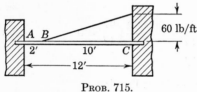

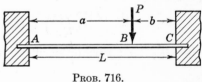

PROB. 715.   PROB. 716.

717. For the restrained beam shown, solve for the end shears and end moments and draw the shear and moment diagrams.

718. In the perfectly restrained beam shown, support B has settled a distance Δ below support A. Show that $M_B = -M_A = \dfrac{6\,EI\Delta}{L^2}$. If the beam is of timber 8 in. wide by 12 in. high, E being 1.5×10^6 psi, what maximum settlement Δ is permissible in a length $L = 12$ ft without exceeding a flexural stress of 1200 psi?

$$Ans. \quad \Delta = 0.46 \text{ in.}$$

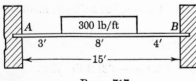

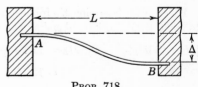

PROB. 717.   PROB. 718.

719. The beam shown is perfectly restrained at A but only partially restrained at B, where the slope is $\dfrac{wL^3}{72\,EI}$ directed up to the right. Solve for the end moments.

720. The restrained beam shown is loaded by a couple M applied where shown. Determine the end moments.

$$Ans. \quad M_A = \frac{Mb}{L}\left(\frac{3\,a}{L} - 1\right); M_B = -\frac{Ma}{L}\left(\frac{3\,b}{L} - 1\right)$$

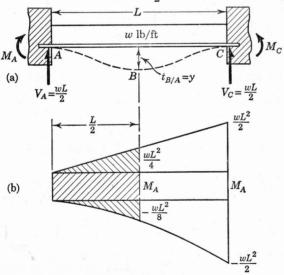

PROB. 719.   PROB. 720.

7–4. Restrained Beams. Symmetrical Loading

Because of symmetry, the end shears are equal to each other, and each equals one-half the applied loads. The end moments also equal each other but are unknown. The simplest method to determine the unknown end moment is to use the principle that, in a symmetrical beam, the tangent to the elastic curve at midspan is horizontal, and therefore the change in slope is zero between this tangent and a tangent drawn at one end.

ILLUSTRATIVE PROBLEM

721. Compute the end moment and maximum deflection for the beam shown in Fig. 7–7a.

Solution: Because of symmetry, $V_A = \dfrac{wL}{2}$. The moment diagram by parts is

FIG. 7–7. — Symmetrical loading.

drawn as in Fig. 7–7*b*. Since the tangent at the midpoint *B* is parallel to the tangent at *A*,

$$[EI\theta_{AB} = (\text{Area})_{AB} = 0] \qquad \frac{1}{2}\left(\frac{wL^2}{4}\right)\left(\frac{L}{2}\right) + M_A\left(\frac{L}{2}\right) - \frac{1}{3}\left(\frac{wL^2}{8}\right)\left(\frac{L}{2}\right) = 0$$

Dividing by $\dfrac{L}{2}$, we obtain

$$M_A = -\frac{wL^2}{8} + \frac{wL^2}{24} = -\frac{wL^2}{12} \quad Ans.$$

The maximum deflection occurs at midspan and is numerically equal to the deviation of *B* from a tangent at *A*.

$$[EIt_{B/A} = (\text{Area})_{BA} \cdot \bar{x}_B]$$

$$EIy = \frac{1}{2}\left(\frac{wL^2}{4}\right)\left(\frac{L}{2}\right)\left(\frac{1}{3}\cdot\frac{L}{2}\right) - \left(\frac{wL^2}{12}\right)\left(\frac{L}{2}\right)\left(\frac{1}{2}\cdot\frac{L}{2}\right) - \frac{1}{3}\left(\frac{wL^2}{8}\right)\left(\frac{L}{2}\right)\left(\frac{1}{4}\cdot\frac{L}{2}\right)$$

from which

$$EIy = -\frac{wL^4}{384} = -\frac{WL^3}{384} \quad Ans.$$

The minus sign indicates that the deflection *y* is directed downward as shown.

PROBLEMS

722. Determine the end moment and midspan value of $EI\delta$ for the restrained beam shown.

$$Ans. \quad M = -\frac{5\,PL}{16}; EI\delta = \frac{PL^3}{96}$$

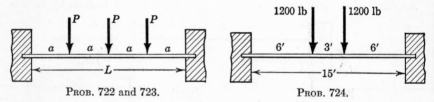

Prob. 722 and 723.   Prob. 724.

723. In Prob. 722, select the lightest WF beam that will limit the midspan deflection to $\frac{1}{360}$ of the span if $P = 3000$ lb, $L = 24$ ft, and $E = 30 \times 10^6$ psi.

724. Compute the dimensions of a timber beam that will support the loads shown, if the width is to be one-half the depth and the allowable flexure stress is 1000 psi.

725. For the restrained beam shown, compute the end moment and maximum $EI\delta$.

$$Ans. \quad M = -2640 \text{ ft-lb}$$

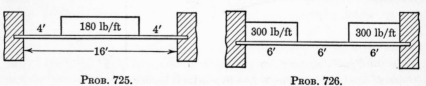

Prob. 725.   Prob. 726.

726. Determine the end moments for the loading shown.

727. A partially restrained beam L ft long carries a uniformly distributed load of w lb/ft over its entire length. The slope at the left end is $\dfrac{wL^3}{48\,EI}$ directed up to the left, whereas at the right end the slope is $\dfrac{wL^3}{48\,EI}$ up to the right. Determine the end moments.

7–5. Restrained Beam Equivalent to Simple Beam with End Moments

Usually the redundant elements in a restrained beam are most easily determined by the method in Art. 7–3, which considers the redundant supports to be the shear and moment at one wall. However, it is sometimes desirable to treat the end moments as the redundant supports. To do this, the restrained beam is considered equivalent to a simple beam acted on not only by the given loading but also by end moments sufficient to rotate the ends of the beam until the slopes at the ends correspond to the slopes at the ends of the restrained beam. Thus the restrained beam in Fig. 7–8a may be considered equivalent to superposing the loadings in Figs. 7–8b and 7–8c.

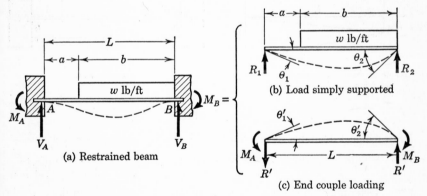

Fig. 7–8. — Restrained beam resolved into simple beam loadings.

It is evident that the unsymmetrical loading in Fig. 7–8b causes a greater slope θ_2 at the right end than the slope θ_1 at the left end. To cancel these end slopes by adding the loading in Fig. 7–8c, we must have $\theta_1 = \theta_1'$ and $\theta_2 = \theta_2'$, which requires that M_B be greater than M_A in order for θ_2' to be greater than θ_1'. In other words, the larger end moment acts at the wall that is closer to the resultant of any single load.

The difference between the end moments M_B and M_A is balanced by the couple $R'L$, consisting of the forces R' applied at the ends of the beam in

Fig. 7–8c. By superposing the reactions in Figs. 7–8b and 7–8c, we obtain $V_A = R_1 - R'$ and $V_B = R_2 + R'$. If the loading were symmetrical, the end slopes θ_1 and θ_2 would be equal, which would require equal end moments M_A and M_B. In this case, there would be no couple reaction R', so the end shears would equal the end reactions of a similarly loaded simple beam. This conclusion agrees with the observation in Art. 7–4 on symmetrical loading.

To consider the end moments as the redundant supports, therefore, the moment diagram by parts for the beam in Fig. 7–8a will be drawn to correspond to the loadings in Figs. 7–8b and 7–8c, and will appear as in Figs. 7–9a and 7–9b. Applying $EI\theta_{AB} = 0$ and $EIt_{B/A} = 0$, we can solve directly for M_A and M_B as the redundant supports, whence V_A and V_B are obtained by applying the equations of static equilibrium. This procedure is not generally as simple as treating the shear and moment at one end as the redundants.

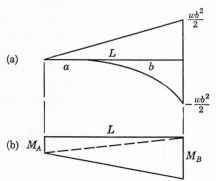

(a)

(b) M_A

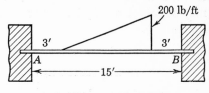

FIG. 7–9. — Moment diagrams for beams of Figs. 7–8(b) and 7–8(c).

PROB. 731.

PROBLEMS

Draw moment diagrams, as described in this article, to solve these problems.

729. Compute the end moments in the beam described in Prob. 713 (page 227).

Ans. $M_A = -427$ ft-lb

730. Determine the moment at the restrained end for the beam described in Prob. 706 (page 224).

Ans. $M = -\dfrac{wL^2}{15}$

731. Determine the end moments for the perfectly restrained beam shown.

Ans. $M_B = -1755$ ft-lb

7–6. Deflections in Restrained Beams

Deflections may be computed by either the area-moment method or the double-integration method. The fact that the tangent to the elastic curve at both walls remains horizontal makes either method simple to apply, although sometimes one is more convenient than the other. Both, however, require that the end shears and end moments first be determined, which is accomplished more easily by the area-moment method than by double-integration. The use of each method is shown by examples.

ILLUSTRATIVE PROBLEMS

732. Determine the deflection equation for portion BC of the restrained beam in Fig. 7–10a. This is the same beam for which the end shears and end moments were computed in Prob. 712.

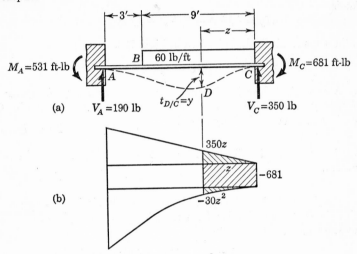

Fig. 7–10. — Deflection by area moment.

Solution: Since the tangent to the elastic curve at C is horizontal, the deviation $t_{D/C}$ at D is numerically equal to the deflection y at D. Therefore

$$[EIt_{D/C} = (\text{Area})_{DC} \cdot \bar{x}_D] \quad EIy = \frac{(350\,z)(z)}{2}\left(\frac{z}{3}\right) - (681)(z)\left(\frac{z}{2}\right) - \frac{(30\,z^2)(z)}{3}\left(\frac{z}{4}\right)$$

or

$$EIy = \tfrac{350}{6} z^3 - \tfrac{681}{2} z^2 - \tfrac{10}{4} z^4 \quad Ans.$$

The deflection at a specific value of z can be found by substituting this value of z in the general deflection equation. However, if the deflection at a particular position is desired, it is usually better to apply the procedure outlined using the numerical value of z rather than a general value.

733. Solve Prob. 732, using the double-integration method.

Solution: Applying the differential equation of the elastic curve to portion CB, we have

$$EI \frac{d^2y}{dz^2} = M = (\Sigma M)_R = 350\,z - 681 - 30\,z^2$$

Integrating to obtain the slope equation gives

$$EI \frac{dy}{dz} = \frac{350}{2} z^2 - 681 z - 10 z^3 + C_1$$

Since the slope is zero at $z = 0$, we find that $C_1 = 0$. Another integration now gives the deflection equation.

$$EIy = \tfrac{3 5 0}{6} z^3 - \tfrac{6 8 1}{2} z^2 - \tfrac{1 0}{4} z^4 + C_2$$

Since the deflection is zero at $z = 0$, we have $C_2 = 0$; hence the final deflection equation is

$$EIy = \tfrac{3 5 0}{6} z^3 - \tfrac{6 8 1}{2} z^2 - \tfrac{1 0}{4} z^4$$

This is the same result as that obtained in Prob. 732.

PROBLEMS

734. A concentrated load P is applied at the center of a perfectly restrained beam L ft long. Determine the maximum deflection and compare it with the deflection of a simple beam similarly loaded.

$$Ans. \quad \delta = \frac{PL^3}{192 \, EI}$$

735. For the beam described in Prob. 714 (page 228), compute the midspan value of $EI\delta$.

$$Ans. \quad EI\delta = \frac{wL^4}{768}$$

736. Starting with the values of end moments found in Prob. 716 (page 228), determine the midspan deflection for a restrained beam carrying a concentrated load anywhere on a span of length L.

$$Ans. \quad \delta = \frac{Pb^2}{48 \, EI} (3 \, L - 4 \, b); \text{ result is valid only for } a \geqq b$$

737. Determine the midspan value of $EI\delta$ for the beam described in Prob. 715 (page 228).

738. Compute the midspan value of $EI\delta$ for the beam described in Prob. 719 (page 228). Note that $V_A = \tfrac{7}{12} wL$ and $M_A = -wL^2/9$.

739. Determine the deflection equation for the beam described in Prob. 718 (page 228). Note that $V_A = 12EI\Delta/L^3$.

7–7. Method of Superposition

By applying the methods described in preceding articles, general values for end moments and deflections may be determined for perfectly restrained beams that carry various general loadings. These values are tabulated in Table VII–1. These general values can be superposed to solve restrained beams supporting various combinations of loads.

ILLUSTRATIVE PROBLEMS

740. Determine the section modulus required for a beam to support the loads shown in Fig. 7–11, without exceeding a flexure stress of 12,000 psi.

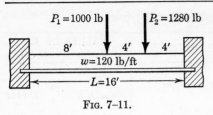

$P_1 = 1000$ lb $P_2 = 1280$ lb

8'   4'   4'

$w = 120$ lb/ft

$L = 16'$

Fig. 7-11.

Solution: The end moments due to the distributed load and the central load P_1 are equal because of symmetry. As discussed in Art. 7-5, the eccentric load P_2 causes a larger end moment at the nearer wall — the right wall, in this case. From Table VII-1, the maximum bending moment occurring at the right end is given by

$$\text{Max. } M = -\frac{wL^2}{12} - \frac{P_1 L}{8} - \frac{P_2 a^2 b}{L^2}$$

$$= -\frac{120(16)^2}{12} - \frac{1000(16)}{8} - \frac{1280(12)^2(4)}{(16)^2}$$

$$\text{Max. } M = -7440 \text{ ft-lb}$$

The negative sign of moment indicates a tensile stress at the top fibers. In an unsymmetrical section like a T beam, this would be important; but in a symmetrical section, only the numerical value of moment need be used. From the flexure formula, the section modulus required is therefore

$$\left[Z = \frac{M}{S} \right] \qquad Z = \frac{7440(12)}{12,000} = 7.44 \text{ in.}^3 \quad Ans.$$

A suitable WF shape to support these loads is a 8 B 10 beam; its section modulus of 7.8 in.³ is ample to include the additional stress resulting from the dead weight of the beam.

741. Select a suitable wide-flange beam to support the loads shown in Fig. 7-12 without exceeding a flexural stress of 18,000 psi. Compute the midspan deflection of this beam. $E = 30,000,000$ psi.

Solution: The end at which the maximum moment occurs is not evident, and computations for moments at each end must therefore be made. At the left end, we obtain

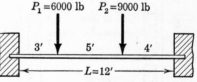

$P_1 = 6000$ lb $P_2 = 9000$ lb

3'   5'   4'

$L = 12'$

Fig. 7-12.

$$M_L = -\frac{P_1 ab^2}{L^2} - \frac{P_2 ab^2}{L^2}$$

$$= -\frac{6000(3)(9)^2}{(12)^2} - \frac{9000(8)(4)^2}{(12)^2} = -18,120 \text{ ft-lb}$$

At the right end, the moment is

$$M_R = -\frac{P_1 a^2 b}{L^2} - \frac{P_2 a^2 b}{L^2}$$

$$= -\frac{6000(3)^2(9)}{(12)^2} - \frac{9000(8)^2(4)}{(12)^2} = -19,340 \text{ ft-lb}$$

TABLE VII–1. Restrained Beam Loadings.

CASE NO.	TYPE OF LOAD	END MOMENTS	VALUES OF EIy (y is positive downward)
1		$M_A = -\dfrac{Pab^2}{L^2}$ $M_B = -\dfrac{Pa^2b}{L^2}$	Midspan $EIy = \dfrac{Pb^2}{48}(3L - 4b)$ Note: only for $a > b$
2		$M_A = M_B = -\dfrac{PL}{8}$	Max. $EIy = \dfrac{PL^3}{192}$
3		$M_A = M_B = -\dfrac{wL^2}{12} = -\dfrac{WL}{12}$	Max. $EIy = \dfrac{wL^4}{384} = \dfrac{WL^3}{384}$
4		$M_A = -\dfrac{5}{192}wL^2 = -\dfrac{5}{96}WL$ $M_B = -\dfrac{11}{192}wL^2 = -\dfrac{11}{96}WL$	Midspan $EIy = \dfrac{wL^4}{768} = \dfrac{WL^3}{384}$
5		$M_A = -\dfrac{wL^2}{30} = -\dfrac{WL}{15}$ $M_B = -\dfrac{wL^2}{20} = -\dfrac{WL}{10}$	Midspan $EIy = \dfrac{wL^4}{768} = \dfrac{WL^3}{384}$
6		$M_A = M_B = -\dfrac{5wL^2}{96} = -\dfrac{5WL}{48}$	Max. $EIy = \dfrac{7wL^4}{3840} = \dfrac{7WL}{1920}$
7		$M_A = \dfrac{Mb}{L}\left(\dfrac{3a}{L} - 1\right)$ $M_B = -\dfrac{Ma}{L}\left(\dfrac{3b}{L} - 1\right)$	
8		$M_A = -\dfrac{6EI\Delta}{L^2}$ $M_B = \dfrac{6EI\Delta}{L^2}$	

Substituting the larger numerical value of end moment in the flexure formula, we find that the required section modulus for live loads is

$$\left[Z = \frac{M}{S} \right] \qquad\qquad Z = \frac{19,340(12)}{18,000} = 12.9 \text{ in.}^3$$

A suitable beam is an 8 WF 17 with $Z = 14.1$ in.^{3} and $I = 56.4$ in.^{4} Table VII–1 gives the midspan deflection,[1] including the dead weight of the beam, as

$$EIy = \sum \frac{Pb^2}{48}(3\,L - 4\,b) + \frac{wL^4}{384}$$

$$EIy = \frac{6000(3)^2}{48}[3(12) - 4(3)] + \frac{9000(4)^2}{48}[3(12) - 4(4)] + \frac{17(12)^4}{384}$$

$$EIy = 27,000 + 60,000 + 918 = 87,918 \text{ lb-ft}^3$$

Substituting numerical values for E and I, we then convert the right-hand side to inches by multiplying by 1728:

$$(30 \times 10^6)(56.4)(y) = 87,918(1728)$$

from which

$$y = 0.0896 \text{ in.} \quad Ans.$$

742. Compute the maximum end moment for the beam shown in Fig. 7–13a.

Solution: This loading was selected as a combination of the loading specified in Prob. 741 and *ten times* that specified in Prob. 712. The simplest solution is obtained by applying the formulas in Table VII–1 to loads P_1 and P_2, and applying

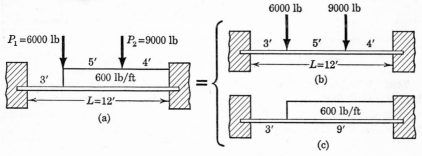

Fig. 7–13.

the area-moment method to the distributed load. Combining by superposition the values computed in Probs. 712 and 741 gives the maximum moment occurring at the right end:

$$M_R = -6810 - 19,340 = -26,150 \text{ ft-lb}$$

If required, the midspan deflection is similarly computed by applying the area-moment method to the partially distributed load, and the formulas in Table VII–1 to the concentrated loads P_1 and P_2.

[1] In computing midspan deflection for a concentrated load, the term b is the smaller of the two segments into which the load divides the length of the beam.

PROBLEMS

743. A restrained beam 16 ft long supports a concentrated load of 12 kips at 4 ft from the left end, and another concentrated load of 10 kips at 6 ft from the right end. Select the lightest WF beam that will support these loads without exceeding a flexural stress of 18,000 psi. Compute the midspan deflection of this beam. $E = 30 \times 10^6$ psi.

744. A timber beam 4 in. wide by 8 in. deep and 12 ft long is perfectly restrained at both ends. It supports a uniformly distributed load of 200 lb/ft over its entire length, and a concentrated load P at 4 ft from the left end. Determine P so as not to exceed a flexural stress of 1800 psi or a midspan deflection of $\frac{1}{360}$ of the span. Assume $E = 1.5 \times 10^6$ psi.

745. A rectangular timber beam whose depth is twice the width supports the loads shown. Determine the dimensions if the allowable flexural stress is 1600 psi. What is the maximum horizontal shearing stress developed in the beam?

Ans. $b = 3.64$ in.; $h = 7.28$ in.; $S_s = 115$ psi

746. Using the method of superposition, check the values of end moment and midspan deflection for the restrained beam in Prob. 722 (page 230).

747. Compute the end moments for the perfectly restrained beam shown.

Ans. $M_A = -2003$ ft-lb

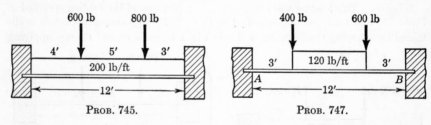

PROB. 745.   PROB. 747.

748. A timber beam 8 in. wide by 12 in. high and 12 ft long supports a total load of 3600 lb uniformly distributed over its entire length. The beam is perfectly restrained against rotation at its ends, but the right end settles $\frac{1}{2}$ in. relative to the left end. If $E = 1.5 \times 10^6$ psi, determine the maximum flexure stress.

Ans. $S_f = 1530$ psi

SUMMARY

The principles of beam deflections studied in Chap. VI are here applied to obtain additional equations which can be combined with the equations of static equilibrium to solve problems involving statically indeterminate beams.

In propped beams, we generally use the fact that the deflection under the redundant support is zero (if the support does not settle), or some known value (if the support does settle). Either the area-moment method or the method of superposition may be used, as indicated in Art. 7–2.

For beams perfectly restrained at both ends, the elastic curve is such that there is no change in slope between the ends, and the deflection of one end relative to the other end is zero. Using the area-moment method, we generally take the shear and moment at one end as the redundant supports. (See Art. 7–3.) For loadings that are combinations of the types in Table VII–1, the method of superposition (Art. 7–7) is usually used.

Deflections in perfectly restrained beams are easily computed from the fact that the tangent to the elastic curve is horizontal at either end. Then, with the area-moment method, the deviation of any point from this tangent equals the deflection. In certain cases, as indicated in Art. 7–6, the double-integration method offers advantages, since the constants of integration are zero for a beam segment starting at a perfectly restrained end. Both methods require that the end shears and moments be known first. When the loading combines the types in Table VII–1, deflections can be obtained immediately by applying the formulas in the table. If a loading consists of types some of which are listed in the table and some not, Table VII–1 may be used to determine results for the types that are listed, and the area-moment method applied for the other loadings.

Chapter VIII
Continuous Beams

8–1. Introduction

In this chapter we consider beams that are continuous over two or more spans, thereby having one or more redundant supports. It is possible to determine these redundancies by applying the deflection relations developed in Chap. VI, but a more convenient method is to consider the unknown bending moments at the supports of the beam as the redundancies. After these bending moments are found, it is comparatively simple to determine the reactions, as we shall show in Art. 8–5.

To solve for the bending moments at the supports, it is necessary to find a general relation among the bending moments at any three sections in a beam. This relation is known as the *three-moment equation*, and it is easily found by applying the area-moment method.

We shall show how this equation is used to solve for deflections as well as for redundancies in any type of beam. The three-moment equation can be used alone to solve all the problems in Chaps. VI and VII; however, in some instances, it is best used in combination with the area-moment method or the double-integration method. Although the three-moment equation provides a complete technique, it is foolish not to supplement it by other methods, especially when they simplify computations. Such combinations of techniques will also be discussed.

8–2. Generalized Form of Three-Moment Equation

A portion of a beam that is loaded and supported in any manner is shown in Fig. 8–1a. At any three points 1, 2, and 3, pass cutting sections and replace the effects of the loads to the left or right of these sections by the proper values of vertical shear and bending moment. Thus the beam segments between points 1 and 2 and between points 2 and 3 (hereafter referred to as spans 1 and 2 respectively) may be isolated by means of the free-body diagrams in Fig. 8–1b. The lengths of the spans (or segments) are L_1 and L_2, and the bending moments at points 1, 2, and 3 are M_1, M_2, M_3; the vertical shears at these points are V_1, V_{-2} (just to the left of point 2), V_2 (just to the right of point 2), and V_{-3} just to the left of point 3.

The technique discussed in Art. 7–5 enables us to resolve the free-body diagrams of the beam segments into simply supported spans that carry the

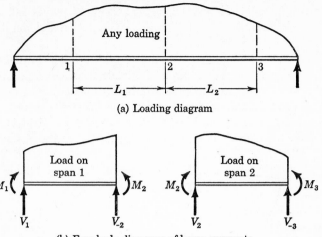

(a) Loading diagram

(b) Free-body diagrams of beam segments

Fig. 8–1. — General loading on any beam.

actual beam loading, and spans loaded only by the bending moments and held in equilibrium by the couple reactions R_1' on span 1 and by R_2' on span 2. This equivalent loading is shown in Figs. 8–2a and 8–2b respectively. When these loadings are superposed, they produce the free-body

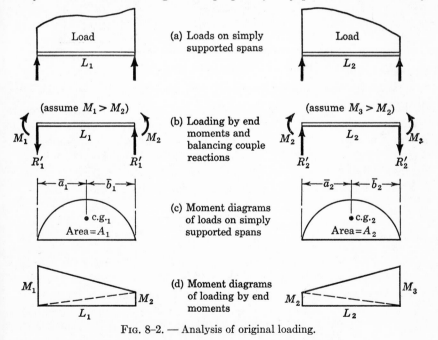

Fig. 8–2. — Analysis of original loading.

diagrams in Fig. 8–1b. Hence the vertical shears at points 1, 2, and 3 are equal to the algebraic sum of the simple beam reaction and couple reaction at these respective points.

In this manner, the moment diagram of each original beam segment is resolved into the moment diagram of the loads assumed to be carried on a simply supported span, and a trapezoidal moment diagram caused by the bending moments in the original beam at the selected points 1, 2, and 3. These diagrams are shown in Figs. 8–2c and 8–2d respectively.

For clarity, the elastic curve of the beam has been drawn separately in Fig. 8–3. The deflection of the curve is greatly exaggerated in order to show the geometric relations. Note that points 1, 2, and 3 lie on it.

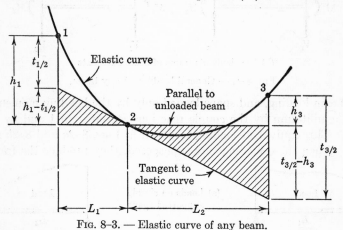

FIG. 8–3. — Elastic curve of any beam.

A tangent drawn to the elastic curve at point 2 determines the tangential deviations $t_{1/2}$ at point 1 and $t_{3/2}$ at point 3. Another line drawn through point 2 parallel to the initial position of the unloaded beam (which has been assumed horizontal for convenience) determines the heights of points 1 and 3 above point 2 to be h_1 and h_3. There are formed the shaded similar triangles having the bases L_1 and L_2 and the altitudes $(h_1 - t_{1/2})$ and $(t_{3/2} - h_3)$.

From the proportions between similar triangles, it is evident that

$$\frac{h_1 - t_{1/2}}{L_1} = \frac{t_{3/2} - h_3}{L_2}$$

which reduces to

$$\frac{t_{1/2}}{L_1} + \frac{t_{3/2}}{L_2} = \frac{h_1}{L_1} + \frac{h_3}{L_2} \qquad (a)$$

The values of the tangential deviations are found from

$$t_{1/2} = \frac{1}{EI} (\text{Area})_{1-2} \cdot \bar{x}_1$$

and

$$t_{3/2} = \frac{1}{EI} (\text{Area})_{3-2} \cdot \bar{x}_3$$

where $(\text{Area})_{1-2} \cdot \bar{x}_1$ is the moment of area about point 1 of the moment diagram between points 1 and 2. As was said previously, this moment diagram has been resolved into the area A_1 (see Fig. 8–2c) and the two triangular areas into which the trapezoidal diagram for the end moments is divided (see Fig. 8–2d). Likewise, $(\text{Area})_{3-2} \cdot \bar{x}_3$ is the moment about point 3 of the area of the moment diagram between points 2 and 3, as represented by area A_2 and the trapezoidal diagram for the end moments which has been subdivided into two triangles.

We can therefore express the tangential deviation $t_{1/2}$ at 1 from a tangent to the elastic curve drawn at 2 as

$$t_{1/2} = \frac{1}{EI} \left[A_1 \bar{a}_1 + \frac{1}{2} M_1 L_1 \times \frac{1}{3} L_1 + \frac{1}{2} M_2 L_1 \times \frac{2}{3} L_1 \right] \qquad (b)$$

and the tangential deviation $t_{3/2}$ at 3 from the *same* tangent drawn at 2 as

$$t_{3/2} = \frac{1}{EI} \left[A_2 \bar{b}_2 + \frac{1}{2} M_2 L_2 \times \frac{2}{3} L_2 + \frac{1}{2} M_3 L_2 \times \frac{1}{3} L_2 \right] \qquad (c)$$

Substituting these values of $t_{1/2}$ and $t_{3/2}$ in Eq. (a) gives

$$M_1 L_1 + 2 M_2 (L_1 + L_2) + M_3 L_2 + \frac{6 A_1 \bar{a}_1}{L_1} + \frac{6 A_2 \bar{b}_2}{L_2} = 6 EI \left(\frac{h_1}{L_1} + \frac{h_3}{L_2} \right) \quad (8\text{-}1)$$

This equation expresses a general relation among moments at any three points in a beam, and hence is known as the *three-moment equation*.

When points 1, 2, and 3 are on the same level in the deflected beam, the heights h_1 and h_3 in Fig. 8–3 become zero and so does the right-hand term in Eq. (8–1). This is the usual condition in which the three-moment equation is applied. The three points selected in applying the equation to continuous beams are the points at the supports (usually assumed as rigid or else as settling the same amount); the equation is used to determine the bending moments in the beam over the supports.

If the three-moment equation is used for deflections, two of the points are selected over supports and the third is chosen at the point whose deflection is desired. Evidently the moments at the three points must first be known in order to compute deflections. We shall expand this application of the three-moment equation in Art. 8–7.

Rules of Sign. Eq. (8–1) was derived under the assumption that the bending moments at the selected points were positive, and that points 1 and 3 were above point 2. Hence, heights h_1 and h_3 must be considered positive when measured upward from point 2. If the moment at any point is actually negative, the negative sign must be used when substituting its value in Eq. (8–1). Conversely, if an unknown moment is actually negative at any point, Eq. (8–1) will give a negative value for that moment; in other words, the sign of the moment at that point is automatically opposite to the positive value assumed in the derivation of the three-moment equation.

8–3. Factors for Three-Moment Equation

The usefulness of the three-moment equation depends on the ease with which the expressions $\dfrac{6\,A\bar{a}}{L}$ and $\dfrac{6\,A\bar{b}}{L}$ in it can be found. It will be recalled that these expressions refer to the moment of area of the moment diagram resulting from carrying the applied loads on a simple span of the same length as the equivalent beam segment. The general expressions in Table VIII–1 were obtained by the following procedure.

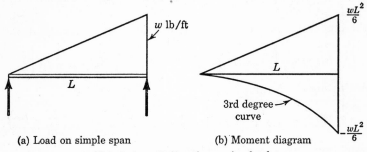

(a) Load on simple span   (b) Moment diagram

Fig. 8–4. — Uniformly varying load.

Case 3. Uniformly Varying Load. The loading over a span L in a continuous beam varies uniformly over the span. If this loading is assumed to be supported on a simple span, the moment diagram is drawn by parts from left to right, as in Fig. 8–4. The moment of area of this moment diagram about the right end is given by

$$A\bar{b} = \frac{1}{2}\left(\frac{wL^2}{6}\cdot L\right)\left(\frac{1}{3}L\right) - \frac{1}{4}\left(\frac{wL^2}{6}\cdot L\right)\left(\frac{1}{5}L\right)$$

$$= \frac{wL^4}{6}\left(\frac{1}{6} - \frac{1}{20}\right) = \frac{7}{360}\,wL^4$$

Multiplying this by $\dfrac{6}{L}$, we obtain the following general value for this type of loading:

$$\frac{6\,A\bar{b}}{L} = \frac{7}{60}\,wL^3 \quad Ans.$$

Special Loadings. For cases not listed in Table VIII–1, or if the table is not available, the following example may be helpful.

TABLE VIII–1. Values of $\dfrac{6A\bar{a}}{L}$ and $\dfrac{6A\bar{b}}{L}$

CASE NO.	TYPE OF LOADING ON SPAN	$\dfrac{6A\bar{a}}{L}$	$\dfrac{6A\bar{b}}{L}$
1		$\dfrac{Pa}{L}(L^2-a^2)$	$\dfrac{Pb}{L}(L^2-b^2)$
2		$\dfrac{wL^3}{4}=\dfrac{WL^2}{4}$	$\dfrac{wL^3}{4}=\dfrac{WL^2}{4}$
3		$\dfrac{8}{60}wL^3=\dfrac{8}{30}WL^2$	$\dfrac{7}{60}wL^3=\dfrac{7}{30}WL^2$
4		$\dfrac{7}{60}wL^3=\dfrac{7}{30}WL^2$	$\dfrac{8}{60}wL^3=\dfrac{8}{30}WL^2$
5		$\dfrac{w}{4L}\left[b^2(2L^2-b^2)-a^2(2L^2-a^2)\right]$	$\dfrac{w}{4L}\left[d^2(2L^2-d^2)-c^2(2L^2-c^2)\right]$
6		$\dfrac{5}{32}wL^3=\dfrac{5}{16}WL^2$	$\dfrac{5}{32}wL^3=\dfrac{5}{16}WL^2$

Assume a continuous beam loaded as in Fig. 8–5, and let it be required to evaluate $\dfrac{6\,A_2\bar{b}_2}{L_2}$ for span 2. Take the loading on span 2 as if it were simply

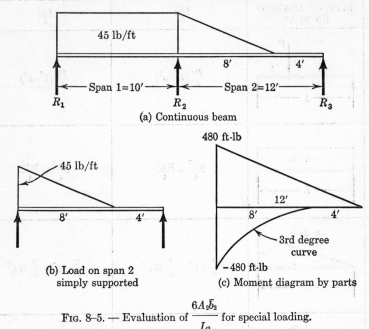

(a) Continuous beam

(b) Load on span 2 simply supported

(c) Moment diagram by parts

FIG. 8–5. — Evaluation of $\dfrac{6A_2\bar{b}_2}{L_2}$ for special loading.

supported on a 12-ft span, and draw the moment diagram by parts from right to left (this is more convenient here). Since $\dfrac{6\,A\bar{b}}{L}$ means multiplying $\dfrac{6}{L}$ by the moment of area of the moment diagram, moments being taken about the right end, we have

$$\frac{6\,A_2\bar{b}_2}{L_2} = \frac{6}{12}\left[\left(\frac{480 \times 12}{2}\right)\left(\frac{2}{3} \times 12\right) - \left(\frac{480 \times 8}{4}\right)\left(4 + \frac{4}{5} \times 8\right)\right]$$

$$= \frac{6}{12}[23{,}040 - 9984] = 6528 \quad Ans.$$

If it had been necessary to evaluate $\dfrac{6\,A_2\bar{a}_2}{L_2}$ for span 2, the symbol $\bar{a}_2$ would have told us to take the moment of area about the left end, since, as Fig. 8–2c shows, the symbols $\bar{a}$ and $\bar{b}$ refer to moment arms measured respectively from the left and right ends of a span.

PROBLEMS

Without referring to Table VIII–1, if the span loadings on a continuous beam reduce to the simply supported loads shown, evaluate the factors $\dfrac{6\,A\bar{a}}{L}$ and $\dfrac{6\,A\bar{b}}{L}$ in each of the following problems.

801. A span loaded as shown.   *Ans.* $\dfrac{6\,A\bar{a}}{L} = 8600\ \text{lb-ft}^2$

802. A span carrying the given loading.   *Ans.* $\dfrac{6\,A\bar{a}}{L} = 2830\ \text{lb-ft}^2$

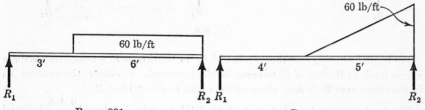

PROB. 801.   PROB. 802.

803. A span loaded as shown.   *Ans.* $\dfrac{6\,A\bar{b}}{L} = 6242\ \text{lb-ft}^2$

804. A span loaded as in Prob. 613 (page 188).

805. A span loaded as in Prob. 614.

806. A span loaded as in Prob. 615.

8–4. Application of the Three-Moment Equation

We shall now see how the three-moment equation may be applied to determine the moments over the supports in various types of continuous beams. Later articles will show how these moments are used to determine the reactions of continuous beams, and will describe a speedy method of drawing shear and moment diagrams.

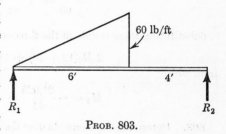

PROB. 803.

ILLUSTRATIVE PROBLEMS

807. For the continuous beam in Fig. 8–6, determine the values of the moments over the supports. The supports are assumed to be rigid or, what amounts to the same thing, to have equal deformations. This assumption applies to all problems unless stated otherwise.

Solution: Apply the three-moment equation to points over the supports. Since the supports remain at the same level, heights h_1 and h_3 are zero, and the equation reduces to

$$M_1L_1 + 2\,M_2(L_1 + L_2) + M_3L_2 + \frac{6\,A_1\bar{a}_1}{L_1} + \frac{6\,A_2\bar{b}_2}{L_2} = 0 \qquad (a)$$

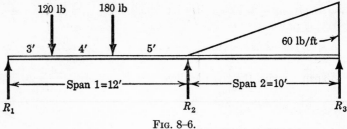

FIG. 8–6.

We begin by noting that the moment M_1 in the beam over R_1 is zero, because there are no loads to the left of R_1 to cause bending moment. Similarly, the moment M_3 in the beam over R_3 is zero, since no forces act to the right of R_3.

The loads on span 1 are in Case 1, Table VIII–1, and the value of $\dfrac{6\,A_1\bar{a}_1}{L_1}$ is found by adding the values of $\dfrac{Pa}{L}(L^2 - a^2)$ as applied to each load. We obtain

$$\frac{6\,A_1\bar{a}_1}{L_1} = \sum \frac{Pa}{L}(L^2 - a^2) = \frac{120 \times 3}{12}(144 - 9) + \frac{180 \times 7}{12}(144 - 49)$$

$$= 4050 + 9975 = 14{,}025 \qquad (b)$$

The load on span 2 is in Case 3; hence, from Table VIII–1, we have

$$\frac{6\,A_2\bar{b}_2}{L_2} = \frac{7}{60}\,wL^3 = \frac{7}{60} \times 60 \times 1000 = 7000 \qquad (c)$$

Substituting these results in the three-moment equation gives

$$2\,M_2(12 + 10) + 14{,}025 + 7000 = 0$$

from which

$$M_2 = -\frac{21{,}025}{44} = -\,448\ \text{lb-ft} \quad Ans.$$

808. Determine the moments over the supports for the continuous beam shown in Fig. 8–7.

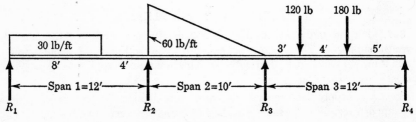

FIG. 8–7.

Preliminary: Writing the three-moment equation between spans 1 and 2, and between spans 2 and 3, we have

$$M_1 L_1 + 2 M_2(L_1 + L_2) + M_3 L_2 + \frac{6 A_1 \bar{a}_1}{L_1} + \frac{6 A_2 \bar{b}_2}{L_2} = 0 \qquad (a)$$

$$M_2 L_2 + 2 M_3(L_2 + L_3) + M_4 L_3 + \frac{6 A_2 \bar{a}_2}{L_2} + \frac{6 A_3 \bar{b}_3}{L_3} = 0 \qquad (b)$$

From the definition of bending moment, both M_1 and M_4 are zero. Hence Eqs. (a) and (b) are a pair of simultaneous equations in M_2 and M_3, which can be solved when the values of $\dfrac{6 A \bar{a}}{L}$ and $\dfrac{6 A \bar{b}}{L}$ for the given loadings are known. Using Table VIII–1, we compute these values as follows:

$$\frac{6 A_1 \bar{a}_1}{L_1} = \frac{wb^2}{4 L}(2 L^2 - b^2) = \frac{30 \times 64}{4 \times 12}(2 \times 144 - 64) = 4960$$

$$\frac{6 A_2 \bar{b}_2}{L_2} = \frac{8}{60} wL^3 = \frac{8}{60} \times 60 \times 1000 = 8000$$

$$\frac{6 A_2 \bar{a}_2}{L_2} = \frac{7}{60} wL^3 = \frac{7}{60} \times 60 \times 1000 = 7000$$

$$\frac{6 A_3 \bar{b}_3}{L_3} = \sum \frac{Pb}{L}(L^2 - b^2) = \frac{120 \times 9}{12}(144 - 81) + \frac{180 \times 5}{12}(144 - 25)$$

$$= 5670 + 8930 = 14{,}600$$

Solution: The values computed above are substituted in Eqs. (a) and (b):

$$2 M_2(12 + 10) + 10 M_3 + 4960 + 8000 = 0$$

$$10 M_2 + 2 M_3(10 + 12) + 7000 + 14{,}600 = 0$$

or

$$44 M_2 + 10 M_3 + 12{,}960 = 0 \qquad (c)$$

$$10 M_2 + 44 M_3 + 21{,}600 = 0 \qquad (d)$$

M_3 is eliminated from these equations by multiplying Eq. (c) by -4.4 and adding the result to Eq. (d). This gives

$$- 183.6 M_2 - 35{,}400 = 0$$

whence

$$M_2 = - 193 \text{ lb-ft} \quad Ans.$$

Similarly M_2 is eliminated by multiplying Eq. (d) by -4.4 and adding this result to Eq. (c), which gives

$$- 183.6 M_3 - 82{,}140 = 0$$

whence

$$M_3 = - 447 \text{ lb-ft} \quad Ans.$$

These values may be checked by substituting them in Eq. (c), as follows:

$$44 \times (- 193) + 10 \times (- 447) + 12{,}960 = 0$$

$$- 8490 - 4470 + 12{,}960 = 0 \quad Check$$

809. Determine the moments over the supports for the continuous beam shown in Fig. 8–8.

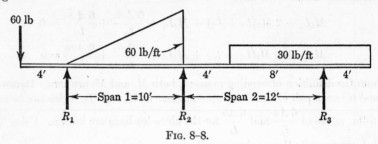

FIG. 8–8.

Preliminary: Since the supports are assumed to remain at the same level, the three-moment equation applied to spans 1 and 2 is

$$M_1 L_1 + 2\,M_2(L_1 + L_2) + M_3 L_2 + \frac{6\,A_1 \bar{a}_1}{L_1} + \frac{6\,A_2 \bar{b}_2}{L_2} = 0 \qquad (a)$$

An important difference between this problem and the preceding ones is the over-hanging loads. From the definition of bending moment, we obtain

$[M = (\Sigma M)_L] \qquad M_1 = -\,60 \times 4 = -\,240 \text{ lb-ft}$

$[M = (\Sigma M)_R] \qquad M_3 = -\,(30 \times 4) \times 2 = -\,240 \text{ lb-ft}$

The minus signs of these moments must be kept when substituting these values in Eq. (a).[1]

From Table VIII–1 we find

$$\frac{6\,A_1 \bar{a}_1}{L_1} = \frac{8}{60}\,wL^3 = \frac{8}{60} \times 60 \times 1000 = 8000$$

$$\frac{6\,A_2 \bar{b}_2}{L_2} = \frac{wd^2}{4\,L}\,(2\,L^2 - d^2) = \frac{30 \times 64}{4 \times 12}\,(2 \times 144 - 64) = 4960$$

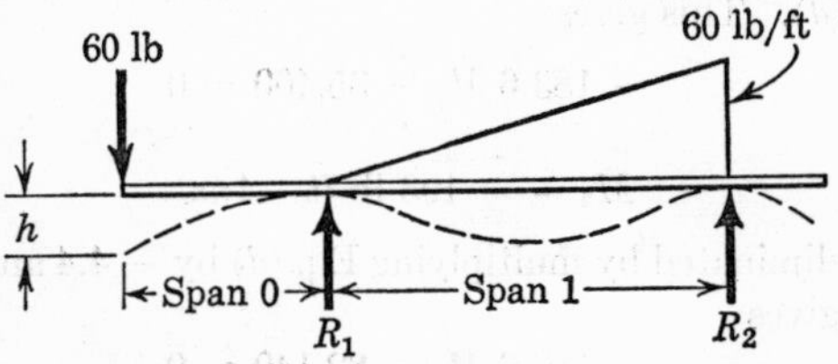

FIG. 8–9.

[1] A common error is to apply the three-moment equation with the right-hand member equal to zero between the overhang and span 1, as shown in Fig. 8–9, thus completely forgetting that the 60-lb load causes the overhang to deflect downward an unknown distance h. Under these conditions, the right-hand member of the general three-moment equation contains the unknown h. Obviously, it is simpler to compute M_1, as indicated above, than to consider both M_1 and h as unknown quantities.

Solution: Our preliminary calculations show that Eq. (*a*) contains only one unknown: M_2. Substituting numerical values in Eq. (*a*) yields

$$- 240 \times 10 + 2 M_2(10 + 12) - 240 \times 12 + 8000 + 4960 = 0$$

whence

$$M_2 = -173.5 \text{ lb-ft} \quad Ans.$$

PROBLEMS

Unless otherwise stated, the continuous beams in the following problems are supported on rigid foundations. In each problem, determine the bending moments in the beam over the supports.

810. Continuous beam loaded as shown.   *Ans.* $M_2 = -1587$ ft-lb

811. Continuous beam loaded as shown.   *Ans.* $M_2 = -408$ ft-lb

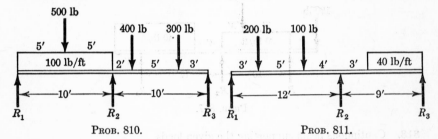

PROB. 810.   PROB. 811.

812. Continuous beam loaded as shown.   *Ans.* $M_2 = -358$ ft-lb

813. Continuous beam loaded as shown.   *Ans.* $M_2 = -653$ ft-lb

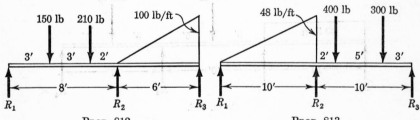

PROB. 812.   PROB. 813.

814. Continuous beam loaded as shown.   *Ans.* $M_2 = -480$ ft-lb

815. Continuous beam loaded as shown.   *Ans.* $M_2 = -174$ ft-lb

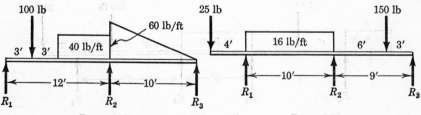

PROB. 814.   PROB. 815.

816. Continuous beam loaded as shown.   *Ans.* $M_2 = -93.4$ ft-lb

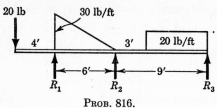

PROB. 816.

817. Continuous beam carrying the indicated loads.

Ans. $M_2 = -287.5$ ft-lb

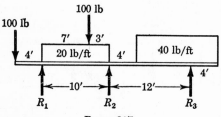

PROB. 817.

818. Continuous beam supporting the given loads.

Ans. $M_2 = -717.5$ ft-lb; $M_3 = -1130$ ft-lb

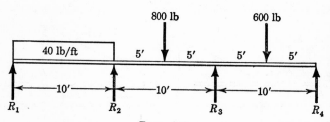

PROB. 818.

819. Continuous beam loaded as shown.

Ans. $M_2 = -275$ ft-lb; $M_3 = -197$ ft-lb

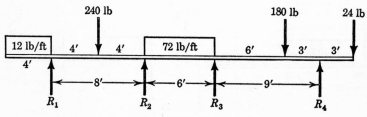

PROB. 819.

820.   Continuous beam supporting the given loads.

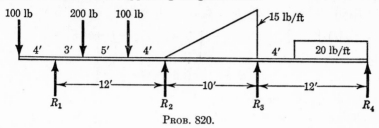

PROB. 820.

821.   Determine the lengths of the overhangs x_1 and x_2 so that the moments over the supports are equal.

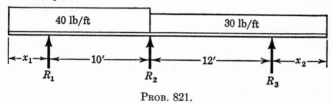

PROB. 821.

8–5. Reactions of Continuous Beams. Shear Diagrams

The major reason for computing the reactions of continuous beams is to be able to draw the shear diagram. Two methods of computing reactions are available; in one, reactions are computed by using the definition of bending moment, and in the other the reaction is divided into parts from which the shear diagram can be drawn easily. The second method is preferred for reasons which will be given later. In both methods the moments over the supports must first be determined.

The definition of bending moment, on which the first method depends, is as follows: The bending moment is the summation of moments about the section of all loads on either side of the section; upward loads produce positive moment, and vice versa. A numerical example will explain this method.

Fig. 8–10 shows the beam whose moments over the supports were computed in Prob. 808 and were found to be $M_2 = -193$ ft-lb and $M_3 = -447$ ft-lb.

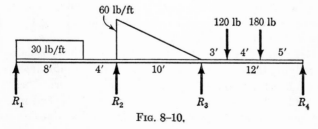

FIG. 8–10.

Applying the definition of bending moment to M_2 by taking moments about R_2 of all loads to the left of R_2, we obtain

$$[M_2 = (\Sigma M)_L] \qquad M_2 = -193 = 12\,R_1 - (30 \times 8) \times 8$$

whence

$$R_1 = 143.9 \text{ lb} \quad Ans.$$

To determine R_2, we apply the definition of M_3 to moments about R_3 of all loads to the left of R_3, as follows:

$$[M_3 = (\Sigma M)_L] \qquad -447 = 22\,R_1 - (30 \times 8) \times 18$$
$$+ 10\,R_2 - \left(\frac{60 \times 10}{2}\right) \times \frac{2}{3} \times 10$$

Substituting in this relation the now known value of $R_1 = 143.9$ lb, we find that

$$R_2 = 270.7 \text{ lb} \quad Ans.$$

The value of R_4 is also obtained from the value of M_3 by expressing M_3 in terms of the moments about R_3 of all loads to the right of R_3:

$$[M_3 = (\Sigma M)_R] \qquad -447 = 12\,R_4 - 120 \times 3 - 180 \times 7$$

whence

$$R_4 = 97.8 \text{ lb} \quad Ans.$$

The value of R_3 can now be found by taking a vertical summation of all forces acting on the entire beam. This gives

$$[\Sigma Y = 0] \qquad R_1 + R_2 + R_3 + R_4 = 30 \times 8 + \frac{60 \times 10}{2} + 120 + 180$$

$$143.9 + 270.7 + R_3 + 97.8 = 240 + 300 + 120 + 180$$

whence

$$R_3 = 327.6 \text{ lb} \quad Ans.$$

It is evident that this method carries through any numerical error, and is also tedious if there are more than three spans to the beam. An alternate method eliminates both of these objections and presents the results in a form suitable for drawing the shear diagram rapidly. This alternate method depends on isolating each span and determining the supporting shear forces at the end of each one.

In Art. 8–2 and Fig. 8–1 we saw that any span can be isolated as a free body by applying to it the proper values of end moments and shears. The isolated span can then be resolved into a simply supported beam carrying the given loads, plus another beam loaded only by the end moments and couple reactions. Span 2 of Fig. 8–10 is thus resolved into its component parts in Fig. 8–11. Because the end moments M_2 and M_3 are negative, they act as shown, and their absolute magnitudes may be used. The term V_2 denotes the vertical shear in the beam to the right of R_2, and V_{-3} is numerically equivalent to the vertical shear in the beam to the left of R_3. The minus sign in the subscript of V_{-3} indicates that it acts opposite to the actual vertical shear in order to create equilibrium in span 2.

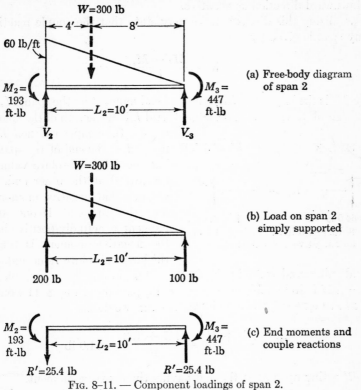

(a) Free-body diagram of span 2

(b) Load on span 2 simply supported

(c) End moments and couple reactions

FIG. 8–11. — Component loadings of span 2.

Since parts (b) and (c) of Fig. 8–11 are superposed to form part (a), it follows that the actual end shears V_2 and V_{-3} are the algebraic sum of the equivalent simple beam reactions and the couple reactions R'. In this example, M_3 is numerically larger than M_2; hence there is an unbalanced clockwise couple acting on part (c) of magnitude $M_3 - M_2$. It can be balanced only by the counterclockwise moment caused by the couple reactions R' acting at the supports and having a moment arm equal to the length L_2 of the span. Evidently the numerical value of R' is given by

$$R'L_2 = M_3 - M_2$$

or

$$R' = \frac{M_3 - M_2}{L_2} = \frac{447 - 193}{10} = 25.4 \text{ lb}$$

The couple reaction R' acts upward at the larger moment M_3 and downward at the smaller moment M_2. In the algebraic summation of reactions referred to previously, we shall take the upward direction as positive and the downward direction as negative.

Generalizing this discussion, we may state that the couple reaction R' on any span is given by

$$R' = \frac{M_l - M_s}{L} \tag{8-2}$$

where M_l is the larger absolute value of end moment on the span, M_s is the smaller absolute value of end moment, and L is the length of the span. As a rule, the couple reaction R' acts

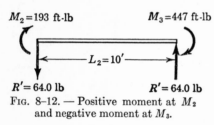

$M_2 = 193$ ft-lb　　　$M_3 = 447$ ft-lb

$L_2 = 10'$

$R' = 64.0$ lb　　　$R' = 64.0$ lb

FIG. 8-12. — Positive moment at M_2 and negative moment at M_3.

upward at the end of the span having the larger absolute value, and downward at the other end. This assumes that negative moments act over the supports. If one support moment is actually positive in sign, the negative moment is taken as the larger absolute value and its numerical value used as M_l in Eq. (8-2). Thus, in the above example, if M_3 were -447 ft-lb but M_2 were $+193$ ft-lb, part (c) of Fig. 8-11 would appear as in Fig. 8-12, whence the value of R' would be

$$R' = \frac{M_3 + M_2}{L_2} = \frac{447 + 193}{10} = 64.0 \text{ lb}$$

with R' acting upward at the end having the negative moment.

A convenient way of arranging the values of simple beam and couple reactions is shown in Fig. 8-13a. The couple reactions were computed as follows, the numerical subscripts referring to the span on which they act. The couple reaction acts upward (or is given a positive sign) at the end having the larger numerical negative end moment.

$$\left[R' = \frac{M_l - M_s}{L} \right]$$

$$R_1' = \frac{193 - 0}{12} = 16.1 \text{ lb}$$

$$R_2' = \frac{447 - 193}{10} = 25.4 \text{ lb}$$

$$R_3' = \frac{447 - 0}{12} = 37.2 \text{ lb}$$

The shear diagram in Fig. 8–13*b* may now be easily plotted. Remember that the values of vertical shear in Fig. 8–13*a* which act to the left of the supports are equal but opposite to the actual vertical shear in the beam. This accounts for the minus values in the shear diagram. If the values of the reaction are desired, they may be obtained by adding the vertical shears acting at the reaction. Thus

$$R_1 = 143.9 \text{ lb}$$
$$R_2 = 96.1 + 174.6 = 270.7 \text{ lb}$$
$$R_3 = 125.4 + 202.2 = 327.6 \text{ lb}$$
$$R_4 = 97.8 \text{ lb}$$

which agree with the values determined by the first method.

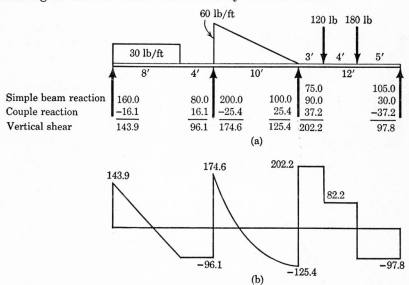

FIG. 8–13. — Method II of computing reactions and drawing shear diagram.

PROBLEMS

In the following problems, determine the reactions and sketch the shear diagrams. Then compute the values of maximum vertical shear V and maximum positive bending moment M. In solving the problems, use the moments determined in the reference problems unless otherwise instructed.

822. A continuous beam carries a uniform load over two equal spans as shown.

$$\text{Ans.} \quad M_2 = -\frac{wL^2}{8}; R_1 = R_3 = \frac{3}{8} wL; R_2 = \frac{5}{4} wL$$

823. A uniform load is carried over three equal spans as shown.

$$\text{Ans.} \quad M_2 = M_3 = -\frac{wL^2}{10}; R_1 = R_4 = 0.4 \, wL; R_2 = R_3 = 1.1 \, wL$$

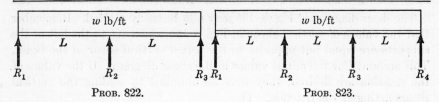

PROB. 822.　　　　　　　　　　　　　　PROB. 823.

824. Refer to Prob. 815.　　*Ans.*　$R_1 = 97.6$ lb; $R_2 = 157.3$ lb; $R_3 = 80.1$ lb

825. Refer to Prob. 817.

826. Refer to Prob. 818.

827. Refer to Prob. 819.

　　Ans.　$R_1 = 145.6$ lb; $R_2 = 371.4$ lb; $R_3 = 276.9$ lb; $R_4 = 130.1$ lb

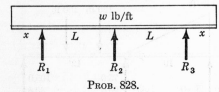

PROB. 828.

828. For the continuous beam loaded as shown, determine the length x of the overhangs that will cause equal reactions.

　　Ans.　$x = 0.44 L$

8–6. Continuous Beams with Fixed Ends

For continuous beams with fixed ends, assume the fixed end to be equivalent to an imaginary span with an imaginary loading. The three-moment equation, when applied to the beam, includes this imaginary span; however, all the terms that refer to the imaginary span have zero values.

The foregoing statement is easily proved by using the last span of the continuous beam shown in Fig. 8–14a. The moment M_1 at V_1 is due to the

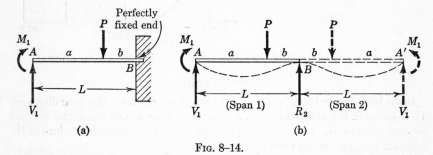

FIG. 8–14.

loads on the beam that lie to the left of V_1. The right end at B is assumed to be perfectly fixed; i.e., a tangent to the elastic curve at B will be perfectly horizontal. The effect of the perfectly fixed end may be duplicated by adding the reflection of the loads (i.e., assuming that the wall at B is a mirror), as shown in Fig. 8–14b. Because of the symmetry of loading thus obtained, the tangent to the elastic curve at B will be horizontal, which is the effect given by a perfectly fixed end.

Applying the three-moment equation to spans 1 and 2 of Fig. 8–14b gives

$$M_1L_1 + 2\,M_2(L_1 + L_2) + M_3L_2 + \frac{6\,A_1\bar{a}_1}{L_1} + \frac{6\,A_2\bar{b}_2}{L_2} = 0 \qquad (a)$$

whence, on substituting values corresponding to those in the figure, we obtain

$$M_1L + 2\,M_2(L + L) + M_1L + \frac{6\,A_1\bar{a}_1}{L_1} + \frac{6\,A_1\bar{a}_1}{L_1} = 0$$

or

$$2\,M_1L + 4\,M_2L + 2 \times \frac{6\,A_1\bar{a}_1}{L_1} = 0$$

Dividing by 2, we obtain

$$M_1L + 2\,M_2L + \frac{6\,A_1\bar{a}_1}{L_1} = 0 \qquad (b)$$

This would have been obtained from Eq. (a) at once if zero had been substituted for all the terms referring to the imaginary span (span 2 in this example). The principle that a fixed end is equivalent to an imaginary span has thus been proved and will now be applied to several examples.

ILLUSTRATIVE PROBLEMS

829. Find the moments over the supports for the propped beam in Fig. 8–15. The right end is assumed to be perfectly fixed.

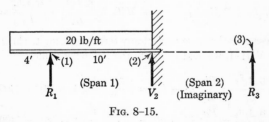

Fig. 8–15.

Solution: This problem can be solved by the basic area-moment method, but it can be solved more easily and more quickly by another method, which will now be explained.

The three-moment equation is applied between spans 1 and 2, whose supports are at the same level, so we obtain

$$M_1L_1 + 2\,M_2(L_1 + L_2) + M_3L_2 + \frac{6\,A_1\bar{a}_1}{L_1} + \frac{6\,A_2\bar{b}_2}{L_2} = 0$$

The moment at R_1 due to the overhang is

$$M_1 = -\,(20 \times 4) \times \tfrac{4}{2} = -\,160 \text{ ft-lb}$$

and zero is substituted for all terms referring to span 2. Table VIII–1 shows that $\dfrac{6\,A_1\bar{a}_1}{L_1} = \dfrac{wL^3}{4}$, so that the three-moment equation reduces to

$$- 160 \times 10 + 2\,M_2 \times 10 + \frac{20 \times 10^3}{4} = 0$$

from which

$$M_2 = -170 \text{ ft-lb} \quad Ans.$$

830. Find the moments over the supports for the continuous beam in Fig. 8–16. Both ends of the beam are assumed to be perfectly fixed.

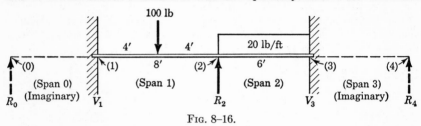

Fig. 8–16.

Solution: The perfectly fixed ends are considered equivalent to the imaginary spans 0 and 3. Writing the three-moment equation for spans 0 and 1, for spans 1 and 2, and for spans 2 and 3, we have

$$M_0 L_0 + 2\,M_1(L_0 + L_1) + M_2 L_1 + \frac{6\,A_0\bar{a}_0}{L_0} + \frac{6\,A_1\bar{b}_1}{L_1} = 0 \qquad (a)$$

$$M_1 L_1 + 2\,M_2(L_1 + L_2) + M_3 L_2 + \frac{6\,A_1\bar{a}_1}{L_1} + \frac{6\,A_2\bar{b}_2}{L_2} = 0 \qquad (b)$$

$$M_2 L_2 + 2\,M_3(L_2 + L_3) + M_4 L_3 + \frac{6\,A_2\bar{a}_2}{L_2} + \frac{6\,A_3\bar{b}_3}{L_3} = 0 \qquad (c)$$

In applying these equations, we neglect any terms referring to the imaginary spans. Using Table VIII–1, we next compute the following values:

$$\frac{6\,A_1\bar{b}_1}{L_1} = \frac{Pb}{L}\,(L^2 - b^2) = \frac{100 \times 4}{8}\,(64 - 16) = 2400$$

$$\frac{6\,A_1\bar{a}_1}{L_1} = \frac{Pa}{L}\,(L^2 - a^2) = \frac{100 \times 4}{8}\,(64 - 16) = 2400$$

$$\frac{6\,A_2\bar{a}_2}{L_2} = \frac{6\,A_2\bar{b}_2}{L_2} = \frac{wL^3}{4} = 1080$$

Substituting these values in the three-moment equations gives

From Eq. (a): $16\,M_1 + 8\,M_2 \qquad\qquad\ + 2400 = 0$ $\qquad\qquad (d)$

From Eq. (b): $8\,M_1 + 28\,M_2 + 6\,M_3 + 3480 = 0$ $\qquad\qquad (e)$

From Eq. (c): $\qquad\quad\ 6\,M_2 + 12\,M_3 + 1080 = 0$ $\qquad\qquad (f)$

Solving Eqs. (d), (e), and (f) simultaneously gives

$$M_1 = - 108.6 \text{ ft-lb}$$
$$M_2 = - 82.8 \text{ ft-lb}$$
$$M_3 = - 48.6 \text{ ft-lb} Ans.$$

PROBLEMS

In the following problems, the ends of the beams are assumed to be perfectly fixed by the walls against rotation. Unless otherwise stated, all supports are assumed to remain at the same level.

831. In the propped beam shown, determine the reaction of the prop.

Ans. $R_1 = 1275$ lb

832. For the propped beam shown, determine the maximum positive bending moment. *Ans.* $M = 160$ ft-lb

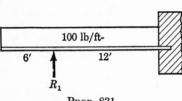

PROB. 831.

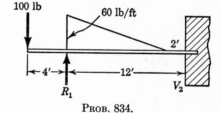

PROB. 832.

833. Determine the wall moment and prop reaction for the given beam.

Ans. $M_2 = - 1383$ ft-lb; $R_1 = 593.5$ lb

834. Determine the wall moment for the propped beam shown.

Ans. $M_2 = - 196$ ft-lb

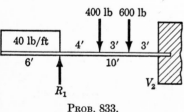

PROB. 833.

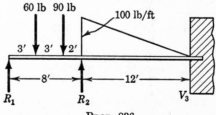

PROB. 834.

835. Determine the wall moment and prop reaction for the given beam.

Ans. $M_2 = 221$ ft-lb; $R_1 = 592$ lb

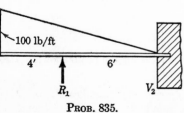

PROB. 835.

PROB. 836.

836. For the continuous beam shown, determine the moments over the supports and the reactions.

　　　　Ans. $M_2 = -472$ ft-lb; $M_3 = -604$ ft-lb; $R_1 = 1.0$ lb; $R_2 = 538$ lb; $V_3 = 211$ lb

837. Determine the moments over the supports for the continuous beam shown.

　　　　　　　　　　　　　　Ans. $M_2 = -82.2$ ft-lb; $M_3 = -138.9$ ft-lb

838. For the beam shown, compute the moments over the supports.

　　　　　　　　　　　　　　Ans. $M_2 = -40$ ft-lb; $M_3 = -146.7$ ft-lb

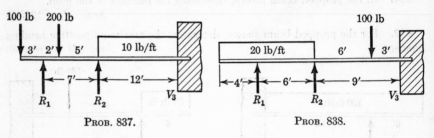

PROB. 837.　　　　　　　　　　PROB. 838.

839. Determine the reaction R_1 for the given beam.

　　　　Ans. $M_2 = -280$ ft-lb; $M_3 = -450.5$ ft-lb; $R_1 = 490$ lb

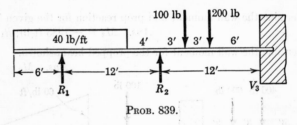

PROB. 839.

840. Sketch the shear diagram for the continuous beam shown.

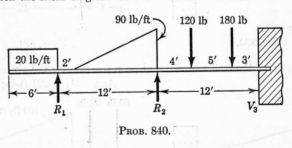

PROB. 840.

841. Compute the support moments and reactions for the beam shown. Also compute the maximum positive bending moment.

842. For the beam shown, determine the support moments and reactions. Also draw the shear diagram and compute the maximum positive bending moment.

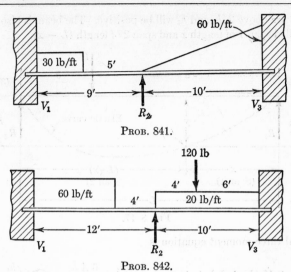

PROB. 841.

PROB. 842.

8-7. Deflections Determined by Three-Moment Equation

Before discussing the use of the general three-moment equation to find deflections let us review a few facts. The three-moment equation determines the relation among the moments at *any* three points in *any* beam. These three points determine two segments of the beam, and the terms $\dfrac{6\,A_1\bar{a}_1}{L_1}$ and $\dfrac{6\,A_2\bar{b}_2}{L_2}$ of the three-moment equation refer to the moment diagram resulting from the loads acting on these segments. The loads are assumed to be simply supported on spans that are as long as the segments. Heights h_1 and h_3 refer to the heights of points 1 and 3 relative to point 2 (see Fig. 8–3, page 242); the heights are considered positive if above point 2 and negative if below it.

The general method for determining deflections by means of the three-moment equation is to select points 1, 2, and 3 so that either (or both) of the heights h_1 and h_3 is equal to the desired deflection. The values of the moments at points 1, 2, and 3 must first be known or computed. This method will now be illustrated.

ILLUSTRATIVE PROBLEMS

843. Determine the deflection at any point of the simply supported beam in Fig. 8–17. This loading is the same as was specified in Case 7 of Table VI–2 and in Prob. 645.

Solution: Selecting point 2 at the position of the desired deflection and points 1 and 3 at the reactions will make h_1 and h_3 each equal the desired deflection. Also since 1 and 3 are above 2, h_1 and h_3 will be positive. The beam is also divided into segments, called span 1 of length x and span 2 of length $(L - x)$.

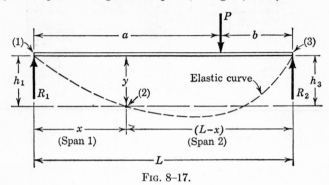

FIG. 8–17.

The general three-moment equation is

$$M_1 L_1 + 2 M_2 (L_1 + L_2) + M_3 L_2 + \frac{6 A_1 \bar{a}_1}{L_1} + \frac{6 A_2 \bar{b}_2}{L_2} = 6 EI \left(\frac{h_1}{L_1} + \frac{h_3}{L_2} \right)$$

Since span 1 in Fig. 8–17 is unloaded, $\dfrac{6 A_1 \bar{a}_1}{L_1}$ is zero. From Case 1 of Table VIII–1, we have for span 2

$$\frac{6 A_2 \bar{b}_2}{L_2} = \frac{Pb}{L - x} [(L - x)^2 - b^2] = \frac{Pb}{L - x} [L^2 - 2 Lx + x^2 - b^2]$$

Since $R_1 = \dfrac{Pb}{L}$, moments about point 2 of all forces to the left of it determine the value of M_2 as $\dfrac{Pbx}{L}$. Since $M_1 = M_3 = 0$ and $h_1 = h_3 = y$, substitution of the above values in the three-moment equation yields

$$2 \frac{Pbx}{L} (x + L - x) + \frac{Pb}{L - x} (L^2 - 2 Lx + x^2 - b^2) = 6 EI \left(\frac{y}{x} + \frac{y}{L - x} \right)$$

or

$$2 Pbx + \frac{Pb}{L - x} (L^2 - 2 Lx + x^2 - b^2) = \frac{6 L}{x(L - x)} \cdot EIy$$

whence

$$EIy = 2 Pbx \cdot \frac{x(L - x)}{6 L} + \frac{Pbx}{6 L} (L^2 - 2 Lx + x^2 - b^2)$$

$$= \frac{Pbx}{6 L} (2 Lx - 2 x^2 + L^2 - 2 Lx + x^2 - b^2)$$

$$= \frac{Pbx}{6 L} (L^2 - b^2 - x^2) \quad Ans. \tag{a}$$

The deflection at any point to the right of the load is obtained from the above result by replacing b with a and measuring x from an origin at the right reaction. The deflection equation becomes

$$EIy = \frac{Pax}{6L}(L^2 - a^2 - x^2) \tag{b}$$

In both Eq. (a) and (b) y has been assumed to be positive downward.

If a is assumed greater than b, the maximum deflection occurs in the left segment and its position is found by differentiating Eq. (a) with respect to x and setting the result equal to zero:

$$x = \sqrt{\frac{L^2 - b^2}{3}} \tag{c}$$

Substituting this value of x in Eq. (a) gives the value of maximum deflection as

$$y_{max} = \frac{1}{EI} \cdot \frac{Pb(L^2 - b^2)^{3/2}}{9\sqrt{3}\,L} \tag{d}$$

844. Determine the midspan product of EIy for the simply supported beam in Fig. 8–18.

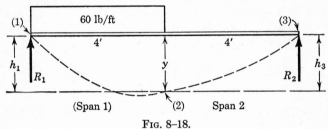

FIG. 8–18.

Solution: The exaggerated position of the deflection curve is shown by the dashed line. Select points 1 and 3 at the supports and point 2 at the midpoint, thereby forming spans 1 and 2.

By taking moments about R_1, we determine $R_2 = 60$ lb; hence $M_2 = 60 \times 4 = 240$ ft-lb. Evidently M_1 and M_3 equal zero, and h_1 and h_3 equal y.

Applying the three-moment equation, we have

$$M_1 L_1 + 2 M_2(L_1 + L_2) + M_3 L_2 + \frac{6\,A_1\bar{a}_1}{L_1} + \frac{6\,A_2\bar{b}_2}{L_2} = 6\,EI\left(\frac{h_1}{L_1} + \frac{h_3}{L_2}\right)$$

Since span 2 is unloaded, $\dfrac{6\,A_2\bar{b}_2}{L_2}$ is zero. Case 2 of Table VIII–1 gives for span 1

$$\frac{6\,A_1\bar{a}_1}{L_1} = \frac{wL^3}{4} = \frac{60 \times 64}{4} = 960$$

Substituting these values in the three-moment equation, we obtain

$$2 \times 240(4 + 4) + 960 = 6\,EI\left(\frac{y}{4} + \frac{y}{4}\right)$$

which reduces to

$$EIy = 1600 \text{ lb-ft}^3 \quad Ans.$$

845. Determine the value of EIy under the 60-lb load of the continuous beam shown in Fig. 8–19.

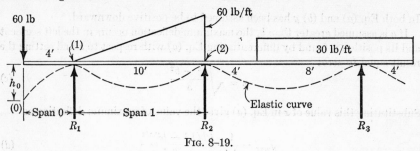

FIG. 8–19.

Solution: This beam is the one for which the support moments were determined in Illus. Prob. 809. Here we select points 0, 1, and 2, encircled as shown, between which to write the three-moment equation. Point 0 on the elastic curve is below point 1; hence $h_0 = -y$ and $h_2 = 0$. Using the results of Prob. 809, we find that $M_0 = 0$, $M_1 = -240$ ft-lb, and $M_2 = -173.5$ ft-lb.

Applying the three-moment equation, we write

$$M_0 L_0 + 2\, M_1(L_0 + L_1) + M_2 L_1 + \frac{6\, A_0 \bar{a}_0}{L_0} + \frac{6\, A_1 \bar{b}_1}{L_1} = 6\, EI\left(\frac{h_0}{L_0} + \frac{h_2}{L_1}\right)$$

In this instance span 0 is unloaded and hence $\dfrac{6\, A_0 \bar{a}_0}{L_0}$ is zero. Case 3 of Table VIII–1 gives for span 1

$$\frac{6\, A_1 \bar{b}_1}{L_1} = \frac{7}{60}\, wL^3 = \frac{7}{60} \times 60 \times 1000 = 7000$$

Substituting these values in the three-moment equation, with careful note of the minus signs of M_1 and M_2, we obtain

$$2(-240)(4+10) + (-173.5) \times 10 + 7000 = 6\, EI\left(\frac{-y}{4} + 0\right)$$

whence

$$EIy = 970 \text{ lb-ft}^3 \quad Ans.$$

The positive value of the result indicates that the deflection is downward as assumed.

846. Use the three-moment equation to determine the value of EIy at a point 6 ft from the wall of the cantilever beam loaded as in Fig. 8–20.

Solution: The equation will be applied here to points 1, 2, and 3. The fixed wall may be replaced by the imaginary span 2 (Art. 8–6). Writing the three-moment equation,

$$M_1 L_1 + 2\, M_2(L_1 + L_2) + M_3 L_2 + \frac{6\, A_1 \bar{a}_1}{L_1} + \frac{6\, A_2 \bar{b}_2}{L_2} = 6\, EI\left(\frac{h_1}{L_1} + \frac{h_3}{L_2}\right)$$

we note that preliminary computations require the following items.

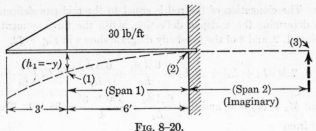

30 lb/ft

$(h_1=-y)$

(1)

(2)

(3)

(Span 1)

(Span 2)
(Imaginary)

3'

6'

Fig. 8-20.

First, by taking moments of all the loads to the left of point 1, we find

$[M = (\Sigma M)_L]$ $\qquad M_1 = -\left(\dfrac{30 \times 3}{2}\right) \times \dfrac{1}{3} \times 3 = -45 \text{ ft-lb}$

The wall moment M_2 is found to be

$[M = (\Sigma M)_L]$ $\qquad M_2 = -\left(\dfrac{30 \times 3}{2}\right) \times \left(\dfrac{1}{3} \times 3 + 6\right) - (30 \times 6) \times \dfrac{6}{2}$

$\qquad = -315 - 540 = -855 \text{ ft-lb}$

Case 2 of Table VIII-1 gives for span 1

$$\frac{6\,A_1\bar{a}_1}{L_1} = \frac{wL^3}{4} = \frac{30 \times 6^3}{4} = 1620$$

Since span 2 is imaginary, $\dfrac{6\,A_2\bar{b}_2}{L_2}$ is zero, as are also M_3 and h_3. Furthermore h_1 is negative, since point 1 lies below point 2.

Watching signs carefully, we substitute these values in the three-moment equation to obtain

$$-45 \times 6 - 2 \times 855 \times 6 + 1620 = 6\,EI\left(\frac{-y}{6} + 0\right)$$

whence

$$EIy = 8910 \text{ lb-ft}^3 \quad Ans.$$

847. The simple beam in Fig. 8-21 carries a load of 300 lb per ft over the right half of the span, and is supported by a steel rod 12 ft long and $\frac{1}{2}$ sq in. in area. The beam is of wood and is 4 in. wide by 8 in. deep. If $E_s = 30 \times 10^6$ psi and $E_w = 1.5 \times 10^6$ psi, determine the maximum stress in the rod and the beam.

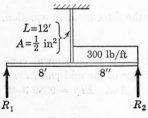

$L=12'$
$A=\frac{1}{2} \text{ in}^2$

300 lb/ft

8'   8''

R_1 R_2

Fig. 8-21.

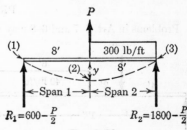

P

(1)   8'   300 lb/ft   (3)

(2) y 8'

Span 1   Span 2

$R_1 = 600 - \dfrac{P}{2}$ $R_2 = 1800 - \dfrac{P}{2}$

Fig. 8-22.

Solution: The elongation of the rod is equal to the midspan deflection of the beam. To determine the midspan deflection, write the three-moment equation between points 1, 2, and 3 of the free-body diagram shown in Fig. 8–22.

$$M_1L_1 + 2\,M_2(L_1 + L_2) + M_3L_2 + \frac{6\,A_1\bar{a}_1}{L_1} + \frac{6\,A_2\bar{b}_2}{L_2} = 6\,EI\left(\frac{h_1}{L_1} + \frac{h_3}{L_2}\right)$$

We note that $M_1 = M_3 = 0$, and that $\dfrac{6\,A_2\bar{b}_2}{L_2} = \dfrac{300 \times 8^3}{4} = 38{,}400$. The value of M_2 is found from

$$[M_2 = (\Sigma M)_L] \qquad M_2 = \left(600 - \frac{P}{2}\right) \times 8 = (4800 - 4\,P) \text{ ft-lb}$$

Substituting these values in the three-moment equation and observing that $h_1 = h_3 = y$, we have

$$2 \times (4800 - 4\,P)(8 + 8) + 38{,}400 = 6\,EI\left(\frac{y}{8} + \frac{y}{8}\right)$$

which reduces to

$$EIy = (128{,}000 - 83.3\,P) \text{ lb-ft}^3$$

The elongation of the rod is given by $\delta = \dfrac{PL}{AE}$. Hence, equating the elongation to the deflection, with careful attention to units, we obtain

$$[\delta = y] \qquad \left(\frac{P \times 12}{\frac{1}{2} \times 30 \times 10^6}\right) \times 12 = \frac{1728}{1.5 \times 10^6 \times \dfrac{4 \times 8^3}{12}}\,(128{,}000 - 83.3\,P)$$

$$9.6\,P = 863{,}000 - 562\,P$$
$$P = 1510 \text{ lb}$$

The stress in the rod is

$$\left[S = \frac{P}{A}\right] \qquad\qquad S = \frac{1510}{\frac{1}{2}} = 3020 \text{ psi} \quad Ans.$$

The maximum moment in the beam occurs 3.41 ft from the right end, and is 1665 ft-lb. Hence, the maximum stress in the beam is

$$\left[S = \frac{Mc}{I} = \frac{6\,M}{bh^2}\right] \qquad S = \frac{6 \times (1665 \times 12)}{4 \times (8)^2} = 585 \text{ psi} \quad Ans.$$

PROBLEMS

Problems in Art. 6–7 and 6–8 may also be solved by the three-moment equation.

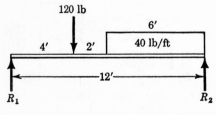

848. For the beam shown, compute the value of the midspan EIy.

Ans. $EIy = 9080$ lb-ft^3

PROB. 848.

849. Determine the value of EIy at a section 6 ft from R_1 for the given beam.

Ans. $EIy = 4759$ lb-ft³

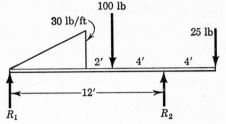

PROB. 849.

850. Determine the value of P that will cause zero deflection under P.

Ans. $P = 202.5$ lb

851. Determine the value of the midspan EIy.   Ans. $EIy = 5570$ lb-ft³

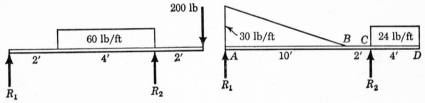

PROB. 850.   PROB. 851.

852. Find the value of EIy under the 200-lb load.   Ans. $EIy = 1280$ lb-ft³

853. In the overhanging beam shown, determine the values of EIy at points B and D.   Ans.   At B, $EIy = 355$ lb-ft³; at D, $EIy = 673$ lb-ft³

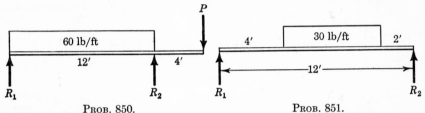

PROB. 852.   PROB. 853.

854. In the propped beam shown, the reaction settles $\frac{1}{2}$ in. as the load is applied. If $E = 2 \times 10^6$ psi, and $I = 10$ in.⁴, find the moment at the wall.

Ans. $M_2 = -1853$ ft-lb

855. The given beam is supported at the left end by a spring which deflects 1 in. for each 300 lb. For the beam, $E = 30 \times 10^6$ psi and $I = 144$ in.⁴ Compute the load and deflection of the spring.

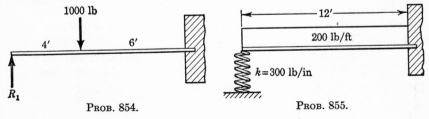

PROB. 854.   PROB. 855.

8–8. Review of Methods

To point out that no one method should be used exclusively, we present a review problem in which the area-moment method, the three-moment equation, and the method of superposition are used.

A beam is loaded as in Fig. 8–23, and the value of EIy at the midpoint is to be determined. The methods are first summarized in the order in which they will be used.

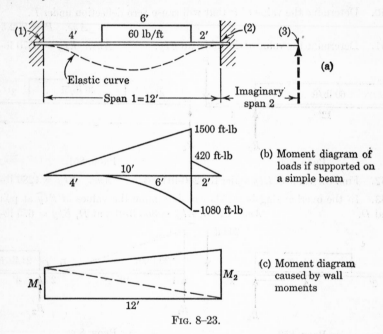

Fig. 8–23.

1. To compute the end moments, apply the three-moment equation to the given span and two imaginary spans. Or preferably, apply it to the given span and one imaginary span to derive one equation involving end moments, and from the area-moment method use the fact that the change in slope between the fixed ends is zero to obtain another equation between these unknown end moments.

2. Determine the end shears, using the second method of Art. 8–5.

3. Sketch the moment diagram by parts so you can use the area-moment method to compute the value of the midspan EIy. It will be found tedious to determine deflections with the three-moment equation in this problem.

4. To check the results, reduce the given loading to two concentrated loads, and apply the method of superposition to verify the values of end moments and midspan deflection.

Solution: Writing the three-moment equation between points 1, 2, and 3 of Fig. 8–23a gives

$$M_1 L_1 + 2 M_2 (L_1 + L_2) + M_3 L_2 + \frac{6 A_1 \bar{a}_1}{L_1} + \frac{6 A_2 \bar{b}_2}{L_2} = 0$$

The right-hand member of the equation is zero, because points 1, 2, and 3 are on the same level. The terms referring to the imaginary span are $\frac{6 A_2 \bar{b}_2}{L_2}$, L_2, and M_3; they also are zero. Thus, one equation involving M_1 and M_2 is set up. To use it, the expression $\frac{6 A_1 \bar{a}_1}{L_1}$ must be computed. This will be computed from Case 5 of Table VIII–1 (page 245), and also by means of the basic method, in order to review how Table VIII–1 was made. According to the table,

$$\frac{6 A_1 \bar{a}_1}{L_1} = \frac{w}{4 L} [b^2 (2 L^2 - b^2) - a^2 (2 L^2 - a^2)]$$

$$= \frac{60}{4 \times 12} [100(288 - 100) - 16(288 - 16)] = 18{,}060 \text{ lb-ft}^2$$

The value of $\frac{6 A_1 \bar{a}_1}{L_1}$ will also be computed from the moment diagram in Fig. 8–23b caused by the loads simply supported. Since $\frac{6 A_1 \bar{a}_1}{L_1}$ means $\frac{6}{L}$ times the moment of the area of the moment diagram about the left end of the beam, we obtain

$$\frac{6 A_1 \bar{a}_1}{L_1} = \frac{6}{12} \left[\frac{1500 \times 10}{2} \left(\frac{2}{3} \times 10 \right) + \frac{420 \times 2}{2} \left(10 + \frac{1}{3} \times 2 \right) \right.$$
$$\left. - \frac{1080 \times 6}{3} \left(4 + \frac{3}{4} \times 6 \right) \right]$$

$$= \tfrac{1}{2}[50{,}000 + 4480 - 18{,}360] = 18{,}060 \text{ lb-ft}^2 \quad \textit{Check}$$

Substituting this value in the three-moment equation gives

$$12 M_1 + 24 M_2 + 18{,}060 = 0$$

which, on being divided by 12, reduces to

$$M_1 + 2 M_2 + 1505 = 0 \tag{a}$$

Another relation between M_1 and M_2 is easily obtained from the fact that tangents to points 1 and 2 of the elastic curve in Fig. 8–23a are each horizontal. Hence, the change in slope between these tangents is zero; and by applying Theorem I of the area-moment method, we obtain

$$\left[\theta_{1-2} = \frac{1}{EI} (\text{Area})_{1-2} = 0 \right] \quad \frac{1500 \times 10}{2} + \frac{420 \times 2}{2} - \frac{1080 \times 6}{3} +$$

$$\frac{12\,M_1}{2} + \frac{12\,M_2}{2} = 0$$

which reduces to

$$M_1 + M_2 + 960 = 0 \qquad\qquad (b)$$

Observe carefully that $(\text{Area})_{1-2}$ refers to the actual moment diagram for the loading in Fig. 8–23a, and hence Theorem I had to be applied to include the areas in Figs. 8–23b and 8–23c.

Subtracting Eq. (b) from Eq. (a) gives

$$M_2 = -\,545 \text{ ft-lb}$$

whence, on substituting M_2 in Eq. (b), we find

$$M_1 = -\,415 \text{ ft-lb}$$

These values agree with our earlier conclusion (see Art. 7–5) that in restrained beams the larger wall moment occurs at the wall closer to the resultant of any single load.

The vertical shears at the walls are found by combining the simple beam reactions with the couple reactions. From $\Sigma M = 0$ taken about each end of the simple beam supporting the loads, the simple beam reactions are found to be 150 lb at the left support and 210 lb at the right support. The couple reactions on span 1 are given by (Art. 8–5)

$$R_1' = \frac{M_l - M_s}{L} = \frac{545 - 415}{12} = 10.8 \text{ lb}$$

This couple reaction acts upward at point 2 (which has the larger numerical value) and downward at point 1. Therefore, the vertical shears are

$$V_1 = 150 - 10.8 = 139.2 \text{ lb}$$

$$V_2 = 210 + 10.8 = 220.8 \text{ lb}$$

The midspan deflection is determined most easily with Theorem II of the area-moment method. Since point 1 in Fig. 8–24a is perfectly fixed, the deviation of point 4 from a tangent to the elastic curve at point 1 equals the deflection. Applying Theorem II to the partial moment diagram drawn by parts only between points 1 and 4, we have

$$\left[t_{4/1} = \frac{1}{EI} (\text{Area})_{1-4} \cdot \bar{x}_4 \right]$$

$$y = \frac{1}{EI} \times \left[\left(\frac{835 \times 6}{2} \right)\left(\frac{6}{3} \right) - (415 \times 6)\left(\frac{6}{2} \right) - \left(\frac{120 \times 2}{3} \right)\left(\frac{2}{4} \right) \right]$$

whence

$$EIy = -\ 2510 \text{ lb-ft}^3 \quad Ans.$$

The minus sign indicates that point 4 on the elastic curve is below the tangent drawn to the curve at point 1, and hence y is directed downward.

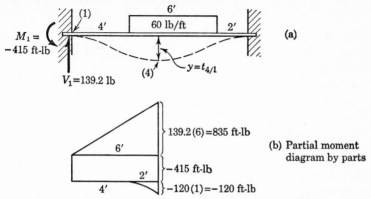

(a)

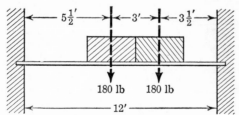

(b) Partial moment diagram by parts

Fig. 8–24. — Deflection by using area-moment method.

We complete this review of methods by checking the above results by the method of superposition. A sufficiently close check may be obtained by considering that the loading in Fig. 8–23a is divided into two concentrated loads, as shown in Fig. 8–25. The given loading is thereby replaced

Fig. 8–25. — Reduction of given load to two concentrated loads for checking by method of superposition.

by two eccentrically placed concentrated loads. Hence, from the formulas of Case 1 from Table VII–1 (restrained beam loadings, page 236), the approximate values of the end moments are

$$M_1 = -\sum \frac{Pab^2}{L^2} = -\ \frac{180 \times 5.5 \times (6.5)^2}{144} - \frac{180 \times 8.5 \times (3.5)^2}{144}$$

$$= -\ 291 - 130 = -\ 421 \text{ ft-lb}$$

$$M_2 = -\sum \frac{Pa^2b}{L^2} = -\ \frac{180 \times (5.5)^2 \times 6.5}{144} - \frac{180 \times (8.5)^2 \times 3.5}{144}$$

$$= -\ 245 - 316 = -\ 561 \text{ ft-lb}$$

These figures agree quite closely with the exact values, − 415 ft-lb and − 545 ft-lb, but are a little larger because of replacing a uniformly distributed load by only two concentrated loads. They would agree even more closely if the given load were divided into three or more segments.

By means of Table VII–1, the approximate value of midspan deflection is determined from

$$EIy = \sum \frac{Pb^2}{48}(3L - 4b) = \frac{180 \times (5.5)^2}{48}(3 \times 12 - 4 \times 5.5) +$$
$$\frac{180 \times (3.5)^2}{48}(3 \times 12 - 4 \times 3.5)$$
$$= 1585 + 1010 = 2595 \text{ lb-ft}^3$$

This result is also in close agreement with the exact value of 2510 lb-ft³, as well as being a little larger.

8–9. Moment Distribution

Modern techniques of designing continuous structures are based on a method of successive approximations popularized by Hardy Cross.[2] This method, which is widely known as the *moment-distribution method*, is applicable to all types of rigid-frame analysis. Its application to continuous beams will serve to introduce this powerful tool of the structural engineer.

Several preliminary concepts are necessary. The first, the *carry-over moment*, is defined as the moment induced at the fixed end of a beam by the action of a moment applied at the other end. Thus consider the beam in

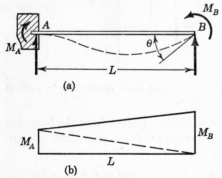

(a)

(b)

Fig. 8–26. — Carry-over moment and beam stiffness.

Fig. 8–26a which is perfectly fixed at A and hinged at B. A moment M_B applied at B flexes the beam as shown and induces the wall moment M_A. The moment diagram, which is drawn as described in Art. 7–5, is shown in Fig. 8–26b. Although M_A is actually negative (because of the downward curvature of the elastic curve at A), it is convenient to consider it positive as shown; consequently the solution will de-

[2] See Cross's papers, "Continuity as a Factor in Reinforced Concrete Design," *Proceedings*, A.C.I., 1929, pp. 669–711; "Simplified Rigid Frame Design," *Proceedings*, A.C.I., 1930, Vol. 26, pp. 170–183; "Analysis of Continuous Frames by Distributing Fixed End Moments," *Transactions*, A.S.C.E.; 1932, Vol. 96, pp. 1–156. See also Hardy Cross and N. D. Morgan, *Continuous Frames of Reinforced Concrete*, Wiley.

termine not only its absolute value but also the correct sign (negative).

The deviation at B from a reference tangent drawn at A is zero because of the perfect wall constraint at A. Hence

$$[EIt_{B/A} = (\text{Area})_{BA} \cdot \bar{x}_B] \qquad (\tfrac{1}{2} M_A L)(\tfrac{2}{3} L) + (\tfrac{1}{2} M_B L)(\tfrac{1}{3} L) = 0$$

whence

$$M_A = -\tfrac{1}{2} M_B \qquad\qquad (8\text{–}3)$$

This result means that a moment applied at the hinged end B "carries over" to the fixed end A a moment that is half the amount and of opposite sign.

A second concept needed for the moment-distribution method is *beam stiffness*. Beam stiffness is the moment required at the simply supported end of a beam to produce unit rotation of that end, the other end being rigidly fixed. Note that this definition implies no relative linear displacement of the two ends of the beam.

The slope at B in Fig. 8–26a is found from the first theorem of the area-moment method and is expressed in terms of the moment diagram in Fig. 8–26b:

$$[EI\theta_{AB} = (\text{Area})_{AB}] \qquad\qquad EI\theta = \tfrac{1}{2} M_A L + \tfrac{1}{2} M_B L$$

Replacing M_A by $-\tfrac{1}{2} M_B$ from Eq. (8–3) gives

$$M_B = \frac{4\,EI\theta}{L}$$

As was said above, the value of M_B when θ equals one radian is known as the *beam stiffness*. It varies with the ratio $\dfrac{I}{L}$ as well as with E. It is denoted by the symbol K; hence

$$\textbf{Absolute } K = \frac{4\,EI}{L} \qquad\qquad (8\text{–}4)$$

However, in many structures E remains constant, so only a relative measure of resistance to rotation is required. This may be called *relative beam stiffness* and is expressed by

$$\textbf{Relative } K = \frac{I}{L} \qquad\qquad (8\text{–}5)$$

We are now ready to describe qualitatively the moment-distribution procedure.

The continuous beam in Fig. 8–27a is perfectly restrained at A and C and simply supported at B. Assume that at B the beam is temporarily locked or rigidified against the rotation caused by the loads P and Q. Under these conditions, segments AB and BC will act as fixed ended beams subjected to the fixed end moments caused by loads P and Q. These fixed end moments (hereafter abbreviated to FEM) are assumed to have the values shown in Fig. 8–27b.

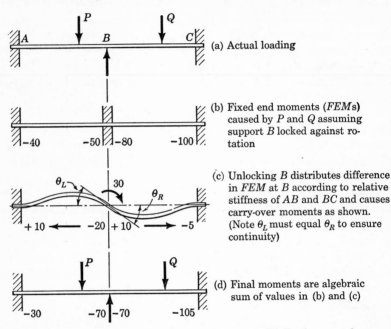

(a) Actual loading

(b) Fixed end moments (*FEM*s) caused by P and Q assuming support B locked against rotation

(c) Unlocking B distributes difference in *FEM* at B according to relative stiffness of AB and BC and causes carry-over moments as shown. (Note θ_L must equal θ_R to ensure continuity)

(d) Final moments are algebraic sum of values in (b) and (c)

FIG. 8–27. — Qualitative description of moment-distribution procedure.

If the support at B is now released or unlocked, the difference in FEM between sections to the left and right of B creates an unbalanced moment of 30 ft-lb which causes the beam at B to rotate, as shown in Fig. 8–27c, until the moments at B are balanced. Obviously, the moment to the left of B will be increased by some amount, say 20 ft-lb; and to the right of B, the moment will be decreased by the remaining 10 ft-lb of the 30 ft-lb difference between the FEM at B in Fig. 8–27b. Thus the unbalanced moment is distributed at the unlocked support. The rotation of B caused by these distributed moments induces, at A and C, carry-over moments of half the amount and of opposite sign. These carry-over moments are indicated by the arrows in Fig. 8–27c.

The ratio of distribution of the unbalanced moment at B is fixed by the fact that the two beams must rotate through the same angle at B. This means that the unbalanced moment must be distributed in the ratio of the stiffness factors of the adjacent beams. The ratio of distribution to any beam is called a *distribution factor*, *DF* and is defined by

$$DF = \frac{K}{\Sigma K} \tag{8-6}$$

where K is the stiffness factor for that beam and ΣK is the sum of the stiffness factors for adjacent beams. If the beams are of the same material (as is generally the case) only relative K need be used. Further, if they are of the same cross-section, relative K (i.e., beam stiffness) is inversely proportional to the length (see Eq. 8–5). In distributing the *FEM*s the object is to secure balance at the unlocked support. The distributed moments are opposite in sign and so applied as to increase the smaller and decrease the larger *FEM* at the locked support.

The final moments in Fig. 8–27*d* are obtained by superposition of the *FEM*s in Fig. 8–27*b* and of the distributed moments and carry-over moments in Fig. 8–27*c*.

The moment-distribution method may be summarized in the following steps:

1. Assume that all supports are fixed or locked and compute *fixed end moments* for each span considered separate from every other span. Table VII–1 (page 236) will be helpful in computing these *FEM*s.

2. Unlock each support and *distribute* the unbalanced moment at each one to each adjacent span by means of Eq. (8–6). Then relock each support.

3. After distributing the unbalanced moment to each adjacent span, carry over one-half this amount, with *opposite* sign, to the other end of each span, as specified in Eq. (8–3).

This completes one cycle of distribution. Steps 2 and 3 must be repeated because of the new unbalance caused by the carry-over moments. Such repetitions are made until the carry-over moments become zero or negligibly small. The process may be stopped when any distribution is completed, the accuracy of the final results depending on the number of cycles. As a rule, no more than four cycles are necessary, since the unbalance caused by the carry-over moments usually decreases rapidly to zero.

The following illustrative problems show the method of recording results, as well as some suggested modifications or shortcuts.

ILLUSTRATIVE PROBLEMS

856. The continuous beam of constant cross-section and material shown in Fig. 8–28 is perfectly restrained at the ends. Compute the moments over the supports.

Solution: Although I is not specified, it is convenient to take I as numerically equal to the greater length, i.e., 18 units. Then the values of relative stiffness $K = \dfrac{I}{L}$ are as shown, and the distribution factors (*DF*) are computed from Eq. (8–6) and also listed.

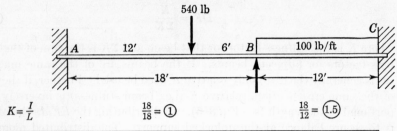

FIG. 8–28.

Assuming all supports locked, and using Table VII–1 (page 236), we compute values for the fixed end moments (*FEM*):

Span *AB*:
$$M_A = -\frac{Pab^2}{L^2} = -\frac{540(12)(6)^2}{(18)^2} = -720 \text{ ft-lb}$$

$$M_B = -\frac{Pa^2b}{L^2} = -\frac{540(12)^2(6)}{(18)^2} = -1440 \text{ ft-lb}$$

Span *BC*:
$$M_B = M_C = -\frac{wL^2}{12} = -\frac{100(12)^2}{12} = -1200 \text{ ft-lb}$$

With *B* unlocked, the unbalanced moment is the numerical difference between the *FEM* at *B*, or $1440 - 1200 = 240$ ft-lb. Using the values of *DF*, we distribute this unbalanced moment to the left of *B* as $0.4(240) = +96$ ft-lb and to the right of *B* as $0.6(240) = -144$ ft-lb. These values are given signs so that combining them with the *FEM* causes equal moments on either side of *B*. One-half the values of these balancing moments are now carried over with the opposite sign. Thus $+96$ applied to the left of *B* is carried over as -48 to *A*, and -144 applied to the right of *B* is carried over as $+72$ to *C*.

Since *A* and *C* are locked or fixed and are specified as remaining so, they absorb these carry-over moments and the distribution is completed. The final values of the bending moment at each support are obtained by algebraic summations of each vertical column, giving the results shown.

857. The continuous beam in Fig. 8–29 carries the same loads as the beam in Prob. 856, but the ends at *A* and *C* are simply supported. Compute the support moments.

Solution: Values of *K* and *DF* are computed and listed as in Prob. 856. Assuming all supports locked. the *FEM*s are also computed and listed.

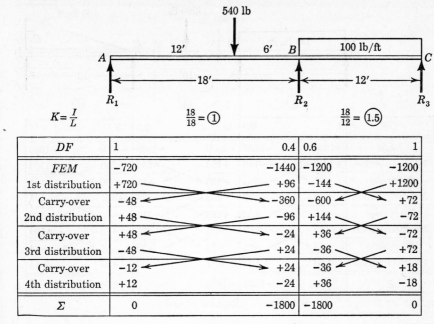

$$K=\frac{I}{L} \qquad \frac{18}{18} = ① \qquad \frac{18}{12} = ⑴.⑸$$

DF	1		0.4	0.6		1
FEM	−720		−1440	−1200		−1200
1st distribution	+720		+96	−144		+1200
Carry-over	−48		−360	−600		+72
2nd distribution	+48		−96	+144		−72
Carry-over	+48		−24	+36		−72
3rd distribution	−48		+24	−36		+72
Carry-over	−12		+24	−36		+18
4th distribution	+12		−24	+36		−18
Σ	0		−1800	−1800		0

Fig. 8–29.

All the supports are now unlocked, which restores the beam to the specified conditions at each support. The unbalanced moment at each support set up by unlocking the supports must now be distributed. At B the distribution is as described in Prob. 856; but releasing A and C is equivalent to adding moments of $+720$ and $+1200$ respectively, so as to cause a final moment of zero at these free ends. When this distribution is completed and all the supports are relocked, the distributed moments cause the carry-over effects indicated by the arrows, and this again introduces unbalance at the locked supports. However, this unbalance is appreciably smaller.

We continue to unlock each support, distribute the unbalanced moment, and relock each support, thus completing another cycle of distribution, until the carry-over moments become negligibly small or, as here in cycle 3, until the sum of the carry-over moment and the distributed moment is zero on each side of a support. Further cycles of distribution will then produce no effect, as cycle 4 shows. Note that the analysis must end with a distribution and not with a carry-over.

858. Apply the moment-distribution method to the continuous beam of three spans with free ends shown in Fig. 8–30.

Solution: There are two solutions. The first, in (a), involves the same procedure that was described in Prob. 857 for free ends on two spans. It is inconvenient to treat a free end as fixed, carry moment over to it, and then release it again. It is simpler to use a modification in which the free end, initially assumed fixed, is re-

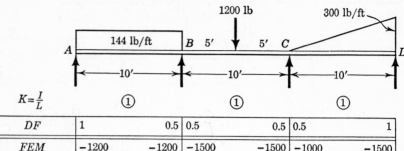

DF	1		0.5	0.5		0.5	0.5		1
FEM	−1200		−1200	−1500		−1500	−1000		−1500
1st distribution	+1200		−150	+150		+250	−250		+1500
Carry-over	+75		−600	−125		−75	−750		+125
2nd distribution	−75		+237	−238		−338	+337		−125
Carry-over	−119		+38	+169		+119	+63		−169
3rd distribution	+119		+65	−66		−28	+28		+169
Carry-over	−33		−60	+14		+33	−85		−14
4th distribution	+33		+37	−37		−59	+59		+14
Σ	0		−1633	−1633		−1598	−1598		0

Solution (a)   Regular procedure

$K=\frac{I}{L}$	$\frac{3}{4}\times 1=\left(\frac{3}{4}\right)$			①			$\frac{3}{4}\times 1=\left(\frac{3}{4}\right)$		
DF	1		$\frac{3}{7}$	$\frac{4}{7}$		$\frac{4}{7}$	$\frac{3}{7}$		1
FEM	−1200		−1200	−1500		−1500	−1000		−1500
Release A & D	+1200	⟶	−600				−750	⟵	+1500
Adjusted FEM	0		−1800	−1500		−1500	−1750		0
1st distribution			+128	−172		−143	+107		
Carry-over				+72		+86			
2nd distribution			+31	−41		−49	+37		
Carry-over				+25		+20			
3rd distribution			+11	−14		−11	+9		
Carry-over				+6		+7			
4th distribution			+3	−3		−4	+3		
Σ	0		−1627	−1627		−1594	−1594		0

Solution (b)   Shortcut procedure

Fig. 8–30.

leased only once and has no moment carried over to it for further distribution. To understand this modification, we shall show how the moment that is distributed to the left of B in the first distribution of solution (a) is carried through the computations. This moment, denoted by M in Fig. 8–31, carries over to A as $-\frac{1}{2} M$ if A is locked. If A is a free end, releasing it causes the distributed moment $+\frac{1}{2} M$ at A, which then carries over to B the moment $-\frac{1}{2}(\frac{1}{2} M) = -\frac{1}{4} M$. A summation of these values gives zero at A (which is now freely hinged) and $\frac{3}{4} M$ at B.

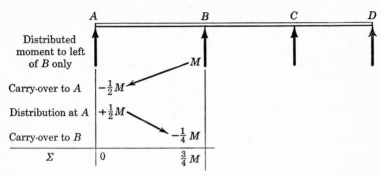

	A	B	C	D
Distributed moment to left of B only		M		
Carry-over to A	$-\frac{1}{2}M$			
Distribution at A	$+\frac{1}{2}M$			
Carry-over to B		$-\frac{1}{4} M$		
Σ	0	$\frac{3}{4} M$		

Fig. 8–31. — Modification of distribution at B to avoid carry-over to free end A.

If the initial distribution at B had been modified so that only $\frac{3}{4} M$ were distributed to B, these results would have been obtained directly, with no moment carried over to A. In other words, if the stiffness factor for AB is multiplied by $\frac{3}{4}$, the distribution at B is modified so that no moment need be carried over to the free end.

This shortcut is applied in the second solution (*b*) shown in Fig. 8–30. As a start, reduce A and D to free ends by releasing them, applying the balancing moments of $+1200$ at A and $+1500$ at D, and carrying over half these amounts with opposite signs to B and C as shown. Now distribute the *FEM*s at B and C, using the distribution factors obtained by modifying the stiffness of AB and CD as described above. Note that no moment is carried over to the free ends under these conditions. Note also that we are approaching the final result more rapidly in the fourth distribution here than in the corresponding fourth distribution in the first solution.

859. The loading in Prob. 858 is modified in Fig. 8–32 by adding an overhang at A and fixing the end at D. The moments of inertia of segments AB and CD are each equal to 20 units, but that of BC is increased to 30 units. The relative stiffnesses are therefore $K_{AB} = 2$, $K_{BC} = 3$, and $K_{CD} = 2$. Compute the moments over the supports.

Solution: This problem illustrates two additional concepts. (1) The cross-section may vary from segment to segment and is taken into account by computing the $\frac{I}{L}$ ratio for each segment.[3] (2) The overhanging end offers no resistance to rotation. Hence, when A is released, the unbalance of 400 ft-lb must be distributed as zero to the left of A and as $+400$ ft-lb to the right of A. When -200 ft-lb is carried over to B, the adjusted fixed end moments are as shown below the first double line. Also, to avoid carrying moments back to A, we multiply K_{AB} by $\frac{3}{4}$, and the shortcut

[3] More complex cases, in which the cross-section varies along the segment, are treated by Cross and Morgan, *Continuous Frames of Reinforced Concrete*, Wiley.

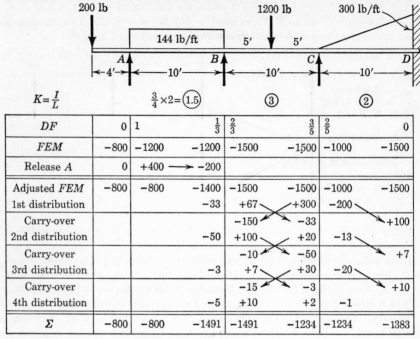

$K = \dfrac{I}{L}$ $\dfrac{3}{4} \times 2 = \boxed{1.5}$ ③   ②

DF	0	1	$\frac{1}{3}$	$\frac{2}{3}$	$\frac{3}{5}$	$\frac{2}{5}$	0
FEM	−800	−1200	−1200	−1500	−1500	−1000	−1500
Release A	0	+400 ⟶	−200				
Adjusted FEM	−800	−800	−1400	−1500	−1500	−1000	−1500
1st distribution			−33	+67	+300	−200	
Carry-over				−150	−33		+100
2nd distribution			−50	+100	+20	−13	
Carry-over				−10	−50		+7
3rd distribution			−3	+7	+30	−20	
Carry-over				−15	−3		+10
4th distribution			−5	+10	+2	−1	
Σ	−800	−800	−1491	−1491	−1234	−1234	−1383

Solution (a)   Regular procedure

DF	0	1	$\frac{1}{3}$	$\frac{2}{3}$	$\frac{3}{5}$	$\frac{2}{5}$	0
FEM	−800	−1200	−1200	−1500	−1500	−1000	−1500
1st distribution	0	+400	−100	+200	+300	−200	
Carry-over			−200	−150	−100		+100
2nd distribution		+17	−33	+60	−40		
Carry-over				−30	+16		+20
3rd distribution			−10	+20	−10	+6	
Carry-over				+5	−10		−3
4th distribution			+2	−3	+7	−3	
Σ	−800	−800	−1491	−1491	−1237	−1237	−1383

Solution (b)   Alternate procedure

FIG. 8–32.

procedure described in Prob. 858 is then applied, as shown in Fig. 8–32. Note that the fixed end at D absorbs the carry-over moments from C but does not transfer any back to C.

An alternate distribution preferred by some engineers gives substantially the same results and is also shown in Fig. 8–32. Here, instead of starting with an adjusted *FEM* at *A* and *B*, the unbalanced moment at all supports is first distributed at each support and then carried over as shown.

PROBLEMS

Solve the following problems, using the moment-distribution method.

860. See Prob. 815 (page 251).

861. See Prob. 818.

862. See Prob. 819.

863. See Prob. 836.

864. See Prob. 837.

865. See Prob. 838.

Chapter IX

Combined Stresses

9–1. Introduction

In preceding chapters we studied three basic types of loading: axial, torsional, and flexural. Each of these types was discussed on the assumption that only one of these loadings was acting on a structure at a time. The present chapter is concerned with cases in which two or more of these loadings act simultaneously upon a structure. The three basic types of loading and the corresponding stress formula may be summarized as follows:

$$\text{Axial loading:} \quad S_a = \frac{P}{A}$$

$$\text{Torsional loading:} \quad S_s = \frac{T\rho}{J}$$

$$\text{Flexural loading:} \quad S_f = \frac{My}{I}$$

There are four possible combinations of these loadings: (1) axial and flexural; (2) axial and torsional; (3) torsional and flexural; and (4) axial, torsional, and flexural, acting simultaneously. We shall consider the axial and flexural combination first because it combines only normal stresses and is therefore the simplest. Each of the others combines shearing and normal stresses and requires a preliminary discussion (see Art. 9–4 to 9–7) before they can be considered.

9–2. Combined Axial and Flexural Loads

The simply supported beam in Fig. 9–1a carries a concentrated load Q. The supports are hinged to the beam at its centroidal surface. At point A, the flexural stress is $S_f = \frac{My}{I}$. It is tensile and is directed normal to the surface of the cross-section, as shown. The force exerted on the element at A is $S_f \, dA$.

If the same beam supported in the same way is loaded only with an axial load P (Fig. 9–1b), the axial stresses are uniformly distributed across any transverse section (Art. 1–3). Their magnitude is $S_a = \frac{P}{A}$; they are tensile and directed normal to the cross-section. The force exerted on the element at A is $S_a\,dA$.

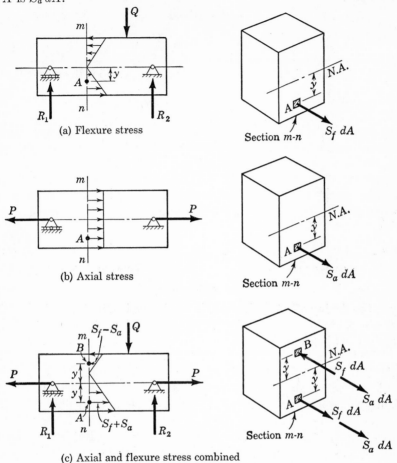

(a) Flexure stress

Section *m-n* $S_f\,dA$

(b) Axial stress

Section *m-n* $S_a\,dA$

(c) Axial and flexure stress combined
Note shift in position of line of zero stress

Fig. 9–1.

If both loads act simultaneously on the beam (Fig. 9–1c), the resultant stress at A is equal to the superposition of the two separate effects. Thus, the resultant force at A is the vector sum of the collinear forces $S_a\,dA$ and $S_f\,dA$. Dividing this by the area dA gives the resultant stress $S = S_a + S_f$ directed normal to the cross-section.

Similarly, at a point B in the same section, also at a distance y from the neutral axis but above it, the resultant stress is the difference between the axial and flexural stresses. If tensile stress is denoted by a positive sign and compressive stress by a negative sign, the resultant stress at any point of the beam is given by the algebraic sum of the axial and flexural stresses at that point:

$$S = S_a \pm S_f$$

or

$$S = \begin{matrix} \oplus \\ \ominus \end{matrix} \frac{P}{A} \pm \frac{My}{I} \tag{9-1}$$

Note that the axial stress may be compressive which is the reason for the circled $\oplus$ and $\ominus$ signs before $\dfrac{P}{A}$. The circling of these signs is a reminder that the axial stress is uniform and of the same type all over a cross-section, whereas the magnitude and type of the flexural stress vary with position.

In Eq. (9-1) we used the method of superposition. One note of caution is necessary, as the following makes clear: Fig. 9-2 shows, in exaggerated

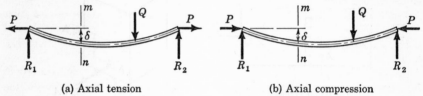

(a) Axial tension   (b) Axial compression

Fig. 9-2.

form, the flexing effect of Q. If P is tensile, as in Fig. 9-2a, the bending moment of P at any section, i.e., $P\delta$, tends to reduce the bending moment due to Q and hence slightly reduces the flexural stress. The opposite effect occurs when the axial load is compressive, as in Fig. 9-2b, where the additional bending moment $P\delta$ slightly increases the flexural stress. In other words, the values given by Eq. (9-1) are slightly high when P is tensile and slightly low when P is compressive. These effects are negligible in the case of most structural members, which are usually so stiff that stresses produced by bending moments like $P\delta$ can be neglected. But in long slender members or columns, the effect is significant, and more exact methods must be used.[1]

ILLUSTRATIVE PROBLEM

901. A cantilever beam (Fig. 9-3) has the profile shown so that it will provide sufficient clearances for large pulleys mounted on the line shaft it supports. The reaction of the line shaft is a load $P = 6000$ lb. Determine the resultant normal stresses at A and B at the wall.

Solution: We begin by computing the bending moment of P. This is computed in terms of its components $P_x = 4800$ lb and $P_y = 3600$ lb by taking moments about the centroidal axis of section AB:

$$[M = (\Sigma M_{cg})_R] \qquad M = -3600(18) + 4800(6) = -36{,}000 \text{ in.-lb}$$

[1] See, for example, Niles and Newell's *Aircraft Structures*, published by Wiley.

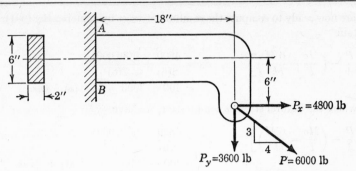

FIG. 9–3.

P_y acts down; hence its moment effect is negative (Art. 4–2) and the opposite moment effect of P_x must be positive. The negative sign of the bending moment at AB indicates that the beam curvature at section AB is concave downward (Art. 4–2), thereby causing tension at A and compression at B. Having thus interpreted the sign of the bending moment, only its absolute value is used in applying Eq. (9–1).

However, it may not as yet be obvious that the axial tensile effect is due solely to P_x. Use the principles of mechanics to convert the given load into either of the equivalent loadings in Fig. 9–4. It is evident from the principle of transmissibility that the entire moment effect is due to P_y in Fig. 9–4b, and therefore the axial effect

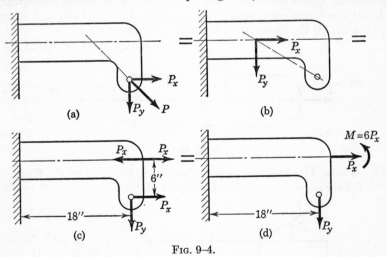

FIG. 9–4.

is caused by P_x alone. Or we may add a pair of collinear forces each equal to P_x, as in Fig. 9–4c, thereby reducing the system to that shown in Fig. 9–4d. Once again we see that the axial effect is caused by P_x, since the bending moment, which consists of $-18 P_y$ plus the couple $6 P_x$, is equivalent to the bending moment as computed above.

We are now ready to compute the resultant stresses by applying Eq. (9–1). At A we obtain

$$\left[S = \frac{P}{A} + \left(\frac{Mc}{I} = \frac{6\,M}{bh^2} \right) \right] \qquad S_A = \frac{4800}{2(6)} + \frac{6(36{,}000)}{2(6)^2}$$
$$= 400 + 3000 = 3400 \text{ psi} \quad Ans.$$

At B, where the flexural stress is compressive, we have

$$\left[S = \frac{P}{A} - \left(\frac{Mc}{I} = \frac{6\,M}{bh^2} \right) \right] \qquad S_B = \frac{4800}{2(6)} - \frac{6(36{,}000)}{2(6)^2}$$
$$= 400 - 3000 = -\,2600 \text{ psi} \quad Ans.$$

The signs indicate that the stress is tensile at A and compressive at B.

PROBLEMS

902. Compare the maximum stress in a bent rod $\frac{1}{2}$ in. square, where the load P is $\frac{1}{2}$ in. off center as shown, with the maximum stress if the rod were straight and the load applied axially. This problem illustrates why lateral deflection in columns is so dangerous.   *Ans.* 7 to 1

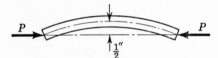

PROB. 902.

903. To avoid interference, a link in a certain machine is designed so that its cross-sectional area is reduced one-half at section A–B, as shown. Compute the maximum tensile stress developed across section A–B if (*a*) the section is a square 4 in. by 4 in., (*b*) the cross-section is a circle 4 in. in diameter.

Ans.   (*a*) 24,000 psi; (*b*) 27,300 psi

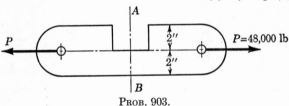

PROB. 903.

904. A beam 4 in. by 12 in., supported as shown, carries a load P. What is the value of P if the maximum stress is not to exceed 1200 psi?   *Ans.* $P = 5430$ lb

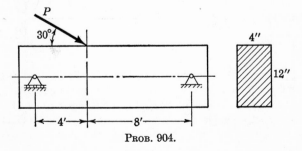

PROB. 904.

905. For the beam 2 in. by 8 in. shown, find the normal stresses at A and B. Are these the points of maximum normal stress? If not, where are they located and what are their values?

Ans. $S_A = -6270$ psi; $S_B = 3850$ psi; max. $S_n = -7510$ psi and 5090 psi

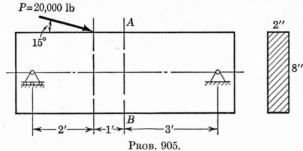

PROB. 905.

906. A punch press has the frame shown. Determine the greatest force P that can be exerted at the jaws of the punch without exceeding a stress of 18,000 psi at section A–B. The properties of the area are as shown and 1–1 is the centroidal axis.

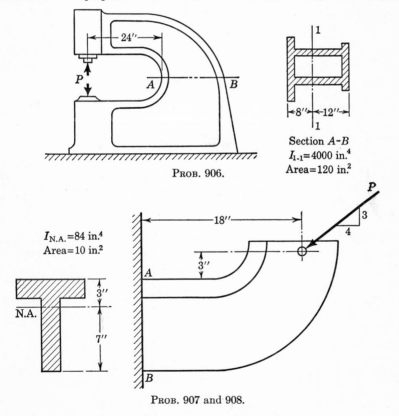

PROB. 906.

Section A-B
$I_{1\text{-}1} = 4000$ in.^{4}
Area = 120 in.^{2}

$I_{\text{N.A.}} = 84$ in.^{4}
Area = 10 in.^{2}

PROB. 907 and 908.

907. If $P = 18,000$ lb for the bracket shown, compute the maximum values of S_t and S_c developed at section A—B.

908. Determine the maximum safe load P that may be applied to the given bracket if the allowable stresses at section A–B are max. $S_t \leq 4000$ psi and max. $S_c \leq 12,000$ psi. $\qquad$ *Ans.* $P = 20,700$ lb

909. Compute the stresses at A and B on the given link if $P = 6000$ lb and $F = 0$. $\qquad$ *Ans.* $S_A = 2400$ psi; $S_B = -1600$ psi

910. Solve Prob. 909 if $P = 6000$ lb and $F = 8000$ lb.

$\qquad$ *Ans.* $S_A = -1200$ psi; $S_B = 2800$ psi

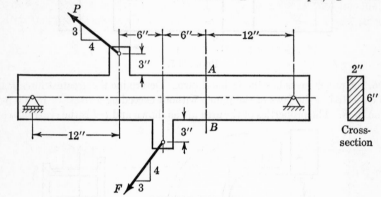

PROB. 909 and 910.

911. A concrete dam has the profile shown. If concrete weighs 150 lb/ft³ and water weighs 62.5 lb/ft³, determine the maximum compressive stress on section m–n if the depth of water behind the dam is $h = 45$ ft.

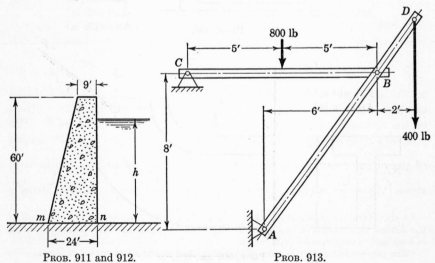

PROB. 911 and 912. $\qquad$ PROB. 913.

912. Compute the maximum depth h of water that can be maintained behind the dam in Prob. 911 without causing a tensile stress on section m–n.

$$Ans. \quad h = 46.7 \text{ ft}$$

913. The structure shown is hinged to fixed supports at A and C. Assume that the pin connections at A, B, and C are frictionless. The bars are each 4 in. by 4 in. in section. Compute the maximum compressive stress developed in bar AD.

$$Ans. \quad S_c = 966 \text{ psi}$$

9–3. Kern of a Section. Loads Applied Off Axes of Symmetry

A special case of combined axial and flexural loads is illustrated in Fig. 9–5a, in which a short strut[2] carries a compressive load P applied with an

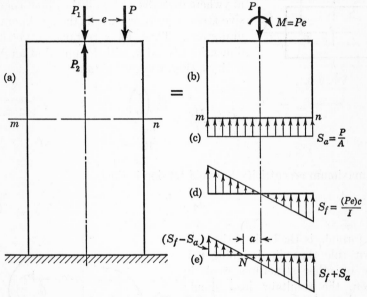

FIG. 9–5.

eccentricity e along one of the principal axes[3] of the section. The addition of a pair of forces P_1 and P_2, each of magnitude P and acting at the centroid of the section, causes the equivalent loading shown in Fig. 9–5b. The stresses across any typical section m–n are the result of the superposition of the direct compressive stress $\left(S_a = \dfrac{P}{A}\right)$ in Fig. 9–5c and the flexural stress $\left(S_f = \dfrac{Mc}{I} = (Pe)\dfrac{c}{I}\right)$ in Fig. 9–5d. If the maximum flexural stress is

[2] A short strut is one whose length is no more than 10 times its least lateral dimension; the flexural deflection is so small that its effect can be neglected. The eccentric loading of long bars is considered in Art. 11–6.

[3] The principal axes are the axes of maximum and minimum moments of inertia.

larger than the direct compressive stress, the resultant stress appears as in Fig. 9–5e. The point of zero stress N is the new location of the neutral axis and is easily found by computing the distance a at which the tensile flexural stress equals the direct compressive stress:

$$\frac{P}{A} = \frac{My}{I} = \frac{(Pe)a}{I}$$

whence

$$a = \frac{I}{Ae} \qquad (9\text{–}2)$$

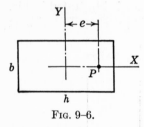

FIG. 9–6.

It is evident that there will be no tensile stress anywhere over the section if the direct compressive stress equals or exceeds the maximum flexural stress. Thus, for a rectangular section of dimensions b and h, with P applied at an eccentricity e (Fig. 9–6), we obtain

$$\frac{P}{A} = \frac{Mc}{I} = \frac{Pe\left(\dfrac{h}{2}\right)}{\dfrac{bh^3}{12}}$$

The maximum eccentricity to avoid tension is thus

$$e = \frac{h}{6} \qquad (9\text{–}3)$$

This formula is the basis of the well-known rule that, in designing masonry or other structures weak in tension, the resultant load should fall in the middle third of the section.

We now consider the general case[4] in which the load P is applied at any point with respect to the principal axes X and Y, as in Fig. 9–7. If e_x and e_y represent the eccentricities of P, the moments of P with respect to the X and Y axes are respectively

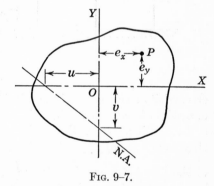

FIG. 9–7.

Pe_y and Pe_x. By superposition, the stress at any point of the cross-section whose coordinates are x and y is

---

[4] Actually, this is an application of unsymmetrical bending, which is discussed at length in Art. 12–8.

$$S = -\frac{P}{A} - \frac{(Pe_x)\,x}{I_y} - \frac{(Pe_y)\,y}{I_x} \qquad (9\text{-}4)$$

To determine the neutral axis or line of zero stress in the cross-section, we set $S = 0$. Using $\dfrac{I_y}{A} = k_y{}^2$ and $\dfrac{I_x}{A} = k_x{}^2$ where k_y and k_x are respectively the radii of gyration relative to the Y and X axes, we obtain

$$0 = 1 + \frac{e_x}{k_y{}^2}x + \frac{e_y}{k_x{}^2}y \qquad (a)$$

The intercepts u and v of the neutral axis with the X and Y axes respectively are found by substituting first $y = 0$ and then $x = 0$ in Eq. (a). This gives

$$u = -\frac{k_y{}^2}{e_x} \quad \text{and} \quad v = -\frac{k_x{}^2}{e_y} \qquad (b)$$

The neutral axis passes through the quadrant which is opposite to that containing P, and in general is *not* perpendicular to the direction OP. For example, the stress distribution on a rectangular section caused by a load P not on the principal axes (Fig. 9–8a) is shown in Fig. 9–8b. If the stresses at A, B, and C are computed, the intersection of the neutral axis with AB and BC (or their extensions) can be easily determined by proportion.

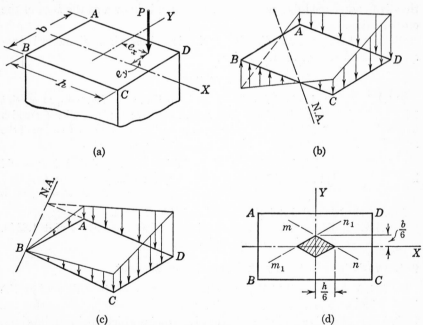

(a) (b)

(c) (d)

Fig. 9–8. — Neutral axis for load P eccentrically applied and kern of rectangular section.

Let us now determine the coordinates e_x and e_y of the load P, for which the neutral axis passes through the corner B, as in Fig. 9–8c. Substituting $S = 0$, $x = -\dfrac{h}{2}$, and $y = -\dfrac{b}{2}$ in Eq. (9–4), we obtain

$$0 = -\frac{P}{bh} + \frac{(Pe_x)\left(\dfrac{h}{2}\right)}{\dfrac{bh^3}{12}} + \frac{(Pe_y)\left(\dfrac{b}{2}\right)}{\dfrac{hb^3}{12}}$$

or

$$\frac{e_x}{\dfrac{h}{6}} + \frac{e_y}{\dfrac{b}{6}} = 1 \qquad\qquad (c)$$

This is the equation of the straight line mn in Fig. 9–8d; it intersects the X and Y axes at $\dfrac{h}{6}$ and $\dfrac{b}{6}$ respectively. This line is the locus of points of application of P, for which corner B has zero stress. Any compressive load above and to the right of this line causes tension at B. Similarly the line $m_1 n_1$ is the locus of loads that cause zero stress in corner C. Continuing this procedure indicates that evidently no corner and no part of the cross-section will be in tension if the resultant compressive load lies on or within the diamond-shaped figure. This shaded area is known as the *kern* of the cross-section.

Show that the kern of a circular section is a circle whose diameter is one-quarter the diameter of the section.

PROBLEMS

914. A compressive load $P = 14{,}400$ lb is applied, as in Fig. 9–8a, at a point 1 in. to the right and 2 in. above the centroid of a rectangular section for which $h = 12$ in. and $b = 6$ in. Compute the stress at each corner and the location of the neutral axis. Illustrate answers with a sketch similar to Fig. 9–8b.

915. From the data in Prob. 914, what additional load applied at the centroid is necessary so that no tensile stress will exist anywhere on the cross-section?

Ans. $P = 21{,}600$ lb

916. Calculate and sketch the kern of a 14 WF 87 beam.

Ans. A diamond-shaped figure having coordinates on axis *1–1* of ± 1.88 in. and on axis *2–2* of ± 5.40 in.

9–4. Variation of Stress with Inclination of Element

In Art. 1–2 we saw that the magnitude and type of stress depend on the inclination of an element. As a review of that discussion, consider that the body in Fig. 9–9a is acted upon by the given forces which are in equilibrium. Pass two exploratory sections a–a and b–b through the body, section a–a

perpendicular to the resultant R of P_1 and P_2 as in Fig. 9–9b, and section b–b inclined to R.   Thus, at the same position in a stressed body (located at the intersection of sections a–a and b–b), an element whose face is oriented as in Fig. 9–9b will be subjected to different stress intensities than the element in Fig. 9–9c.

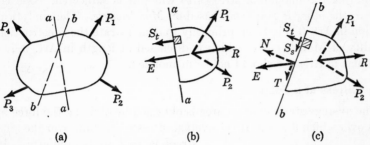

| (a) | (b) | (c) |

Fig. 9–9. — Stress at a point varies with inclination of plane through the point.

It is evident that the average normal stress in Fig. 9–9b is greater than that in Fig. 9–9c.   With combined loadings, however, it is not simple to predetermine the angular position of an element that is subjected to maximum stress; moreover no formulas exist for computing directly the stresses on any arbitrarily chosen surface.   In beams, for example, the flexure formula determines stresses only on planes normal to the longitudinal axis of the beam.   So also for torsional shearing stresses; the torsion formula determines shearing stresses only on sections normal to the longitudinal axis of a twisted bar.   Thus, in a bar subjected to simultaneous bending and twisting, as in Fig. 9–10, we can compute the flexural and shearing stresses

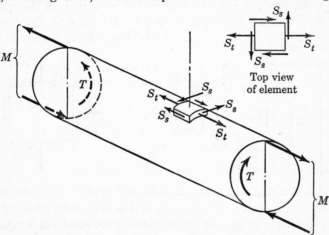

Top view
of element

Fig. 9–10. — Stresses caused by simultaneous flexure and torsion.

only for elements in the position shown. But the discussion of Fig. 9–9 indicates that if the element in Fig. 9–10 were rotated about the axis shown, there would be a particular position at which maximum normal stress would exist.

There are two methods of determining this position of the element and computing the maximum stresses to which it is subjected. One is analytical; the other is graphical, based on *Mohr's circle*. The analytical discussion in Art. 9–6 is given primarily to demonstrate the construction and validity of Mohr's circle, which is discussed at length in Art. 9–7. The formulas in Art. 9–6 should *not* be memorized.

9–5. Stress at a Point

The average stress over an area is obtained by dividing the force by the area over which it acts. If the average stress is constant over the area, the

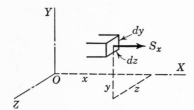

FIG. 9–11. — Stress at a point.

stress is said to be uniform. If the stress is not uniform, the stress at any point is found by permitting the area enclosing the point to approach zero as a limit. In other words, *stress at a point* really defines the uniform stress distributed over a differential area. In Fig. 9–11, for example, the normal stress in an X direction acting at the point whose coordinates are x, y, and z means the uniform stress acting over the differential area $dy\, dz$.

When the stress at a point is defined by components acting in several directions, the stresses may be represented as acting on the differential element (i.e., volume) enclosing the point. For example, let the stresses at a point be S_x, S_y, and S_{xy}; Fig. 9–12a shows these stresses as they act

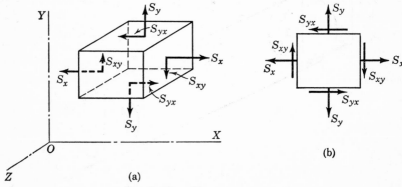

(a)

(b)

FIG. 9–12. — Stress components.

on the differential element enclosing the point. The element is usually represented by its front view, as in Fig. 9–12b. Note the shearing stress S_{yx} acting on the Y face in the X direction. This is due to the fact that a shearing stress on any plane induces an equal shearing stress on a plane perpendicular to the first one. (See Art. 5–7, page 154.)

The notation used here defines a *normal* stress by means of a single sub-script corresponding to the face on which it acts. A face takes the name of the axis normal to it, e.g., the X face is perpendicular to the X axis. A *shearing* stress is denoted by a double subscript, the first letter correspond-ing to the face on which the shearing stress acts and the second indicating the direction in which it acts. Thus the shearing stress on the X face act-ing in the Y direction is denoted by S_{xy}, and the shearing stress on the Y face acting in the X direction is denoted by S_{yx}. Of course $S_{xy} = S_{yx}$, since the shearing stresses on perpendicular planes are equal.

In this and succeeding articles, we consider only plane stress in which the stresses act parallel to a single plane such as the XY plane. In a tri-axial stress, the Z face of an element may be subject to the normal stress S_z as well as to shearing stresses S_{zx} and S_{zy}. These shearing stresses then induce the numerically equal shearing stresses S_{xz} and S_{yz} which act respectively on the X and Y faces.

9–6. Variation of Stress at a Point. Analytical Derivation

The stress acting at a point is represented by the stresses acting on the faces of the element enclosing the point. As we saw in Art. 9–4, the stresses change with the inclination of the planes passing through that point; i.e., the stresses on the faces of the element vary as the angular position of the element changes.

In determining these stress variations analytically, a plane is passed that cuts the original element into two parts and the conditions of equilibrium are applied to either part. Fig. 9–13b shows the normal and shearing stress components acting on the plane whose normal N makes an angle θ with the X axis (see Fig. 9–13a). The triangular element in Fig. 9–13b is in equi-librium under the action of the forces arising from the stresses that act over its faces. The area of the inclined face being denoted by A, these forces are shown in the free-body diagram in Fig. 9–13c. The point diagram of these forces is shown in Fig. 9–13d.

Applying the conditions of equilibrium to axes chosen as in Fig. 9–13d, we obtain

$$[\Sigma N = 0] \qquad AS_n = (S_x A \cos \theta) \cos \theta + (S_y A \sin \theta) \sin \theta -$$
$$(S_{xy} A \cos \theta) \sin \theta - (S_{yx} A \sin \theta) \cos \theta \qquad (a)$$

and

$$[\Sigma T = 0] \qquad AS_s = (S_x A \cos \theta) \sin \theta - (S_y A \sin \theta) \cos \theta +$$
$$(S_{xy} A \cos \theta) \cos \theta - (S_{yz} A \sin \theta) \sin \theta \qquad (b)$$

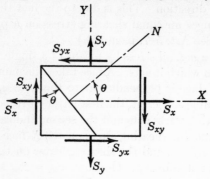

(a) Original state of stress

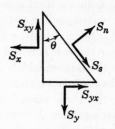

(b) Stresses acting on wedge

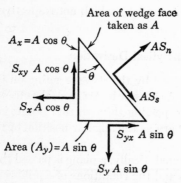

(c) Free-body diagram of forces on wedge   (d) Point diagram of forces

Fig. 9–13. — Variation of stress components.

Since the common term A can be canceled and since S_{yz} is numerically equal to S_{xy}, we use the relations

$$\cos^2 \theta = \frac{1 + \cos 2\theta}{2}, \ \sin^2 \theta = \frac{1 - \cos 2\theta}{2}, \ \sin \theta \cos \theta = \frac{1}{2} \sin 2\theta$$

to reduce Eqs. (a) and (b) to

$$S_n = \frac{S_x + S_y}{2} + \frac{S_x - S_y}{2} \cos 2\theta - S_{xy} \sin 2\theta \qquad (9\text{–}5)$$

and

$$S_s = \frac{S_x - S_y}{2} \sin 2\theta + S_{xy} \cos 2\theta \qquad (9\text{–}6)$$

The planes defining maximum or minimum normal stresses are found by differentiating Eq. (9–5) with respect to θ and setting the derivative equal to zero, whence

$$\tan 2\,\theta = -\frac{2\,S_{xy}}{S_x - S_y} \qquad (9\text{–}7)$$

Similarly, the planes of maximum shearing stress are defined by

$$\tan 2\,\theta_s = \frac{S_x - S_y}{2\,S_{xy}} \qquad (9\text{–}8)$$

Eq. (9–7) gives two values of $2\,\theta$ that differ by 180°. Hence, the planes on which maximum and minimum normal stresses occur are 90° apart. Similarly, from Eq. (9–8), the planes on which the maximum shearing stress occurs are also found to be 90° apart.

The planes of zero shearing stress may be determined by setting S_s equal to zero in Eq. (9–6); this gives

$$\tan 2\,\theta = -\frac{2\,S_{xy}}{S_x - S_y}$$

which is identical with Eq. (9–7). Hence *maximum and minimum normal stresses occur on planes of zero shearing stress.* The maximum and minimum normal stresses are called the *principal stresses*, sometimes referred to as the p and q stresses.

Eq. (9–8) is also the negative reciprocal of Eq. (9–7). This means that the values of $2\,\theta$ defined by Eqs. (9–7) and (9–8) differ by 90°. In other words, *the planes of maximum shearing stress are at 45° with the planes of principal stress.*

Substituting values of $2\,\theta$ from Eqs. (9–7) and (9–8) respectively in Eqs. (9–5) and (9–6), we obtain the following expressions for maximum stresses:

$$(S_n)_{\substack{max \\ min}} = \frac{S_x + S_y}{2} \pm \sqrt{\left(\frac{S_x - S_y}{2}\right)^2 + (S_{xy})^2} \qquad (9\text{–}9)$$

$$(S_s)_{max} = \pm \sqrt{\left(\frac{S_x - S_y}{2}\right)^2 + (S_{xy})^2} \qquad (9\text{–}10)$$

9–7. Mohr's Circle

The formulas developed in the preceding article may be used for any case of two-dimensional stress. A visual interpretation of them, devised by the German engineer Otto Mohr in 1882, eliminates the necessity for remembering them.[5] In this interpretation a circle is used; accordingly, the construc-

[5] Equations (9–5) and (9–6), as well as the succeeding variations of them, are identical with the equations that express the variations in moments of inertia with respect to U and V axes inclined at an angle θ to the reference axes X and Y. Replacing normal stress by the moment of inertia I and the shearing stress by the product of inertia P,

tion is called Mohr's circle. If this construction is plotted to scale, the results can be obtained graphically; usually, however, only a rough sketch is drawn, analytical results being obtained from it by following the rules given below.

Mohr's circle provides a simple method of showing the various combinations of normal and shearing stresses to which an element at a given point in a stressed body is subjected as the element is rotated about an axis perpendicular to the plane of stress. The construction of Mohr's circle is governed by the following rules, which will be applied to several problems to illustrate their use. Illus. Prob. 917 will demonstrate that these rules give the same results as the equations in Art. 9–6, thus constituting a proof of the construction.

Rules for Applying Mohr's Circle to Combined Stresses

1. On rectangular $S_n - S_s$ axes, plot points having the coordinates (S_x, S_{xy}) and (S_y, S_{yx}). These points represent the normal and shearing stresses acting on the X and Y faces of an element for which the stresses are known. In plotting these points, assume tension as plus, compression as minus, and shearing stress as plus when its moment about the center of the element is clockwise.[6]

2. Join the points just plotted by a straight line. This line is the diameter of a circle whose center is on the S_n axis.

3. As different planes are passed through the selected point in a stressed body, the normal and shearing stress components on these planes are represented by the coordinates of points whose position shifts around the circumference of Mohr's circle.

4. The radius of the circle to any point on its circumference represents the axis directed normal to the plane whose stress components are given by the coordinates of that point.

5. The angle between the radii to selected points on Mohr's circle is twice the angle between the normals to the actual planes represented by these points, or to twice the space angularity between the planes so represented.

---

we obtain

$$I_u = \frac{I_x + I_y}{2} + \frac{I_x - I_y}{2} \cos 2\theta - P_{xy} \sin 2\theta$$

and

$$P_{uv} = \frac{I_x - I_y}{2} \sin 2\theta + P_{xy} \cos 2\theta$$

A Mohr's circle treatment of these equations is described in detail in Appendix A, page 441.

[6] This rule of sign for shearing stress makes $S_{xy} = -S_{yx}$.

ILLUSTRATIVE PROBLEMS

917. For the state of stress shown in Fig. 9–14, determine the values of maximum normal and shearing stresses.

Solution: Applying rule 1, the stresses acting on the X face are represented by point A in Fig. 9–15, and the stresses acting on the Y face are represented by point B. Note that the moment sense of S_{xy} about O in Fig. 9–14 is clockwise, whereas that of S_{yx} about O is counterclockwise; hence, S_{xy} is plus, and the numerically equal S_{yx} is minus.

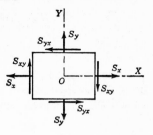

Fɪɢ. 9–14. — State of stress.

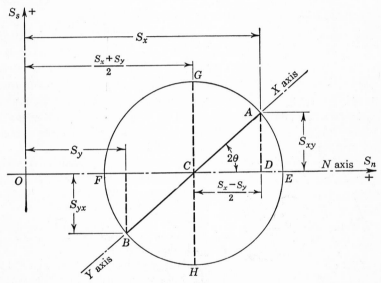

Fɪɢ. 9–15. — Mohr's circle for state of stress represented by Fig. 9–14.

The radius AC of Mohr's circle is the hypotenuse of the right triangle ACD, and its length, from the Pythagorean theorem, is

$$AC = \sqrt{\left(\frac{S_x - S_y}{2}\right)^2 + (S_{xy})^2} \qquad (a)$$

Points E and F (see rule 3) represent planes on which zero S_s acts, and thus will give the values of the principal stresses. Hence the maximum normal stress represented by point E is equivalent to

$$(S_n)_{max} = OE = OC + CE = OC + CA$$

$$= \frac{S_x + S_y}{2} + \sqrt{\left(\frac{S_x - S_y}{2}\right)^2 + (S_{xy})^2} \qquad (b)$$

Similarly, the minimum normal stress represented by point F is equivalent to

$$(S_n)_{min} = OF = OC - CF = OC - CA$$

$$= \frac{S_x + S_y}{2} - \sqrt{\left(\frac{S_x - S_y}{2}\right)^2 + (S_{xy})^2} \qquad (c)$$

The maximum shearing stress is determined by points G or H. (Note that these points, in accordance with rule 5, are actually on planes 90° apart and, although numerically equal, are of opposite sign.) Hence

$$(S_s)_{max} = CG = CH = CA = \pm \sqrt{\left(\frac{S_x - S_y}{2}\right)^2 + (S_{xy})^2} \qquad (d)$$

By rule 4, the radius CA represents the X axis, which is the normal to the X face, and the radius CB represents the Y axis. The angle between these radii is 180°, or twice the angle between the X and Y axes. Similarly, the radius CE represents the N axis, which is normal to the plane of maximum normal stress. The angle θ between the N and X axes (see rule 5) is given by

$$\tan 2\theta = \frac{AD}{CD} = -\frac{2 S_{xy}}{S_x - S_y} \qquad (e)$$

The sign is negative because the N axis (of maximum normal stress) is reached by moving in a clockwise direction from the X axis. Hence, the principal planes relative to the X and Y axes are represented as in Fig. 9–16.

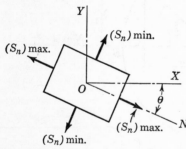

FIG. 9–16. — Principal stresses.

Comparison of Eqs. (*b*), (*c*), (*d*), and (*e*) with Eqs. (9–9), (9–10), and (9–7) shows that Mohr's circle represents in nomographic fashion the equations of combined stresses. At first it may seem more difficult for you to remember the rules for Mohr's circle than the equations it replaces. After you have used them, however, you will find the rules much easier to apply (and remember) than the equations. Mohr's circle has the further advantage of presenting a picture of the equations that the average student interprets more readily than the equations themselves.

918. At a certain point in a stressed body, the principal stresses are $S_x = 8000$ psi and $S_y = -4000$ psi. Determine S_n and S_s on the faces whose normals are at $+30°$ and $+120°$ with the X axis.

Solution: The given state of stress is shown in Fig. 9–17a. Point A in Fig. 9–17b represents the stress components on the X face, and point B those on the Y face. These points are plotted on the S_n axis because the shearing stresses on these faces are zero. The diameter of Mohr's circle is AB (from rule 2) and its center C is 2000 psi from the origin O. The radius of the circle is one-half of AB or 6000 psi. From rule 4, the radius CA represents the X axis. In accordance with rules 4 and 5, point D represents the stress components acting on the face whose normal is inclined at $+ 30°$ to the X axis, and point E represents the stress components on the perpendicular face. Observe that positive angles are plotted in a counterclockwise direction from the X axis and are laid off to double size.

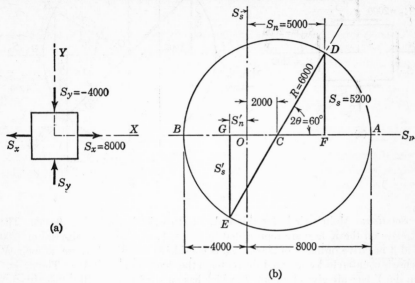

(a)

(b)

Fig. 9–17.

From the geometry of Mohr's circle, the required stresses on the 30° face are

$$S_n = OF = OC + CF = 2000 + 6000 \cos 60° = 5000 \text{ psi}$$
$$S_s = DF = 6000 \sin 60° = 5200 \text{ psi}$$

On the perpendicular 120° face we have

$$S_n' = OG = OC - CG = 2000 - 6000 \cos 60° = - 1000 \text{ psi}$$
$$S_s' = GE = - 6000 \sin 60° = - 5200 \text{ psi}$$

Both sets of stress components are shown in Fig. 9–18. Note particularly the clockwise and counterclockwise moments of S_s and S_s' respectively, relative to the center of the element (see rule 1).

919. A state of stress is specified in Fig. 9–19a. Determine the normal and shearing stresses on (a) the principal planes, (b) the planes of maximum shearing stress, and (c) the plane whose normal is at $+ 36.8°$ with the X axis.

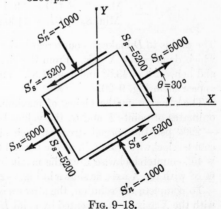

Fig. 9–18.

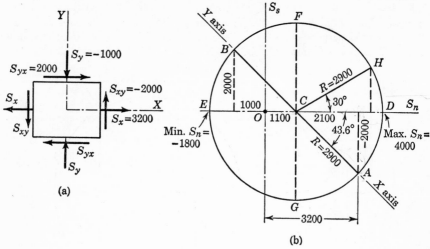

FIG. 9–19.

Solution: Mohr's circle for this state of stress is shown in Fig. 9–19*b*. The stresses on the X face are represented by point A, which has an abscissa of 3200 and a negative ordinate of 2000. S_{xy} is considered negative because its moment sense is counterclockwise about the center of the element in Fig. 9–19*a*. The stresses on the Y face are given by point B, which has an abscissa of $-$ 1000 (negative because compressive) and an ordinate of 2000 (positive because the moment sense of S_{yx} is clockwise). Joining A and B gives the diameter of Mohr's circle, its center C being midway between the ordinates of A and B, or at 1100 psi from the origin O. Hence the radius R is computed from the right triangle whose sides are 2100 and 2000; the radius is 2900 psi.

The principal stresses are represented by points D and E, where the shearing stress coordinates are zero. From the geometry of the circle, we obtain

$$\text{Max. } S_n = OD = 1100 + 2900 = + 4000 \text{ psi}$$
$$\text{Min. } S_n = OE = 1100 - 2900 = - 1800 \text{ psi}$$

The radius to D makes a counterclockwise angle $2\,\theta$ measured from the radius CA, which denotes the X axis. From the circle, we see that $\tan 2\,\theta = \frac{2000}{2100} = 0.952$, and hence $2\,\theta = 43.6°$ and $\theta = 21.8°$. The principal stresses and principal planes appear as in Fig. 9–20.

The stresses on the planes of maximum shearing stress are given by the coordinates of points F and G, the values being max. $S_s = 2900$ psi and min. $S_s = - 2900$ psi; the normal stress on each plane is 1100 psi. The radius CF is 90° counterclockwise from CD, so the normal to the plane of maximum shearing stress is 45° counterclockwise from the maximum principal plane, or at $45° + 21.8° = 66.8°$ with the X axis, as shown in Fig. 9–21.

To complete the solution, the stresses on the plane whose normal is at $+ 36.8°$ with the X axis are represented by point H, located at the intersection of the radius

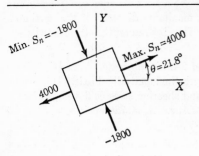

FIG. 9–20. — Principal stresses.

FIG. 9–21. — Maximum shear stresses.

CH with Mohr's circle (see rule 3). From rule 5, the angle between the normals to any two faces is laid off to double size on the circle; hence angle $ACH = 2 \times 36.8 = 73.6°$, and angle $HCD = 73.6 - 43.6 = 30°$. The coordinates of point H therefore are

$$S_n = 1100 + 2900 \cos 30° = 3610 \text{ psi}$$
$$S_s = 2900 \sin 30° = 1450 \text{ psi}$$

PROBLEMS

920. Two wooden joists 2 in. by 4 in. are glued together along the joint *AB*. What axial tensile force *P* may be applied if the maximum shearing stress along *AB* is 433 psi?   *Ans.* $P = 8000$ lb

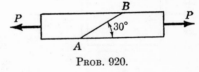

PROB. 920.

921. A short 2-in. circular bar is made of a material for which max. $S_c = 16,000$ psi and max. $S_s = 6000$ psi. Determine the safe axial compressive force that may be applied.

922. An element is subjected to the principal stresses $S_x = 12,000$ psi and $S_y = -4000$ psi. Compute the stress components on the face inclined at 30° with the X face. What max. S_s is developed?

Ans. $S_n = 8000$ psi; $S_s = 6930$ psi; max. $S_s = 8000$ psi

923. A small block is 1.6 in. long, 1.2 in. high, and 0.2 in. thick. It is in equilibrium under the action of the tensile forces shown. Compute S_n and S_s developed along the diagonal *AB*.

Ans. $S_n = 7440$ psi; $S_s = -1920$ psi

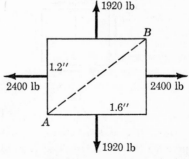

924. Solve the preceding problem if the tensile forces of 1920 lb are reversed to act in compression.

925. A closed cylindrical tank is fabricated from $\frac{1}{2}$-in. plate and subjected to an

PROB. 923 and 924.

internal pressure of 200 psi. Determine the maximum diameter if the maximum shearing stress is limited to 6000 psi. *Hint:* The circumferential stress is twice the longitudinal stress (Art. 2–1). *Ans.* $D = 120$ in.

926. A tube with an external diameter of 2 in. is fabricated from $\frac{1}{8}$-in. plate; the spiral weld used makes an angle of 30° with the longitudinal axis. If a torque of 450 ft-lb is applied, compute the normal and shearing stresses developed in the weld. *Ans.* $S_n = 7200$ psi; $S_s = 4150$ psi

927. If the spiral weld in the tube in Prob. 926 makes an angle of 60° with the longitudinal axis, determine the maximum torque that may be applied without exceeding a shearing stress of 6000 psi along the weld. *Ans.* $T = 652$ ft-lb

928. A state of stress is defined by $S_x = 12{,}000$ psi, $S_y = -8000$ psi, and $S_{xy} = 6000$ psi. Compute the values of the principal stresses and the maximum shearing stress. Sketch the planes on which these stresses act.

Ans. Max. $S_n = 13{,}640$ psi; min. $S_n = -9640$ psi; max. $S_s = 11{,}640$ psi

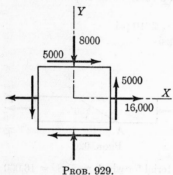

PROB. 929.

929. The state of stress at a certain point in a stressed body is shown in psi. Determine the principal stresses, the maximum shearing stress, and the stress components on the plane at 30° with the X face.

Ans. Max. $S_n = 17{,}000$ psi; min. $S_n = -9000$ psi; max. $S_s = 13{,}000$ psi; $S_n = 14{,}300$ psi; $S_s = 7900$ psi

930. The state of stress at a point is the result of two separate actions; one produces the pure shear of 4000 psi shown in (*a*) and the other produces the pure shear of 4000 psi shown in (*b*). Find the resultant stress by rotating the state of stress in (*b*) to coincide with that in (*a*), so that the stresses can be added directly. Then determine the principal stresses and principal planes for the combined state of stress.

Ans. Max. $S_n = 6930$ psi at $\theta = 30°$; min. $S_n = -6930$ psi at $\theta = 120°$

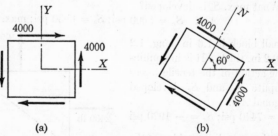

PROB. 930.

931. The state of stress at a point is the result of three separate actions that produce the three tensile stresses shown. Determine the principal stresses and principal planes caused by the superposition of these stresses. [Ans. on p. 307.]

932. Solve the preceding problem if the stress in (c) is changed to 8000 psi compression.

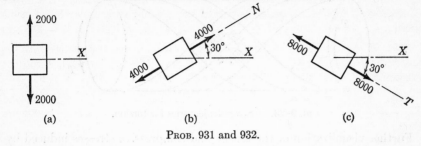

(a)   (b)   (c)

Prob. 931 and 932.

9–8. Applications of Mohr's Circle to Combined Loadings

The mathematical analysis of combined stresses that is summarized in Mohr's circle may be visually confirmed by subjecting a brittle material to torsion. Failure will occur because of the tensile stress induced by the torsional shear, since the tensile strength of brittle materials, such as cast iron, is usually less than their shear strength. We can predict the plane of failure with Mohr's circle, and then confirm it experimentally by twisting a cylindrical piece of chalk, another brittle material that is weakest in tension.

Thus an element on the surface of the cylinder in Fig. 9–22a is subjected to the indicated torsional shearing stress. Fig. 9–22b shows Mohr's circle

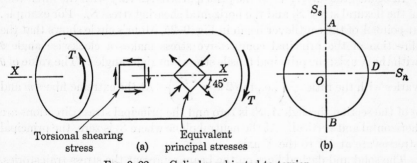

Torsional shearing   Equivalent
stress   (a)   principal stresses   (b)

Fig. 9–22. — Cylinder subjected to torsion.

for this state of stress. The radius OA specifies the X axis. The maximum tensile stress is denoted by point D, whose radius OD is 90° clockwise from OA. Hence, the normal to the plane of maximum tensile stress is 45° clockwise from the X axis, as shown. The lines in Fig. 9–23 that follow the directions of the principal stresses are called *stress trajectories*. For torsion, they are 45° helices. If the material is weakest in tension, failure occurs along a 45° helix such as AB. This may be confirmed by twisting a piece of chalk until it breaks.

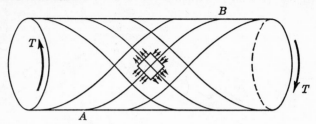

FIG. 9–23. — Stress trajectories for torsion.

Further visualization of the tensile and compressive stresses induced by pure shear is provided in Fig. 9–24. The distorted appearance of the ele-

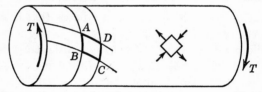

FIG. 9–24.

ment $ABCD$, originally rectangular, indicates that the diagonal AC has been lengthened and BD shortened. These deformations agree with the directions of the tensile and compressive stresses previously obtained.

In beams, the directions of the principal stresses vary with the intensities of the flexural stress S_f and the horizontal shearing stress S_s. For example, at point A of the cantilever beam in Fig. 9–25, Mohr's circle shows that the direction of the principal compressive stress makes a clockwise angle θ with the X axis; the principal tensile stress is at right angles. The value of θ varies with the ratio $\dfrac{S_s}{S_f}$ $\left(\text{i.e., } \tan 2\,\theta = \dfrac{2\,S_s}{S_f}\right).$ At the extreme fibers m and n of the section through A, S_s is zero and the principal stress directions are horizontal and vertical. At the neutral plane where S_f is zero, the principal stresses are at 45° to the X axis.

The solid and dashed lines on the beam represent the stress trajectories. They consist of two systems of orthogonal curves whose tangents at each point are in the direction of the principal stresses at that point. The solid lines indicate the direction of the maximum compressive stresses, and the dashed lines indicate the direction of the maximum tensile stresses. Be careful not to confuse stress trajectories with lines of constant stress. *Stress trajectories are lines of principal stress direction but of variable stress intensity.*

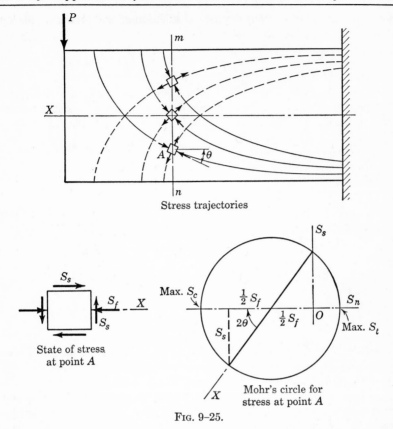

FIG. 9–25.

The most important use of combined stresses is in the design of members subjected to combined loadings or the determination of safe loads. Here Mohr's circle enables a visualization of conditions that is superior to mere analytical manipulation. The usual procedure is to consider an element on which the effect of the three fundamental loadings — axial, torsional, and flexural — can be computed. Study of Mohr's circle for this element indicates the procedure to be used. The following illustrative problems are typical of the procedures involved.

ILLUSTRATIVE PROBLEMS

933. A shaft 4 in. in diameter that rotates at 1800 rpm is subjected to bending loads that produce a maximum bending moment of 2000 π ft-lb. Determine the torque and hp that can also act simultaneously on the shaft without exceeding a resultant shearing stress $S_s = 12,000$ psi or a resultant normal stress $S_n = 16,000$ psi.

Solution: The bending moment produces a maximum flexural stress at the top or bottom of the shaft. Its value is

$$\left[S_f = \frac{Mc}{I} = \frac{4\,M}{\pi r^3} \right] \qquad\qquad S_f = \frac{4(2000\,\pi \times 12)}{\pi(2)^3} = 12{,}000 \text{ psi}$$

An applied torque T, as yet undetermined, produces a torsional shearing stress, maximum at the periphery of the shaft, which also acts on the element at the top or bottom of the shaft.[7] This state of stress is shown in Fig. 9–26a. Although the

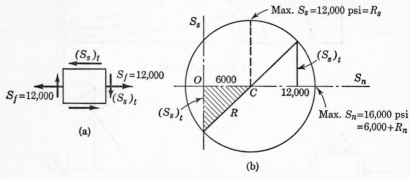

FIG. 9–26.

torsional shearing stress (denoted by $(S_s)_t$ to distinguish it from the maximum resultant shearing stress S_s which the shaft can withstand) is not yet known, Mohr's circle can be drawn in terms of it, as in Fig. 9–26b.

To produce the maximum permitted resultant shearing stress, the radius of the circle must be $R_s = 12{,}000$ psi. However, the radius that will produce the maximum permitted normal stress must satisfy the condition $S_n = 16{,}000 = OC + R_n = 6000 + R_n$, whence $R_n = 10{,}000$ psi.

It should be clear that the proper radius of Mohr's circle is R_s or R_n, whichever is smaller, so that the allowable values of max. S_s or max. S_n will not be exceeded. Having thus determined the proper radius, i.e., $R = 10{,}000$, we compute, from the shaded right triangle in Fig. 9–26b, the torsional shearing stress $(S_s)_t$ that can be combined with the flexural stress. Hence

$$(S_s)_t{}^2 = R^2 - (6000)^2 = (10{,}000)^2 - (6000)^2$$

or

$$(S_s)_t = 8000 \text{ psi}$$

The torsion formula shows that the torque required to produce this torsional shearing stress is

[7] At the extremities of the neutral axis, the torsional shearing stress is added to the shearing stress caused by the vertical shear, thereby forming a resultant shearing stress. In a short heavily loaded shaft, this can be the maximum resultant shearing stress that limits the value of the torsional shearing stress. However, this possibility is ignored here.

$$\left[T = \frac{S_s J}{r} = \frac{S_s \pi r^3}{2} \right] \qquad T = \frac{(8000)\pi(2)^3}{2} = 101{,}000 \text{ in.-lb}$$

whence, in terms of the torque, the required hp that may be applied is

$$\left[hp = \frac{TN}{63{,}000} \right] \qquad hp = \frac{101{,}000(1800)}{63{,}000} = 2875 \quad Ans.$$

934. A solid shaft is subjected to simultaneous twisting and bending due to a torque T and a maximum bending moment M. Express the maximum resultant shearing stress S_s and the maximum resultant normal stress S_n in terms of T, M, and the radius r of the shaft. By means of these relations, determine the proper diameter of a solid shaft to carry simultaneously $T = 900$ ft-lb and $M = 600$ ft-lb, if $S_s \leq 10{,}000$ psi and $S_n \leq 16{,}000$ psi.

Solution: The simultaneous bending and twisting in this problem is commonly encountered in designing shafts. The formulas that will be developed are very useful, but their use should be limited to those cases in which both M and T are known. Under any other conditions, Mohr's circle should be used.

The state of stress of an element subjected to simultaneous flexure and torsion is shown in Fig. 9–27a, and the equivalent Mohr's circle in Fig. 9–27b. The maximum resultant shearing stress S_s is equal to the radius R, which, from the shaded right triangle, is

$$\text{Max.} \, S_s = R = \sqrt{(\tfrac{1}{2} S_f)^2 + (S_{s_t})^2} \tag{a}$$

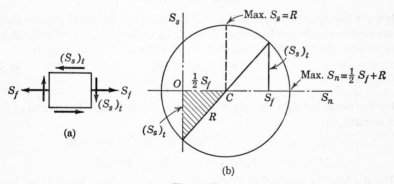

(a)

(b)

Fig. 9–27.

The following variations of the flexure and torsion formulas as applied to a circular shaft are used:

$$S_f = \frac{4 M}{\pi r^3} \quad \text{and} \quad S_{s_t} = \frac{2 T}{\pi r^3} \tag{b}$$

Substituting these values in Eq. (a) yields

$$\text{Max.} \, S_s = \sqrt{\left(\frac{2 M}{\pi r^3}\right)^2 + \left(\frac{2 T}{\pi r^3}\right)^2}$$

which reduces to

$$\text{Max. } S_s = \frac{2}{\pi r^3} \sqrt{M^2 + T^2}$$

Letting $T_e = \sqrt{M^2 + T^2}$, we obtain finally

$$\textbf{Max. } \textbf{\textit{S}}_s = \frac{2\,T_e}{\pi r^3} \tag{9-11}$$

The similarity between Eq. (9–11) and the torsion formula in Eq. (b) suggests *equivalent torque* as a suitable name for T_e.

An equation for maximum resultant normal stress that is similar to the flexure formula but involves an *equivalent moment* M_e, is obtained as follows: In Fig. 9–27b, the maximum resultant normal stress is max. $S_n = \frac{1}{2} S_f + R$. Substituting $S_f = \dfrac{4\,M}{\pi r^3}$ and $R = \dfrac{2\,T_e}{\pi r^3}$, we have

$$\text{Max. } S_n = \frac{2}{\pi r^3}\,(M + T_e)$$

Multiplying and dividing the right side by 2 gives

$$\textbf{Max. } \textbf{\textit{S}}_n = \frac{4\,M_e}{\pi r^3} \tag{9-12}$$

which is equivalent to the flexure formula in Eq. (b) if the equivalent moment M_e is expressed by

$$M_e = \tfrac{1}{2}(M + T_e)$$

It is not necessary to memorize Eqs. (9–11) and (9–12) because they are so similar to the torsion and flexure formulas. In using them, however, the following definitions of equivalent torque and equivalent moment must be remembered:

$$\textbf{\textit{T}}_e = \sqrt{\textbf{\textit{M}}^2 + \textbf{\textit{T}}^2} \tag{9-13}$$

$$\textbf{\textit{M}}_e = \tfrac{1}{2}(\textbf{\textit{M}} + \textbf{\textit{T}}_e) \tag{9-14}$$

For the numerical data given in this problem, the equivalent torque and equivalent moment are

$$T_e = \sqrt{M^2 + T^2} = \sqrt{(600)^2 + (900)^2} = 1080 \text{ ft-lb}$$

$$M_e = \tfrac{1}{2}(M + T_e) = \tfrac{1}{2}(600 + 1080) = 840 \text{ ft-lb}$$

The shaft radius required so that the maximum shearing stress will not be exceeded is found from Eq. (9–11):

$$\left[S_s = \frac{2\,T_e}{\pi r^3} \right] \qquad 10{,}000 = \frac{2(1080 \times 12)}{\pi r^3}$$

$$r^3 = 0.825 \quad \text{and} \quad r = 0.939 \text{ in.}$$

The radius that will avoid exceeding the maximum normal stress is, from Eq. (9–12),

$$\left[S_n = \frac{4\,M_e}{\pi r^3} \right] \qquad 16{,}000 = \frac{4(840 \times 12)}{\pi r^3}$$

$$r^3 = 0.802 \quad \text{and} \quad r = 0.930 \text{ in.}$$

The larger of these two radii will satisfy both stress conditions; hence the proper diameter is

$$d = 2 \times 0.939 = 1.878 \text{ in.} \quad Ans.$$

935. Design a solid shaft to carry the loads shown in Fig. 9–28, if max. $S_s \leq$ 10,000 psi and max. $S_n \leq$ 18,000 psi. The belt pulls on pulleys B and C are vertical, and those on pulley E are horizontal. Neglect the weight of the pulleys and shaft.

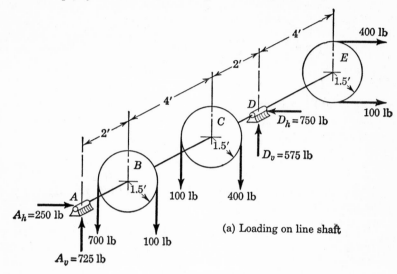

(a) Loading on line shaft

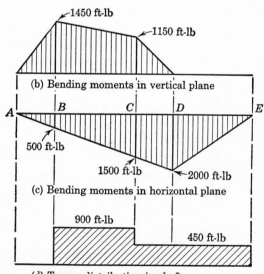

(b) Bending moments in vertical plane

(c) Bending moments in horizontal plane

(d) Torque distribution in shaft

Fig. 9–28.

Solution: The given loading produces bending in both the vertical and horizontal planes. The bending moment diagrams in these planes are given in Fig. 9–28(*b*) and (*c*). The resultant moment at any section is expressed by $M = \sqrt{M_h^2 + M_v^2}$. Therefore the resultant bending moments at *B*, *C*, and *D* are $M_B = 1535$ ft-lb, $M_C = 1890$ ft-lb, and $M_D = 2000$ ft-lb. Combining these values with the torque distribution in the shaft (Fig. 9–28*d*) shows that the dangerous sections are at *C* and *D*.

Since both moment and torque values are known, it is advantageous to use the method in Prob. 934. Applying Eqs. (9–13) and (9–14), we find the equivalent torque and equivalent moment to be

At *C*:
$$T_e = \sqrt{M^2 + T^2} = \sqrt{(1890)^2 + (900)^2} = 2090 \text{ ft-lb}$$
$$M_e = \tfrac{1}{2}(M + T_e) = \tfrac{1}{2}(1890 + 2090) = 1990 \text{ ft-lb}$$

and at *D*:
$$T_e = \sqrt{M^2 + T^2} = \sqrt{(2000)^2 + (450)^2} = 2050 \text{ ft-lb}$$
$$M_e = \tfrac{1}{2}(M + T_e) = \tfrac{1}{2}(2000 + 2050) = 2025 \text{ ft-lb}$$

The largest of these values is applied to Eqs. (9–11) and (9–12). Since max. T_e occurs at *C*, and max. M_e at *D*, we obtain

$$\left[S_s = \frac{2\,T_e}{\pi r^3} \right] \qquad 10{,}000 = \frac{2(2090 \times 12)}{\pi r^3} \qquad r^3 = 1.6$$

$$\left[S_n = \frac{4\,M_e}{\pi r^3} \right] \qquad 18{,}000 = \frac{4(2025 \times 12)}{\pi r^3} \qquad r^3 = 1.72$$

The larger of these values of r^3 determines the proper radius. Its value is $r = \sqrt[3]{1.72} = 1.198$ in., and the required diameter is 2.396 in. In view of the standard sizes of shafting, a shaft $2\frac{7}{16}$ in. in diameter would be selected.

PROBLEMS

936. Explain why the stress trajectories in Fig. 9–25 tend to become horizontal as they approach the wall. Where are they exactly horizontal? What are the stress trajectories for axial tension or compression?

937. A portion of a propeller shaft is hollow; it has a 12-in. outside diameter and an 11-in. inside diameter. At maximum power, the propeller thrust exerts a compressive force of 100,000 lb on the shaft, which is also twisted through 1.146° in a length of 20 ft. If $G = 12 \times 10^6$ psi, compute the maximum normal and shearing stresses in the shaft. *Ans.* Max. $S_s = 6600$ psi; max. $S_n = -9370$ psi

938. Compute the principal stresses and maximum shearing stress at points *A* and *B* of the section $x = 6$ in. due to $P = 6000$ lb. The beam is rectangular, 4 in. by 1 in., and points *A* and *B* are each 1 in. from the neutral surface. *Hint:* Include the shearing stress due to *P*.

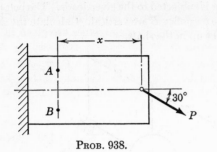

PROB. 938.

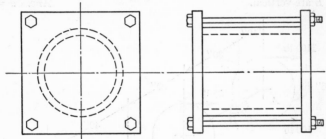

PROB. 939.

939. Repeat Prob. 938 if $P = 24,000$ lb, $x = 4$ ft, and the cross-section is the wide-flanged section shown. Assume points A and B to be where the web joins the upper and lower flanges respectively.

Ans. At A: Max. $S_n = 9220$ psi; min. $S_n = -140$ psi; max. $S_s = 4680$ psi

940. A plastic cylinder is sealed at both ends by gaskets fastened in place by two rigid plates that are held together by four long bolts, as shown. The cylinder is pumped full of oil which, at a pressure of 200 psi, leaks out from the gaskets. To maintain the oil pressure and stop the leak, the four bolts are tightened until they each carry 7950 lb tension. What is the maximum shearing stress developed in the cylinder if inside diameter is 10 in. and $t = \frac{1}{4}$ in.?   *Ans.* $S_s = 3000$ psi

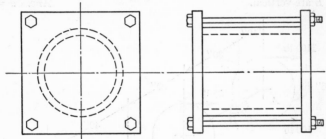

PROB. 940 and 941.

941. If the allowable stresses permitted in the cylinder in Prob. 940 are $S_t = 8000$ psi, $S_c = 4000$ psi, and $S_s = 3500$ psi, what maximum internal pressure may be applied if each of the bolts carries an initial tensile load of 8000 lb?

Ans. $p = 298$ psi

942. Twenty hp are transmitted through a speed reducer. At one part of the machine, the pinion drives the gear A of shaft AB at 252 rpm. Determine the diameter of shaft AB if max. $S_s \leqq 6000$ psi and max. $S_n \leqq 10,000$ psi.   *Ans.* $d = 2.34$ in.

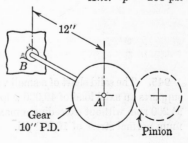

PROB. 942.

943. A line shaft 2 in. in diameter is subjected to the given loads. The belt pulls on pulley A are horizontal, and those on pulley B are vertical. Calculate the maximum shearing and normal stresses set up in the shaft.

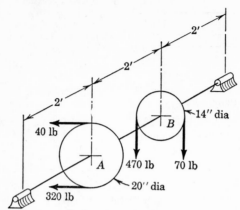

PROB. 943.

944. Design a solid shaft to carry the loads shown if max. $S_s \leq 8000$ psi and max. $S_n \leq 12,000$ psi. The belt pulls on pulleys A and C are horizontal, and those on pulley E are vertical. *Ans.* $d = 2.48$ in.

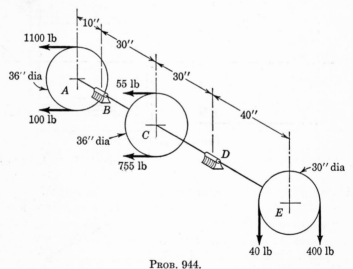

PROB. 944.

945. The solid shaft of a small vertical hydraulic turbine is 4 in. in diameter and supports an axial load of $40,000 \, \pi$ lb. Determine the safe hp that can be developed at 200 rpm without exceeding a maximum shearing stress of 12,000 psi and a maximum normal stress of 16,000 psi. *Ans.* hp = 390

946. In a certain machine, a shaft 4.30 in. in diameter carries a bending moment of 2500π ft-lb. What torque may be applied without exceeding a maximum shearing stress of 15,000 psi and a maximum normal stress of 20,000 psi?

Ans. $T = 16{,}570$ ft-lb

947. A shaft 6 in. in diameter carries simultaneously an axial compressive load of 113,200 lb, a maximum bending moment of 14,140 ft-lb, and a torque of 35,400 ft-lb. Compute max. S_t, max. S_c, and max. S_s produced in the shaft.

Ans. $S_t = 12{,}200$ psi; $S_c = 17{,}670$ psi; $S_s = 11{,}670$ psi

948. A shaft 4 in. in diameter is subjected to a maximum bending moment of 2000π ft-lb and an axial compressive load of $16{,}000\pi$ lb. Find the safe torque that can also be applied if max. $S_n \le 20{,}000$ psi and max. $S_s \le 15{,}000$ psi.

Ans. $T = 9350$ ft-lb

9–9. Components of Strain

Consider an element subjected only to the principal stresses S_x and S_y. The strains accompanying these stresses (assumed to be tensile) elongate the element by $\epsilon_x\, dx$ in the X direction and by $\epsilon_y\, dy$ in the Y direction, as shown in Fig. 9–29. These strains cause A to move to A', thereby increas-

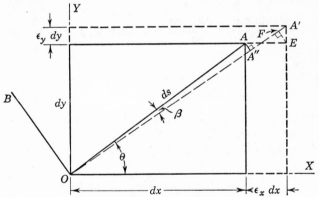

Fig. 9–29. — Components of strain.

ing the length of OA and changing its angular position by β. This change in angular position is so small that the increase in length of OA may be considered equal to $A'A''$. The magnitude of $A'A''$ may be found by projecting $\epsilon_x\, dx$ and $\epsilon_y\, dy$ on the direction of OA', whence

$$A'A'' = A''F + FA' = \epsilon_x\, dx\, \cos\theta + \epsilon_y\, dy\, \sin\theta \qquad (a)$$

The increase in length of OA divided by its original length ds is defined as the strain ϵ_a in the direction OA:

$$\epsilon_a = \frac{A'A''}{ds} = \frac{\epsilon_x\, dx\, \cos\theta}{ds} + \frac{\epsilon_y\, dy\, \sin\theta}{ds} \qquad (b)$$

But from Fig. 9–29, $\dfrac{dx}{ds} = \cos\,\theta$ and $\dfrac{dy}{ds} = \sin\,\theta$. With these relations, Eq. (b) reduces to

$$\epsilon_a = \epsilon_x \cos^2\theta + \epsilon_y \sin^2\theta \tag{c}$$

which, if we substitute for $\cos^2\theta$ and $\sin^2\theta$ their equivalents in terms of $2\,\theta$, becomes

$$\epsilon_a = \frac{\epsilon_x + \epsilon_y}{2} + \frac{\epsilon_x - \epsilon_y}{2}\cos 2\,\theta \tag{9–15}$$

The angular deviation of OA (i.e., β) may be computed from

$$\beta = \frac{AA''}{OA''} \approx \frac{AA''}{OA} = \frac{AA''}{ds} \tag{d}$$

Projecting $AE = \epsilon_x\,dx$ and $EA' = \epsilon_y\,dy$ on the direction EF, which is perpendicular to OA', we obtain

$$AA'' = \epsilon_x\,dx \sin\,\theta - \epsilon_y\,dy \cos\,\theta$$

Hence Eq. (d) becomes

$$\beta = \frac{\epsilon_x\,dx \sin\,\theta}{ds} - \frac{\epsilon_y\,dy \cos\,\theta}{ds} = \epsilon_x \cos\,\theta \sin\,\theta - \epsilon_y \sin\,\theta \cos\,\theta$$

whence finally

$$\beta = \frac{\epsilon_x - \epsilon_y}{2}\sin 2\,\theta \tag{9–16}$$

If now we write the equations of normal and shearing stress along the plane OA in terms of the principal stresses S_x and S_y, Eqs. (9–5) and (9–6) become (since $S_{xy} = 0$ on the principal planes)

$$S_n = \frac{S_x + S_y}{2} + \frac{S_x - S_y}{2}\cos 2\,\theta \tag{9–5a}$$

and

$$S_s = \frac{S_x - S_y}{2}\sin 2\,\theta \tag{9–5b}$$

These are identical in form with Eqs. (9–15) and (9–16) respectively, from which we conclude that the normal and shearing *strains* can also be represented by a Mohr's circle for strain, constructed in the same manner as Mohr's circle for stress. This has been done in Fig. 9–30; from it we see that for two perpendicular directions OA and OB in Fig. 9–29, the values of β must be equal but opposite in angular sense. Therefore, the right angle AOB in Fig. 9–29 will be increased by the numerical amount $2\,\beta$. Since shearing strain was defined in Art. 1–6 as the change in the right angle of a

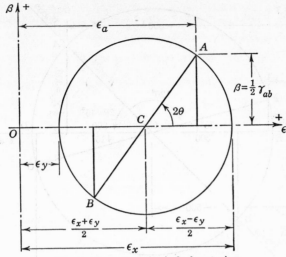

Fig. 9–30. — Mohr's circle for strains.

stressed element, the angular deviation β is actually one-half the shearing strain, or

$$\beta = \tfrac{1}{2}\gamma \tag{9–17}$$

In applying Mohr's circle for strain, we use the following rules of sign: Extensional strains are considered positive, compressive strains negative, and shearing strains positive when they *increase* the original right angle of an unstrained element. A more general rule of sign for shearing strain is obtained by denoting the strain between two perpendicular directions OA and OB by γ_{ab}, the first subscript indicating the direction OA associated with the angle θ. The shearing strain is considered positive if the directional line associated with the first subscript (OA in this case) moves clockwise, and vice versa. This rule of sign makes $\gamma_{ab} = -\gamma_{ba}$. However, as shown in Fig. 9–30, only *half values* of shearing strain are plotted.

ILLUSTRATIVE PROBLEM

949. In a body subjected to plane strain, there act at a certain point $\epsilon_x = 800$ micro-inches per inch, or 800×10^{-6}, $\epsilon_y = 200 \times 10^{-6}$, and $\gamma_{xy} = 600 \times 10^{-6}$ radians. Compute (*a*) the principal strains and the principal strain axes; also (*b*) the strain ϵ_a in a direction of $60°$ with the X axis, the strain ϵ_b perpendicular to ϵ_a, and the shearing strain γ_{ab}.

Solution: Mohr's circle for the given state of strain is shown in Fig. 9–31. The factor 10^{-6} being omitted, the coordinates of point A are $\epsilon_x = 800$ and $\beta = \tfrac{1}{2}\gamma_{xy} = 300$, and the coordinates of B are $\epsilon_y = 200$ and $\beta = \tfrac{1}{2}\gamma_{yx} = -300$. The X axis is represented by the radius CA, and the Y axis by the radius CB. The radius of the circle is computed to be 424, whence the maximum principal strain ϵ_1, denoted by

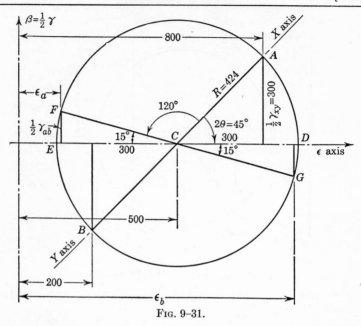

FIG. 9–31.

point D, equals $500 + 424 = 924 \times 10^{-6}$. The minimum principal strain ϵ_2 denoted by point E, equals $500 - 424 = 76 \times 10^{-6}$. The angle between the maximum strain axis and the X axis is one-half the angle ACD, or 22.5°, in a clockwise direction from the X axis, as shown in Fig. 9–32.

To determine the strain ϵ_a, lay off the radius CF at twice 60°, or 120°, counterclockwise from CA. The strain coordinates of point F are $\epsilon_a = 500 - 424 \cos 15° = 90 \times 10^{-6}$, and $\beta = 424 \sin 15° = 110$, whence $\gamma_{ab} = 220 \times 10^{-6}$ radians. Laying off the 90° angle between the directions of ϵ_a and ϵ_b to double scale locates G as diametrically opposite from F; hence $\epsilon_b = 500 + 424 \cos 15° = 910 \times 10^{-6}$.

FIG. 9–32.

Except for changing the symbols and plotting only half values of shearing strain, the procedure is the same as that given in Art. 9–7 describing Mohr's circle for stress.

PROBLEMS

950. Determine the results in Prob. 949 if $\epsilon_x = -500 \times 10^{-6}$, $\epsilon_y = 100 \times 10^{-6}$, and $\gamma_{xy} = 800 \times 10^{-6}$ radians.

$Ans.$ $\epsilon_1 = 300$ at $\theta = -63.45°$; $\epsilon_2 = -700$; $\epsilon_a = -396$; $\epsilon_b = -4$;
$\gamma_{ab} = -920$. (*Note:* In this and subsequent problems, the multiplying factor 10^{-6} should be added to strains.)

951. The state of strain is defined by $\epsilon_x = 600 \times 10^{-6}$, $\epsilon_y = -300 \times 10^{-6}$, and $\gamma_{xy} = -400 \times 10^{-6}$. Determine the principal strains and the maximum shearing strain. *Ans.* $\epsilon_1 = 642$ at $\theta = +12°$; $\epsilon_2 = -242$; $\gamma = 984$

952. Solve Prob. 950 if ϵ_y is a compressive strain of 200×10^{-6}.

$\quad$*Ans.* $\epsilon_1 = 78$ at $\theta = -55.28°$; $\epsilon_2 = -778$; $\epsilon_a = -622$; $\epsilon_b = -78$;
$\quad\quad\gamma_{ab} = -660$

9–10. The Strain Rosette

The stress in a bar subjected to uni-axial stress can be determined experimentally by attaching a strain gage oriented in the direction of the stress. The stress is then computed, in terms of the strain, from $S = E\epsilon$. The strain is generally small (under 1 part in 1000); hence sensitive instruments are required for measuring it. Until recently, strain gages were mechanical or optical, but these have now been almost completely replaced by electrical gages. This type of gage contains a wire element whose electrical resistance varies with its deformation. The gage is cemented to the test specimen, the strain in the specimen being measured as a function of the change in the electrical resistance of the wire element. This type of gage has been brought to a high state of perfection by the Baldwin Southwark Division of the Baldwin Locomotive Works, which markets it as the SR–4 strain gage.

As was said above, a single strain gage oriented in the direction of a uni-axial stress is sufficient for computing the stress. For bi-axial stress, we might suppose that two strain gages would be sufficient; this would be true if the directions of the principal stresses were known, but this is not usually the case. To determine the magnitude of the principal stresses and the angle between S_{max} and a reference direction, three values of strain are required. From these three strains we construct a Mohr's circle of strain from which we compute the magnitudes of the principal strains and their directions. When the principal strains are known, Hooke's law for bi-axial stress (see page 17) may be used to compute the principal stresses by means of the following equations:

$$S_x = \frac{E(\epsilon_x + \mu\epsilon_y)}{1 - \mu^2}, \qquad S_y = \frac{E(\epsilon_y + \mu\epsilon_x)}{1 - \mu^2} \qquad (1\text{–}13)$$

Three strain readings are obtained by using either of two combinations of three resistance strain gages: (1) three gages set with their axes at 45° with each other, and (2) three gages whose axes are at 60° with each other, as in Fig. 9–33. These combinations are known as *strain rosettes*. The three gages are electrically insulated from each other, and are used to determine the strain at the surface of the structure to which they are attached. We shall now construct Mohr's circle for each of these rosettes.

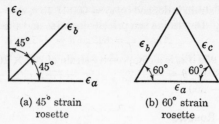

(a) 45° strain   (b) 60° strain
rosette   rosette

FIG. 9–33. — Strain rosettes.

The 45° or Rectangular Strain Rosette. A Mohr's circle for three extensional strains ϵ_a, ϵ_b, and ϵ_c, 45° apart, will have radii CA, CB, and CD 90° apart, as shown in Fig. 9–34. The center C is midway between G and E, so

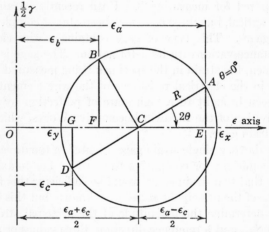

FIL. 9–34. — Mohr's circle for 45° strain rosette.

one side (CE) of triangle ACE is known. To construct the circle, the other side AE must be computed. Evidently, triangles CBF and CAE are congruent, so that $AE = CF$. From the geometry of the circle, $CF = OC - OF$; hence

$$AE = \frac{\epsilon_a + \epsilon_c}{2} - \epsilon_b \qquad (a)$$

Also

$$CE = \frac{\epsilon_a - \epsilon_c}{2} \qquad (b)$$

Therefore the radius $R = CA$ is determined from

$$R = \sqrt{(CE)^2 + (AE)^2} \qquad (c)$$

To apply this, assume that the three strains from a 45° strain rosette are $\epsilon_a = 700$ at 0°, $\epsilon_b = 400$ at 45°, and $\epsilon_c = 300$ at 90°, expressed in micro-inches per inch. Determine the principal strains and principal axes of strain. Also compute the principal stresses if $E = 30 \times 10^{-6}$ psi and $\mu = 0.3$.

We start by locating the center of the circle, which is at a distance $OC = \dfrac{\epsilon_a + \epsilon_c}{2} = \dfrac{700 + 300}{2} = 500$ to the right of the origin. The radius R is computed from the right triangle whose sides are $CE = \dfrac{\epsilon_a - \epsilon_c}{2} = \dfrac{700 - 300}{2} = 200$ and $AE = OC - \epsilon_b = 500 - 400 = 100$. Hence

$$R = \sqrt{(200)^2 + (100)^2} = 224$$

and

$$2\,\theta = \tan^{-1}\frac{AE}{CE} = \frac{100}{200} = 26.6°$$

The direction of the maximum principal strain ϵ_x is $\theta = 13.3°$ clockwise with respect to the direction of ϵ_a.

The principal strains are $\epsilon_x = OC + R = 500 + 224 = 724$ and $\epsilon_y = OC - R = 500 - 224 = 276$.

From Eq. (1–13), the principal stresses are

$$S_x = \frac{E(\epsilon_x + \mu\epsilon_y)}{1 - \mu^2} = \frac{30 \times 10^6 (724 + 0.3 \times 276)10^{-6}}{1 - (0.3)^2} = 26,600 \text{ psi}$$

and

$$S_y = \frac{E(\epsilon_y + \mu\epsilon_x)}{1 - \mu^2} = \frac{30 \times 10^6 (276 + 0.3 \times 724)10^{-6}}{1 - (0.3)^2} = 16,200 \text{ psi}$$

The 60° or Equiangular Strain Rosette. If the three known strains ϵ_a, ϵ_b, and ϵ_c are each 60° apart, they will appear on Mohr's circle so that radii CA, CB, and CD are 120° apart, as in Fig. 9–35. If ϵ_a is the largest of the three strains, $2\,\theta$ can never be more than 60°. From the geometry of the circle, we obtain

$$\epsilon_a = OC + R \cos 2\,\theta \qquad\qquad (d)$$
$$\epsilon_b = OC + R \cos (2\,\theta + 120°) \qquad\qquad (e)$$
$$\epsilon_c = OC + R \cos (2\,\theta + 240°) \qquad\qquad (f)$$

Expanding the cosines of the double angles and adding these three equations eliminates R and determines the center of Mohr's circle as

$$OC = \frac{\epsilon_a + \epsilon_b + \epsilon_c}{3} \qquad\qquad (g)$$

To determine $2\,\theta$, we bring OC to the left side of Eqs. (d) and (e), giving

$$\epsilon_a - OC = \tfrac{1}{3}(2\,\epsilon_a - \epsilon_b - \epsilon_c) = R \cos 2\,\theta$$
$$\epsilon_b - OC = \tfrac{1}{3}(2\,\epsilon_b - \epsilon_a - \epsilon_c) = R \cos (2\,\theta + 120°)$$

Dividing them eliminates R and leaves 2θ as the only unknown. We then obtain

$$\tan 2\theta = \sqrt{3}\,\frac{\epsilon_c - \epsilon_b}{2\,\epsilon_a - \epsilon_b - \epsilon_c} \qquad (h)$$

from which 2θ can be determined from the test data. Since 2θ and OC are now known, and since $R = \dfrac{\epsilon_x - \epsilon_y}{2}$, it is relatively simple to compute the principal strains ϵ_x and ϵ_y.

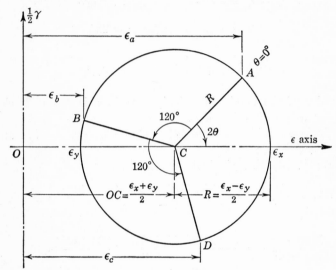

FIG. 9–35. — Mohr's circle for strains from a 60° rosette.

As an example, assume that the three readings on a 60° strain rosette are $\epsilon_a = 800$, $\epsilon_b = 600$, and $\epsilon_c = 400$, expressed in micro-inches per inch. If $E = 30 \times 10^6$ psi and $\mu = 0.30$, determine the principal strains and the principal stresses.

We start by computing OC and 2θ. From Eq. (g)

$$OC = \frac{\epsilon_a + \epsilon_b + \epsilon_c}{3} = \frac{800 + 600 + 400}{3} = 600$$

and from Eq. (h)

$$\tan 2\theta = \sqrt{3}\,\frac{\epsilon_c - \epsilon_b}{2\,\epsilon_a - \epsilon_b - \epsilon_c} = \sqrt{3}\,\frac{400 - 600}{1600 - 600 - 400} = -0.577;$$
$$2\theta = -30°$$

The value of R is computed from Eq. (d):

$$[\epsilon_a = OC + R \cos 2\theta] \qquad 800 = 600 + R \cos(-30) \qquad R = 231$$

From Fig. 9–35, we see that

$$OC = \frac{\epsilon_x + \epsilon_y}{2} = 600$$

and

$$R = \frac{\epsilon_x - \epsilon_y}{2} = 231$$

whence, first adding and then subtracting these relations, we obtain $\epsilon_x = 831$ and $\epsilon_y = 369$. The direction of ϵ_x is at $\theta = 15°$ counterclockwise from the direction of ϵ_a. Substituting the principal strains in Eq. (1–13), we compute the principal stresses as $S_x = 31,100$ psi and $S_y = 20,400$ psi.

PROBLEMS

953. The strains measured on a 45° strain rosette and expressed in micro-inches per inch are: $\epsilon_a = 600$, $\epsilon_b = -400$, and $\epsilon_c = -200$. If $E = 30 \times 10^6$ psi and $\mu = 0.30$, determine the principal stresses.
    Ans. $\epsilon_x = 922; \epsilon_y = -522; \theta = -28.15°; S_x = 25,200$ psi$; S_y = -8080$ psi

954. Repeat Prob. 953, the strains being $\epsilon_a = 700$, $\epsilon_b = 480$, and $\epsilon_c = -340$.
    Ans. $\epsilon_x = 780; \epsilon_y = -420; \theta = 15°; S_x = 21,600$ psi$; S_y = -6140$ psi

955. The three readings in micro-inches per inch on a 60° strain rosette are: 600, 600, and -300. If $E = 30 \times 10^6$ psi and $\mu = 0.30$, compute the maximum shearing stress.   *Ans.*   Max. $S_s = 13,850$ psi

956. A 60° strain rosette attached to the aluminum skin of an airplane fuselage measures the following strains in micro-inches per inch: $\epsilon_a = 640$, $\epsilon_b = -300$, and $\epsilon_c = -100$. If $E = 10 \times 10^6$ psi and $\mu = \frac{1}{3}$, compute the principal stresses and maximum shearing stress.
    Ans. $\epsilon_x = 652; \epsilon_y = -492; \theta = -5.85°; S_x = 5260$ psi$; S_y = -3090$ psi; max. $S_s = 4165$ psi

9–11. Relation Between Modulus of Rigidity and Modulus of Elasticity

In Art. 1–6 we said that $G = \dfrac{E}{2(1 + \mu)}$; we are now ready to prove this relation. The state of stress shown in Fig. 9–36a consists of a tensile stress S_x and a compressive stress S_y of the same magnitude. Mohr's circle for this (Fig. 9–36b) indicates that an element rotated 45° counterclockwise as in Fig. 9–36c is subjected to pure shear in which S_s is numerically equal to S_x and S_y. These shearing stresses deform the element *abcd* to the dashed outline $a'b'c'd'$ in Fig. 9–36a. The right angle at a has decreased to $90° - \gamma$, where γ is the shearing strain. Simultaneously, the right angle at b has increased to $90° + \gamma$.

Consider now the deformation of the right triangle *aob* that has equal legs. Since $S_x = -S_y = S_s$, we obtain, with Eqs. (1–11) and (1–12), (see page 17), the normal strains

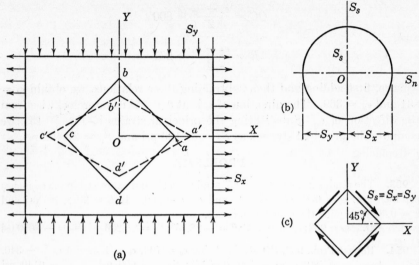

FIG. 9–36. — Prue shear and shearing strain.

$$\epsilon_x = \frac{S_s(1+\mu)}{E}, \qquad \epsilon_y = -\frac{S_s(1+\mu)}{E}$$

Hence the deformed lengths of sides oa and ob respectively are

$$\overline{oa'} = \overline{oa}\left[1 + \frac{S_s(1+\mu)}{E}\right], \qquad \overline{ob'} = \overline{ob}\left[1 - \frac{S_s(1+\mu)}{E}\right]$$

Therefore, from the right triangle $oa'b'$, we have

$$\tan oa'b' = \tan\left(45° - \frac{\gamma}{2}\right) = \frac{\overline{ob'}}{\overline{oa'}} = \frac{1 - \frac{S_s(1+\mu)}{E}}{1 + \frac{S_s(1+\mu)}{E}} \qquad (a)$$

From trigonometry, the expanded form of the tangent is

$$\tan\left(45° - \frac{\gamma}{2}\right) = \frac{\tan 45° - \tan\frac{\gamma}{2}}{1 + \tan 45° \tan\frac{\gamma}{2}} = \frac{1 - \frac{\gamma}{2}}{1 + \frac{\gamma}{2}} \qquad (b)$$

since for small angles γ like those that occur with shearing strain, $\tan\frac{\gamma}{2}$ is practically equivalent to $\frac{\gamma}{2}$ expressed in radians. Equating this expanded value of $\tan\left(45° - \frac{\gamma}{2}\right)$ to the right side of Eq. (a) gives

$$\frac{1 - \dfrac{\gamma}{2}}{1 + \dfrac{\gamma}{2}} = \frac{1 - \dfrac{S_s(1 + \mu)}{E}}{1 + \dfrac{S_s(1 + \mu)}{E}}$$

which, with a little algebra, reduces to

$$\gamma = \frac{2\,S_s(1 + \mu)}{E} \quad \text{or} \quad \frac{S_s}{\gamma} = \frac{E}{2(1 + \mu)}$$

Replacing $\dfrac{S_s}{\gamma}$ by G, as specified in Hooke's law for shear (Eq. 1–8), we obtain finally

$$G = \frac{E}{2(1 + \mu)} \tag{1–15}$$

which expresses the desired relation between the three elastic constants G, E, and μ.

SUMMARY

The normal stresses caused by a combination of axial and flexural loads are determined from

$$S = \overset{\oplus}{\underset{\ominus}{}} \frac{P}{A} \pm \frac{My}{I} \tag{9–1}$$

The positive sign refers to tension and the negative sign to compression. The circled signs indicate that the axial stress is uniform and of the same type all over the cross-section, whereas the magnitude and type of the flexural stress vary with position.

The kern of a section (Art. 9–3) is the part of a cross-section through which the resultant compressive force must pass if no tensile stress is to be developed over the section.

For bodies subjected to other than axial and flexural combinations of loading, the elements of the body are subject to both shearing and normal stresses. The stresses on such elements (in fact, on any element) vary with the angular position of the element and are expressed by the following equations which were derived in Art. 9–6.

$$S_n = \frac{S_x + S_y}{2} + \frac{S_x - S_y}{2} \cos 2\theta - S_{xy} \sin 2\theta \tag{9–5}$$

$$S_s = \frac{S_x - S_y}{2} \sin 2\theta + S_{xy} \cos 2\theta \tag{9–6}$$

However, the rules for Mohr's circle (page 300) make it unnecessary to remember these equations, and the more important conditions which determine the maximum resultant normal and shearing stresses. A drawing of the circle provides all the information needed to compute the variations in stress at any element. Further applications of Mohr's circle in practical designing are given in Art. 9–8.

The use of Mohr's circle of strain is described in Art. 9–9. The procedure is similar to that with the circle of stress except that *half values* of shearing strain are plotted as ordinates. Mohr's circle of strain is used principally in the strain rosette (Art. 9–10). The normal strains in three predetermined directions are used to compute the principal strains from which, by means of Eq. (1–13), the principal stresses may be found.

Chapter X

Reinforced Beams

10–1. Introduction

It was once common to strengthen timber beams by bolting strips of steel to them. With increasingly lower prices for steel, this practice has ceased except where timber is plentiful and the cost of transporting steel to the construction site is high. The most common type of reinforced beam used today is the concrete beam reinforced with steel rods.

The theory of flexure does not apply to composite beams, because it was based on the assumption that the beam was homogeneous and that plane transverse sections remained plane, whence the strains varied directly with their distance from the neutral axis. In investigating the bending of composite beams, only one assumption is retained: that plane sections remain plane, i.e., the strains vary directly with their distance from the neutral axis. The effect of this on the stress distribution in a reinforced concrete beam is shown in Fig. 10–1, where the greater modulus of elasticity of the steel reinforcing bars causes the abrupt change in stress intensity.

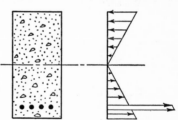

The most common method of dealing with a nonhomogeneous beam is to transform it into an equivalent homogeneous beam to which the flexure formula may be applied. The basic principle involved here is that the strains and load capacities must remain unchanged. We shall discuss first reinforced timber beams and then reinforced concrete beams, applying to the latter a procedure more fundamental and more commonly used than a modification of the flexure formula.

Fig. 10–1. — Stress distribution in composite beam.

10–2. Reinforced Timber Beams

The timber beam in Fig. 10–2a is reinforced with a steel strip, the steel being securely fastened to the timber so that no slip occurs between them as the beam is bent. From page 124 we see that the ordinary theory of flexure is restricted to beams of homogeneous material, and hence does not apply to the beam under consideration. However, by suitable modifications we can obtain an equivalent section in terms of one material to which the theory can be applied.

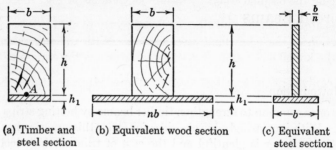

(a) Timber and   (b) Equivalent wood section   (c) Equivalent
steel section   steel section

FIG. 10–2. — Equivalent sections.

To obtain an equivalent section, consider a longitudinal steel fiber of the beam at A. Since the steel and wood are assumed to be firmly bolted together, the strains of the steel and wood fibers at A must be equal, i.e., $\epsilon_s = \epsilon_w$. Expressing this relation in terms of the stresses and moduli of elasticity, we have

$$\frac{S_s}{E_s} = \frac{S_w}{E_w} \tag{a}$$

Furthermore, in order to be equivalent, the loads carried by the steel fiber and the equivalent wood fiber must be equal, so

$$P_s = P_w$$

or, in terms of the areas,

$$A_s S_s = A_w S_w \tag{b}$$

Combining Eqs. (a) and (b), we obtain

$$A_s \left(\frac{E_s}{E_w}\right) S_w = A_w S_w$$

from which, by canceling out S_w and denoting the ratio of the moduli of elasticity $\dfrac{E_s}{E_w}$ by n, we finally have

$$A_w = nA_s \tag{10–1}$$

This indicates that the area of the equivalent wood is n times the area of the steel. The location of the equivalent area is governed by the condition that the equivalent wood fibers must be at the same distance from the neutral axis as the steel fibers they replace in order to satisfy the criterion of equal deformations in Eq. (a). In other words, the equivalent wood area is n times as wide as the steel it replaces; the equivalent wood section is shown in Fig. 10–2b. If desired, an equivalent steel section can be set up by replacing the original wood by steel $\frac{1}{n}$ as wide, as in Fig. 10–2c.

The flexure formula can now be applied directly to either the equivalent wood section or the equivalent steel section. With the equivalent wood section, the actual steel stress is n times the stress in the equivalent wood; with the equivalent steel section, the actual wood stress is $\frac{1}{n}$ times the stress in the equivalent steel.

ILLUSTRATIVE PROBLEM

1001. A timber beam 6 in. by 12 in. is reinforced, on the bottom only, with a steel strip 3 in. wide by $\frac{1}{2}$ in. thick. Determine the maximum resisting moment if the allowable stresses are $S_s \leq 18{,}000$ psi and $S_w \leq 1200$ psi. Assume $\frac{E_s}{E_w} = n = 20$.

Solution: Although only rarely is steel used to reinforce one side of a timber beam, this problem illustrates many of the concepts encountered later in reinforced concrete beams. The first of these involves the location of the neutral axis. Since the neutral axis coincides with the centroidal axis of the equivalent section shown in Fig. 10–3, the moments of area about an axis through the base gives

$$[A\bar{y} = \Sigma ay] \qquad (72 + 30)\bar{y} = 72(6.5) + 30(\tfrac{1}{4}) \qquad \bar{y} = 4.67 \text{ in.}$$

(a) Original section   (b) Equivalent section

Fɪɢ. 10–3.

First finding the moment of inertia about an axis through the top of the flange, and then using the transfer formula, we compute the moment of inertia about the neutral axis:

$$\left[I = \Sigma \frac{bh^3}{3} \right] \qquad I = \frac{6(12)^3}{3} + \frac{60(\tfrac{1}{2})^3}{3} = 3459 \text{ in.}^4$$

$$[I_0 = I - Ad^2] \qquad I_{N.A.} = 3459 - (102)(4.17)^2 = 1685 \text{ in.}^4$$

The resisting moment in terms of the maximum wood stress is

$$\left[M = \frac{SI}{y} \right] \qquad M_w = \frac{1200(1685)}{7.83} = 258{,}000 \text{ in.-lb}$$

The maximum stress in the wood equivalent of the steel is

$$S_w = \frac{S_s}{n} = \frac{18,000}{20} = 900 \text{ psi.}$$

Hence the resisting moment that will not exceed the permissible steel stress is

$$\left[M = \frac{SI}{y} \right] \qquad M_s = \frac{900(1685)}{4.67} = 324,000 \text{ in.-lb}$$

The smaller resisting moment (i.e., $M_w = 258,000$ in.-lb) is the safe resisting moment. In this case there is an excess of steel; hence the beam may be said to be over-reinforced.

PROBLEMS

1002. A timber beam is reinforced with steel plates rigidly attached at the top and bottom for the full length of the beam, as shown. Determine the maximum uniformly distributed load that can be carried on a simply supported span 16 ft long, if $n = 15$ and the allowable stresses in the wood and steel are not to exceed 1000 psi and 16,000 psi, respectively. *Ans.* $w = 2130$ lb/ft

1003. In the preceding problem, if $w = 2000$ lb/ft, compute the maximum stresses in the wood and the steel.

1004. A timber beam 8 in. by 12 in. is reinforced by a steel strip only at the bottom, as shown. Determine the safe centrally applied load that can be carried on a simply supported span 18 ft long, if $n = 20$, $S_s \leq 18,000$ psi, $S_w \leq 1200$ psi. Show that the neutral axis is 8.41 in. below the top and that $I_{N.A.} = 2600$ in.⁴
Ans. $P = 6870$ lb

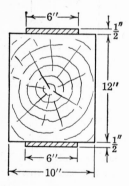

PROB. 1002 and 1003.

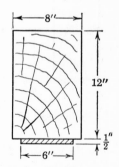

PROB. 1004, 1005,
and 1006.

1005. Determine the width b of the $\frac{1}{2}$-in. steel strip fastened to the bottom of the beam in Prob. 1004 that will simultaneously stress the wood and the steel to their permissible limits of 1200 psi and 18,000 psi respectively.
Ans. $b = 2.16$ in.

1006. A uniformly distributed load of 300 lb/ft (including the weight of the beam) is simply supported on a 20-ft span. The cross-section of the beam is as described in Prob. 1004. If $n = 20$, determine the maximum stresses produced in the wood and the steel.

1007. A pair of 12-in. 20.7-lb channels are securely bolted to a beam 10 in. by 12 in., as shown. If bending occurs about axis 1–1, determine the safe resisting moment, with $\dfrac{E_s}{E_w} = n = 20$, the allowable stresses being $S_s = 18,000$ psi and $S_w = 1200$ psi.

Ans. $M = 82,000$ ft-lb

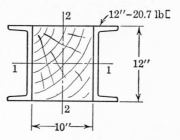

Prob. 1007 and 1008.

1008. In Prob. 1007, determine the safe resisting moment if bending occurs about axis 2–2.   *Ans.* $M = 85,000$ ft-lb

10–3. Shearing Stress and Deflection in Composite Beams

The formula for horizontal shearing stress (Eq. 5–4, page 153) developed for homogeneous beams applies equally well to the equivalent section of a composite beam, because its derivation was based on the difference in normal forces between two adjacent sections. Since the forces on the original composite section and on the equivalent section are the same (see page 330), Eq. (5–4) is valid for either section.

Deflections in composite beams can also be computed, as in homogeneous beams, by using the flexural rigidity EI of the equivalent section. This is true because the deflection is the result of the changes in length of the fibers in the beam, and one of the basic principles of composite beams is that the strains of fibers are identical at corresponding points in the original and equivalent beams.

PROBLEMS

1009. Compute the allowable total vertical shear for a beam having the same cross-section as in Prob. 1004, if $n = 20$ and the maximum shear stress is 120 psi.
                              Ans. $V = 8820$ lb

1010. In the beam section in Prob. 1007, assume that the channels are bolted to the wood by two rows of $\frac{3}{4}$-in. bolts spaced 1 ft apart and located 3 in. above and below axis 1–1. Assume $n = 20$, and compute the shearing stress in the bolts caused by a central load of 20,000 lb applied to a simply supported span 10 ft long, if bending takes place (*a*) about axis 1–1, and (*b*) about axis 2–2.
                       Ans. (*b*) $S_s = 10,400$ psi

1011. The beam in Prob. 1002 carries a uniformly distributed load of 2000 lb/ft on a simply supported span 16 ft long. If $E_s = 30 \times 10^6$ psi and $E_w = 1.5 \times 10^6$ psi, compute the midspan deflection.   *Ans.* $\delta = 0.320$ in.

10–4. Reinforced Concrete Beams

Concrete is an excellent building material because it is cheap and fire-proof and does not rust or rot. It has about the same strength in compression as soft wood, but its tensile strength is practically zero. For this reason, the tensile side of concrete beams is reinforced with steel bars. Ideally, these steel bars should follow the tensile stress trajectories, but practically they are placed in one layer on the tensile side. Fortunately there is a natural adhesion or bond between concrete and steel; hence no slipping occurs between them during bending,[1] and the principles developed in the preceding article can be used here. Fortunately also, both concrete and steel have about the same coefficient of temperature expansion.

It is usually assumed that the concrete carries no tensile stress, the tensile side of the concrete beam serving merely to position the steel which carries the entire tensile load. The steel is assumed to be uniformly stressed (since it is all at nearly the same distance from the neutral axis), so the line of action of the tensile force acts through the center of the reinforcing steel. The compressive stress in the concrete is assumed to vary linearly from the neutral axis, which places the resultant compressive force at the centroid of the compressive stress triangle (see Fig. 10–4a). The value of E for

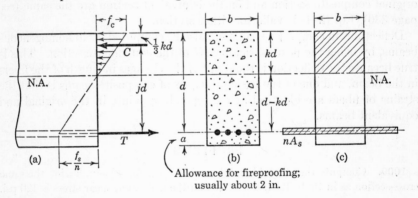

FIG. 10–4. — Reinforced concrete beam and equivalent section.

concrete is usually assumed to be $\frac{1}{15}$ that for steel, but it may vary from $\frac{1}{15}$ to $\frac{1}{8}$, depending upon the quality of the concrete.

The portion of a reinforced concrete beam in Fig. 10–4a has the cross-section shown in Fig. 10–4b. The equivalent section in terms of concrete, shown in Fig. 10–4c, is obtained by using Eq. (10–1) to transform the steel area A_s into the equivalent concrete area nA_s. As before, n is the ratio of

---

[1] Sufficient bond is developed in long beams to permit the steel bars to be laid straight, but in short beams the ends are usually bent over to anchor the steel more securely in the concrete.

the moduli of elasticity, i.e., $n = \dfrac{E_s}{E_c}$. The shaded portions of Fig. 10–4c indicate the areas that are effective in resisting bending. The distance from the top of the beam to the center of the reinforcing steel is conventionally denoted by the symbol d, and the location of the neutral axis is specified as being a fractional part k of this distance.

If the quantities b, d, A_s, and n are known, the neutral axis (the centroidal axis of the shaded areas in Fig. 10–4c) is located by applying the principle that the moment of area above the neutral axis equals the moment of area below this axis:

$$(b\ kd)\left(\frac{kd}{2}\right) = nA_s(d - kd) \tag{10–2}$$

This is a quadratic equation in terms of the distance kd. Sometimes the equation is solved directly for k, but it is more useful to determine kd.

The resultant compressive force C in the concrete acts at the centroid of the stress triangle in Fig. 10–4a, and is therefore at a distance $\frac{1}{3}\ kd$ from the top of the beam.[2] The resisting couple, composed of the equal compressive and tensile forces C and T, therefore has a moment arm jd equal to

$$jd = d - \tfrac{1}{3}(kd) \tag{10–3}$$

The notation for stresses in reinforced concrete differs from that used elsewhere in this book, it being conventional to denote the stress in the concrete by f_c and the stress in the steel by f_s. The neutral axis having been located, the moment of inertia of the equivalent section may be computed and the flexure formula applied, as in the preceding article. However, it is more direct to compute the resisting moment from the couple composed of the compressive force C and the tensile force T; this value is $C\ (jd)$ or $T\ (jd)$.

According to this concept, the average compressive stress in the concrete is $\frac{1}{2}\ f_c$, where f_c is the maximum compressive stress. The compressive force C in the concrete is the product of the average compressive stress multiplied by $b\ kd$, (the area under compression):

$$C = \tfrac{1}{2}\ f_c(b\ kd) \tag{10–4}$$

The resisting moment based on the maximum compressive stress is therefore

$$M_c = C(jd) = \tfrac{1}{2}\ f_c(b\ kd)(jd) \tag{10–5}$$

The tensile force T in the steel is the product of the steel area A_s multiplied by the steel stress f_s; hence the resisting moment in terms of the steel is

$$M_s = T(jd) = f_s A_s(jd) \tag{10–6}$$

[2] This statement and the procedure which follows should be compared with the discussion of a homogeneous rectangular section on pages 128 and 130.

The safe bending moment is the lower of the two values M_c and M_s.

In solving problems, it is better to follow numerically the steps in the derivations above rather than to use these equations directly. The first step is to locate the neutral axis, after which the moment arm of the resisting couple is easily computed. The resisting moment is then determined by means of the concept of force (C or T) times the moment arm jd.

ILLUSTRATIVE PROBLEMS

1012. In a reinforced concrete beam, $b = 12$ in., $d = 20$ in., $A_s = 2$ sq. in., $n = 15$. Determine the maximum stresses in the concrete and steel produced by a bending moment of 50,000 ft-lb.

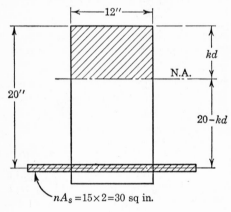

$nA_s = 15 \times 2 = 30$ sq in.

FIG. 10–5.

Solution: The equivalent section of the beam is shown in Fig. 10–5. Since the total moment of area about the neutral axis is zero,

$$[\Sigma ay = 0] \qquad 12\, kd \left(\frac{kd}{2}\right) = 30(20 - kd)$$

which reduces to

$$(kd)^2 + 5\, kd - 100 = 0$$

from which

$$kd = 7.8 \text{ in.}$$

The moment arm of the resisting moment is

$$[jd = d - \tfrac{1}{3} kd] \qquad jd = 20 - \tfrac{1}{3}(7.8) = 17.4 \text{ in.}$$

In terms of the concrete, the resisting moment is

$$[M = \tfrac{1}{2} f_c(b\, kd)(jd)] \qquad 50{,}000 \times 12 = \tfrac{1}{2} f_c(12)(7.8)(17.4)$$

from which the maximum compressive stress is

$$f_c = 736 \text{ psi}$$

In terms of the steel, the resisting moment is

$[M = f_s A_s jd]$ $50,000 \times 12 = f_s(2)(17.4)$

from which the steel stress is

$$f_s = 17,250 \text{ psi}$$

1013. In a reinforced concrete beam, $b = 10$ in., $d = 15$ in., $A_s = 1.5$ sq. in., and $n = 15$. If the allowable stresses are $f_c \leq 600$ psi and $f_s \leq 16,000$ psi, determine the maximum bending moment that may be applied. Is the beam over- or under-reinforced, or in balanced reinforcement?

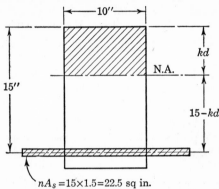

$nA_s = 15 \times 1.5 = 22.5$ sq in.

Fig. 10–6.

Solution: The equivalent section of this beam is shown in Fig. 10–6. Proceeding as in Prob. 1012, we begin by computing the factors kd and jd:

$[\Sigma ay = 0]$ $10\,kd\left(\dfrac{kd}{2}\right) = 22.5(15 - kd)$

whence

$$kd = 6.27 \text{ in.}$$

$[jd = d - \tfrac{1}{3}kd]$ $jd = 15 - \tfrac{1}{3}(6.27) = 12.91 \text{ in.}$

To stress the concrete to its maximum limit will require a bending moment

$[M_c = \tfrac{1}{2}f_c(b\,kd)(jd)]$ $M_c = \tfrac{1}{2}(600)(10)(6.27)(12.91) = 243,000$ in.-lb

To stress the steel to its limit, the required bending moment is

$[M_s = f_s A_s jd]$ $M_s = 16,000(1.5)(12.91) = 310,000$ in.-lb

The safe bending moment is therefore 243,000 in.-lb. The concrete governs, because there is too much steel; hence the beam is over-reinforced.

PROBLEMS

1014. In a reinforced concrete beam, $b = 10$ in., $d = 18$ in., $A_s = 2$ sq. in. Find the values of kd and jd if (a) $n = 15$, and (b) $n = 12$.

                          Ans.   (b) $kd = 7.2$ in.; $jd = 15.6$ in.

1015. Determine the maximum stresses produced in the concrete and steel of a reinforced beam by a bending moment of 40,000 ft-lb if $b = 12$ in., $d = 18$ in., $A_s = 2$ sq. in., and $n = 15$. *Ans.* $f_c = 705$ psi; $f_s = 15,400$ psi

1016. In a reinforced concrete beam, $b = 20$ in., $d = 30$ in., $A_s = 6$ sq. in., and $n = 12$. What are the maximum stresses developed in the concrete and the steel by a bending moment of 200,000 ft-lb? *Ans.* $f_c = 796$ psi; $f_s = 15,300$ psi

1017. The dimensions of a reinforced concrete beam are $b = 12$ in., $d = 24$ in., $A_s = 2.7$ sq. in., and $n = 12$. If the allowable stresses are $f_c \leq 800$ psi and $f_s \leq 18,000$ psi, determine the maximum bending moment that may be applied. In what state of reinforcement is the beam?

Ans. $M = 906,000$ in.-lb; over-reinforced

1018. In a reinforced concrete beam, $b = 10$ in., $d = 16$ in., $A_s = 1.6$ sq. in., and $n = 15$. Determine the safe uniformly distributed load that can be carried on a simply supported span 12 ft long if $f_c \leq 600$ psi and $f_s \leq 16,000$ psi. Assume 2 in. of concrete below the reinforcing steel and include the weight of the beam. Concrete weighs 150 lb/ft.^{3} *Ans.* $w = 1100$ lb/ft

1019. In a reinforced concrete beam, $b = 16$ in., $d = 24$ in., and $n = 12$. If a maximum stress of 600 psi is developed in the concrete when resisting a bending moment of 80,000 ft-lb, what stress is developed in the steel? What area of reinforcing steel is required? *Ans.* $f_s = 10,730$ psi; $A_s = 4.30$ sq. in.

1020. Solve Prob. 1019 if the bending moment is 60,000 ft-lb, all other data remaining unchanged. *Ans.* $f_s = 17,860$ psi; $A_s = 1.85$ sq. in.

1021. Solve Prob. 1016 by computing the moment of inertia of the transformed section, and then applying the flexure formula according to the procedure in Art. 10–2. The distance of the equivalent concrete area from the neutral axis of the transformed section can be taken as its radius of gyration with respect to this axis.

1022. Solve Prob. 1017 using the procedure outlined in Prob. 1021.

10–5. Design of Reinforced Concrete Beams

In the preceding article the dimensions of the reinforced beam were specified. This fixed the location of the neutral axis. Inasmuch as the stresses vary directly with their distance from the neutral axis, the applied bending moment may stress the concrete to its permissible limit while leaving the steel understressed — a condition known as over-reinforcement. The opposite condition, under-reinforcement, may occur when the steel reaches its permissible limit first, the concrete remaining understressed. For maximum economy, both materials should reach their limiting stresses simultaneously — a condition known as *balanced reinforcement*.

In designing a concrete beam with balanced reinforcement, therefore, we start with the assumption that the position of the neutral axis is such that the maximum f_c and the maximum stress $\dfrac{f_s}{n}$ in the equivalent concrete occur simultaneously; this is shown in the stress diagram in Fig. 10–7. From this, by the proportional relations between the triangles ABC and ADE, we obtain

$$\frac{kd}{d} = \frac{f_c}{\dfrac{f_s}{n} + f_c}$$

or

$$k = \frac{f_c}{\dfrac{f_s}{n} + f_c} \qquad (10\text{–}7)$$

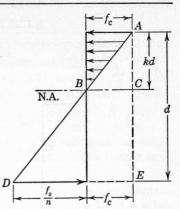

Fig. 10–7. — Stress distribution.

Having computed k in terms of the allowable stresses, we obtain the value of j by canceling out the term d in Eq. (10–3):

$$j = 1 - \tfrac{1}{3} k \qquad (10\text{–}8)$$

Once the values of k and j are determined, Eq. (10–5) is used to compute the quantity bd^2. The deeper the beam, the greater will be the moment arm of the resisting couple and the smaller the force. A deep beam therefore requires less concrete and steel than a shallow beam. Because of practical limits to the depth, however, d is usually made about 1.5 b. From this and the now computed value of bd^2, the dimensions b and d are found.

As the final step, the area of the reinforcing steel is computed from Eq. (10–6) or, preferably, from the condition that $C = T = A_s f_s$, in which A_s is now the only unknown. However, the reinforcing rods generally available are not of such size as to equal precisely the steel area required. As a consequence, balanced reinforcement can be only closely approximated.

For most well-designed rectangular beams, the values of k and j are very close to $k = \tfrac{3}{8}$ and $j = \tfrac{7}{8}$. If these values are used, dimensions may be rapidly estimated by substituting them in Eq. (10–5) thereby giving[3]

$$bd^2 = \frac{6\,M}{f_c} \qquad (10\text{–}9)$$

Having thus found bd^2 and assigning values to b and d, we compute the tensile force in the steel and the steel area from

$$T = \frac{M}{\tfrac{7}{8}\,d} \quad \text{and} \quad A_s = \frac{T}{f_s} \qquad (10\text{–}10)$$

[3] The similarity of this result to the flexure formula for rectangular beams, $S = \dfrac{6\,M}{bh^2}$, makes it simple to remember.

ILLUSTRATIVE PROBLEM

1023. Design a concrete beam with balanced reinforcement to resist a bending moment of 70,000 ft-lb. The allowable stresses are $f_c = 650$ psi, $f_s = 18,000$ psi, and $n = 15$.

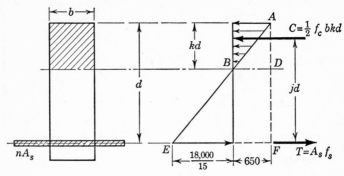

FIG. 10–8.

Solution: With balanced reinforcement, the stresses in the concrete and the concrete equivalent of the steel have the values shown in Fig. 10–8. From the proportional relations between the similar triangles ABD and AEF, the value of k is found to be

$$\frac{kd}{d} = \frac{650}{\dfrac{18,000}{15} + 650}, \qquad k = 0.351$$

from which the value of j is

$$j = 1 - \frac{1}{3}k = 1 - \frac{0.351}{3} = 0.883$$

In terms of the concrete, the resisting moment is $C \cdot (jd)$, so

$$[M_c = C \cdot (jd) = (\tfrac{1}{2}f_c\,bkd)(jd)] \qquad (70,000)(12) = \tfrac{650}{2}(bd^2)(0.351)(0.883)$$

$$bd^2 = 8340 \qquad\qquad (a)$$

Assuming that $d = 1.5\,b$, we now obtain from Eq. (a), $d^3 = 12,510$, from which $d = 23.2$ in. and $b = 15.46$ in. However, in constructing forms for the reinforced beam, it is common to make the value of b a whole number — say $b = 16$ in. in this case. Entering this value in Eq. (a), we obtain

$$d^2 = \frac{8340}{16} = 521, \qquad d = 22.8\,\text{in.}$$

The area of reinforcing steel is now the only unknown. Since the compressive force C in the concrete equals the tensile force T in the steel, we obtain, using $b = 16$ in. and $d = 22.8$ in.,

$[\frac{1}{2} f_c \, bkd = A_s f_s]$ $\frac{650}{2}(16)(0.351 \times 22.8) = A_s(18,000)$

whence

$$A_s = 2.31 \text{ sq in.}$$

Usually the available stock sizes of reinforcing steel do not produce exactly this area of steel, so the final design only closely approximates balanced reinforcement.

PROBLEMS

1024. A reinforced concrete beam is designed so as to reach $f_c = 700$ psi and $f_s = 18,000$ psi simultaneously. If $n = 15$ and $d = 18$ in., compute the moment arm of the resisting couple.   *Ans.   jd = 15.79 in.*

1025. In a reinforced concrete beam, $d = 21$ in. and $n = 12$. Find the dimensions b and A_s that will resist a bending moment of 40,000 ft-lb with balanced reinforcement, if $f_c = 750$ psi and $f_s = 18,000$ psi. *Ans.   b = 9.8 in.; A_s = 1.43 sq. in.*

1026. In a reinforced beam, $b = 10$ in., $d = 18$ in., and $n = 20$; the allowable stresses are $f_c = 600$ psi and $f_s = 18,000$ psi. Determine A_s for balanced design, and the safe resisting moment.   *Ans.   A_s = 1.2 sq. in.; M = 28,100 ft-lb*

1027. Design a reinforced concrete beam with balanced reinforcement that will resist a bending moment of 100,000 ft-lb, assuming $d = 1.5 \, b$. Assume $f_c = 600$ psi, $f_s = 16,000$ psi, and $n = 15$.

1028. Solve Prob. 1027, if $b = \frac{3}{4} d$ and $n = 13$.

1029. A simply supported beam 16 ft long is designed to carry a central load of 14,000 lb. Compute b and A_s for a depth $d = 18$ in., using balanced reinforcement, with $f_c = 1000$ psi, $f_s = 18,000$ psi, and $n = 10$. Allow 2 in. of concrete below the steel and include the weight of the beam, assuming concrete weighs 150 lb/ft.[3]   *Ans.   b = 15.62 in.; A_s = 2.79 sq. in.*

1030. A reinforced concrete beam 24 ft long and perfectly restrained at the ends is to carry a live load of 1000 lb/ft in addition to its weight. Assuming $b = 16$ in., design a beam with balanced reinforcement using $f_c = 800$ psi, $f_s = 18,000$ psi, $n = 12$. Allow 2 in. of concrete below the reinforcing rods. Concrete weighs 150 lb/ft.[3]   *Ans.   d = 20 in.; A_s = 2.48 sq. in.*

10–6. Tee Beams of Reinforced Concrete

The method used for rectangular reinforced concrete beams become quite involved when applied to tee beams. Because of the flange of the tee, the centroid of the compressive area is no longer $\frac{1}{2} kd$ from the neutral axis, nor is the line of action of the resultant compressive force $\frac{1}{3} kd$ from the top of the beam. As a consequence, it is cumbersome to use the basic procedure described in Art. 10–4, although textbooks on reinforced concrete do develop equations in terms of k and j. It is preferable for the beginner to apply the flexure formula directly to an equivalent section, as indicated in Art. 10–2 and as done in the following problem.

ILLUSTRATIVE PROBLEM

1031. The tee beam in Fig. 10–9 is reinforced with 2.5 sq. in. of steel. Assuming $n = 12$, $f_c \leq 600$ psi, and $f_s \leq 18,000$ psi, determine the maximum resisting moment.

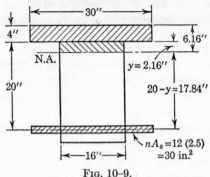

FIG. 10–9.

Solution: Denoting the distance from the bottom of the flange to the neutral axis by y, we compute the moments of area about the neutral axis:

$$[\Sigma ay = 0] \qquad (30 \times 4)(y + 2) + (16\,y)\left(\frac{y}{2}\right) - 30(20 - y) = 0$$

This reduces to

$$8\,y^2 + 150\,y - 360 = 0$$

from which

$$y = 2.16 \text{ in.}$$

The moment of inertia about the neutral axis is computed by resolving the compressive area into a rectangle 30 in. by 6.16 in., reduced by a rectangle 14 in. by 2.16 in. Thus we have

$$I = \frac{30(6.16)^3}{3} - \frac{14(2.16)^3}{3} + 30(17.84)^2 \approx 11,840 \text{ in.}^4$$

The distance 17.84 may be taken as the radius of gyration of the concrete equivalent of the steel.

In terms of the permissible concrete stress, the flexure formula gives

$$\left[M = \frac{SI}{y}\right] \qquad M_c = \frac{600(11,840)}{6.16} = 1,154,000 \text{ in.-lb}$$

In terms of the concrete equivalent of the steel, the permissible limit is $\dfrac{f_s}{n} = \dfrac{18,000}{12} = 1500$ psi, and the flexure formula gives

$$\left[M = \frac{SI}{y}\right] \qquad M_s = \frac{1500(11,840)}{17.84} = 996,000 \text{ in.-lb}$$

This, being smaller than M_c, is the maximum resisting moment.

The portion of the compression area in the stem contributes very little to the resisting moment. Neglecting this area leads to a simplified solution whose results are nevertheless close to those obtained with the exact solution. As an exercise, show that this simplified procedure gives a resisting moment of 1,000,000 in.-lb.

PROBLEMS

1032. In a reinforced tee beam, $b_1 = 20$ in., $h_1 = 6$ in., $b = 10$ in., $h = 20$ in., $A_s = 3$ sq. in., and $n = 15$. Compute the maximum stresses produced in the concrete and the steel by a bending moment of 100,000 ft-lb.

Ans. $f_c = 608$ psi; $f_s = 17,200$ psi

1033. The dimensions of a reinforced concrete tee beam are $b_1 = 30$ in., $h_1 = 4$ in., $b = 12$ in., and $h = 18$ in. If $n = 12$ and $A_s = 3.5$ sq. in., determine the maximum bending moment that may be applied without exceeding $f_c = 800$ psi and $f_s = 18,000$ psi.   *Ans.* $M = 96,700$ ft-lb

1034. In a reinforced concrete tee beam, $b_1 = 36$ in., $h_1 = 3$ in., $b = 12$ in., $h = 21$ in., and $n = 15$. Find A_s and the maximum resisting moment for a balanced design, using $f_c = 600$ psi and $f_s = 16,000$ psi.

Ans. $A_s = 4.18$ sq in.; $M = 122,000$ ft-lb

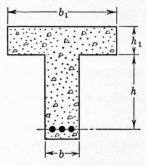

PROB. 1032, 1033, and 1034.

10–7. Shearing Stress and Bond Stress

In the bending of reinforced concrete beams, the steel is prevented from sliding by the grip of the enveloping concrete. The stress developed by dividing this gripping force by the surface area of the reinforcing bars per

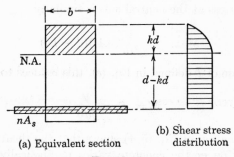

(a) Equivalent section

(b) Shear stress distribution

FIG. 10–10.

linear inch is the *bond stress*. The bond stress is analogous to the shearing stress in a homogeneous beam; it may be computed by applying Eq. (5–4) (page 153) to the equivalent section of concrete shown in Fig. 10–10. Thus

$$\left[S_s = \frac{V}{Ib} A'\bar{y} \right] \qquad\qquad S_s = \frac{V}{Ib'}(nA_s)(d - kd) \qquad\qquad (a)$$

where b' is the effective width of the steel bars, equivalent to the sum of the perimeters of the steel bars, usually expressed by Σo.

The moment of inertia of the transformed section is found from the flexure formula. Thus, at the concrete equivalent of the steel, the stress is $\dfrac{f_s}{n}$, so

$$\left[S = \frac{My}{I} \right] \qquad\qquad \frac{f_s}{n} = \frac{M(d - kd)}{I} \qquad\qquad (b)$$

But $M = T(jd) = A_s f_s\, jd;$ hence Eq. (b) reduces to

$$I = nA_s(d - kd)(jd) \qquad\qquad (c)$$

Since $nA_s(d - kd) = (bkd)\left(\dfrac{kd}{2}\right)$ (see Eq. 10–2, page 335), the moment of inertia can also be expressed by

$$I = \tfrac{1}{2} b(kd)^2(jd) \qquad\qquad (d)$$

Substituting in Eq. (a) the value of I from Eq. (c) gives

$$S_s = \frac{V(nA_s)(d - kd)}{[nA_s(d - kd)(jd)]\, b'}$$

from which the bond stress is given by

$$S_s = \frac{V}{jdb'} = \frac{V}{jd\Sigma o} \qquad\qquad (10\text{–}11)$$

The shearing stress at the neutral axis is similarly

$$\left[S_s = \frac{V}{Ib} A'\bar{y} \right] \qquad\qquad \text{Max. } S_s = \frac{V}{Ib}(nA_s)(d - kd)$$

By using the value of I defined in Eq. (c), this reduces to

$$\textbf{Max. } S_s = \frac{V}{jdb} \qquad\qquad (10\text{–}12)$$

Further examination of Eq. (5–4) shows that the shearing stress in the compressive portion of the concrete varies parabolically as in a homogeneous rectangular section, whereas it remains constant below the neutral axis, as shown in Fig. 10–10b. Comparison of Eqs. (10–11) and (10–12) shows that the bond stress becomes larger than the shearing stress on the neutral surface if Σo is smaller than the width b of the beam. To increase Σo and keep A_s constant, more reinforcing bars of smaller diameter may be used.

PROBLEMS

1035. The reinforced beam in Prob. 1016 is subjected to a vertical shear $V = 30,000$ lb. Calculate the maximum shearing stress and bond stress if the reinforcement consists of six bars 1 in. square. *Ans.* 57.2 psi; 47.8 psi

1036. Determine the vertical shear that can be sustained by the beam in Prob. 1015 if the reinforcing consists of four bars $\frac{1}{2}$ in. square. Assume that allowable shearing stress is 50 psi and the allowable bond stress is 80 psi. *Ans.* $V = 9330$ lb

SUMMARY

Nonhomogeneous beams of two materials may be transformed into equivalent sections of one material by using the relation

$$A_c = A_w = nA_s \tag{10-1}$$

where n is the ratio of the moduli of elasticity of the transformed material to that of the equivalent material. The flexure formula may then be applied directly to the transformed section as shown in Arts. 10–2 and 10–6.

The basic procedure in Art. 10–4 is usually used with reinforced concrete beams. The principles outlined in deriving the following equations should be followed numerically, rather than slavishly applying the equations themselves.

$$(b\,kd)\left(\frac{kd}{2}\right) = nA_s(d - kd) \tag{10-2}$$

$$jd = d - \tfrac{1}{3}(kd) \tag{10-3}$$

The stresses are found from the following equations. If the allowable stresses are specified, the safe resisting moment of the beam is the smaller of the two values.

$$M_c = C(jd) = \tfrac{1}{2} f_c(b\,kd)(jd) \tag{10-5}$$

$$M_s = T(jd) = f_s A_s(jd) \tag{10-6}$$

In designing a concrete beam with balanced reinforcement, the dimensions of the section are unknown, so the above equations cannot be applied. Nevertheless, a stress diagram can be drawn in terms of the specified maximum stresses, as in Fig. 10–7 in Art. 10–5, whence the position of the neutral axis is defined in terms of k as follows:

$$k = \frac{f_c}{\dfrac{f_s}{n} + f_c} \tag{10-7}$$

Eq. (10–7) is based on the assumption of balanced reinforcement, i.e., that both concrete and steel reach their allowable stresses simultaneously. This relation between the stresses does not exist when the dimensions of a beam are specified; hence Eq. (10–7) cannot be used as a shortcut substitute for Eq. (10–2) in locating the neutral axis.

The maximum shearing stress in reinforced rectangular concrete beams is given by

$$\text{Max. } S_s = \frac{V}{jdb} \tag{10–12}$$

and the bond stress by

$$S_s = \frac{V}{jd\Sigma o} \tag{10–11}$$

where Σo is the sum of the perimeters of the reinforcing steel bars.

Chapter XI
Columns

11–1. Introduction

A column is a compression member that is so slender compared to its length that under gradually increasing loads it fails by buckling at loads considerably less than those required to cause failure by crushing. In this respect it differs from a short compression member, which, even if eccentrically loaded, undergoes negligible lateral deflection. Although there is no sharp line of demarcation between short compression members and columns, a compression member is generally considered to be a column when its unsupported length is more than 10 times its least lateral dimension.

Columns are usually subdivided into two groups: *long* and *intermediate;* sometimes the short compression block is considered to be a third group. The distinction between the three is determined by their behavior. Long columns fail by buckling or excessive lateral bending; intermediate columns, by a combination of crushing and buckling; short compression blocks, by crushing. We shall now examine these differences in detail.

An ideal column is assumed to be a homogeneous member of constant cross-section that is initially straight and is subjected to axial compressive loads. However, actual columns always have small imperfections of material and fabrication, as well as unavoidable accidental eccentricities of load, which produce the effect shown, greatly exaggerated, in Fig. 11–1. The initial crookedness of the column, together with the placement of the load, causes an indeterminate eccentricity e with respect to the centroid of a typical section m–n. The loading on this section is similar to that on an eccentrically loaded short strut (Art. 9–3,

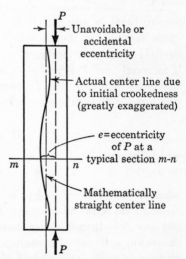

FIG. 11–1. — Factors contributing to eccentricity of loads in columns.

347

page 291) and the resultant stress is due to a combination of a direct compressive stress and a flexure stress.

If the eccentricity is small and the member short, the lateral deflection is negligible, and the flexural stress is insignificant compared with the direct compressive stress. A long member, however, is quite flexible, because deflection is proportional to the cube of the length; hence a relatively low value of P may cause a large flexural stress accompanied by a negligible direct compressive stress. Thus, at the two extremes, a short column carries principally direct compressive stress, and a long column is subjected primarily to flexural stress. As the length of a column increases, the importance of the direct compressive stress decreases, and that of the flexural stress increases. Unfortunately, in the intermediate column range it has not been possible to determine the rates of change in these stresses or the proportion of each stress that constitutes the resultant stress. It is this indeterminateness that gives rise to the many formulas for intermediate columns; these are discussed in Art. 11–5.

For the present, we have deliberately refrained from establishing any criterion for the difference between long and intermediate columns, except the fact that the long column is subjected principally to flexural stress and the intermediate column to a combination of direct and flexural stress. The distinction between them in terms of actual length can be discussed intelligently only after we have studied the action in a long column.

11–2. Critical Load

A long beam is mounted vertically and hinged at the ends so that it is free to bend in any direction. A central horizontal load H is applied to cause bending in its most limber plane, as shown in Fig. 11–2a. Since flexural stress is proportional to deflection, there will be no change in stress if an axial load P is added at each end, as in Fig. 11–2b, H being simultaneously decreased as P increases so that the midspan deflection δ is unaltered. The midspan bending moment is then

$$M = \frac{H}{2}\left(\frac{L}{2}\right) + P\delta$$

which becomes

$$M = (P_{cr})\delta$$

when H has been reduced to zero. Here, as shown in Fig. 11–2c, P_{cr} is the critical load required to maintain the column in its deflected position without any side thrust. Any increase in P beyond this value increases the deflection δ, thereby increasing M, thence δ, etc., until the column buckles or fails. On the other hand, if P is decreased slightly below this critical value, the deflection is decreased, thereby decreasing the bending moment, thence the deflection, etc., and the column straightens out. A critical load, therefore, can be interpreted as the maximum axial load to which a column may be subjected and still remain straight, although in such an unstable condition that a slight sideways thrust will cause it to bow out, as in Fig. 11–2c. The next article discusses the computation of this critical load.

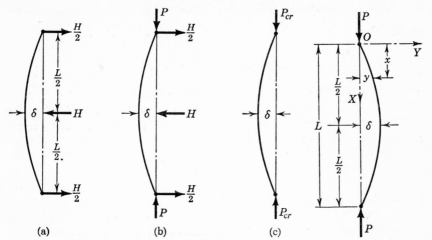

(a)   (b)   (c)

Fig. 11–2. — Beam and column sustaining equal deflections   Fig. 11–3.

11–3. Long Columns by Euler's Formula

A theoretical analysis of the critical load for long columns was made by the great Swiss mathematician Leonhard Euler in 1757. His analysis is based on the differential equation of the elastic curve $EI \dfrac{d^2y}{dx^2} = M$. As we know now, such an analysis is valid only up to the stress at the proportional limit.[1] In Euler's time, neither the concept of stress nor the limiting stress at the proportional limit had been formulated; hence he did not emphasize the concept of an upper limit to the critical load P. This upper limit is considered in Art. 11–4.

Fig. 11–3 shows the center line of a column in equilibrium under the action of its critical load P. The column is assumed to have hinged ends (sometimes called round, pivoted, or pinned) restrained against lateral movement. The maximum deflection δ is so small that there is no appreciable difference between the original length of the column and its projection on a vertical plane. Under these conditions the slope $\dfrac{dy}{dx}$ is so small that we

---

[1] More recent investigations by Professor J. A. Van den Broek have indicated methods of utilizing the strength of structures loaded beyond the proportional limit. See his *Theory of Limit Design*, published by Wiley.

may apply the differential equation of the elastic curve of a beam, viz.,

$$EI \frac{d^2y}{dx^2} = M = - Py \tag{a}$$

M is negative in accordance with the sign convention adopted in Art. 4–2; also mathematically, the minus sign before Py is required because in the region where the slope $\frac{dy}{dx}$ is positive, it is decreasing with increasing x, so $\frac{d^2y}{dx^2} = \frac{d}{dx}\left(\frac{dy}{dx}\right)$ must be negative.

Eq. (a) cannot be integrated directly, as was done in Art. 6–2, because here M is not a function of x. However, we present two methods of solving it. Students who are familiar with dynamics will find Eq. (a) similar to the equation of a simple vibrating body:

$$\frac{W}{g} \frac{d^2x}{dt^2} = - kx$$

for which the general solution is

$$x = C_1 \sin\left(t\sqrt{\frac{kg}{W}}\right) + C_2 \cos\left(t\sqrt{\frac{kg}{W}}\right)$$

Hence, by analogy, the solution of Eq. (a) can be written at once as

$$y = C_1 \sin\left(x\sqrt{\frac{P}{EI}}\right) + C_2 \cos\left(x\sqrt{\frac{P}{EI}}\right) \tag{b}$$

Substituting $y = 0$ at $x = 0$ in Eq. (b) gives $C_2 = 0$. If we apply $y = 0$ at $x = L$, we obtain

$$0 = C_1 \sin\left(L\sqrt{\frac{P}{EI}}\right)$$

This is satisfied if $C_1 = 0$ (in which case there is no bending of the column), or by

$$L\sqrt{\frac{P}{EI}} = n\pi \quad (n = 0, 1, 2, 3, \text{etc.})$$

from which

$$P = n^2 \frac{EI\pi^2}{L^2} \tag{c}$$

Students not familiar with dynamics can solve Eq. (a) by rewriting it in the form

$$EI \frac{d}{dx}\left(\frac{dy}{dx}\right) = - Py$$

After multiplying this by $2\,dy$ to obtain perfect differentials, we get, by integration,

$$EI\left(\frac{dy}{dx}\right)^2 = -Py^2 + C_1 \qquad\qquad (d)$$

Since, according to Fig. 11–3, $y = \delta$ when $\dfrac{dy}{dx} = 0$, substitution in Eq. (d) gives $C_1 = P\delta^2$, whence Eq. (d) becomes

$$EI\left(\frac{dy}{dx}\right)^2 = P(\delta^2 - y^2)$$

or

$$\frac{dy}{dx} = \sqrt{\frac{P}{EI}}\ \sqrt{\delta^2 - y^2}$$

Separating the variables, we obtain

$$\frac{dy}{\sqrt{\delta^2 - y^2}} = \sqrt{\frac{P}{EI}}\ dx$$

which is integrated to yield

$$\sin^{-1}\frac{y}{\delta} = x\sqrt{\frac{P}{EI}} + C_2$$

To evaluate C_2 we use the relationship $y = 0$ at $x = 0$; hence $C_2 = 0$, so

$$\sin^{-1}\frac{y}{\delta} = x\sqrt{\frac{P}{EI}} \quad\text{or}\quad y = \delta\sin\left(x\sqrt{\frac{P}{EI}}\right) \qquad (e)$$

This indicates that the column has the shape of a sine curve.

Setting $y = 0$ at $x = L$ in Eq. (e) gives

$$\sin\left(L\sqrt{\frac{P}{EI}}\right) = 0$$

or

$$L\sqrt{\frac{P}{EI}} = n\pi \quad (n = 0, 1, 2, 3, \ldots)$$

from which

$$P = n^2\frac{EI\pi^2}{L^2} \qquad\qquad (f)$$

This agrees with the value found previously in Eq. (c).

The value $n = 0$ is meaningless, because then the load P is zero. For the other values of n, the column bends into the shapes shown in Fig. 11–4. Of these, the most important is (a); the others occur with larger loads and

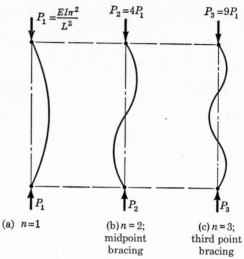

FIG. 11–4. — Effect of n on load.

are possible only if the column is braced at the middle or third points respectively.[2] The critical load for a hinged-ended column is therefore

$$P = \frac{EI\pi^2}{L^2} \tag{11–1}$$

The critical load for columns with other end conditions can be expressed in terms of the critical load for a hinged column, which is taken as the fundamental case. Thus, from symmetry, the column with fixed ends in Fig. 11–5a has inflection points at the quarter points of its unsupported length. Since the bending moment is zero at a point of inflection, the free-body diagrams show that the middle half of the fixed-ended column is equivalent to a hinged column having an effective length $L_e = \dfrac{L}{2}$. If this is substituted in Eq. (11–1), the critical load on a fixed-ended column is

$$P = \frac{EI\pi^2}{L_e^2} = \frac{EI\pi^2}{\left(\dfrac{L}{2}\right)^2} = 4\frac{EI\pi^2}{L^2} \tag{11–2}$$

This is 4 times the strength of the column if its ends were hinged.

Fig. 11–5a also provides a means of determining the load capacity of a column built in at one end and free at the other — the flagpole type of

---

[2] Bracing Fig. 11–4b at the midpoint reduces it to the shape in Fig. 11–4a with an equivalent length $\frac{1}{2} L$. Substituting $\frac{1}{2} L$ in place of L in Eq. (11–1) increases the critical load 4 times, which checks Eq. (f) for $n = 2$.

column. The critical loads on it (Fig. 11–5*b*) and on the fixed-ended column (Fig. 11–5*a*) are equal, provided the fixed-ended column is 4 times as long as the flagpole type. In other words, by substituting in Eq. (11–2) an

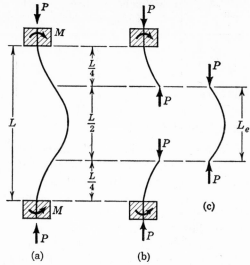

(a)   (b)   (c)

FIG. 11–5. — Built-in column and free-body diagrams.

equivalent length L_e that is 4 times its actual length, the critical load on a flagpole column is given by

$$P = \frac{4\,EI\pi^2}{L_e^2} = \frac{4\,EI\pi^2}{(4\,L)^2} = \frac{1}{4}\frac{EI\pi^2}{L^2} \qquad (11\text{–}3)$$

This load is $\frac{1}{4}$ the critical load on a hinged column of the same length.

One other type of column is hinged at one end and built in at the other, as in Fig. 11–6. For it, the point of inflection can be shown to be nearly 0.7 L from the hinged end. Hence substituting an effective length $L_e = 0.7\,L$ in Eq. (11–1) gives

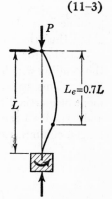

FIG. 11–6. — Column hinged at one end and built-in at the other.

$$P = \frac{EI\pi^2}{L_e^2} = \frac{EI\pi^2}{(0.7\,L)^2} = 2\,\frac{EI\pi^2}{L^2}\ \text{(very nearly)} \qquad (11\text{–}4)$$

The effect of end conditions on the critical load can therefore be expressed in terms of the critical load for the fundamental type of hinged column of the same length. All we need do is apply Eq. (11–1) multiplied by a factor n which varies with end conditions as summarized in the table on page 354, or, preferably, replace L in Eq. (11–1) by the tabulated value of an effective or modified length L_e; i. e., $P = n \dfrac{EI\pi^2}{L^2} = \dfrac{EI\pi^2}{L_e^2}.$

End Condition	n = Number of Times Strength of Hinged Column	$L_e =$ Effective Length
Fixed ends	4	$\frac{1}{2}L$
One end fixed, the other hinged	2	$0.7\,L$
Both ends hinged	1	L
One end fixed, the other free	$\frac{1}{4}$	$2\,L$

11–4. Limitations of Euler's Formula

A column always tends to buckle in its most limber direction. For this reason, and since flexural resistance varies with moment of inertia, the value of I in the column formulas is always the least moment of inertia of the cross-section. Any tendency to buckle therefore occurs about the least axis of inertia of the cross-section.

Euler's formula also shows that the critical load which causes buckling depends not upon the strength of the material but only upon its dimensions and modulus of elasticity. For this reason, two dimensionally identical slender struts, one of high-strength steel and the other of ordinary structural steel, will buckle under the same critical load because, although their strengths are different, they have the same modulus of elasticity. Good design also requires that a section have as large a moment of inertia as possible. Hence, for a given area, the material should be distributed as far as possible from the centroid, and in such a way that the moments of inertia about the principal axes are equal or as nearly equal as possible.

In order for Euler's formula to be applicable, the stress accompanying the bending which occurs during buckling must not exceed the proportional limit. This stress may be found by replacing in Euler's formula the moment of inertia I by its equivalent Ak^2, where A is the cross-sectional area and k the least radius of gyration. Doing this for the fundamental case of a hinged column, Eq. (11–1) becomes

$$\frac{P}{A} = \frac{E\pi^2}{\left(\dfrac{L}{k}\right)^2} \qquad\qquad (11\text{–}5)$$

For other end conditions, substitute in this equation the equivalent length of a hinged column from the table on this page.

Here $\dfrac{P}{A}$ is the *average stress* in the column when carrying its critical load. This stress is often called the *critical stress*. Its limiting value is the stress

at the proportional limit.   The ratio $\dfrac{L}{k}$ is called the slenderness ratio of the
column.   Since the column buckles about the axis of least moment of
inertia, the least radius of gyration should be used in computing the slenderness ratio.

The limiting slenderness ratio can be found easily for any material by
substituting in Eq. (11–5) the known values of the proportional limit and
the modulus of elasticity for the material.   For example, for steel that has a
proportional limit about 30,000 psi and with $E = 30 \times 10^6$ psi, we obtain

$$\left(\frac{L}{k}\right)^2 = \frac{(30 \times 10^6)\pi^2}{30,000} \approx 10,000 \quad \text{or} \quad \frac{L}{k} \approx 100$$

This indicates that Eq. (11–5) can be used to determine the critical load for
hinged columns only if $\dfrac{L}{k} \geqq 100$.   If $\dfrac{L}{k} < 100$, the critical stress reaches the
proportional limit before buckling can occur and Eq. (11–5) is not ap-
plicable.   Thus, the dashed portion of Euler's curve in Fig. 11–7 represents

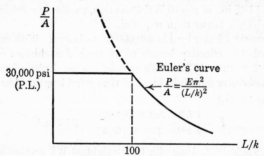

FIG. 11–7. — Critical or allowable stress is given by the solid line. Dashed portion of
Euler's curve is not valid.

values that are not valid.   The curve also shows that the critical or allowable stress on a column decreases rapidly as the slenderness ratio increases;
hence it is good design to keep the slenderness ratio as small as possible,
thereby increasing the load capacity of the column.

Finally, it should be remembered that Euler's formulas determine critical loads, not safe working loads.   It is therefore necessary to divide the
right side of each formula by a suitable factor of safety, usually $2\frac{1}{2}$ to 3, in
order to obtain practical allowable values.

ILLUSTRATIVE PROBLEM

1101.   Select the lightest WF section that can act as a column 22 ft long (*a*) with
both ends hinged and (*b*) with one end fixed and the other hinged. The column is to
support an axial load of 100,000 lb with a factor of safety of 3.

Solution: Part a. The specified working load, when multiplied by the factor of safety, gives a critical Euler load of 300,000 lb. For hinged ends, Euler's formula is

$$P = \frac{EI\pi^2}{L^2} \quad \text{or} \quad I = \frac{PL^2}{E\pi^2}$$

whence

$$I = \frac{300,000(22 \times 12)^2}{(30 \times 10^6)\pi^2} = 70.7 \text{ in.}^4$$

The lightest WF section with this least value of I is the 10 WF 49 section, with least $I = 93.0$ in.^{4} and least $k = 2.54$ in. Before concluding that this is the proper section, we must check the slenderness ratio. Its value is $\dfrac{L}{k} = \dfrac{22 \times 12}{2.54} = 104.$ This is larger than the lower limit of $\dfrac{L}{k} = 100$ permitted for hinged Euler columns of steel and the section is therefore satisfactory.

That this section is satisfactory may be checked from another viewpoint. Substituting $\dfrac{L}{k} = 104$ in $\dfrac{P}{A} = \dfrac{E\pi^2}{\left(\dfrac{L}{k}\right)^2}$ yields a critical stress of 27,400 psi. Multiplying this by the area 14.40 in.^{2} of the 10 WF 49 section, we obtain a critical load capacity of 395,000 lb, which is larger than required.

Part b. The critical Euler load is 300,000 lb, as before. With one end fixed and the other hinged, the effective length of an equivalent hinged column is $L_e = 0.7 L = 0.7 \times 22 \times 12 = 185$ in. We may now apply Euler's formula for hinged ends, using this effective length in place of the actual length. The least I now required is

$$I = \frac{PL^2}{E\pi^2} = \frac{300,000(185)^2}{(30 \times 10^6)\pi^2} = 34.7 \text{ in.}^4$$

According to Table B–2, Appendix B, the lightest WF section with a least moment of inertia larger than this value is an 8 WF 31 section, with $I = 37.0$ in.^{4}, least $k = 2.01$ in. and area $A = 9.12$ in.^{2} Again, however, we must check the slenderness ratio to insure that Euler's formula is applicable. Here $\dfrac{L}{k} = \dfrac{185}{2.01} = 92.$ This indicates that Euler's formula does not apply, since, as shown in Fig. 11–7, the criterion is $\dfrac{L}{k} \geqq 100$ for steel with a P.L. of 30,000 psi (see page 355). The selected section is therefore not acceptable.

This conclusion may also be checked as follows: To support a critical load of 300,000 lb without exceeding the limiting stress of 30,000 psi requires an area of at least 10 in.^{2}, whereas for the 8 WF 31 section $A = 9.12$ in.^{2}

This column should be handled as an intermediate column. This will be discussed in the next article (see Prob. 1118). As an introduction, however, we may obtain a solution here by assuming that if $\dfrac{L}{k} < 100$, the column section is governed by a limiting stress which is the proportional limit of 30,000 psi. (See Fig. 11–7.) The lightest satisfactory WF section with $\frac{L}{k} < 100$ and an area greater than 10 in.² (obtained by dividing the load of 300,000 lb by the stress of 30,000 psi) is therefore the 8 WF 35 section with least $k = 2.03$ (giving $\frac{L}{k} = 91$) and $A = 10.30$ in.²

Query: Why could not the area be used as the basis for selecting the column in part (a)?

PROBLEMS

1102. A rectangular steel bar 2 in. by 3 in. is used as a column with fixed ends. Determine the minimum length at which Euler's formula can be used if $E = 30 \times 10^6$ psi and the proportional limit is 40,000 psi. What central load can be carried with a factor of safety of $2\frac{1}{2}$ if the length is 10 ft?

Ans. $L = 99.3$ in.; $P = 65,800$ lb

1103. A steel strut 6 ft long has a rectangular section $\frac{3}{4}$ in. by 2 in. A bolt through each end secures the strut so that it acts as a hinged column about an axis perpendicular to the 2-in. dimension, and as a fixed-ended column about an axis perpendicular to the $\frac{3}{4}$-in. dimension. Determine the safe central load, using a factor of safety of 3.   *Ans.* $P = 5360$ lb

1104. Two 10-in. 25-lb channels are latticed together so they have equal moments of inertia about the principal axes. Determine the minimum length of a column having this section, using pinned ends, if $E = 30 \times 10^6$ psi and the proportional limit is 35,000 psi. What safe load will it carry for a length of 30 ft, the factor of safety being $2\frac{1}{2}$?   *Ans.* $L = 27$ ft; $P = 166,000$ lb

1105. Repeat Prob. 1104 if one end is fixed and the other hinged.

1106. Select the lightest WF section that will act as a column 20 ft long with hinged ends, and support an axial load of 60,000 lb with a factor of safety of $2\frac{1}{2}$.

1107. Select the lightest WF section that will act as a column 30 ft long with fixed ends, and support an axial load of 120,000 lb with a factor of safety of 3. Assume P.L. = 30,000 psi.   *Ans.* 14 WF 43 (P.L. governs)

11–5. Intermediate Columns. Empirical Formulas

The preceding discussion showed that long columns can be treated by Euler's formula provided that the slenderness ratio is larger than the value at which the average stress reaches the proportional limit. For hinged steel columns, this limit is $\frac{L}{k} = 100$ at 30,000 psi. Euler's formula is not valid for smaller slenderness ratios. The definition of a short column as one whose length does not exceed 10 times the least lateral dimension sets the upper limit of the slenderness ratio at about 30 for a rectangular section. For all practical purposes, the limiting stress on a short column has been found to be the stress at the yield point; extreme care is required to prevent buckling when stressed to this point. Fig. 11–8 shows these conditions for steel having a yield point of 40,000 psi and a proportional limit of 30,000 psi.

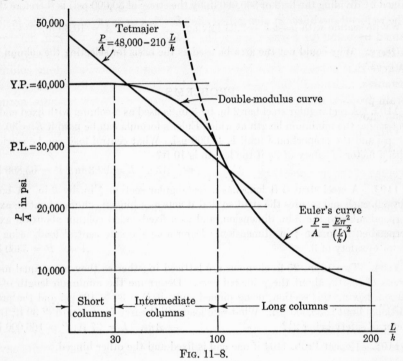

FIG. 11–8.

Various methods have been proposed for bridging the gap between the short column range and the long column range. However, none of them have been accepted universally for intermediate columns, partly because of their departure from the stress-strain relationship when the stresses exceed the proportional limit, and partly because of their indeterminate mixture of direct and flexural stresses when loads are reduced by an appropriate factor of safety to bring the stresses below the proportional limit.

Most empirical formulas for intermediate columns have been developed for steel, because it is such a common structural material. We shall discuss these first, and then indicate their extension to other structural materials.

In one proposed method — that of the double-modulus theory[3] — the Euler formula is extended to intermediate columns stressed above the proportional limit by replacing the constant modulus E by a reduced modulus $\bar{E}$, viz.,

[3] See a paper by W. R. Osgood, "The Double-Modulus Theory of Column Action," *Civil Engineering*, March, 1935.

$$\frac{P}{A} = \frac{\bar{E}\pi^2}{\left(\dfrac{L}{k}\right)^2} \tag{11–6}$$

The reduced modulus $\bar{E}$, also called the effective or tangent modulus, is obtained by using for $\bar{E}$ the slope of the tangent to the stress-strain diagram at the point corresponding to the average stress in the column. This yields a curve that connects those curves representing the short and long column formulas. Although this method is empirical because it violates the stress-strain proportionality assumed in the derivation of Euler's formula, actual tests show close agreement with the theoretical curve.

Other methods are frankly empirical. One of the simplest, proposed by T. H. Johnson in 1886, consists of drawing a straight line through the average of the test points obtained by plotting values of $\dfrac{P}{A}$ (when failure due to buckling appeared imminent) against the corresponding values of $\dfrac{L}{k}$. The general equation of this straight-line formula is

$$\frac{P}{A} = S - C\frac{L}{k}$$

where S is the intercept for $\dfrac{L}{k} = 0$ and C is the magnitude of the slope.

The results obtained by Tetmajer and Bauschinger with tests on structural steel bars with hinged ends have been widely used. Their results gave for the critical load:

$$\frac{P}{A} = 48,000 - 210\frac{L}{k} \tag{11–7}$$

This equation is shown in Fig. 11–8. As mentioned previously, the yield point is the practical limit to $\dfrac{P}{A}$; this is recognized in the formula by setting a lower limit to $\dfrac{L}{k}$ that corresponds to 38 for a yield point of 40,000 psi.

Eq. (11–7) divided by a factor of safety of 3 has been incorporated into the building codes of many communities. Its best-known advocate today is the Chicago Building Code, whence it has become known as the Chicago formula:

$$\frac{P}{A} = 16,000 - 70\frac{L}{k} \tag{11–8}$$

This equation for safe working loads is limited to a slenderness range of

$30 \leq \dfrac{L}{k} \leq 120$ for main members, and up to $\dfrac{L}{k} = 150$ for secondary mem-

bers used for bracing. Below $\dfrac{L}{k} = 30$, $\dfrac{P}{A} = 14{,}000$ psi is used.

Another widely used empirical column formula is the Rankine-Gordon formula developed about 1860. It has the form

$$\frac{P}{A} = \frac{S}{1 + \varphi \left(\dfrac{L}{k}\right)^2}$$

in which S is the critical compressive stress for short bars and φ is a constant that depends upon the material and end conditions. The formula specified in the New York City Building Code for 1945, hereafter referred to as the New York formula, is

$$\frac{P}{A} = \frac{18{,}000}{1 + \dfrac{1}{18{,}000}\left(\dfrac{L}{k}\right)^2} \tag{11-9}$$

This formula, which includes a factor of safety, is valid for main members with $\dfrac{L}{k}$ between 60 and 120 and for secondary members with $\dfrac{L}{k}$ up to 200.

Below $\dfrac{L}{k} = 60$, a working stress of $\dfrac{P}{A} = 15{,}000$ psi is specified.

Still another variation of the intermediate column formula is the parabolic type proposed in 1892 by Professor J. B. Johnson (not related to T. H. Johnson of straight-line fame). This formula has the general form:

$$\frac{P}{A} = S - C\left(\frac{L}{k}\right)^2$$

in which S is the stress at the yield point and C is a constant chosen to make the parabola tangent to Euler's curve.

The American Institute of Steel Construction (AISC) recommends the adoption of this formula in the following form:

$$\frac{P}{A} = 17{,}000 - 0.485\left(\frac{L}{k}\right)^2 \tag{11-10}$$

This is valid for columns with slenderness ratios up to 120 for main members, and is supplemented by the New York formula (Eq. 11-9) for secondary members with $\dfrac{L}{k}$ from 120 up to 200. This equation permits a little

heavier safe load than does the New York formula.   For main members
having slenderness ratios between 120 and 200, Eq. (11–9) may be used by
modifying it to

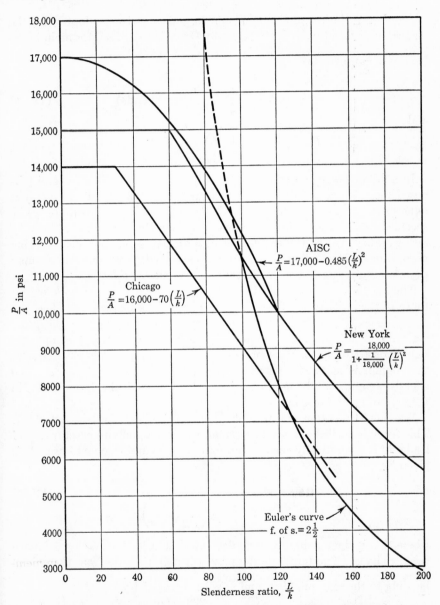

FIG. 11–9. — Comparison of unit loads of various column formulas.

$$\frac{P}{A} = \left(1.6 - \frac{1}{200}\frac{L}{k}\right)\frac{18,000}{1 + \frac{1}{18,000}\left(\frac{L}{k}\right)^2} \tag{11-9a}$$

Another variation of the parabolic formula has been adopted by the American Association of State Highway Officials (AASHO) for main members with $\frac{L}{k}$ up to 120:

$$\frac{P}{A} = 15,000 - \frac{1}{3}\left(\frac{L}{k}\right)^2 \quad \text{(pinned ends)} \tag{11-11}$$

and

$$\frac{P}{A} = 15,000 - \frac{1}{4}\left(\frac{L}{k}\right)^2 \quad \text{(riveted ends)} \tag{11-12}$$

In addition to the specific variations given above for these several proposed formulas, a great many other equations are used. However, it is unnecessary to memorize them, for the formula to be used must always be specified. All the equations have one feature in common: they reduce the safe working load as the slenderness ratio increases, although in varying proportions. Depending on the formula specified, the same column may therefore support any one of several different safe *legal* loads.

The above formulas are all based on columns with hinged ends, except those of the AASHO. Although fixity of the ends increases the load capacity (see Art. 11–3), structural columns — which compose the great majority of intermediate columns — practically never have completely rigid ends. Hence it is good practice to assume hinged ends, even though the column is actually riveted or otherwise rigidified at its ends. The effective length may be used occasionally for economical column design in the case of partial or complete end restraints.

We should mention one formula that will be developed in Art. 11–7. This formula, called the *secant formula*, assumes a definite eccentricity of load and is theoretically correct, but exceedingly cumbersome to use. It is given by

$$\frac{P}{A} = \frac{S_{max}}{1 + \frac{ec}{k^2}\sec\left(\frac{L}{2k}\sqrt{\frac{P}{EA}}\right)} \tag{11-13}$$

where S_{max} is the maximum stress developed by a load P having a known eccentricity e. The term c is the perpendicular distance from the axis of bending to the extreme fiber, and $\frac{ec}{k^2}$ is the eccentricity ratio.

After a careful study of existing column data supplemented by additional tests, the following variation of the secant formula was proposed in 1933 by a special committee of the American Society of Civil Engineers:

$$\frac{P}{A} = \frac{\frac{1}{f}\,(\text{Yield point})}{1 + 0.25 \sec\left(\frac{nL}{2\,k}\sqrt{\frac{fP}{EA}}\right)} \tag{11–14}$$

This formula determines safe loads with a factor of safety f. An eccentricity ratio $\frac{ec}{k^2} = 0.25$ is assumed to account for any initial crookedness in the column or any accidental eccentricity of load. The additional factor n makes it possible to obtain equivalent lengths corresponding to different end conditions. For pinned ends, n is specified as $\frac{7}{8}$; and for riveted ends as $\frac{3}{4}$.

To use Eq. (11–14) directly requires a method of trial and error. Therefore, a curve is usually plotted to show the relation between $\frac{P}{A}$ and $\frac{L}{k}$, the values of $\frac{L}{k}$ corresponding to assumed values of $\frac{P}{A}$ being computed from Eq. (11–14). However, a parabolic formula (which is much more convenient for computation than the secant formula) can be set up to fit the graph of Eq. (11–14) very closely. Formulas like those in Eqs. (11–11) and (11–12) are therefore the most logical ones to use. But however logical we may consider them, nevertheless we still must follow the legal specifications of the various building codes.

We now consider some column formulas for materials other than steel. For the various aluminum alloys, the Alcoa Structural Handbook specifies formulas of the straight-line type. A typical formula is that for columns with hinged ends made of the alloy 14S–T4:

$$\frac{P}{A} = 43{,}800 - 350\,\frac{L}{k} \tag{11–15}$$

for $\frac{L}{k} < 83$. Above this limit, use the Euler formula:

$$\frac{P}{A} = \frac{102{,}000{,}000}{\left(\frac{L}{k}\right)^2} \tag{11–16}$$

This is based on $E = 10.3 \times 10^6$ psi and applies to all aluminum alloys regardless of their strength. Both of these equations give critical loads, and must be divided by a suitable factor of safety to find safe working loads.

For magnesium alloy columns, the American Magnesium Corporation specifies the safe working load for $\dfrac{L}{k} < 120$ to be

$$\frac{P}{A} = 11{,}000 - 53.6\,\frac{L}{k} \qquad\qquad (11\text{--}17)$$

For cast-iron columns, the New York City Building Code specifies

$$\frac{P}{A} = 9000 - 40\,\frac{L}{k} \qquad\qquad (11\text{--}18)$$

for $\dfrac{L}{k} < 70$.

For rectangular wood columns, the Forest Products Laboratory has developed the following formulas which are expressed in terms of the *least lateral dimension*, b, of the cross-section. For short columns having a ratio $\dfrac{L}{b} < 10$, $\dfrac{P}{A} = S$ is used, S being the safe compressive stress specified in Table XI–1 on page 365.

For intermediate columns, use

$$\frac{P}{A} = S\left[1 - \frac{1}{3}\left(\frac{L}{Kb}\right)^{4}\right] \qquad\qquad (11\text{--}19)$$

where S is the safe compressive stress for short blocks, and K is a constant[4] evaluated from

$$K = \frac{\pi}{2}\sqrt{\frac{E}{6\,S}}$$

where E is the modulus of elasticity. Values of S, K, and E are given in Table XI–1. Eq. (11–19) is valid for slenderness ratios between $\dfrac{L}{b} = 10$ and $\dfrac{L}{b} = K$.

For long wood columns between slenderness ratios $\dfrac{L}{b} = K$ and $\dfrac{L}{b} = 50$, the following Euler formula, which includes a factor of safety of 3, is used:

$$\frac{P}{A} = \frac{E\pi^{2}}{36\left(\dfrac{L}{b}\right)^{2}} \qquad\qquad (11\text{--}20)$$

---

[4] Actually, K is the value of $\dfrac{L}{b}$ that makes $\dfrac{P}{A} = \dfrac{2}{3}\,S$ in Eq. (11–20). Substituting these values in Eq. (11–20) gives $\dfrac{2}{3}\,S = \dfrac{E\pi^{2}}{36\,K^{2}}$, whence $K = \dfrac{\pi}{2}\sqrt{\dfrac{E}{6\,S}}$. At this value of K or $\dfrac{L}{b}$, the fourth degree parabola in Eq. (11–19) is tangent to the Euler curve in Eq. (11–20).

TABLE XI–1.   For Use with Forest Products Laboratory Formula
(Common structural grade, kept continuously dry)

Species	S	K	E
Douglas fir	880	27.3	1,600,000
Western hemlock	720	28.3	1,400,000
White oak	880	27.8	1,650,000
Longleaf pine	1025	25.3	1,600,000
Shortleaf pine	880	27.3	1,600,000
Redwood	800	24.8	1,200,000
Spruce	640	27.8	1,200,000

ILLUSTRATIVE PROBLEMS

1108.   Using the AISC formula, determine the safe axial loads on a 14 WF 78 section used as a column under the following conditions: (*a*) hinged ends and a length of 30 ft; (*b*) built-in ends and an unsupported length of 50 ft; (*c*) built-in ends and a length of 50 ft braced at the midpoint.

Solution: Table B–2, Appendix B, gives, for a 14 WF 78 section, an area $A = 22.94$ in.^{2} and a least k of 3.00 in.

Part a.   The slenderness ratio is $\dfrac{L}{k} = \dfrac{30 \times 12}{3.00} = 120$, which is the upper limit of the AISC formula.   Hence, the average stress permitted is

$$\frac{P}{A} = 17{,}000 - 0.485 \left(\frac{L}{k}\right)^2 = 17{,}000 - 0.485(120)^2 = 10{,}000 \text{ psi}$$

and the allowable load is

$$P = (22.94)(10{,}000) = 229{,}400 \text{ lb}$$

Part b.   Using the concept of an effective length, a column with built-in or fixed ends is equivalent to a hinged column of half the actual length.   Hence, with $L_e = \frac{1}{2} L = \frac{1}{2}(50 \times 12) = 300$ in., the slenderness ratio is $\dfrac{L}{k} = \dfrac{300}{3.00} = 100$, which is within the specified $\dfrac{L}{k}$ range of the column formula.   Applying the formula, the average stress or allowable unit load is

$$\frac{P}{A} = 17{,}000 - 0.485(100)^2 = 12{,}150 \text{ psi}$$

and the allowable load is

$$P = (22.94)(12{,}150) = 279{,}000 \text{ lb}$$

Part c.   Braced at the midpoint, the column is equivalent to one having a length of 25 ft. fixed at one end and hinged at the other.   The effective length $L_e =$

$0.7 L = 0.7(25 \times 12) = 210$ in., whence $\dfrac{L}{k} = \dfrac{210}{3.00} = 70$. The allowable unit load is therefore

$$\frac{P}{A} = 17,000 - 0.485(70)^2 = 14,620 \text{ psi}$$

and the allowable load is

$$P = (22.94)(14,620) = 336,000 \text{ lb}$$

This problem illustrates the increased strength of a column whose ends can be perfectly rigidified. Since this condition is never realized in practice, it is better, in determining allowable loads, always to assume hinged ends, or to be more realistic in selecting the effective length with fixed ends as about $\frac{3}{4} L$ instead of $\frac{1}{2} L$.

1109. Select the lightest WF section that will support an axial load of 200,000 lb on a length of 15 ft. Use the AISC formula.

Solution: Substituting the given data in the column formula, we have

$$\left[\frac{P}{A} = 17,000 - 0.485 \left(\frac{L}{k} \right)^2 \right] \qquad \frac{200,000}{A} = 17,000 - 0.485 \left(\frac{180}{k} \right)^2$$

Since both the area A and the least radius of gyration k are unknown and no convenient relation between them can be set up, a method of trial and error is required. Since the unit load $\dfrac{P}{A}$ in the AISC formula varies from 17,000 psi at $\dfrac{L}{k} = 0$ to 10,000 psi at $\dfrac{L}{k} = 120$, we may estimate the required area, assuming an average value of, say, 13,000 psi. Therefore we look up WF sections having an area of $A = \dfrac{200,000}{13,000} = 15.4$ in.^{2}

Try a 12 WF 53 section having $A = 15.59$ in.^{2} and least $k = 2.48$ in. This section has a slenderness ratio $\dfrac{L}{k} = \dfrac{180}{2.48} = 72.5$, and hence the unit load permitted is

$$\frac{P}{A} = 17,000 - 0.485(72.5)^2 = 14,450 \text{ psi}$$

giving a load capacity of

$$P = (15.59)(14,450) = 225,000 \text{ lb (too high)}$$

We try next a 10 WF 49 section, a lighter one that has approximately the same k, 2.54 in., with an area $A = 14.40$ in.^{2} Hence $\dfrac{L}{k} = \dfrac{180}{2.54} = 70.9$, and the unit load permitted is

$$\frac{P}{A} = 17,000 - 0.485(70.9)^2 = 14,560 \text{ psi}$$

giving a load capacity of

$$P = (14.40)(14,560) = 210,000 \text{ lb (too high)}$$

The load capacity of the 10 WF 49 section is slightly high, but no lighter section is available. The procedure of selecting a section is greatly simplified by using tables giving the allowable axial loads for different sections of various lengths. Such tables are found in a steel handbook such as that published by the AISC.

PROBLEMS

1110. What factor of safety should be used with Euler's column formula so that it will give the same load capacity as is given by the upper limit of (*a*) the Chicago formula; (*b*) the New York formula; (*c*) the AISC formula?

1111. An 8 WF 40 beam is used as a column with hinged ends. Compute the safe axial load that may be applied for lengths of 4.5 ft, 15 ft, 25 ft, using (*a*) the Chicago formula and (*b*) the AISC formula.

     Ans. (*a*) 164,600 lb; 115,300 lb; 67,000 lb (secondary member only);
           (*b*) 195,700 lb; 155,400 lb; 83,100 lb ~~(secondary member only)~~

1112. A 14 WF 78 beam is used as a column 50 ft long with built-in ends. (*a*) Compute the safe load that may be applied, using the effective length and the AISC formula. (*b*) What is the safe load if the column is also braced at the mid-point?   *Ans.* (*a*) 279,000 lb; (*b*) 336,000 lb

1113. Solve Prob. 1103 if the strut is 4 ft long. Use the AISC formula and apply the concept of an effective length.   *Ans.* *P* = 16,530 lb

1114. Using the Chicago formula, what is the maximum length of a 12 WF 65 section if it is used as a column to support a load of (*a*) 200,000 lb, (*b*) 100,000 lb?   *Ans.* (*a*) 19.9 ft; (*b*) 30.2 ft

1115. The end chord *AB* of a bridge truss is made of two 10-in. 30-lb channels latticed together so that the resultant section has equal moments of inertia about the axes of symmetry. Compute the safe load it can sustain (*a*) without and (*b*) with the collision strut *CD*. Use the AASHO formula with pinned ends.   *Ans.* (*a*) 199,000 lb; (*b*) 237,000 lb

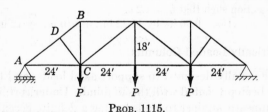

PROB. 1115.

1116. Select a WF section to act as a column carrying an axial load of 160,000 lb on a length of 14 ft. Use the AISC formula.

1117. Repeat Prob. 1116 for a length of 20 ft, using the Chicago formula.   *Ans.* 14 WF 61 section

1118. Solve Illus. Prob. 1101 for both specified end conditions, using (*a*) the Chicago formula and (*b*) the AISC formula.

1119. Four angles 3 in. by 3 in. by $\frac{1}{2}$ in. are riveted back to back as shown. (a) Determine the safe load when used as a column 12 ft long. Apply the AISC formula. (b) Multiply by 4 the safe load on one angle acting alone and compare with (a). *Ans.* (a) 120,400 lb

PROB. 1119.   PROB. 1120.

10 *WF* 49   15 ⊏ 50

1120. A steel column 40 ft long is fabricated from a 10 WF 49 beam and two 15-in. 50-lb. channels arranged as shown. Determine the safe axial load, using the AASHO formula with (a) pinned ends and (b) riveted ends. Show that the maximum and minimum moments of inertia are 1005 in.⁴ and 896 in.⁴

Ans. (a) 490,000 lb

1121. A 14S–T4 aluminum alloy column has the same dimensions as a 12-in. 50-lb steel I beam and is 6 ft long. What safe load may be applied, the factor of safety being $2\frac{1}{2}$? *Ans.* $P = 115,200$ lb

1122. Determine the safe load on a round hollow cast-iron column 14 ft long if it is 8 in. in outside diameter and 1 in. thick.

1123. Determine the safe axial loads on an oak column 8 in. by 10 in. for lengths of (a) 6 ft, (b) 14 ft, (c) 22 ft. *Ans.* (a) 70,400 lb; (b) 62,800 lb; (c) 33,300 lb

1124. Repeat Prob. 1123, using red cedar for which $S = 560$ psi and $E = 1,000,000$ psi.

1125. Design a redwood column 12 ft long to support an axial load of 80,000 lb. Assume a cross-section such that $h = 1.2\,b$.

Ans. 9.36 in. by 11.22 in.; use 10 in. by 12 in. nominal size

11–6. Eccentrically Loaded Columns

Columns are usually designed to support axial loads, and the preceding formulas have been presented with this in mind. Under certain conditions, however, columns are subject to loads having a definite eccentricity. This occurs, for example, in the case of a beam riveted to the column flange in a building. The secant formula derived in the next article is especially adapted to such cases, but it is so unwieldy that the following simplified procedure is used instead.

The maximum compressive stress in an eccentrically loaded column is computed as though the column were a short strut; the effect of deflection on the moment arm of the loads is neglected. Thus, for a column carrying an axial load P_o and a load P at an eccentricity e, (Fig. 11–10), the maximum stress developed is

$$S = \frac{\Sigma P}{A} + \frac{Mc}{I} = \frac{P_o + P}{A} + \frac{(Pe)c}{I} = \frac{P_o + P}{A} + \frac{Pe}{Z} \quad (11\text{–}21)$$

Note that I is the moment of inertia with respect to the axis about which the eccentric load causes bending (axis 1–1 in Fig. 11–10), and that Z is the section modulus with respect to that axis.

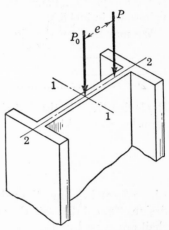

The maximum stress from Eq. (11–21) must not exceed the safe working stress. If the column were a short strut, a working stress of 16,000 to 18,000 psi might be used, but for longer members this must be reduced because of the danger of buckling. The extent of this reduction varies with the slenderness ratio. Consequently, the maximum working stress permitted in Eq. (11–21) is assumed to be equal to the unit loading as computed with the specified column formula. In computing the slenderness ratio, the least radius of gyration is *always* used, regardless of the axis about which the eccentric load causes bending. Proper attention must also be

Fig. 11–10. — Axial load P_o and eccentric load P on column.

given to the limiting range of $\dfrac{L}{k}$ for which the column formula is valid.

A refinement of this method is as follows: With **no** eccentricity, the total stress in Eq. (11–21) is $S = \dfrac{\Sigma P}{A}$ and its maximum value is the safe working stress S_w for a column of length L as determined by the specified column formula. With large eccentricities the term $\dfrac{\Sigma P}{A}$ is negligible compared with $\dfrac{Mc}{I}$; hence the column is almost in a condition of pure bending and Eq. (11–21) reduces to $S = \dfrac{Mc}{I}$. Here S may be taken as the working compressive stress S_b permitted in bending. As was said on page 135, the possibility of lateral buckling of the compression flange in long beams limits the value of S_b to the following values specified by the American Institute of Steel Construction.

For $\dfrac{Ld}{bt} < 600$, use $S_b = 20,000$ psi

For $\dfrac{Ld}{bt} > 600$, use $S_b = \dfrac{12,000,000}{\dfrac{Ld}{bt}}$ $\qquad$ (5-3)

where L is the unsupported length, d the depth of the beam, b the breadth of the compression flange, and t the thickness of the compression flange (all values are in inches).

We may now rewrite Eq. (11-21) in the following form:

$$1 = \frac{\dfrac{\Sigma P}{A}}{S} + \frac{\dfrac{Mc}{I}}{S}$$

Replacing the S in the first right-hand term by S_w and the S in the second term by S_b, we obtain

$$1 = \frac{\dfrac{\Sigma P}{A}}{S_w} + \frac{\dfrac{Mc}{I}}{S_b} \qquad (11\text{-}22)$$

where S_w and S_b have the values assigned in the preceding paragraph. In design, Eq. (11-22) sets the criterion that the sum of the right-hand terms shall not exceed unity.

ILLUSTRATIVE PROBLEM

1126. A 14 WF 87 section is used as a column 22 ft long to support one track of a traveling crane in a factory. Determine the maximum permissible reaction P if the column also carries a load of 90,000 lb from an upper floor, as shown in Fig. 11-11. Use the AISC formula and (a) Eq. (11-21) and then (b) Eq. (11-22).

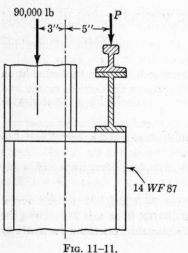

90,000 lb $\quad$ P

$\leftarrow 3'' \rightarrow \leftarrow 5'' \rightarrow$

14 WF 87

Fig. 11-11.

Solution: Part a. Table B-2, Appendix B, gives the properties of a 14 WF 87 section as $A = 25.56$ in.^{2}, $Z_{1-1} = 138.1$ in.^{3}, and least $k = 3.70$ in. The slenderness ratio is $\dfrac{L}{k} = \dfrac{22 \times 12}{3.70} = 71.3$. Assuming the maximum safe working stress to equal the unit loading specified by the AISC formula, we have

$$S_w = 17,000 - 0.485\left(\frac{L}{k}\right)^2 = 17,000 - $$
$$0.485(71.3)^2 = 14,530 \text{ psi}$$

We now consider that the column acts as an eccentrically loaded short compression member limited to this maximum stress of 14,530 psi. Applying Eq. (11–21) we obtain

$$\left[S = \frac{\Sigma P}{A} + \frac{M}{Z} \right] \qquad 14{,}530 = \frac{90{,}000 + P}{25.56} + \frac{(5\,P - 3 \times 90{,}000)}{138.1}$$

whence

$$P = 172{,}000 \text{ lb.} \quad \textit{Ans.}$$

Part b. The given section has a value of $\dfrac{d}{bt} = 1.40.$ Hence $\dfrac{Ld}{bt} = (22 \times 12)(1.40) = 370$, which, being less than 600, determines S_b (Eq. 5–3) to be 20,000 psi. This conclusion may also be obtained directly from Table B–2, since the listed value $L_u = 35.5$ ft is greater than the specified column length, 22 ft.

Before applying Eq. (11–22) it is convenient to multiply the equation by S_w so that it takes the following form:

$$S_w = \frac{\Sigma P}{A} + \left(\frac{S_w}{S_b} \right) \frac{M}{Z}$$

This is the same as Eq. (11–21), except for the ratio $\dfrac{S_w}{S_b}$ by which the second right-hand term is multiplied. Substituting values, we obtain

$$14{,}530 = \frac{90{,}000 + P}{25.56} + \left(\frac{14{,}530}{20{,}000} \right) \frac{(5\,P - 3 \times 90{,}000)}{138.1}$$

whence

$$P = 190{,}000 \text{ lb} \quad \textit{Ans.}$$

PROBLEMS

1127. A 14 WF 87 beam is used as a column 30 ft long. Use the New York formula and Eq. (11–21) to determine the maximum load that can be carried at an eccentricity of 12 in.   *Ans.* $P = 93{,}700$ lb

1128. A steel column 2 in. by 3 in. in section is 5 ft long. Using the AISC formula and Eq. (11–21), compute the maximum load that can be carried at an eccentricity of 5 in. from the geometric axis. The column also carries a central load of 10,000 lb.   *Ans.* $P = 5500$ lb

1129. A steel pipe 9 ft long, built in at its lower end and free at its upper end, supports a sign whose center of gravity is 2 ft from the axis of the pipe. Determine the maximum weight of the sign; use the Chicago formula and Eq. (11–21). Apply the concept of an effective length. The outside diameter of the pipe is 5.56 in., its area is 4.30 in.^{2}, and its moment of inertia is 15.2 in.^{4} *Ans.* $W = 1720$ lb

1130. A 14 WF 68 section is used as a column 24 ft long. It carries a central load of 50,000 lb and also an eccentric load of 100,000 lb on axis 2–2. Using the Chicago formula and Eq. (11–21), determine the maximum permissible eccentricity of the load.

1131. Solve Prob. 1130 with the AISC formula and Eq. (11–22).

Ans. e = 5.68 in.

1132. Determine the maximum length of a 12 WF 58 section used as a column to support a central load of 50,000 lb and an eccentric load of 40,000 lb acting at 10 in. off center on axis 2–2. Use the AISC formula and Eq. (11–21).

Ans. $L = 24.4$ ft

1133. Solve Prob. 1132 if the eccentric load is reduced to 20,000 lb.

1134. A steel column 40 ft long has the section specified in Prob. 1120. It carries an axial load of 100,000 lb. Using the New York formula and Eq. (11–21), determine the maximum load that may also be carried with an eccentricity of 12 in.

Ans. P = 96,600 lb

1135. A 15-in. 33.9-lb channel is used as a hinged-ended column 8 ft long. How far off center can a load of 10,000 lb be placed on axis 1–1? On which side of axis 2–2 must it be placed? Use the AISC formula and Eq. (11–21).

Ans. 11.0 in. on the web side (but only 6.60 in. if tensile stress is limited to 20,000 psi)

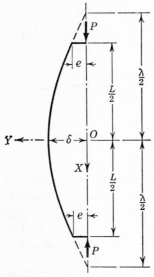

FIG. 11–12. — Eccentrically loaded column.

1136. Determine the lightest WF section that will act as a column 25 ft long supporting a central load of 80,000 lb and an eccentric load of 60,000 lb acting 10 in. off center on axis 2–2. Use the Chicago formula and Eq. (11–21).

Ans. 14 WF 87

1137. Solve Prob. 1136 with the AISC formula and Eq. (11–22). Assume $S_b = 20,000$ psi initially; correct if necessary by means of Eq. (5–3).

11–7. The Secant Formula

A theoretically correct formula for eccentrically loaded columns can be obtained by extending Euler's analysis in the following manner. Fig. 11–12 shows the center line of a column carrying a load P with an eccentricity e on a length L. If this column is extended as indicated by the dashed lines, it becomes equivalent to a hinged Euler column having a length λ. The value of P shown is the critical load for this unknown length λ. Such a column has the shape of a sine curve whose equation with respect to an origin at one end was shown in Eq. (*e*), Art. 11–3, to be

$$y = \delta \sin\left(x\sqrt{\frac{P}{EI}}\right)$$

Since from Eq. (11–1) $\sqrt{\dfrac{P}{EI}} = \dfrac{\pi}{L}$ for the fundamental shape of a hinged column, we obtain

$$y = \delta \sin\left(\frac{\pi x}{L}\right) \qquad (a)$$

If the origin is taken at the center, Eq. (a), in terms of the equivalent but unknown length λ, becomes:

$$y = \delta \cos\left(\frac{\pi x}{\lambda}\right) \qquad (b)$$

Applying the condition that $y = e$ at $x = \dfrac{L}{2}$ gives

$$e = \delta \cos\left(\frac{\pi L}{2\lambda}\right)$$

from which the value of δ is obtained for substitution in Eq. (b), thereby yielding

$$y = e\,\frac{\cos\left(\dfrac{\pi x}{\lambda}\right)}{\cos\left(\dfrac{\pi L}{2\lambda}\right)} \qquad (c)$$

The value of λ is found by applying the Euler formula in Eq. (11–1) with a length λ so that

$$P = \frac{EI\pi^2}{\lambda^2}, \qquad \text{or} \qquad \lambda = \pi\sqrt{\frac{EI}{P}}, \qquad \text{and} \qquad \frac{\pi}{\lambda} = \sqrt{\frac{P}{EI}}$$

When this is substituted in Eq. (c) we obtain the following equation for the column in Fig. 11–12:

$$y = e\,\frac{\cos\left(x\sqrt{\dfrac{P}{EI}}\right)}{\cos\left(\dfrac{L}{2}\sqrt{\dfrac{P}{EI}}\right)} \qquad (d)$$

The curvature is found by differentiating Eq. (d) twice, whence

$$\frac{d^2y}{dx^2} = -\frac{eP}{EI}\,\frac{\cos\left(x\sqrt{\dfrac{P}{EI}}\right)}{\cos\left(\dfrac{L}{2}\sqrt{\dfrac{P}{EI}}\right)}$$

Hence, from the differential equation of the elastic curve, the maximum bending moment at $x = 0$ is

$$M = EI \left(\frac{d^2y}{dx^2}\right)_{x=0} = - \frac{eP}{\cos\left(\frac{L}{2}\sqrt{\frac{P}{EI}}\right)} = - eP \sec\left(\frac{L}{2}\sqrt{\frac{P}{EI}}\right) \quad (e)$$

The maximum stress in the eccentrically loaded column is composed of a direct stress and a flexural stress as in a short strut, so

$$S_{\max.} = \frac{P}{A} + \frac{Mc}{I}$$

whence, using $I = Ak^2$ and the value of M from Eq. (e), we obtain

$$S_{\max.} = \frac{P}{A}\left[1 + \frac{ec}{k^2} \sec\left(\frac{L}{2\,k}\sqrt{\frac{P}{EA}}\right)\right] \quad (11\text{--}23)$$

This equation is known as the *secant formula*. The buckling load P specified in it is converted to a working load P_w by replacing P by fP_w where f is the factor of safety. Doing this and taking the maximum stress as the yield point we reduce Eq. (11–23) to

$$S_{y.p.} = \frac{fP_w}{A}\left[1 + \frac{ec}{k^2} \sec\left(\frac{L}{2\,k}\sqrt{\frac{fP_w}{EA}}\right)\right] \quad (11\text{--}24)$$

Trial and error methods are necessary in using these equations. Their

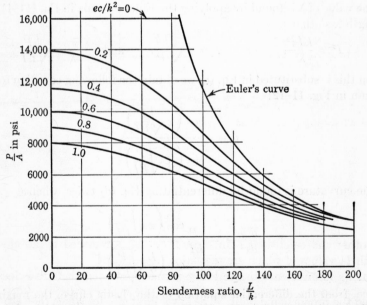

Fig. 11–13. — Design curves for secant formula with factor of safety = $2\frac{1}{2}$.

use is facilitated by calculating the values of $\dfrac{L}{k}$ corresponding to assumed

values of $\dfrac{P}{A}$ for various values of the eccentricity ratio $\dfrac{ec}{k^2}$, such as 0.2, 0.4,

etc., to 1.0. This procedure gives the data in the table on this page, from which design curves like those in Fig. 11–13 may be plotted.

Design Data for Eq. (11–24) Using $S_{y.p.} = 40{,}000$ psi, $f = 2.5$, and $E = 30 \times 10^6$ psi.

$\dfrac{P}{A}$ (psi)	$\dfrac{L}{k}$				
	$\dfrac{ec}{k^2} = 0.2$	0.4	0.6	0.8	1.0
3000	194	187	181	177	169
4000	165	158	150	142	135
5000	145	136	127	118	108
6000	130	119	108	96	83
7000	117	104	90	75	56
8000	106	90	72	50	0
9000	96	75	50		
10,000	85	58	0		
11,000	74	33			
12,000	59				

SUMMARY

Long slender columns are solved by Euler's column formula. For columns with hinged ends it is

$$P = \frac{EI\pi^2}{L^2} \tag{11-1}$$

or

$$\frac{P}{A} = \frac{E\pi^2}{\left(\dfrac{L}{k}\right)^2} \tag{11-5}$$

For other end conditions L in these formulas is replaced by an effective length L_e values of which are tabulated on page 354.

Euler's formulas are theoretically correct, provided the stress does not exceed the proportional limit. The lower limit of $\dfrac{L}{k}$ for which they are valid may be obtained by assuming that $\dfrac{P}{A}$ represents the actual stress in a

straight, axially loaded column, and replacing $\dfrac{P}{A}$ in Eq. (11–5) by the value

of the proportional limit.

Columns with a slenderness ratio less than the limit thus obtained are known as intermediate columns. No theoretically correct formulas have yet been developed; the closest approach, so far, is the secant formula (Eq. 11–14). However, this formula is too unwieldy, various empirical formulas being used instead. These empirical formulas are specified by the building codes of various communities, and the *legal* specifications of these codes must be adhered to.

Eccentrically loaded columns are solved like eccentrically loaded short struts (see Art. 9–3), except that the allowable stress is assumed to be the

value of $\dfrac{P}{A}$ obtained by solving the specified column formula. A variation of

this technique, which is also commonly used, is given by Eq. (11–22).

Chapter XII
Special Topics

12–1. Introduction

The preceding chapters have dealt with topics that comprise the usual undergraduate course in strength of materials, but the subject does not end there. We now consider briefly some additional topics[1] that properly belong in an advanced course in strength of materials; some, such as photo-elasticity, constitute a field of study in themselves.

12–2. Repeated Loading. Fatigue

Many machine parts are subjected to varying stresses caused by repeated loading and unloading. Parts subjected to such loading frequently fail at a stress much smaller than the ultimate strength determined by a static tensile test. Failures of this type are known as *fatigue failures*. In order properly to design members that are subjected to stress reversals, it is necessary to know the stress that can safely be carried an indefinite number of times (or a somewhat higher stress that may be carried safely for a limited number of reversals, as when a machine is used only occasionally and may therefore have a long life).

Testing to determine these values is called *fatigue testing*. The simplest method involves reversed bending. In it, a round specimen S is mounted in bearings, as shown in Fig. 12–1, and subjected to bending couples by the load W. As the motor M rotates the specimen, a fiber that was originally on top passes from compression to tension and back to compression, thereby

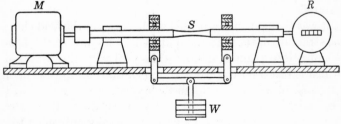

Fig. 12–1. — Rotating beam fatigue-testing machine.

[1] For extended discussions of these topics, see one or more of the following books: *Advanced Mechanics of Materials*, by F. B. Seely, Wiley; *Strength of Materials*, Vols. I and II, by S. P. Timoshenko, Van Nostrand; *Advanced Mechanics of Materials*, by Glenn Murphy, McGraw-Hill.

undergoing a complete reversal of stress for each revolution. A revolution counter, R, registers the number of revolutions until failure occurs. The motor then stops automatically. In testing a given material, about a dozen identical specimens are prepared and rotated in the machine, each at a different load W, until failure occurs or until four to five million cycles have been recorded. A typical result obtained in this way is shown in the S–N diagram in Fig. 12–2, where stress versus number of cycles is plotted

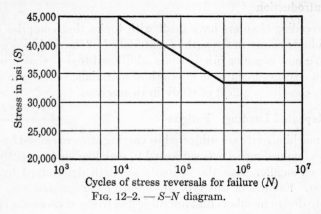

FIG. 12–2. — S–N diagram.

with semi-logarithmic scales. The point at which this diagram[2] levels off is called the *endurance limit*, denoted by S_e. Although no definite relation exists between the endurance limit and the ultimate strength, tests show that the endurance limit is between 40 and 50% of the ultimate strength.

When a ductile steel specimen is subjected to a gradually increasing load, yielding of the specimen is evident considerably before actual failure occurs. But a specimen of the same material that is subjected to stress reversals fails suddenly, without any plastic deformation or any other warning. Thus the fatigue failure of ductile steel is similar to the static failure of a brittle material.

At first it was thought that repeated applications of the load changed the crystalline structure of the material, but we now know that this is not true. Fatigue failure is explained more satisfactorily by the localized stress theory, which is based on the stress concentrations that occur (*a*) inside a material because of discontinuities in the material itself and (*b*) at the surface of a material because of abrupt changes in section. These stress concentrations are not serious when a ductile material is subjected to a static load; but when the load is repeatedly applied, they cause minute cracks which spread with each repetition until the member suddenly fractures.

---

[2] A log-log plot may be used for this diagram, but a Cartesian plot does not show the endurance limit so clearly.

For example, a flat steel bar with a small central hole is loaded by axial tensile forces. As shown in the next article, the stress at the edge of the hole is three times the stress across the full section. However, if this bar is subjected to a gradually increasing static tensile load, it will sustain practically the same ultimate load as a similar bar without a hole. The apparent insignificance of the stress concentration at the hole is due to the fact that although the material there does yield at one-third of the load at which the whole bar yields, this yielding is purely local and the stress at the edge of the hole remains constant during it. With increasing load, the whole bar finally yields; then the effect of a small hole on the strength of the bar is negligible. But if two bars, one solid and the other with a small hole, were subjected to a tensile fatigue test, the failure load of the bar with the hole would actually be about one-third that of the solid bar.

12–3.   Stress Concentration

As we said in the preceding article, the effect of stress concentration on ductile steel subjected to repeated loading is similar to its effect on a brittle material subjected to static loading. We consider now the effect of abrupt change in section upon the stress distribution. In Fig. 12–3, a small circular hole in a rectangular plate subjected to a uniform tensile stress S causes a stress distribution across a section through the hole as shown by the shaded area. This stress distribution is expressed by[3]

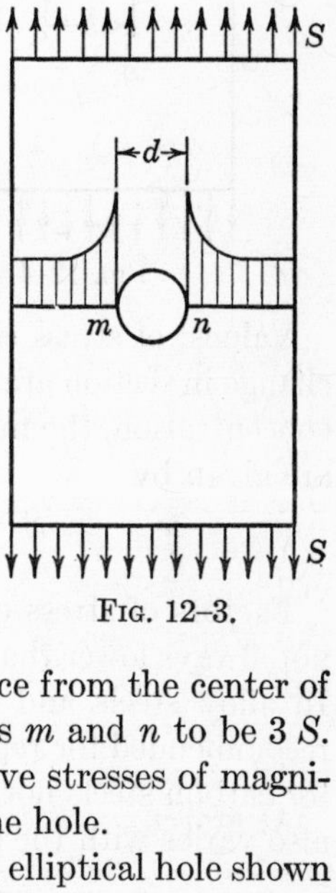

Fig. 12–3.

$$S' = \frac{S}{2}\left(2 + \frac{d^2}{4\,r^2} + \frac{3}{16}\frac{d^4}{r^4}\right) \qquad (a)$$

where d is the diameter of the hole and r is the distance from the center of the hole. From Eq. (a) we find the stresses at points m and n to be $3\,S$. Because of bending action around the hole, compressive stresses of magnitude S are created at the top and bottom points of the hole.

A similar stress concentration is caused by the small elliptical hole shown in Fig. 12–4. The maximum stress at the ends of the horizontal axis of the hole is given by

$$S_{\max} = S\left(1 + 2\frac{b}{a}\right) \qquad (b)$$

This stress increases with the ratio $\dfrac{b}{a}$; hence a very high stress concentration is produced by a narrow hole or crack perpendicular to the direction of the

[3] See *Theory of Elasticity*, by S. Timoshenko, McGraw-Hill, p. 78.

tensile stress and therefore such cracks tend to spread. This spreading may be stopped by drilling small holes at the ends of the crack, thus replacing a high stress concentration by a relatively smaller one.

Small semicircular grooves in a plate (Fig. 12–5) produce stress concentrations at points m and n that are about three times the average stress S applied at the ends of the plate.

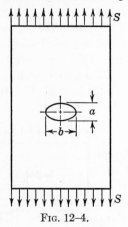

FIG. 12–4.

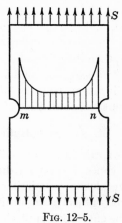

FIG. 12–5.

Values[4] of stress concentration factors for several other cases of abrupt change in section are listed in Table XII–1. If k denotes the factor of stress concentration, the maximum stresses for axial, torsional, and flexural loads are given by

$$S = k\frac{P}{A}, \qquad S_s = k\frac{Tr}{J}, \qquad S = k\frac{Mc}{I}$$

Factors of stress concentration for repeated loading are sometimes but not always lower than the theoretical values for static loading given above. In alloy steels and quenched-carbon steels, these theoretical values are recommended for repeated loading; somewhat lower values are permissible for carbon steels not quenched. The fatigue factor of stress concentration also varies with the size and type of material.[5]

12–4. Theories of Failure

Various theories of failure have been proposed, their purpose being to establish, from the behavior of a material subjected to simple tension or

[4] These values are taken from a more complete tabulation for these and other cases on pp. 330–347 of R. J. Roark's *Formulas for Stress and Strain*, McGraw-Hill.

[5] A more complete discussion of fatigue will be found in *Prevention of Fatigue of Metals*, Battelle Memorial Institute, published by Wiley. See also Timoshenko's *Strength of Materials*, Part II, Arts. 78 to 81, for a discussion of fatigue, and his Chap. VII for stress concentration. A fairly complete bibliography on the subject of stress concentration is given in Roark's *Formulas for Stress and Strain*, Wiley, p. 348.

TABLE XII–1. Stress Concentration Factors

I. Square shoulder with fillet in rectangular bar.

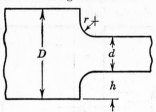

(a) Tension

$\dfrac{h}{r}$ \ $\dfrac{r}{d}$	0.05	0.10	0.20	0.27	0.50	1.0
0.5	1.70	1.60	1.53	1.47	1.39	1.21
1.0	1.93	1.78	1.67	1.59	1.42	1.22
1.5		1.89	1.72	1.65	1.43	1.23
2.0		1.95	1.80	1.70	1.44	1.23

(b) Bending

$\dfrac{h}{r}$ \ $\dfrac{r}{d}$	0.05	0.10	0.20	0.27	0.50	1.0
0.5	1.61	1.49	1.39	1.34	1.22	1.07
1.0	1.91	1.70	1.48	1.38	1.22	1.08
1.5	2.00	1.73	1.50	1.39	1.23	1.08
2.0		1.74	1.52	1.39	1.23	1.09

II. Square shoulder with fillet in circular shaft.

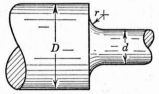

(a) Tension: Approximately same as Case I(a)
(b) Bending: Approximately same as Case I(b)

(c) Torsion

$\dfrac{D}{d}$ \ $\dfrac{r}{d}$	0.005	0.01	0.02	0.03	0.04	0.10
2.00		3.0	2.25	2.00	1.82	1.44
1.33		2.7	2.16	1.91	1.76	1.40
1.20	3.00	2.5	2.00	1.75	1.62	1.34
1.09	2.20	1.88	1.53	1.40	1.30	1.15

TABLE XII–1—(*Continued*)

III. Semicircular notch in circular shaft.

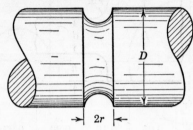

(a) Tension	$\dfrac{r}{D-2r}$	0.05	0.15	0.30	0.40	0.52	0.75
	k	2.57	2.16	1.81	1.65	1.51	1.36

(b) Bending	$\dfrac{r}{D-2r}$	0.05	0.10	0.20	0.30	0.50	0.75
	k	2.20	1.86	1.59	1.45	1.30	1.18

(c) Torsion: $\qquad k = \dfrac{2D}{D+2r}$

compression tests, the point at which failure will occur under any type of combined loading. By failure we mean either yielding (resulting in excessive permanent deformation) or actual rupture, whichever occurs first. Failure resulting from local crippling or elastic instability is not considered here.

The Maximum Stress Theory. The maximum stress theory proposed by Rankine is the oldest as well as the simplest of all the theories. It is based on the assumption that failure occurs when the maximum principal stress on an element reaches a limiting value, the limit being the yield point in a simple tension test (or ultimate strength, if the material is brittle). The theory disregards the effect of possible other principal stresses, and of the shearing stresses on other planes through the element. For example, Mohr's circles for the pure shear and pure tension in (*a*) and (*b*) in Fig. 12–6 show that although both are equally strong according to the maximum principal stress theory, (*a*) has twice the maximum shearing stress of (*b*). This indicates that the maximum tensile or compressive stress alone is not sufficient to define yielding. Nevertheless, this theory does give results that agree well with test results from brittle materials.

The Maximum Strain Theory. According to the maximum strain theory, which is credited to Saint Venant, a ductile material begins to yield when

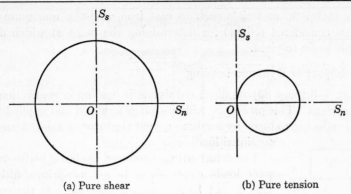

(a) Pure shear   (b) Pure tension

FIG. 12–6. — Although principal stresses are equal in (a) and (b), (a) has twice the shearing stress of (b).

the maximum principal strain ϵ reaches the strain at which yielding occurs in simple tension, or when the minimum principal strain (i.e., the compressive strain) equals the yield point strain in simple compression. However, if we examine Hooke's law for tri-axial stress expressed by the following equations:

$$
\left.
\begin{aligned}
\epsilon_x &= \frac{1}{E}\left[S_x - \mu(S_y + S_z)\right] \\[4pt]
\epsilon_y &= \frac{1}{E}\left[S_y - \mu(S_z + S_x)\right] \\[4pt]
\epsilon_z &= \frac{1}{E}\left[S_z - \mu(S_x + S_y)\right]
\end{aligned}
\right\} \tag{1-14}
$$

we see that when $S_x = -S_y = -S_z$, the maximum strain is $(1 + 2\,\mu)\dfrac{S}{E}$. On the other hand, when $-S_x = -S_y = -S_z$, as in hydrostatic compression, the maximum strain is $(1 - 2\,\mu)\dfrac{S}{E}$. Thus, different strains may appear with the same maximum stress.

The Maximum Shear Theory. Sometimes called Guest's theory, the maximum shear theory assumes that yielding begins when the maximum shearing stress equals the maximum shearing stress developed at yielding in simple tension. Since the maximum shearing stress is equal to one-half the difference between the principal stresses, the condition for yielding is

$$
(S_s)_w = \tfrac{1}{2}(S_{\max.} - S_{\min.}) = \tfrac{1}{2}\,S_{\text{y.p.}}
$$

Summary. Of the several other proposed theories of failure, the most important is the maximum strain energy theory. However, the maximum stress theory is generally considered to give reliable results for determining rupture in brittle materials such as cast iron, and the maximum shear theory is considered reliable for determining the point at which ductile materials begin to yield.

12–5.   Impact or Dynamic Loading

In Art. 3–5 (page 85) we discussed dynamic loading in connection with helical springs. This procedure will now be generalized and applied to the dynamic effects produced by a falling weight that causes axial, flexural, or torsional loading.

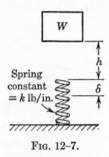

FIG. 12–7.

The deformations produced in elastic bodies by impact loads cause them to act as springs, although that is not their designed function. If the equivalent spring constant for such members is defined as the load required to cause a unit deformation, the spring constant in each case can be determined from our earlier study of deformations. Actually, however, as we shall see, it is unnecessary to determine the equivalent spring constant. For the present, we may consider the problem of impact as analogous to that of a falling body stopped by a spring (Fig. 12–7). The weight W has zero velocity when first dropped, and also when the spring is deflected through the maximum dynamic deflection δ. Equating the resultant work done on W to the zero change in kinetic energy, we therefore obtain[6]

$$W(h + \delta) - \tfrac{1}{2} k\delta^2 = 0 \qquad (a)$$

where $W(h + \delta)$ is the work done by gravity on the weight, and $\tfrac{1}{2} k\delta^2$ is the resisting work done by the equivalent spring.

If Eq. (a) is rearranged in the form

$$\delta^2 - 2\frac{W}{k}\delta - 2\frac{W}{k}h = 0$$

and $\dfrac{W}{k}$ is replaced by δ_{st}, which is the static deformation produced by a gradual application of the load W, the following general value of δ is obtained:

$$\delta = \delta_{st} + \sqrt{(\delta_{st})^2 + 2\,\delta_{st}h} \qquad (b)$$

Two extreme cases are of interest. If h is large compared with δ, we may neglect the work $W\delta$ in Eq. (a), which then reduces to

$$\delta = \sqrt{2\frac{W}{k}h} = \sqrt{2\,\delta_{st}h} \qquad (c)$$

---

[6] The weight is assumed to remain in contact with the spring. Also, some energy is dissipated by the impact, so the actual deflection is always less than that given by Eq. (a).

In the other extreme case, $h = 0$ (i.e., the load is suddenly applied), and Eq. (a) reduces to

$$\delta = 2\frac{W}{k} = 2\,\delta_{st} \tag{d}$$

Due to a suddenly applied load, the deflection, and consequently the stress which is directly proportional to it, is therefore twice as great as that caused by the same load gradually applied.

The ratio of the maximum dynamic deformation δ to the static deformation δ_{st} gives a value which may be called the impact factor. This is easily determined by rearranging Eq. (b) in the form

$$\delta = \delta_{st} + \delta_{st}\sqrt{1 + \frac{2\,h}{\delta_{st}}} = \delta_{st}\left(1 + \sqrt{1 + \frac{2\,h}{\delta_{st}}}\right)$$

Hence the impact factor is

$$\frac{\delta}{\delta_{st}} = 1 + \sqrt{1 + \frac{2\,h}{\delta_{st}}} \tag{12–1}$$

Multiplying W by this factor gives an equivalent impact load P, which may be used in the formulas for static loading to compute the maximum stress and deflection. Or, if preferred, the static stress due to a gradual application of W may be multiplied by the impact factor to give the maximum stress:

$$S_{\max} = S_{st}\left(1 + \sqrt{1 + \frac{2\,h}{\delta_{st}}}\right) \tag{12–2}$$

We now apply these results to various types of impact loading.

Tension.   The most usual type of impact loading is shown in Fig. 12–8. A weight W drops freely through a height h before striking a stop on the end of the rod, thereby producing the dynamic deflection δ. Assuming that the stresses remain within the elastic range, and that δ is negligible compared with h, we replace δ_{st} in Eq. (c) by its value from the deformation equation $\delta_{st} = \dfrac{WL}{AE}$, whence we obtain

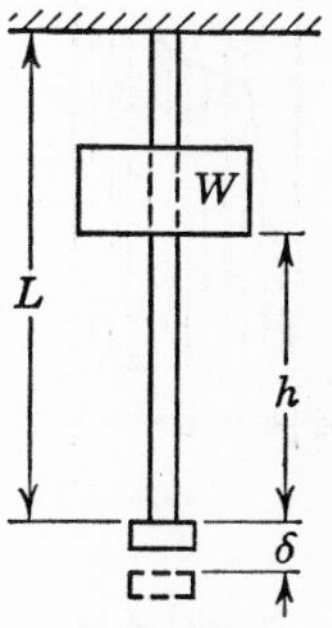

$$\delta = \sqrt{\frac{2\,L}{A E}\,Wh} \tag{e}$$

The corresponding stress in the rod is

$$S = \frac{\delta}{L}\,E = \sqrt{\frac{2\,E}{AL}\,Wh} \tag{f}$$

Fig. 12–8. — Impact loading of a rod.

By replacing Wh by the kinetic energy $\dfrac{Wv^2}{2g}$ (expressed in in.-lb), this may also be used to determine the shock stress caused by the sudden stopping of a weight W that is moving with a velocity v:

$$S = \sqrt{\frac{2E}{AL} \cdot \frac{Wv^2}{2g}} \qquad\qquad (g)$$

These equations show that the stress due to impact can be reduced by using a material with a lower value of E or by increasing the area A or the length L of the rod. This is quite different from static tension where the stress is independent of E or L.

The above discussion assumes that the stress remains below the proportional limit. When the stress is above the proportional limit the problem is more complex, because the elongation is no longer proportional to the load. Nevertheless, we can still find a basis for determining actual rupture due to impact. Thus, it being assumed that the shape of a tensile test diagram does not depend upon the speed with which the bar is strained, the area $OABC$ in Fig. 12–9 represents the work done upon the bar to produce an elongation δ; this must be equal to the work $W(h + \delta)$ done by the falling weight W. When $W(h + \delta)$ equals or exceeds the total area $OADE$, the falling weight will rupture the bar.

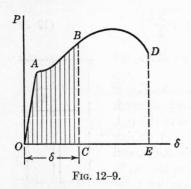

FIG. 12–9.

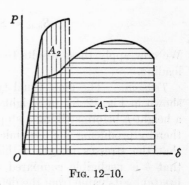

FIG. 12–10.

A bar's resistance to impact also depends upon the ductility of the material. Fig. 12–10 shows the tensile test diagram of a high-strength steel of low ductility superimposed upon the diagram for a steel of lower strength but high ductility. The horizontally shaded area A_1 is much larger than the vertically shaded area A_2, showing that the more ductile steel will absorb more energy before rupture than the less ductile steel. For this reason, ductile materials are usually selected for members subject to impact or shock loading.

In connection with the above, the total area of a stress-strain diagram is called the *modulus of toughness;* it represents the energy absorbed per unit volume. Its value is equal approximately to

$$U_r = \frac{S_y + S_u}{2} \cdot \epsilon_u \qquad (h)$$

where S_y and S_u are respectively the yield point and the ultimate strength, and ϵ_u is the ultimate strain. The partial area of a stress-strain diagram up to the stress S_e at the elastic limit is called the *modulus of resilience;* it represents the energy that can be absorbed per unit volume without creating a permanent distortion. If the stress-strain relation is linear, its value is

$$U = \frac{1}{2} S_e \epsilon = \frac{1}{2} S_e \cdot \frac{S_e}{E} = \frac{S_e^2}{2E} \qquad (i)$$

Flexure. In Fig. 12–11 a simply supported beam is subjected to the impact of a load W falling freely through the height h before striking the midpoint of the beam and causing the dynamic deflection δ. If the proportional limit is not exceeded, Eqs. (b), (c), and (d) apply here also. Assuming that h is large compared with δ_{st}, we obtain

$$\delta = \sqrt{2 h \delta_{st}}$$

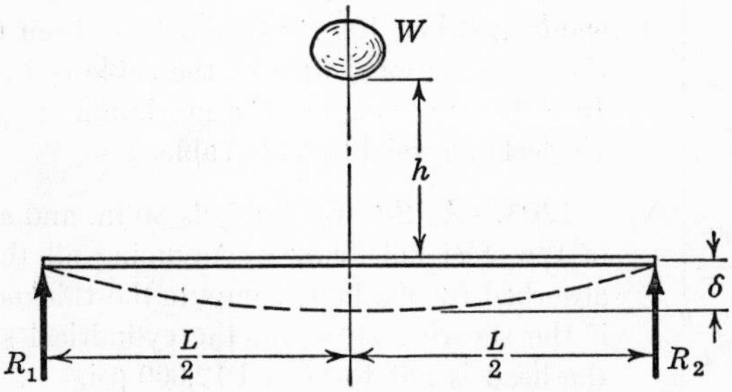

Fig. 12–11. — Impact loading of a beam.

Hence the impact factor for a centrally loaded simple beam where $\delta_{st} = \dfrac{WL^3}{48\,EI}$ (Case 6, Table VI–2, page 212) becomes

$$\frac{\delta}{\delta_{st}} = \sqrt{\frac{2 h}{\delta_{st}}} = \sqrt{\frac{96\,EIh}{WL^3}}$$

The static stress found from the flexure formula is

$$S_{st} = \frac{Mc}{I} = \frac{WL}{4} \cdot \frac{c}{I}$$

and the maximum stress is

$$S = \frac{\delta}{\delta_{st}} S_{st} = \sqrt{\frac{6 \ WhEc^2}{LI}} \qquad (j)$$

Limitations. The preceding discussions assumed that the work done by a falling weight or the kinetic energy of a moving body can be stored in the resisting member in the form of strain energy. This assumption can never be realized for the following reasons: If the velocity of impact is high, the deceleration of the moving body may be so rapid as to transform the kinetic energy into partly heat and partly local deformations, largely inelastic, of both the moving body and the resisting member. Even if the velocity of impact is low, the resisting member may have great stiffness, causing the same results. Finally, if the mass of the resisting member is large compared to that of the moving body, the *inertia* of the resisting member may also cause the same result.

PROBLEMS

1201. A weight of 100 lb falls through 6 ft and is then caught on the end of a steel wire rope 100 ft long having a cross-sectional area of 0.4 sq in. Compute the maximum stress in the rope. Assume $E = 15 \times 10^6$ psi.

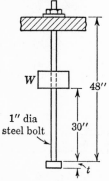

PROB. 1203.

1202. An elevator weighing 4000 lb is being lowered at the rate of 10 ft/sec. The hoisting drum is stopped suddenly when 100 ft of cable have been unwrapped. If the cross-sectional area of the cable is 1 sq in. and $E = 15 \times 10^6$ psi, compute the maximum stress in the cable. Neglect the weight of the cable.

1203. A 12-lb weight falls 30 in. and strikes the head of the steel bolt shown. Assuming all the energy to be absorbed by the bolt, compute the thickness t of its head if the shearing stress on the cylindrical surface through the head is not to exceed 12,000 psi.

Ans. $t = 0.498$ in.

1204. A simply supported rectangular beam L ft long is struck at the middle by a weight W falling through a height h. Show that the relation between the cross-sectional area A and the maximum stress S in the beam is given by $A = \dfrac{18 \ WhE}{LS^2}$. Use this relation to determine the area A for a timber beam ($E = 1.5 \times 10^6$ psi) if $W = 48$ lb, $h = 1$ ft, and max. $S = 1200$ psi. *Ans.* $A = 90$ in.²

1205. A 5-in. 10-lb I beam is used as a cantilever 6 ft. long. A weight of 100 lb falls through a height of 6 in. before striking the free end. Compute the maximum stress and deflection caused by the impact. Neglect the mass of the beam and assume that the weight remains in contact with the beam.

Ans. $S = 29,600$ psi; $\delta = 0.675$ in.

1206. Compute the impact factor for a simply supported beam 20 ft long subjected to an impact from a weight $W = 2000$ lb that drops through a height of 1 ft on a point 5 ft from one end. Assume the beam section is 8 WF 17 and $E = 30 \times 10^6$ psi. Neglect the weight of the beam.   *Ans.* 12.2

12–6. Shearing Stresses in Thin-Walled Members Subjected to Bending. Shear Flow

The formula developed in Art. 5–7 (page 151) for determining the shearing stress induced by flexure can also be used to determine the shearing stress across the flanges of wide-flange beams or channels or other sections. The existence of this shearing stress is explained in Fig. 12–12, which shows

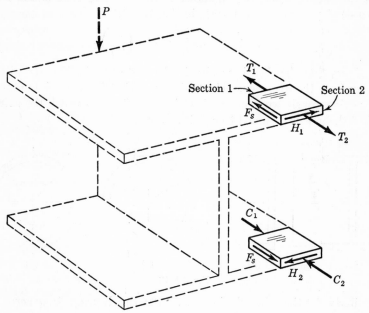

FIG. 12–12. — Lateral shear forces H_1 and H_2 in flanges of cantilever beam. External vertical shear acts downward.

the free-body diagrams of portions of the flanges cut out by two adjacent sections. The dashed lines indicate a phantom view of the cantilever beam from which these sections were cut. When the external vertical shear acts downward, the upper flange is in tension, the tensile force T_2 being larger than T_1 because the bending moment is greater at section 2 than at section 1. For equilibrium of the upper flange segment, a longitudinal shearing force F_s must act as shown, thereby inducing the lateral shear force H_1. The direction of H_1 determines the directions of the shearing stresses in the upper flange. Similarly, the compressive forces C_2 and C_1 developed in the lower flange segment require a leftward lateral shear H_2, and hence the shearing stresses are here directed leftward. Because of tension in the upper flange and compression in the lower flange, therefore, the shearing stresses in these flanges point in opposite directions.

The magnitude of the longitudinal shearing stress across the flange is given by Eq. (5–4) (page 153) if the flange is assumed to be relatively thin so that, as was done in deriving this equation, the shearing stress may without serious error be considered uniform across the thickness of the flange. From Eq. (5–5), relating to shearing stresses on perpendicular planes, we conclude that an equal shearing stress acts across the flange perpendicular to its thickness. Thus, at a distance z from the free edge of the flange, Eq. (5–4) gives for either (a) or (b) in Fig. 12–13:

$$S_s = \frac{V}{It} A'\bar{y} = \frac{V}{It}(tz)y = \left(\frac{Vh}{2I}\right)z \tag{a}$$

This shows that the shearing stress in the flanges varies linearly with the distance from the free edge. The variation of shearing stress intensity and its direction are shown in (a) and (b) in Fig. 12–14, in which the external vertical shear V is assumed to act downward.

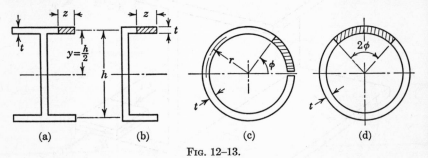

(a)   (b)   (c)   (d)

FIG. 12–13.

Similarly, for the split tube in Fig. 12–13c, the shearing stress across any radial section defined by φ is

$$S_s = \frac{V}{It} A'\bar{y} = \frac{V}{It} \int_o^\varphi r \sin \varphi(tr\, d\varphi) = \frac{Vr^2}{I}(1 - \cos \varphi) \tag{b}$$

When an external vertical shear acts upward, Fig. 12–14c shows how the shearing stress varies from zero at the split to a maximum value at a section opposite the split.

Show that the shearing stress for the solid tube varies as shown in Fig. 12–14d.

In all these cases the shearing stress vectors point or "flow" in the same direction. This has given rise to *shear flow*, a term common in aeronautics. Shear flow is the shear force across the section per unit length along the section. It is denoted by the symbol q (expressed in lb/in.) and

equals $\dfrac{S_s t\, dx}{dx}$, which reduces to

$$q = S_s t = \frac{V}{I} A' \bar{y} = \frac{VQ}{I} \tag{12–3}$$

A detailed application of this equation is given in Illus. Prob. 1207 (page 395).

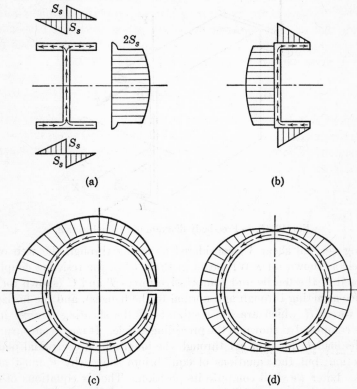

(a)   (b)

(c)   (d)

Fig. 12–14. — Intensity and flow of shear stresses. In (a) and (b), external vertical shear V is down; in (c) and (d), V is up.

12–7. Shear Center

We are now ready to consider the bending of members that have only one axis of symmetry, the loading being such as to cause this axis to become the neutral axis. On any section of a beam subjected to other than pure bending, there exist shearing stresses. These stresses create internal shearing forces whose resultant must be equal, opposite, and collinear to the external shear; otherwise the bending is accompanied by twisting of the beam.

Bending without twisting occurs only when the resultant of the shearing forces passes through the shear center (also called the center of twist and sometimes the flexural center). The shear center is defined as the point in the cross-section of a beam through which the plane of the transverse bending loads must pass so that the beam will bend without twisting.

We begin by considering a channel section used as a cantilever; the free-body diagram is shown in Fig. 12–15. The resisting forces consist of the

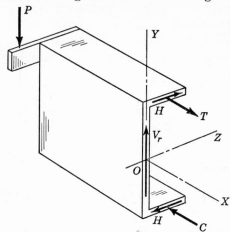

FIG. 12–15. — Free-body diagram of channel section.

resisting vertical shear V_r considered as acting through the web of the channel (as shown for a WF beam in Prob. 546), the resisting couple M_r composed of the tensile and compressive forces T and C (shown for convenience as acting through and normal to the flanges), and the horizontal flange forces H which are the resultants of the shearing stresses in the flanges computed as shown in the preceding article. It may seem surprising that the load P does not act through the longitudinal centroidal plane of the section; but the equations of equilibrium show why P must act as shown. Later we shall compute its position. The six equations of equilibrium, and the reasons they are satisfied, are as follows:

1. $\Sigma X = 0$, satisfied by balance between the equal and oppositely directed tensile and compressive forces T and C.

2. $\Sigma Y = 0$, satisfied by the resisting vertical shear V_r balancing the vertical shear V caused by P.

3. $\Sigma Z = 0$, satisfied by the balance of the equal and oppositely directed flange forces H.

4. $\Sigma M_y = 0$, satisfied because vertical loads cause no moment about the Y axis, and the moments of the horizontal forces T and C about Y cancel each other, as do the flange forces H.

5. $\Sigma M_z = 0$, satisfied because the applied bending moment M is balanced by the resisting moment M_r supplied by T and C.

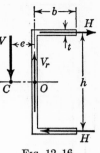

6. $\Sigma M_x = 0$. This condition must be satisfied to prevent the beam from twisting as it bends. It can be satisfied only if the moment of the applied load balances the moments of the shearing forces developed over the section. Selecting the X axis through the web eliminates the moment of V_r. In the end view of Fig. 12–15 which is shown in Fig. 12–16, we set a moment summation about O equal to zero and obtain

Fig. 12–16.

$$[\Sigma M_o = 0] \qquad\qquad Ve = Hh \qquad\qquad (a)$$

The value of the flange force H is the product of the average shearing stress in the flange multiplied by the flange area. Using Eq. (a) of Art. 12–6, we have

$$H = (S_s)_{\text{ave}}\cdot (\text{Area})_{\text{flange}} = \left(\frac{1}{2}\cdot\frac{Vh}{2\,I}\cdot b\right)(bt) = \frac{Vhb^2t}{4\,I}$$

This value of H may now be substituted in Eq. (a) to yield

$$e = \frac{Hh}{V} = \frac{h^2b^2t}{4\,I} \qquad\qquad (12\text{–}4)$$

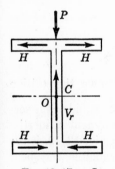

Fig. 12–17. — In a section having two axes of symmetry, the shear center C coincides with the centroid O.

Point C on the N.A. located a distance e from the center of the web is the shear center for the channel.

In a WF beam or an I beam, flexure loads develop a lateral shearing stress in each outstanding flange as in a channel section, but the shearing forces are equal and oppositely directed, as in Fig. 12–17. (See also Fig. 12–14a for the direction of the shear flow.) Hence, moments of the shearing forces about the centroid of the section balance out, and the plane of the loads must also contain the centroid if twisting is to be avoided. We conclude that the shear center coincides with the centroid of the WF section. In general, the shear center is located at the intersection of two axes of symmetry, if they exist.

For an unequal flanged H section with relatively thin flanges and web, like that in Fig. 12–18, the bending resistance of the web may be assumed to be negligible and the total vertical shear V may be assumed to be resisted by the internal shears V_1 and V_2 acting along the center lines of the flanges. To prevent twisting,

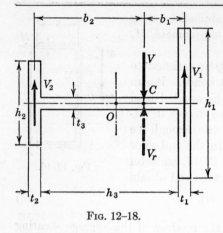

FIG. 12–18.

the resultant V_r of the flange shears must be equal, opposite, and collinear with the external shear V. Hence, taking moments about the shear center C, we have

$$V_1 b_1 = V_2 b_2 \qquad (b)$$

Another relation between V_1 and V_2 may be found from the fact that the two flanges bend as though they were separate beams which have identical radii of curvature. Hence, applying $\rho = \dfrac{EI}{M}$ gives

$$\frac{\rho}{E} = \frac{I_1}{M_1} = \frac{I_2}{M_2} \qquad (c)$$

But the bending moments M_1 and M_2 at any section along the beam are equal respectively to the product of the vertical shears V_1 and V_2 in the flanges and the distance to the section. Hence Eq. (c) becomes

$$\frac{I_1}{V_1} = \frac{I_2}{V_2} \qquad (d)$$

which when combined with Eq. (b) yields

$$\frac{b_1}{b_2} = \frac{I_2}{I_1} \qquad (12\text{–}5)$$

Therefore, since the ratio $\dfrac{b_1}{b_2}$ and the sum of b_1 and b_2 are known, the position of the shear center is easily located. It lies between the centroid of the section and the centroid of the flange that has the larger moment of inertia.

When there is only one flange, as in the T section in Fig. 12–19, if the bending resistance of the web is again assumed to be negligible, the shear center coincides with the centroid of the flange. In general, for any section composed of two narrow rectangles, where the shear flow is along the longer center lines of the rectangles, the shear center is at the intersection of these center lines, as shown in Fig. 12–20.

The procedure for a Z section is the same as for a channel section; the shear flow is shown in Fig. 12–21a and the resultant shear forces in Fig. 12–21b. The resultant of the two flange forces is $2H$ acting through the centroid of the section. Combining this resultant with the shear force in the web gives the resultant shear force R in the section. Evidently the

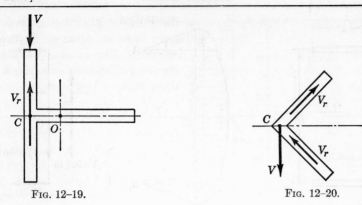

FIG. 12–19.   FIG. 12–20.

shear center C coincides with the centroid O, and the plane of the transverse loads must coincide with R to produce simple bending in the vertical plane. The somewhat surprising fact that an inclined load causes bending in a vertical plane is discussed more fully in the next article, dealing with un-

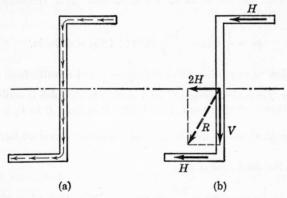

(a)   (b)

FIG. 12–21. — Shear center of a Z section coincides with the centroid.

symmetrical loading. That article also describes a simpler method of determining the plane of loading that causes bending in a vertical plane of a given section.

ILLUSTRATIVE PROBLEM

1207. If the vertical shearing force acting on the thin-walled channel section in Fig. 12–22 is 566 lb, compute and illustrate the shear flow and determine the shear center.

Solution: The moment of inertia about the neutral axis is computed from

$$I = \frac{(0.10)(10)^3}{12} + 2(0.10)(4)(5)^2 = 28.3 \text{ in.}^4$$

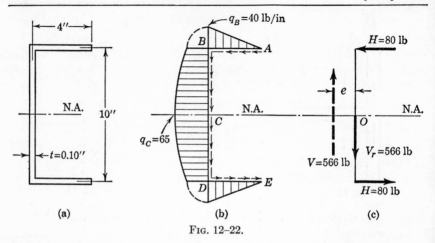

FIG. 12–22.

Because of the thin wall, the shear flow may be assumed to act along the center line $ABCDE$ of the section, as shown in Fig. 12–22b. At A, the shear flow is zero; at B, Eq. (12–3) gives

$$q_B = \frac{V}{I} Q_{AB} = \frac{566}{28.3} (0.10 \times 4)(5) = 40 \text{ lb/in.}$$

The shear flow at any other point C may be found directly from $q_C = \frac{V}{I} Q_{AC}$. However, since Q_{AC} is the moment of area from A to C, which is equivalent to the sum of the moment of area from A to B plus that from B to C, we may write $q_C = \frac{V}{I} (Q_{AB} + Q_{BC})$, which then reduces to the more convenient form $q_C = q_B + \frac{V}{I} Q_{BC}$. Thus the shear flow at C is

$$q_C = q_B + \frac{V}{I} Q_{BC} = 40 + \frac{566}{28.3} (0.10 \times 5) \frac{5}{2} = 40 + 25 = 65 \text{ lb/in.}$$

As shown in Fig. 12–22b, the shear flow from A to B varies directly with the distance from A; but from B to C to D it varies along a parabolic arc. The average shear flow in the web is therefore $40 + \frac{2}{3}(25) = 56.6$ lb/in. The shear force in the web is $V_r = q_{\text{ave.}} \cdot L = 56.6(10) = 566$ lb, which agrees with the applied vertical shear $V = 566$ lb. The shear force in each flange is $H = q_{\text{ave.}} \cdot L = (\frac{1}{2} \times 40)(4) = 80$ lb.

To avoid twisting of the section, the external shear V must lie a distance e to the left of O (Fig. 12–22c) so that the twisting moments exerted by the internal shear forces will be balanced. Hence,

$$[\Sigma M_o = 0] \qquad\qquad 566 \, e = 80(10) \qquad\qquad e = 1.414 \text{ in.}$$

The value of e can be computed more easily from Eq. (12–4):

$$e = \frac{h^2 b^2 t}{4\,I} = \frac{(10)^2(4)^2(0.10)}{4(28.3)} = 1.414 \text{ in.}$$

However, the above numerical computations are presented in order to emphasize the principle of shear flow and to indicate its extension to the more complex problems below.

PROBLEMS

1208. Locate the shear center for the section shown in Fig. 12–18 if $t_1 = t_2 = t_3 = \frac{1}{2}$ in., $h_1 = 6$ in., $h_2 = 4$ in., $h_3 = 7$ in.

1209. Determine the position of the shear center for a section composed of a thin-walled cylinder of thickness t and mean radius r which is split along one longitudinal element, as in Fig. 12–13c.

    Ans. $e = 2\,r$ measured along the axis of symmetry from the center of the cylinder in a direction opposite to the split element.

1210. Show that the position of the shear center for the given semicircular thin ring is $e = \dfrac{4\,r}{\pi}$ to the left of O.

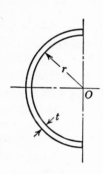

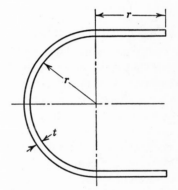

PROB. 1210.   PROB. 1211.

1211. The thin-walled section shown consists of a semicircular ring of mean radius r and two straight pieces of length r. Show that the shear center is $e = \dfrac{tr^4}{I}(\pi + 3)$ to the left of O, and hence for $r = 2$ in. and $t = 0.10$ in., that $e = 4.78$ in. Need the value of t be specified?

1212. If the vertical shear on the given section is 576 lb, construct a shear flow diagram and locate the shear center.

    Ans. $q = 12$ and 24 lb/in. at the junction of flange and web; $e = 0.75$ in. to the left of the web center

1213. If the vertical shear on the given section is 2560 lb, construct a shear flow diagram and locate the shear center. *Note:* Shear flow along AB and FE may be assumed to be linear without serious error, although it is actually parabolic.

    Ans. $q_B = q_E = 62$ lb/in.; $q_C = q_D = 172.2$ lb/in.; $e = 2.48$ in. to the left of web center

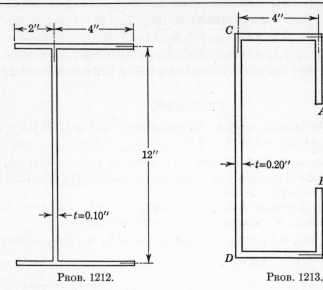

PROB. 1212.   PROB. 1213.

12–8. Unsymmetrical Bending

The theory of flexure developed in Chap. V was restricted to loads lying in a plane that contained an axis of symmetry of the cross-section. With this restriction, the neutral axis passes through the centroid of the section and is perpendicular to the plane of loading. The preceding article extended the application of the flexure formula to sections with only one axis of symmetry that were loaded so that this axis became the neutral axis. In either case, bending without twist is possible only if the plane of loading contains the shear center, a requirement that is automatically satisfied when the axis of symmetry coincides with the plane of loading.

There is a further restriction which so far has been adhered to, although not mentioned. The plane of loading must be parallel to or contain a principal axis of inertia of the beam cross-section. We first consider the case in which the plane of loading contains an axis of symmetry, such as the Y axis in Fig. 12–23. In deriving the flexure formula (Art. 5–2), we applied the condition of equilibrium that the applied bending moment about the X axis is balanced by the resisting moment exerted by the flexure stresses, i.e., $M_x = \int y(S\, dA)$.

If the bending loads are restricted so that they lie in the longitudinal plane containing the Y axis, the external moment M_y must be zero.[7] However, the flexure force $S\, dA$ on a typical element of the section has a moment

---

[7] When the section has only one axis of symmetry which becomes the neutral axis, the plane of loading is offset from, but parallel to, the longitudinal centroidal plane so that it contains the shear center; but even then M_y is zero.

$x(S\,dA)$ about the Y axis. If the Y axis is an axis of symmetry, this moment about Y is neutralized by an identical force (not shown) acting through the point of symmetry. For sections that do not have an axis of symmetry, the resultant moment of the flexure forces about the Y axis is

$$M_y = \int x(S\,dA) = \int x\left(\frac{E}{\rho}y\right) dA = \frac{E}{\rho}\int xy\,dA$$

M_y will be zero and equilibrium satisfied only if the integral $\int xy\,dA$ is zero. This integral is the product of inertia P_{xy}, which is zero only if X and Y are the principal axes of
inertia of the section. We conclude that the flexure formula may be applied only if the bending loads act in a longitudinal plane parallel to or containing one of the principal axes of the section. These planes are called the principal planes of bending.

We are now ready to discuss unsymmetrical bending, which is defined as bending caused by loads that are inclined to the principal planes of bending. Examples of unsymmetrical bending are roof purlins that, because of the inclination of the roof, are subjected to loads whose planes make large angles with the principal axes of

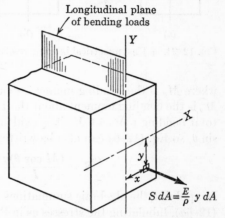

Fig. 12–23. — Flexure stress causes resisting moment about Y axis as well as about X axis. $M_y = 0$ if Y is an axis of symmetry (or a principal axis, if there is no axis of symmetry).

inertia of the section; and beams in structures and machines that are subjected to loads which, because of deformation or design, are inclined to the principal planes.

We consider first the case shown in Fig. 12–24, in which a symmetrical section is subjected to loads inclined to the axes of symmetry. Resolving the loading into horizontal and vertical components, we obtain the two loading conditions shown in (b) and (c), which can each be solved directly by the flexure formula. In (b), the X axis is the neutral axis, whereas in (c) the Y axis becomes the neutral axis. Each of these conditions produces flexure stresses that are normal to the cross-section; hence the resultant stress at any point is the algebraic sum of the stresses at that point caused by each case considered separately, i.e.,

$$S = \frac{M_x y}{I_x} + \frac{M_y x}{I_y} \tag{12–6}$$

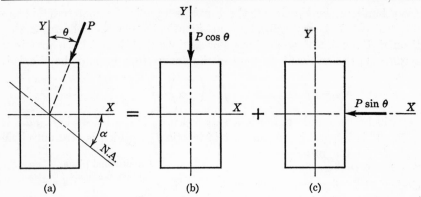

Fig. 12–24. — Unsymmetrical bending resolved into symmetrical bending about X and Y axes.

where M_x is the bending moment about the x axis caused by $P \cos \theta$, and M_y is the bending moment about the Y axis due to $P \sin \theta$. In terms of the total bending moment M, it is evident that $M_x = M \cos \theta$ and $M_y = M \sin \theta$, so Eq. (12–6) can also be written as

$$S = \frac{(M \cos \theta)y}{I_x} + \frac{(M \sin \theta)x}{I_y} \qquad (12\text{–}6a)$$

In applying the algebraic summations of stress indicated by Eqs. (12–6) or (12–6a), tabulating the stresses as in Prob. 1214 below will avoid confusion regarding signs.

To determine the deflection at any point, we combine vectorially the deflections caused by the horizontal and vertical components of the load. The components of the deflection are generally unequal because they are proportional to the relative ratio of $\dfrac{\sin \theta}{I_y}$ to $\dfrac{\cos \theta}{I_x}$. Consequently the neutral axis, which is perpendicular to the resultant deflection as shown in Fig. 12–25, is usually *not* perpendicular to the applied load. The inclination of the neutral axis is found from Fig. 12–25 to be

$$\tan \alpha = \frac{\delta_x}{\delta_y} = \frac{\dfrac{\sin \theta}{I_y}}{\dfrac{\cos \theta}{I_x}} = \frac{I_x}{I_y} \tan \theta \qquad (12\text{–}7)$$

From this, we see that unless $I_x = I_y$ or $\tan \theta = 0$ or ∞, the neutral axis is not perpendicular to the load.

We now consider the nonsymmetrical section like the vertically loaded Z section in Fig. 12–26. For this section, the principal axes are 1–1 and 2–2; hence the load P is inclined at the angle θ with one of the principal planes of bending.   This loading, therefore, also causes unsymmetrical bending. The stresses may be determined, as shown below in Prob. 1215, by resolving P into components directed along the 1–1 and 2–2 axes, and Eq. (12–6) may then be applied.

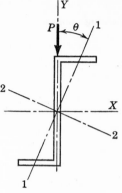

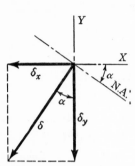

Fig. 12–25. — Neutral axis is perpendicular to resultant deflection δ.

Fig. 12–26. — Unsymmetrical bending produced in a nonsymmetrical section. Axes 1–1 and 2–2 are principal axes.

ILLUSTRATIVE PROBLEMS

1214.   A 10 WF 21 section is used as a cantilever beam to support the given loads inclined to the Y axis, as shown in Fig. 12–27.   Compute the stresses at the corners A, B, C, and D of the wall section.

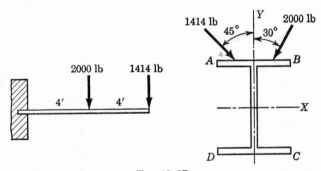

Fig. 12–27.

Solution: Resolve the loads into their X and Y components and compute M_x and M_y:

$$M_x = -\,(1414 \cos 45°)8 - (2000 \cos 30°)4 = -\,14{,}930 \text{ ft-lb}$$

The negative sign for M_x indicates downward curvature at the wall, and hence the bending causes tension at A and B and compression at C and D.

Taking moments of the X components of the loads about a Y axis at the wall, we obtain

$$M_y = (1414 \sin 45°)8 - (2000 \sin 30°)4 = 4000 \text{ ft-lb}$$

This bending moment causes tension at A and D and compression at B and C.

From Appendix B, Table B–2, we find $\left(\dfrac{I}{c}\right)_x = 21.5 \text{ in.}^3$ and $\left(\dfrac{I}{c}\right)_y = 3.4 \text{ in.}^3$ The stresses caused by M_x and M_y are therefore

$$S_x = \frac{M_x}{\left(\dfrac{I}{c}\right)_x} = \frac{14{,}930 \times 12}{21.5} = 8330 \text{ psi}$$

$$S_y = \frac{M_y}{\left(\dfrac{I}{c}\right)_y} = \frac{4000 \times 12}{3.4} = 14{,}100 \text{ psi}$$

As indicated by Eq. (12–6), these stresses are combined algebraically. For this purpose, tensile stresses in the accompanying tabulation are denoted by a positive sign and compressive stresses by a negative sign.

Stress Due to	A	B	C	D
M_x	+ 8330	+ 8330	− 8330	− 8330
M_y	+ 14,100	− 14,100	− 14,100	+ 14,100
Σ	+ 22,430	− 5770	− 22,430	+ 5770

1215. A cantilever beam 6 ft long carries a vertical load $P = 200$ lb at the free end. The cross-section is a structural Z 5 x $3\frac{1}{4}$ x 17.9 whose dimensions are shown in Fig. 12–28. Compute the maximum stress at the corner A.

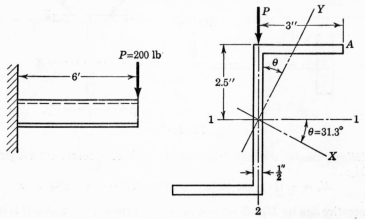

P=200 lb

6′

P

Y

3″

A

2.5″

θ

1 — — — — 1

θ=31.3°

X

$\frac{1}{2}$″

2

FIG. 12–28.

Solution: We start by determining the direction and values of the principal moments of inertia. From a structural steel handbook, we obtain $I_1 = 19.2$, $I_2 = 9.0$, and $I_y = 2.95$, all in in.^{4} These values are sufficient to enable us to plot a Mohr's circle of inertia, as in Fig. 12–29, from which we obtain $I_x = 25.25$ in.^{4} and $\theta = 31.3°$.

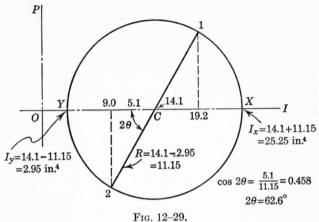

$$I_x = 14.1 + 11.15 = 25.25 \text{ in.}^4$$

$$I_y = 14.1 - 11.15 = 2.95 \text{ in.}^4$$

$$R = 14.1 - 2.95 = 11.15$$

$$\cos 2\theta = \frac{5.1}{11.15} = 0.458$$

$$2\theta = 62.6°$$

FIG. 12–29.

From Fig. 12–28, the coordinates of point A are

$$x_A = 3 \cos 31.3° - 2.5 \sin 31.3° = 1.26 \text{ in.}$$

$$y_A = 3 \sin 31.3° + 2.5 \cos 31.3° = 3.69 \text{ in.}$$

and the components of P are

$$P_x = P \sin \theta = 200 \sin 31.3° = 104 \text{ lb}$$

$$P_y = P \cos \theta = 200 \cos 31.3° = 171 \text{ lb}$$

Hence the components of the maximum bending moment are

$$M_x = P_y L = 171(6 \times 12) = 12,300 \text{ in.-lb}$$

$$M_y = P_x L = 104(6 \times 12) = 7500 \text{ in.-lb}$$

We now apply Eq. (12–6), noting that M_x produces tension and that M_y produces compression at A. Substituting the values previously computed, we obtain

$$S_A = \frac{M_x y}{I_x} - \frac{M_y x}{I_y} = \frac{12,300(3.69)}{25.25} - \frac{7500(1.26)}{2.95}$$
$$= 1800 - 3200 = -1400 \text{ psi}$$

The negative sign indicates that the stress at A is compressive.

PROBLEMS

In all these problems the loading passes through the shear center.

1216. Compute the horizontal and vertical components of deflection at the free end of the cantilever beam in Illus. Prob. 1214.

1217. A beam simply supported at the ends, has the cross-section and is loaded with a concentrated load P as shown. If the maximum flexural stress is not to exceed 18,000 psi, determine the safe value of P.   *Ans.* $P = 9080$ lb

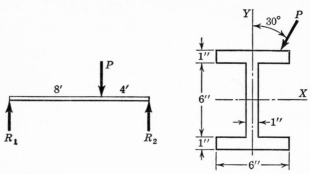

PROB. 1217.

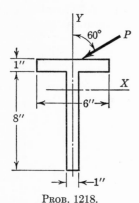

PROB. 1218.

1218. The T section shown is the cross-section of a simply supported beam 16 ft long carrying a central concentrated load inclined at 60° to the Y axis. If $S_c \leqq 12,000$ psi and $S_t \leqq 5000$ psi, what is the maximum load that will not overstress the beam?

Ans. $P = 803$ lb

1219. A cantilever beam 10 ft long with the same T section as in Prob. 1218 carries two concentrated loads inclined at the given angles with the Y axis of symmetry. The centroidal X axis is 3.07 in. below the top of the section; $I_x = 112.6$ in.⁴ and $I_y = 18.7$ in.⁴ Compute the inclination of the neutral axis at the wall, and the maximum compressive and tensile stresses.

Ans. $\alpha = 70.1°$; max. $S_t = 18,450$ psi; max. $S_c = 11,860$ psi

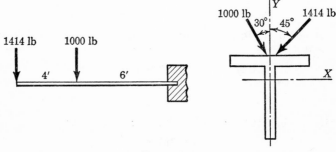

PROB. 1219.

1220. The Z beam in Illus. Prob. 1215 is used as a roof purlin. It carries a vertical uniformly distributed load of 200 lb/ft on a simply supported span 12 ft

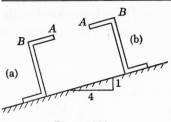

PROB. 1220.

long. If the slope of the roof is 1 to 4, compute the stress at corner A if (*a*) leg AB points up and (*b*) leg AB points down. Which design is better?

1221. An angle 7 in. by 4 in. by $\frac{1}{2}$ in. is used as a cantilever beam 6 ft long with the 7-in. leg vertical. It supports a vertical load of 1000 lb applied at the free end. Compute the maximum stress and the horizontal and vertical components of deflection at the free end. *Hint:* Compute the inclination of the *N.A.* to determine the point of maximum stress.

Ans. $S = 16,500$ psi; $\delta_h = 0.271$ in.; $\delta_v = 0.233$ in.

12–9. Curved Beams

Members subjected to bending are not always straight; sometimes, as in the case of crane hooks, they are curved before a bending moment is applied. If the member is sharply curved, the stress distribution is markedly different from that given by the flexure formula $S = \dfrac{Mc}{I}$, which was derived for beams that are initially straight.

For example, a sharply curved beam is subjected to bending couples, as shown in Fig. 12–30. It is usually assumed that plane radial sections

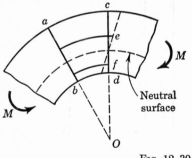

FIG. 12–30.

remain plane after bending. Although not strictly accurate, this assumption gives results that agree closely with actual strain measurements. In accordance with this assumption, bending causes section cd to rotate, relative to section ab, to the dashed position. Consequently, the two fibers e and f, each equidistant from the neutral surface, will have equal deformations, i.e., $\delta_e = \delta_f$. Applying Hooke's law, $\delta = \dfrac{SL}{E}$, we have

$$\frac{S_e L_e}{E} = \frac{S_f L_f}{E}$$

From Fig. 12–30 it is evident that the length L_e of fiber e is greater than the length L_f of fiber f, the difference in length depending on how sharply the beam is curved initially. Consequently, S_e is less than S_f, and the result is the nonlinear stress distribution shown.

As a consequence of the nonlinear stress distribution, there can be no balance between the tensile and compressive forces over the section if the neutral surface passes through the centroid of the section; the neutral surface must shift from the centroid of the section toward the axis of curvature O. The dashed linear stress distribution shows not only this shift, but the relatively increased stress at the inner fibers and the decreased stress at the outer fibers, in comparison with the stresses computed from the flexure formula.

To determine the shift in position of the neutral axis and to express the stress at any fiber in terms of the applied bending moment, we proceed as follows: In Fig. 12–31, ab and cd represent two adjacent sections of a curved

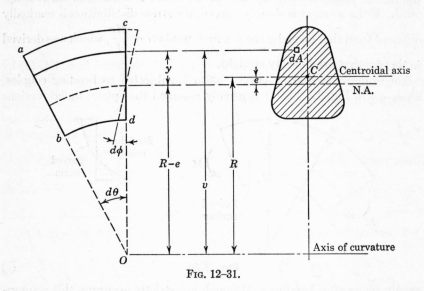

FIG. 12–31.

beam. Let $d\theta$ be the angle between these sections before bending, and $d\varphi$ the angle of rotation of cd relative to ab caused by bending. Let y denote the coordinate of a typical element dA with respect to the neutral axis, which is at an as yet undetermined distance e from the centroid of the section. R represents the radius of curvature of the centroidal axis.

The total elongation of a fiber at a distance y from the neutral axis is $y\,d\varphi$. The original length of this fiber is $(R - e + y)\,d\theta$. Hence, the unit elongation or strain is

$$\epsilon = \frac{\delta}{L} = \frac{y\,d\varphi}{(R - e + y)d\theta} \qquad (a)$$

and from Hooke's law, the stress is

$$S = E\epsilon = \frac{E\,d\varphi}{d\theta} \cdot \frac{y}{R - e + y} \qquad (b)$$

If the beam is loaded in pure bending, the conditions of equilibrium require that the sum of the normal forces over a cross-section be equal to zero, and that the moment of these normal forces balance the applied bending moment. In accordance with the first of these conditions, a force summation over the entire area yields

$$\int S\,dA = \frac{E\,d\varphi}{d\theta} \int \frac{y\,dA}{R - e + y} = 0 \qquad (c)$$

Since $\dfrac{E\,d\varphi}{d\theta}$ cannot be zero, we obtain

$$\int \frac{y\,dA}{R - e + y} = 0 \qquad (d)$$

in which e is the only unknown. Its value may be found from Eq. (d) by letting v denote the distance from the axis of curvature to the element dA. Then $y = v - (R - e)$ and Eq. (d) is rewritten as

$$\int \frac{y\,dA}{R - e + y} = \int \frac{v - (R - e)}{v}\,dA = \int dA - (R - e)\int \frac{dA}{v} = 0$$

from which we obtain

$$e = R - \frac{A}{\displaystyle\int \frac{dA}{v}} \qquad (12\text{–}8)$$

Equating the applied bending moment to the resisting moment gives

$$M = \int y S\,dA = \frac{E\,d\varphi}{d\theta} \int \frac{y^2\,dA}{R - e + y} \qquad (e)$$

This integral is simplified by adding and subtracting $(R - e)$ to one of the two y's in the numerator so that $y = (R - e + y) - (R - e)$. The integral is then rewritten as

$$\int \frac{y^2\,dA}{R - e + y} = \int y\,dA - (R - e)\int \frac{y\,dA}{R - e + y} \qquad (f)$$

The first integral on the right side of Eq. (f) is the moment of the entire cross-sectional area about the neutral axis and equals Ae. The second integral, from Eq. (d), equals zero. Eq. (e) can now be rewritten as

$$\frac{E\,d\varphi}{d\theta} = \frac{M}{Ae}$$

This value of $\dfrac{E\,d\varphi}{d\theta}$ is then substituted in Eq. (b) to yield finally

$$S = \frac{M}{Ae} \cdot \frac{y}{R - e + y} \qquad (12\text{–}9)$$

Eqs. (12–8) and (12–9) are theoretically adequate to determine the stresses in curved beams, but are limited in usefulness by the difficulty of computing the value of e. This difficulty may be avoided by means of a study made by Wilson and Quereau.[8] These men computed the extreme fiber stresses in curved beams of various cross-sections with the curved beam theory and with the ordinary flexure formula. From a comparison of the results they determined values of a correction factor K by which stresses computed with the flexure formula can be multiplied to give the actual stress in a curved beam. A modified equation for computing the extreme fiber stresses in curved beams is therefore

$$S = K\frac{Mc}{I} \qquad (12\text{–}10)$$

Values of K in Eq. (12–10) vary with the ratio $\dfrac{R}{c}$, where R is the radius of curvature of the centroidal axis and c is the distance from the centroidal axis to the inner fiber. As Fig. 12–30 shows, these stress correction factors are greater than unity for the inner fibers and less than unity for the outer fibers. At values of $\dfrac{R}{c}$ greater than 20, these factors approach unity, and the flexure formula may be applied directly to such slightly curved beams. Table XII–2 lists correction factors for various cross-sections.

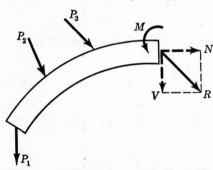

FIG. 12–32. — Reduction of applied forces to a single force R and a bending couple M.

For beams subjected to other than pure bending, as in Fig. 12–32, the system of coplanar forces acting in the plane of curvature is reduced to a single force R acting at the centroid of the section, plus a bending couple M. The moment of this couple is equivalent to the summation of moments about the centroidal axis of the external forces acting to one side of the

[8] See "A Simple Method of Determining Stresses in Curved Beams," Circular 16, Engineering Experiment Station, University of Illinois.

Cross-Section						
R/c	Circle or Ellipse		Rectangle		Other Sections (Ave. values)	
	Inside	Outside	Inside	Outside	Inside	Outside
1.2	3.41	0.54	2.89	0.57	When section is unsymmetrical, R/c refers to the inside fiber.	
1.4	2.40	0.60	2.13	0.63		
1.6	1.96	0.65	1.79	0.67		
1.8	1.75	0.68	1.63	0.70	—	—
2.0	1.62	0.71	1.52	0.73	1.63	0.74
3.0	1.33	0.79	1.30	0.81	1.36	0.81
4.0	1.23	0.84	1.20	0.85	1.25	0.86
6.0	1.14	0.89	1.12	0.90	1.16	0.90
8.0	1.10	0.91	1.09	0.92	1.12	0.93
10.0	1.08	0.93	1.07	0.94	1.10	0.94
20.0	1.03	0.97	1.04	0.96	1.05	0.95

cross-section. The normal stresses produced by this couple are found as in pure bending.

The force R is resolved into two components: a shearing force V in the plane of the cross-section, and a normal force N perpendicular to the plane of the cross-section. The normal force acting at the centroid of the section produces tensile or compressive stresses, uniformly distributed over the section, of the magnitude $S = \dfrac{N}{A}$, where A is the cross-sectional area. The total normal stress is found by superposing this uniform stress algebraically upon the stresses produced by the bending couple. The shearing stresses produced by the transverse shear V may be calculated as for a straight beam, using $S_s = \dfrac{V}{Ib} Q$.

ILLUSTRATIVE PROBLEM

1222. The circular link shown in Fig. 12–33 has a rectangular section 4 in. wide by 2 in. thick. Using Eq. (12–10) and values of K from Table XII–2, compute the stresses at A and B and at C and D. Check the stresses at A and B by means of Eqs. (12–8) and (12–9).

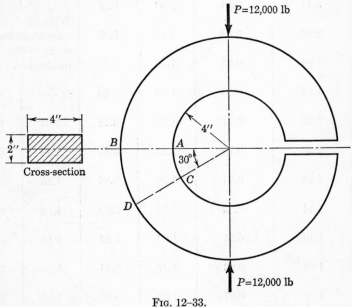

FIG. 12–33.

Solution: The radius of curvature of the centroidal axis is $R = 4 + 2 = 6$ in. The ratio $\dfrac{R}{c} = \dfrac{6}{2} = 3$; hence, from Table XII–2, $K_i = 1.30$ and $K_o = 0.81$. The bending moment at section AB is caused by the moment of P about the centroidal axis of the section. Hence $M = 6 P = 6(12,000) = 72,000$ in.-lb. Applying Eq. (12–10), we obtain

$$\left[S = K \frac{Mc}{I} = K \frac{6 M}{bh^2} \right] \qquad S_A = 1.30 \frac{6(72,000)}{2(4)^2} = 17,530 \text{ psi compression}$$

$$S_B = 0.81 \frac{6(72,000)}{2(4)^2} = 10,920 \text{ psi tension}$$

Adding these results (Fig. 12–34a) to the uniform axial stress $S_a = -\dfrac{P}{A} = -\dfrac{12,000}{2(4)} = -1500$ psi gives the final values, $S_A = -19,030$ psi and $S_B = +9420$ psi.

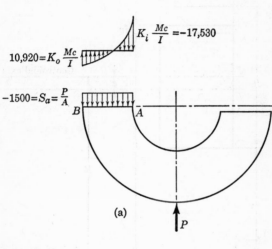

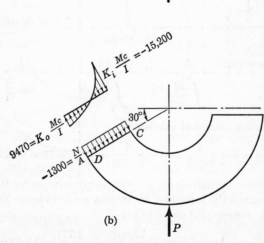

Fig. 12–34.

At section CD, the bending moment $M = P(6 \cos 30°) = 62,400$ in.-lb. The component of P normal to CD is $N = P \cos 30° = 12,000\,(0.866) = 10,400$ lb. Hence, the stresses at C and D (Fig. 12–34b) are

$$\left[S = -\frac{N}{A} \pm K\frac{6\,M}{bh^2} \right]$$

$$S_C = -\frac{10,400}{2(4)} - 1.30\,\frac{6(62,400)}{2(4)^2}$$
$$= -1300 - 15,200 = -16,500\,\text{psi}$$

$$S_D = -\frac{10,400}{2(4)} + 0.81\,\frac{6(62,400)}{2(4)^2}$$
$$= -1300 + 9470 = +8170\,\text{psi}$$

Applying Eq. (12–8) to Fig. 12–35, we have

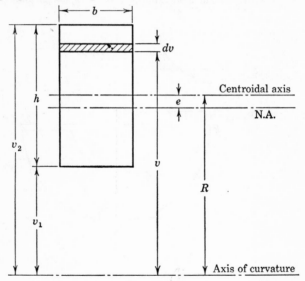

FIG. 12–35.

$$e = R - \frac{A}{\displaystyle\int \frac{dA}{v}} = R - \frac{bh}{\displaystyle\int_{v_1}^{v_2} \frac{b\,dv}{v}} = R - \frac{h}{\log_e \dfrac{v_2}{v_1}}$$

whence, substituting numerical values,

$$e = 6 - \frac{4}{\log_e \frac{8}{4}} = 6 - \frac{4}{0.6931} = 6 - 5.771 = 0.229$$

Note that slide rule calculations are not sufficiently accurate for this computation.

Having determined the value of e, we are now ready to apply Eq. (12–9), which shows the flexure stresses at A and B to be:

$$\left[S = \frac{M}{Ae} \cdot \frac{y}{R - e + y} \right]$$

$$S_A = \frac{72,000}{(2 \times 4)(0.229)} \cdot \frac{1.771}{4} = 17,400\,\text{psi compression}$$

$$S_B = \frac{72,000}{(2 \times 4)(0.229)} \cdot \frac{2.229}{8} = 10,960 \text{ psi tension}$$

To these values we must add the axial stress, − 1500 psi, giving finally $S_A =$ − 18,900 psi and $S_B = +$ 9460 psi.

Thus Eq. (12–10) and Table XII–2 give results that agree closely with those obtained with Eqs. (12–8) and (12–9), and in addition are simpler to use.

PROBLEMS

1223. A sharply curved beam of rectangular section is $\frac{1}{2}$ in. thick by 2 in. deep. If the radius of curvature is $R = 2$ in., compute the stress in terms of M at a point $1\frac{1}{2}$ in. from the outer surface.

1224. For the hook of circular section shown, (*a*) determine the maximum load P that may be supported without exceeding a stress of 18,000 psi at A. (*b*) What stress then exists at B?   *Ans.* (*a*) $P = 11,060$ lb

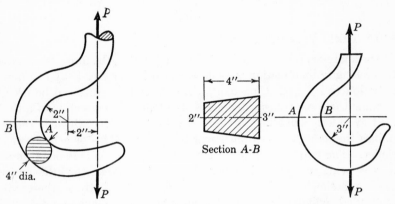

PROB. 1224.   Section A-B   PROB. 1227.

1225. Repeat Prob. 1224 if the hook has a circular section 3 in. in diameter. Obtain the values of K_i and K_o from a graph of K_i and K_o plotted against $\dfrac{R}{c}$.

1226. Determine the diameter of a round steel rod that is to be used as a hook to lift a 1-ton load acting through the center of curvature of the axis of the hook. Assume $\dfrac{R}{c} = 4$ and that the maximum stress permitted is 16,000 psi.
    Ans. $d = 1.82$ in.

1227. A crane hook has a cross-section that is approximated by the trapezoidal section shown. What is the maximum load P that will not exceed a stress of 12,000 psi?

1228. The cross-section of a ring is the T section shown. The inside diameter of the ring is 15.6 in. Determine the value of P that will cause a maximum stress of 18,000 psi.   *Ans.* $P = 22,300$ lb

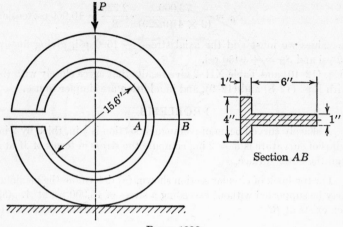

PROB. 1228.

12–10. Thick-Walled Cylinders

In the analysis of thin-walled cylinders in Art. 2–1, the forces transmitted across a longitudinal section were determined from a free-body diagram of the section (see Fig. 2–2, page 39). A similar procedure can be used to determine the force transmitted across the longitudinal section of a thick-walled cylinder. Dividing this force by the area over which it acts determines the *average* tangential stress for *either* a thin- or a thick-walled cylinder. The two cases differ in that in a thin-walled cylinder (the wall thickness being equal to or less than $\frac{1}{20}$ the internal diameter) this average stress is practically equal to the maximum tangential stress, whereas in a thick-walled cylinder it is much smaller than the maximum tangential stress; moreover the stress distribution is nonlinear.

The problem of determining the tangential stress S_t and the radial stress S_r at any point on a thick-walled cylinder, in terms of the applied pressures and the dimensions, was solved by the French elastician Gabriel Lamé in 1833. The cylinder shown in Fig. 12–36 has radii a and b subjected to both a uniformly distributed internal pressure of p_i psi and an external pressure of p_o psi. This cylinder may be assumed composed of thin shells. Fig. 12–37 shows a half section of a typical shell, the radius of which is r, the thickness dr, and the length unity. The tangential stress in this shell is S_t; the radial stress on the inner surface is S_r and that on the outer surface is $S_r + dS_r$, where dS_r is the increment in S_r due to the variation of pressure across the cylinder wall. The radial stresses are assumed (incorrectly) to be tensile, so a negative result for S_r will denote compression.

This shell may be treated as a thin cylinder; hence, for equilibrium, a vertical summation of forces must equal zero. Thus

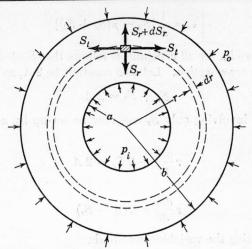

FIG. 12–36. — Thick-walled cylinder subjected to uniform internal pressure P_i and uniform external pressure P_o.

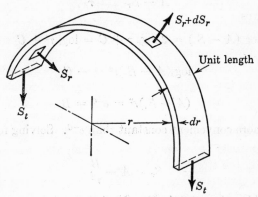

FIG. 12–37. — Stresses on half shell of Fig. 12–36.

$$(S_r + dS_r) \cdot 2(r + dr) - S_r(2\,r) - 2\,S_t\,dr = 0$$

The product $dr \cdot dS_r$ being neglected because it is very small compared to the other quantities, this reduces to

$$r\frac{dS_r}{dr} + S_r - S_t = 0 \qquad\qquad (a)$$

Another relation between S_r and S_t is obtained from the assumption that plane cross-sections remain plane, and hence that the longitudinal strain ϵ_z is constant for all fibers. Applying Hooke's law for tri-axial stress (see page 17), we have

$$\epsilon_z = \frac{1}{E}[S_z - \mu(S_r + S_t)]$$

Since ϵ_z, E, S_z, and μ are all constant, it follows that $S_r + S_t$ is a constant throughout the cross-section. Let this constant be $2\,A$, so that

$$S_r + S_t = 2\,A \tag{b}$$

An equation involving only S_r can now be set up by adding Eqs. (a) and (b):

$$r\frac{dS_r}{dr} + 2\,S_r = 2\,A$$

or

$$r\frac{dS_r}{dr} = 2(A - S_r)$$

whence, separating the variables, we obtain

$$\frac{dS_r}{A - S_r} = 2\frac{dr}{r}$$

Integration gives

$$-\log_e(A - S_r) = 2\log_e r + C = \log_e r^2 + C$$

or

$$\log_e(A - S_r)r^2 = -C$$

and

$$(A - S_r)r^2 = e^{-C} = B$$

where B is a more convenient constant than e^{-C}. Solving for S_r we finally obtain

$$S_r = A - \frac{B}{r^2} \tag{c}$$

Substituting this value of S_r in Eq. (b) gives

$$S_t = A + \frac{B}{r^2} \tag{d}$$

The values of the constants A and B are determined by substituting in Eq. (c) the known values of S_r at the inner and outer surfaces of the cylinder. These values are:

$$\left.\begin{array}{rcl} S_r = -p_i & \text{at} & r = a \\ S_r = -p_o & \text{at} & r = b \end{array}\right\}$$

The minus sign for S_r indicates a compressive stress.

Applying these values, we obtain

$$\left.\begin{array}{l} -\,p_i = A - \dfrac{B}{a^2} \\[2mm] -\,p_o = A - \dfrac{B}{b^2} \end{array}\right\}$$

which, when solved simultaneously for A and B, produce the following values:

$$A = \frac{a^2 p_i - b^2 p_o}{b^2 - a^2}$$

$$B = \frac{a^2 b^2 (p_i - p_o)}{b^2 - a^2}$$

Substituting these values of A and B in Eqs. (c) and (d) gives the following general expressions for S_r and S_t at any point:

$$\left.\begin{array}{l} S_r = \dfrac{a^2 p_i - b^2 p_o}{b^2 - a^2} - \dfrac{a^2 b^2 (p_i - p_o)}{(b^2 - a^2) r^2} \\[3mm] S_t = \dfrac{a^2 p_i - b^2 p_o}{b^2 - a^2} + \dfrac{a^2 b^2 (p_i - p_o)}{(b^2 - a^2) r^2} \end{array}\right\} \qquad (12\text{–}11)$$

Special Cases: Maximum Stresses

Case I: Internal Pressure Only. If the internal pressure is p_i and the external pressure is zero ($p_o = 0$), Eq. (12–11) reduces to

$$\left.\begin{array}{l} S_r = \dfrac{a^2 p_i}{b^2 - a^2}\left(1 - \dfrac{b^2}{r^2}\right) \\[3mm] S_t = \dfrac{a^2 p_i}{b^2 - a^2}\left(1 + \dfrac{b^2}{r^2}\right) \end{array}\right\} \qquad (12\text{–}12)$$

Note that S_r is always a compressive stress, and that S_t is always a tensile stress. Obviously S_t is always larger than S_r and is maximum at the inside surface of the cylinder, where

$$(S_t)_{\text{max.}} = \left(\frac{b^2 + a^2}{b^2 - a^2}\right) p_i \qquad (12\text{–}13)$$

By representing the ratio $\dfrac{b}{a}$ by K, Eq. (12–13) may be rewritten:

$$(S_t)_{\text{max.}} = \frac{K^2 + 1}{K^2 - 1}\, p_i$$

The *average* tangential stress may be found by the method used for thin cylinders in Art. 2–1. Its value is

$$(S_t)_{\text{ave.}} = \frac{a p_i}{b - a} = \frac{p_i}{K - 1}$$

Hence the ratio of the maximum to the average tangential stress is

$$\frac{(S_t)_{\text{max.}}}{(S_t)_{\text{ave.}}} = \frac{K^2 + 1}{K + 1} \tag{12–14}$$

Thus, for a wall thickness equal to $\frac{1}{20}$ of the internal diameter, or $K = \frac{b}{a} = 1.1$, the maximum S_t is only about 5% larger than the average S_t. Hence we may assume, without appreciable error, that where the wall thickness is $\frac{1}{20}$ of the internal diameter or less, the tangential stresses are uniformly distributed, which justifies the procedure used in Art. 2–1.

As a Mohr's circle of stress shows, the shearing stress is one-half the difference of the principal stresses, and since ductile materials like steel (of which most cylinders are made) usually fail because of shear, the value of the maximum shearing stress is important in design. It is maximum at the inner surface of the cylinder where S_t and S_r are both maximum and is given by

$$(S_s)_{\text{max.}} = \frac{S_{t\text{max.}} - S_{r\text{max.}}}{2} = \frac{b^2}{b^2 - a^2} p_i \tag{12–15}$$

Case II: External Pressure Only. If the external pressure is p_o and the internal pressure $p_i = 0$, Eq. (12–11) reduces to

$$\left. \begin{array}{l} S_r = -\dfrac{p_o b^2}{b^2 - a^2}\left(1 - \dfrac{a^2}{r^2}\right) \\[2mm] S_t = -\dfrac{p_o b^2}{b^2 - a^2}\left(1 + \dfrac{a^2}{r^2}\right) \end{array} \right\} \tag{12–16}$$

In this case, both S_r and S_t are always compressive, and S_t is always larger than S_r. The maximum compressive stress (S_t) occurs at the inner surface of the cylinder (at this position S_r is zero) and is given by

$$(S_t)_{\text{max.}} = -\frac{2\, b^2 p_o}{b^2 - a^2} \tag{12–17}$$

$(S_t)_{\text{max.}}$ approaches the value $-2\, p_o$ as b becomes very large compared with a, as in a cylinder with a small central hole.

PROBLEMS

1229. The cylinder for a hydraulic press has an inside diameter of 12 in. Determine the wall thickness required if the cylinder is to withstand an internal pressure of 5000 psi without exceeding a maximum shearing stress of 12,000 psi.

1230. Plot a curve showing the percentage increase in maximum S_t over average S_t for ratios of thickness to inside radius of thick-walled cylinders varying from 0 to 3.

1231. A hoop shrunk onto a hollow tube exerts a contact pressure of 3000 psi on the tube. An internal pressure of 10,000 psi is then applied to the tube. The inner and outer radii of the tube are 1.5 in. and 2.5 in., and 2.5 in. and 4.0 in. for the hoop. What is the maximum tangential stress in the tube (*a*) before and (*b*) after the internal pressure is applied? (*c*) If the 3000-psi pressure is the only pressure acting on the hoop, what is the maximum stress in the hoop?

Ans.   (*a*) $S_t = -9380$ psi; (*b*) $S_t = 3900$ psi; (*c*) $S_t = 6840$ psi

1232. A thick-walled cylinder is built up by shrinking a tube 1 in. thick upon a hollow cylinder having an outside diameter of 6 in. and an inside diameter of 4 in., thereby causing a contact pressure of 3000 psi. What is the greatest internal pressure that can be applied to the assembly without exceeding a tangential stress of 16,000 psi at the inner surface?   *Ans.* $p = 16,100$ psi

1233. The inner and outer radii of a hollow shaft are 2 in. and 4 in., respectively. The hub of a gear wheel that is shrunk onto the hollow shaft has an outer radius of 6 in. The maximum tangential stress developed by shrinking the gear wheel onto the hollow shaft is 30,000 psi. The length of hub parallel to the shaft axis is 5 in., and the coefficient of static friction between hub and shaft is 0.40. Determine the maximum torque that may be transmitted by the gear wheel without slipping on the shaft.   *Ans.* $T = 188,000$ ft-lb

Appendix A
Moments of Inertia

A-1. Definition of Moment of Inertia

Many engineering formulas, such as those relating to strength of beams, columns, deflection of beams, etc., involve the use of a mathematical expression of the form $\int \rho^2\, dA$, where ρ is the perpendicular distance from dA to the axis of inertia. This integral appears so frequently that it has been named *moment of inertia*.[1] Moment of inertia applied to areas has no real meaning when examined by itself; it is merely a mathematical expression usually denoted by the symbol I. However, when used in combination with other terms, as in the flexure formula for beam stresses, $S = \dfrac{Mc}{I}$, it begins to have significance.

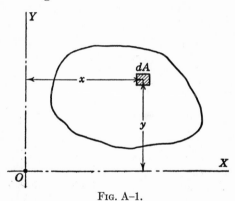

Fig. A-1.

The mathematical definition of moment of inertia, $I = \int \rho^2\, dA$, indicates that an area is divided into small parts such as dA, and each area is multiplied by the square of its moment arm about the reference axis. Thus, as shown in Fig. A-1, if the coordinates of the center of the differential

---

[1] The term *moment of inertia* is derived as follows: Force is related to the mass (i.e., inertia) of a body and its acceleration by the equation $F = Ma$. The equation relating applied forces to the angular acceleration α of rotating bodies is $F \cdot d = [\int \rho^2\, dM] \cdot \alpha$. If the first equation is stated as force equals inertia times acceleration, then by analogy the second equation may be stated as moment of force equals moment of inertia times acceleration. By comparison of the above statements, the expression $\int \rho^2\, dM$ is termed moment of inertia. Similarly, for areas, the expression $\int \rho^2\, dA$ is known as the moment of inertia.

area dA are (x, y), the moment of inertia about the X axis is the summation of the product of each area dA by the square of its moment arm y. This gives

$$I_x = \int y^2 \, dA \tag{A-1}$$

Similarly, the moment of inertia about the Y axis is given by

$$I_y = \int x^2 \, dA \tag{A-2}$$

The moment of inertia (of area) is sometimes called the *second moment of area*, because each differential area multiplied by its moment arm gives the moment of area; when multiplied a second time by its moment arm it gives the moment of inertia. The term *second moment of area* is preferable to the expression *moment of inertia;* the latter is confusing when applied to an area having no inertia. The term *moment of inertia*, however, is long established, and it is not likely to be superseded by the other.

Units and Signs. Examination of the integral $\int \rho^2 \, dA$ shows it to be a fourth-dimensional term, because it is composed of a distance squared multiplied by an area. Thus, if L is the unit of distance, the unit of I is $(L)^4$. A convenient unit of L is inches or feet; this gives quartic inches (in.⁴) or quartic feet (ft⁴) as the dimensional unit of I.

The sign of I is obviously independent of the sign of the moment arm ρ (since if ρ is minus, squaring it makes it plus); it depends entirely on the sign of the area. We define a positive area as one which adds to the area of a figure, and a negative area as one which reduces the area of the figure. For a net area, the moment of inertia must always be positive.

A-2. Polar Moment of Inertia

The moment of inertia for an area relative to a line or axis perpendicular to the plane of the area is called the *polar moment of inertia* and is denoted by the symbol J. In Fig. A-2 the moment of inertia of an area in the XY plane with respect to the Z axis is

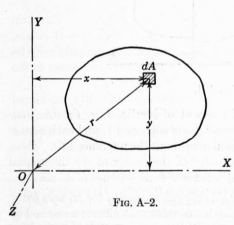

FIG. A-2.

$$[I = \int \rho^2 \, dA]$$
$$J_z = \int r^2 \, dA = \int (x^2 + y^2) \, dA$$
$$= \int x^2 \, dA + \int y^2 \, dA$$

whence from Eqs. (A-1) and (A-2) we finally obtain

$$J_z = I_x + I_y \tag{A-3}$$

Expressed in words, this equation states that the polar moment of inertia for an area, with respect to an axis perpendicular to its plane, is equal to the sum of the moments of inertia about any two mutually perpendicular axes in its plane that intersect on the polar axis.

A–3. Radius of Gyration

The term *radius of gyration* is used to describe another mathematical expression and appears most frequently in column formulas. Radius of gyration is usually denoted by the symbol k (sometimes by r) and is defined by the relation

$$k = \sqrt{\frac{I}{A}} \quad \text{or} \quad I = Ak^2 \tag{A–4}$$

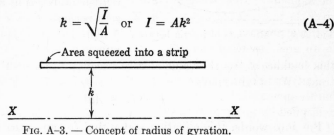

Fig. A–3. — Concept of radius of gyration.

where I is the moment of inertia and A the cross-sectional area.

The following is a geometrical interpretation of this relation. Assume the area of Fig. A–1 to be squeezed into a long narrow strip as shown in Fig. A–3. Each differential element of area dA will be the same distance from the axis of inertia. The moment of inertia is given by

$$I = \int \rho^2 \, dA = k^2 \int dA = Ak^2$$

because each differential element has the same moment arm. The strip may be placed on either side of the reference axis, since if k is minus, squaring it will automatically make it plus. Or part of the strip may be at a distance k from one side of the reference axis, and the remainder of the strip at an equal distance k from the other side of the axis.

In view of this discussion, the radius of gyration is frequently considered to be the distance from the reference axis at which the entire area may be assumed to be concentrated. For example, the symbol ρ in the definition $I = \int \rho^2 \, dA$ could be called the radius of gyration for the area dA.

A–4. Transfer Formula for Moment of Inertia

It is often necessary to transfer the moment of inertia for an area from one axis to another parallel axis. The transfer formula affords a method of doing this without further integration. For example, in Fig. A–4, the moment of inertia with respect to a centroidal X axis (X_o) is given by the expression $I_{x_o} = \int y^2 \, dA$. The moment of inertia for the same area with respect to a *parallel* axis (X) located a distance d from the centroidal axis is given by the equation

$$[I = \int \rho^2 \, dA] \qquad I_x = \int (y + d)^2 \, dA$$

$$= \int y^2 \, dA + 2 \, d \int y \, dA + d^2 \int dA \qquad (a)$$

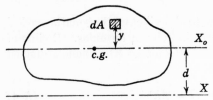

FIG. A–4. — Moments of inertia between parallel axes.

The d is written outside the integral sign because it is a constant that represents the distance separating the axes. The second of the right-hand terms in Eq. (a) becomes zero because $\int y \, dA = A \cdot \bar{y}$, where $\bar{y}$ represents the distance from the reference axis X_o to the centroid. In this instance $\bar{y}$ has the value of zero because X_o passes through the centroid. We obtain finally

$$I_x = I_{x_o} + Ad^2 \qquad \text{(A–5)}$$

Put into words, this equation states that for any area the moment of inertia, with respect to any axis in the plane of the area, is equal to the moment of inertia with respect to a *parallel centroidal axis*, plus a transfer term composed of the product of the area multiplied by the square of the distance between the axes. Evidently the least moment of inertia for any given direction of an axis is the centroidal moment of inertia. Note carefully that the centroidal axis involved in the transfer formula is always the centroidal axis of the area used in the transfer term Ad^2.

A similar relation exists between the radii of gyration with respect to parallel axes, one of which is a centroidal axis. Replacing I_x by Ak_x^2 and I_{x_o} by $Ak_{x_o}^2$ in Eq. (A–5), we obtain

$$Ak_x^2 = Ak_{x_o}^2 + Ad^2$$

whence

$$k_x^2 = k_{x_o}^2 + d^2 \qquad \text{(A–6)}$$

In like fashion, for polar moments of inertia and polar radii of gyration we obtain the following analogous relations between any axis and a parallel centroidal axis:

$$\left. \begin{array}{l} J = J_o + Ad^2 \\ k^2 = k_o^2 + d^2 \end{array} \right\} \qquad \text{(A–7)}$$

A–5. Moments of Inertia by Integration

In determining the moment of inertia by integration, it is desirable to choose the differential area so that either

1. All parts of the differential area are at the same distance from the reference axis,[2] or

2. The moment of inertia of the differential area with respect to the reference axis is known. The moment of inertia of the area is then the summation of the moments of inertia of its elements.

The moment of inertia of a composite figure may be found by combining the moments of inertia of its parts. When the evaluation of I for a particular part is known, the transfer formula (Art. A–4) is used to refer the moments of inertia of the various parts of the figure to a common reference axis.

ILLUSTRATIVE PROBLEMS

A1. Determine the moment of inertia for a rectangle of base b and depth h with respect to (a) an axis coinciding with the base, and (b) a centroidal axis parallel to the base.

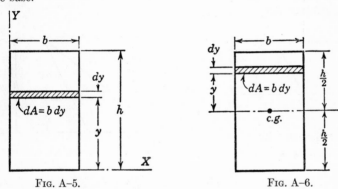

FIG. A–5.   FIG. A–6.

Solution: Axis Coinciding with the Base. Select the differential element, as shown in Fig. A–5. Each part of it is the same distance from the axis of inertia. The moment of inertia with respect to the X axis is obtained from Eq. (A–1) as follows:

$$[I_x = \int y^2 \, dA] \qquad I_x = \int_o^h y^2 \, b \, dy = b \left[\frac{y^3}{3}\right]_o^h$$

$$I_x = \frac{bh^3}{3} \quad Ans.$$

Centroidal Axis. Select the differential element, as shown in Fig. A–6. All parts of the element are a uniform distance from the centroidal axis. The moment of inertia with respect to the centroidal axis X_o is found by applying Eq. (A–1).

$$[I_{x_o} = \int y^2 \, dA] \qquad I_{x_o} = \int_{-h/2}^{+h/2} y^2 \, b \, dy = b \left[\frac{y^3}{3}\right]_{-h/2}^{+h/2}$$

[2] When all parts of an element are at the same distance from an axis, this distance is really the radius of gyration for the element. See Fig. A–3.

$$I_{x_o} = \frac{b}{3}\left[\frac{h^3}{8} + \frac{h^3}{8}\right] = \frac{bh^3}{12} \quad Ans.$$

The moment of inertia of the parallelogram in Fig. A–7 has the same values as for a rectangle, because the elemental strips composing the parallelogram have merely shifted their position laterally from the dashed rectangle of corresponding dimensions.

A2. Determine the moment of inertia for a triangle of base b and altitude h with respect to (a) an axis coinciding with its base, and (b) a centroidal axis parallel to its base.

Solution: Axis Coinciding with the Base. Select the differential element, as shown in Fig. A–8. From similar triangles, the length $x = \dfrac{b}{h}(h - y)$. The moment of inertia with respect to the X axis is obtained from

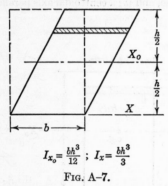

$$I_{x_o} = \frac{bh^3}{12} \; ; \; I_x = \frac{bh^3}{3}$$

FIG. A–7.

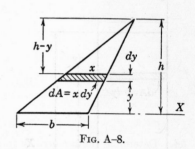

FIG. A–8.

$$[I_x = \int y^2 \, dA]$$

$$I_x = \int_o^h y^2 \cdot x \, dy = \int_o^h y^2 \cdot \frac{b}{h}(h - y)\, dy$$

$$= \frac{b}{h}\left[\int_o^h hy^2 \, dy - \int_o^h y^3 \, dy\right]$$

$$= \frac{b}{h}\left[\frac{hy^3}{3} - \frac{y^4}{4}\right]_o^h$$

$$I_x = \frac{bh^3}{12} \quad Ans.$$

Centroidal Axis. Referring to Fig. A–9 and using the transfer formula, we obtain

$$[I_x = I_{x_o} + Ad^2]$$

$$\frac{bh^3}{12} = I_{x_o} + \left(\frac{bh}{2}\right) \cdot \left(\frac{h}{3}\right)^2$$

$$I_{x_o} = \frac{bh^3}{36} \quad Ans.$$

A3. Determine the moment of inertia of a circular area of radius r with respect to an axis coinciding with a diameter.

Solution: Using polar coordinates, select the differential element, as shown in Fig. A–10. From the figure, $y = \rho \sin \theta$. The moment of inertia with respect to the diameter is

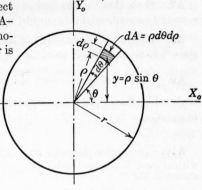

FIG. A–10.

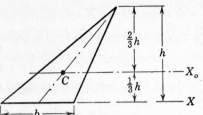

FIG. A–9.

$$[I_x = \int y^2 \, dA]$$

$$I_{x_o} = \int_o^r \int_o^{2\pi} \rho^2 \sin^2\theta \, \rho \, d\theta \, d\rho$$

$$= \int_o^r \int_o^{2\pi} \rho^3 \, d\rho \cdot \sin^2\theta \, d\theta$$

$$= \frac{r^4}{4} \int_o^{2\pi} \sin^2\theta \, d\theta = \frac{r^4}{4} \cdot \pi$$

$$I_{x_o} = \frac{\pi r^4}{4} \quad Ans.$$

PROBLEMS

A4. Determine the moment of inertia of a triangle of base b and altitude h with respect to an axis through the apex parallel to the base. Use the transfer formula and the results of Illus. Prob. A2.   *Ans.* $I = \dfrac{bh^3}{4}$

A5. Determine the moment of inertia of the quarter circle shown with respect to the given axes.   *Ans.* $I_x = I_y = \dfrac{\pi r^4}{16}$

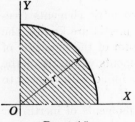

PROB. A5.

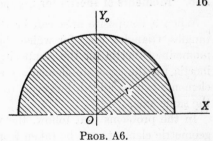

PROB. A6.

A6. Determine the moment of inertia of the semicircle shown with respect to the given axes.   *Ans.* $I_x = I_{y_o} = \dfrac{\pi r^4}{8}$

A7. Show that the moment of inertia of a semicircle of radius r is $0.11\,r^4$ with respect to a centroidal axis parallel to the diameter.

A8. Determine the moment of inertia for the quarter circle in Prob. A5 with respect to a centroidal X axis.   *Ans.* $I_{x_0} = 0.055\,r^4$

A9. Determine the moment of inertia with respect to the X axis for the area enclosed by the ellipse whose equation is $\dfrac{x^2}{a^2} + \dfrac{y^2}{b^2} = 1$. Also determine the radius of gyration.

$$Ans.\quad I_{x_0} = \frac{\pi ab^3}{4};\ k_{x_0} = \frac{b}{2}$$

A10. Determine the polar moment of inertia of the area of a circle of radius r with respect to the centroidal polar axis; also its radius of gyration.

$$Ans.\quad J_o = \frac{\pi r^4}{2};\ k_{z_0} = \frac{r}{\sqrt{2}}$$

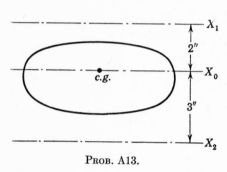

PROB. A13.

A11. Determine the moment of inertia and the radius of gyration, with respect to the Y axis, of the area cut from the first quadrant by the curve $y = 4 - x^2$, where x and y are in inches.

$$Ans.\quad I_y = \tfrac{64}{15}\ \text{in.}^4;\ k_y = \sqrt{\tfrac{4}{5}}\ \text{in.}$$

A12. A rectangle is 3 in. by 6 in. Determine the polar moment of inertia and the radius of gyration with respect to a polar axis through one corner.

$$Ans.\quad J = 270\ \text{in.}^4;\ k_z = 3.88\ \text{in.}$$

A13. The cross-sectional area shown is 4 in.² Its X centroidal axis is located as shown. It is known that $I_{x_1} = 25$ in.⁴ Determine the value of I_{x_2}.

$$Ans.\quad I_{x_2} = 45\ \text{in.}^4$$

A–6. Moments of Inertia for Composite Areas

When a composite area can be divided into geometric elements (rectangles, triangles, etc.) for which the moments of inertia are known, the moment of inertia for the composite area is the sum of the moments of inertia for the separate elements. Before the moments of inertia of the elements can be added, however, they must all be found with respect to the same axis.

In the problems that follow, the values of the moments of inertia for geometric elements can be taken from the results of the problems in Art. A–5); these are summarized in Table A–1. When the geometric shape is the cross-section of a structural element such as an I beam, angle, or channel, its properties are given in Appendix B.

Shape	Moment of Inertia	Radius of Gyration
Rectangle	$I_{x_0} = \dfrac{bh^3}{12}$ $I_x = \dfrac{bh^3}{3}$	$k_{x_0} = \dfrac{h}{\sqrt{12}}$ $k_x = \dfrac{h}{\sqrt{3}}$
Any triangle	$I_{x_0} = \dfrac{bh^3}{36}$ $I_x = \dfrac{bh^3}{12}$	$k_{x_0} = \dfrac{h}{\sqrt{18}}$ $k_x = \dfrac{h}{\sqrt{6}}$
Circle	$I_{x_0} = \dfrac{\pi r^4}{4}$	$k_{x_0} = \dfrac{r}{2}$
Semicircle	$I_x = I_{y_0} = \dfrac{\pi r^4}{8}$ $I_{x_0} = 0.11\, r^4$	$k_x = k_{y_0} = \dfrac{r}{2}$ $k_{x_0} = 0.264\, r$
Quarter circle	$I_x = I_y = \dfrac{\pi r^4}{16}$ $I_{x_0} = I_{y_0} = 0.055\, r^4$	$k_x = k_y = \dfrac{r}{2}$ $k_{x_0} = k_{y_0} = 0.264\, r$
Ellipse	$I_{x_0} = \dfrac{\pi a b^3}{4}$ $I_{y_0} = \dfrac{\pi b a^3}{4}$	$k_{x_0} = \dfrac{b}{2}$ $k_{y_0} = \dfrac{a}{2}$

ILLUSTRATIVE PROBLEMS

A14. Determine the moments of inertia of the area shown in Fig. A–11 with respect to its centroidal axes.

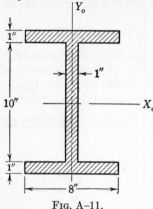

FIG. A–11.

Solution: The moment of inertia of a composite area is the sum of the moments of inertia of the various parts of the area, all the moments of inertia being referred to the same axis of inertia before the addition is made. In this case, the figure can be resolved into a large rectangle whose dimensions are 8 by 12 in., from which two smaller rectangles, each 3.5 by 10 in., are subtracted to give the net area of the figure.

The X axis of the given area happens to be the centroidal axis for each part; hence the transfer terms of the transfer formula are zero. Using the result of Prob. A1, we therefore obtain

$$\left[I_o = \frac{bh^3}{12}\right] \qquad \text{8 by 12 in. rectangle: } I_x = \frac{8 \times (12)^3}{12} = 1152 \text{ in.}^4$$

$$\text{Two 3.5 by 10 in. rectangles: } I_x = 2 \times \left[\frac{3.5 \times (10)^3}{12}\right] = 583 \text{ in.}^4$$

$$\text{Hence, for shaded area: } I_x = 1152 - 583 = 569 \text{ in.}^4 \quad \textit{Ans.}$$

With respect to the Y axis, assume the figure to be composed of a 1 by 10 in. rectangle and two 1 by 8 in. rectangles. The Y axis is also the centroidal axis for each of these rectangles. Again using the result of Prob. A1, we have

$$\left[I_o = \frac{bh^3}{12}\right] \qquad \text{1 by 10 in. rectangle: } I_y = \frac{10 \times (1)^3}{12} = 0.833 \text{ in.}^4$$

$$\text{Two 1 by 8 in. rectangles: } I_y = 2 \times \left[\frac{1 \times (8)^3}{12}\right] = 85.4 \text{ in.}^4$$

$$\text{Net area: } I_y = 0.833 + 85.4 = 86.233 \text{ in.}^4 \quad \textit{Ans.}$$

Such extreme accuracy is not required; the answer would usually be given as 86.2 in.^{4}

A15. Compute the moment of inertia for the composite area shown in Fig. A–12 with respect to the indicated X axis.

Solution: The area is composed of a semicircle S whose radius is 3 in., a 6 by 9 in. rectangle R, and a 4 by 9 in. triangle T. With respect to the X axis, the moment of inertia for the area is the sum of the moments of inertia of these elements, each moment of inertia being referred to the X axis before addition:

$$I_x = I_R + I_S + I_T \tag{a}$$

Expressing the moment of inertia of each element in terms of its centroidal moment of inertia, plus a transfer term, we obtain

$$I_R = (I_o)_R + (Ad^2)_R$$
$$I_S = (I_o)_S + (Ad^2)_S$$
$$I_T = (I_o)_T + (Ad^2)_T$$

Adding the left- and right-hand members of these equations results in

$$I_x = \Sigma I_o + \Sigma Ad^2 \tag{b}$$

Eq. (b) indicates that the moment of inertia of a composite figure is the summation of the centroidal moments of inertia of the elements, plus the summation of the transfer terms for these elements. This equation is readily adapted to tabular computation, as shown below. From Table A-1, the values of I_o for each of these elements are $I_{o_R} = \dfrac{bh^3}{12}$, $I_{o_S} = 0.11\,r^4$, and $I_{o_T} = \dfrac{bh^3}{36}$. The transfer distances are indicated on Fig. A-12.

Item	I_o	Area	d	d^2	Ad^2
Rectangle	365	54	2.5	6.25	337.5
Semicircle	8.91	14.14	3.27	10.7	151.3
Triangle	81	18	4.0	16	288
Totals	454.91				776.8

Taking the summations from the table and substituting in Eq. (b), we obtain

$$[I_x = \Sigma I_o + \Sigma Ad^2] \qquad I_x = 454.91 + 776.8 \qquad I_x = 1231.71 \text{ in.}^4 \quad Ans.$$

A16. The cross-section of a beam is composed of the elements shown in Fig. A-13. The angles are 4 by 4 by $\frac{3}{4}$ in., for which $I_{x_o} = I_{y_o} = 7.7$ in.^{4}, the area = 5.44 in.^{2}, and $\bar{x} = \bar{y} = 1.27$ in. Compute the moment of inertia with respect to the centroidal X axis.

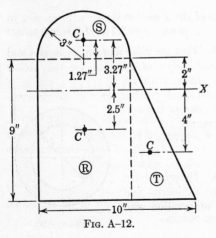

FIG. A-12.

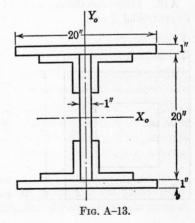

FIG. A-13.

Solution: The tabular computation used in Prob. A15 is well suited for cases in which there are many elements. In the present problem, the elements are symmetrically placed so that a table is hardly justified.

Direct application of the transfer formula to each element gives

$$[I = I_o + Ad^2]$$

For web plate: $I = \dfrac{1 \times (20)^3}{12} + 20 \times (0)^2 = 667 \text{ in.}^4$

For two cover plates: $I = 2 \times \left[\dfrac{20 \times (1)^3}{12} + 20 \times (10.5)^2 \right] = 4413.33 \text{ in.}^4$

For four angles: $I = 4 \times [7.7 + 5.44 \times (8.73)^2] = 1688.8 \text{ in.}^4$

For entire figure: $I_{x_0} = 667 + 4413.33 + 1688.8 \approx 6769 \text{ in.}^4$ *Ans.*

PROBLEMS

A17. The cross-section of an equal leg angle 6 by 6 by 1 in. is shown. Determine the moment of inertia about the centroidal X axis.

Ans. $\bar{y} = 1.86$ in.; $I_{x_0} = 35.5$ in.^{4}

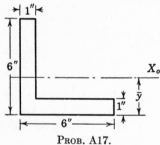

PROB. A17.

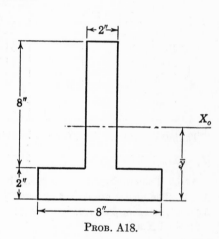

PROB. A18.

A18. Determine the moment of inertia of the T section shown with respect to its centroidal X axis.   *Ans.* $\bar{y} = 3.5$ in.; $I_{x_0} = 290.66$ in.^{4}

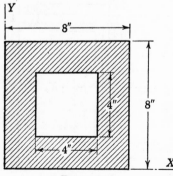

PROB. A19.

A19. Find the polar moment of inertia and the polar radius of gyration for the hollow square shown with respect to a Z axis passing through one of the outside corners.

Ans. $J = 2176$ in.^{4}; $k = 6.74$ in.

A20. Determine the moment of inertia and radius of gyration with

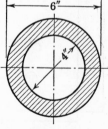

PROB. A20.

respect to a polar centroidal axis for the hollow circular area shown.

A21.   Determine the moment of inertia of the area shown with respect to its centroidal axes.   *Ans.* $\bar{y} = 5.7$ in.; $I_{x_o} = 855$ in.^{4}

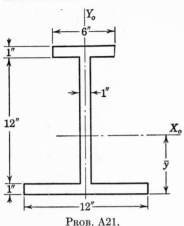

PROB. A21.

A22.   Find the moment of inertia about the indicated X axis for the shaded area shown.   *Ans.* $I_x = 908$ in.^{4}

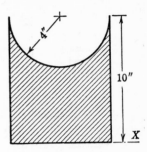

PROB. A22.

A23.   Find the centroidal moment of inertia of the trapezoid shown.
Ans. $\bar{y} = 2.55$ in.; $I_{x_o} = 184.4$ in.^{4}

A24.   The cross section shown is that of a structural member known as a Z section.   Determine the values of I_{x_o} and I_{y_o}.
Ans. $I_{x_o} = 42.1$ in.^{4}; $I_{y_o} = 15.4$ in.^{4}; Area = 8.63 in.^{2}

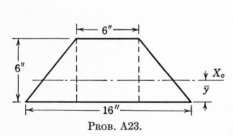

PROB. A23.

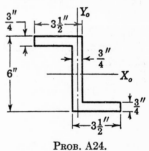

PROB. A24.

A25.   The built-up section shown is composed of two 8 by 6 by 1 in. angles riveted to a 12 by 1 in. web plate.   Determine the moment of inertia with respect to the centroidal X axis.

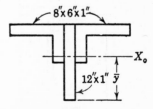

PROB. A25.

A26. Two 12-in., 20.7-lb channels are latticed together to form the column section shown. Determine how far apart the channels should be placed so as to make I_x equal to I_y for the section. (Neglect the lattice bars, which are indicated by the dashed lines.)   *Ans.* $d = 7.69$ in.

A27. The short legs of four 6 by 4 by $\frac{1}{2}$ in. angles are connected to a web plate $23\frac{1}{2}$ in. by $\frac{5}{16}$ in. to form the plate and angle girder shown. Compute the value of I_{x_0}.
Ans. $I_{x_0} = 2666$ in.[4]

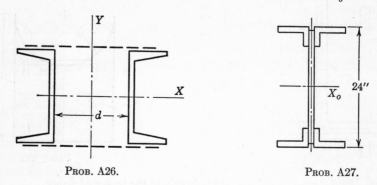

PROB. A26.   PROB. A27.

A28. A plate and angle column is composed of four 8 by 4 by 1 in. angles with the short legs connected to a web plate 14 in. by 1 in. plus two cover plates each 18 in. by $2\frac{1}{4}$ in. Determine the values of I_{x_0} and I_{y_0}.
Ans. $I_{x_0} = 7682$ in.[4]; $I_{y_0} = 3021$ in.[4]

A29. Determine the centroidal moments of inertia of the built-up column section shown. It is composed of two 16 by 1 in. plates riveted to two 12-in. 20.7-lb channels.   *Ans.* $I_{x_0} = 1609$ in.[4]; $I_{y_0} = 956.4$ in.[4]

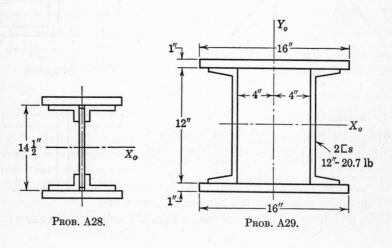

PROB. A28.   PROB. A29.

A30. Four Z bars, each having the size and properties given in Prob. A24, are riveted to a 12 by 1 in. plate to form the section shown. Determine the centroidal moments of inertia. *Ans.* $I_{x_0} = 1300$ in.[4]; $I_{y_0} = 592$ in.[4]

A31. A 10-in. 15.3-lb channel is welded to the top of a 10 WF 21 beam as shown. Compute $\bar{y}$ and the moment of inertia about the centroidal X axis. *Ans.* $\bar{y} = 6.86$ in.; $I_{x_0} = 162.3$ in.[4]

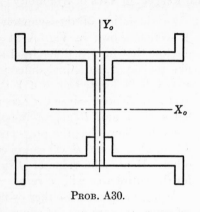

PROB. A30.

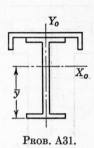

PROB. A31.

A32. Two 10-in. 15.3-lb channels are welded together as shown. Compute the values of I_{x_0} for (a) and (b). *Ans.* (a) $\bar{y} = 7.30$ in., $I_{x_0} = 116.5$ in.[4]; (b) $\bar{y} = 7.82$ in., $I_{x_0} = 140.3$ in.[4]

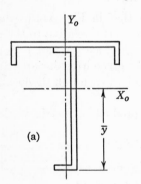

(a)

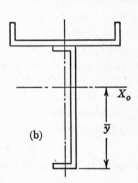

(b)

PROB. A32.

A–7. Product of Inertia

The product of inertia is a mathematical expression of the form $\int xy\, dA$ and is denoted by the symbol P. The product of inertia is not used as commonly as the moment of inertia, because it is generally limited to problems requiring values of maximum and minimum moments of inertia, to cases involving unsymmetrical bending of beams, etc.

Units and Signs. The unit of the product of inertia is of the same form as that for the moment of inertia, namely, (length)[4]. Unlike the moment of inertia, however, the sign for the product of inertia depends upon the location of the area relative to the axes; as will be seen, it may be plus or minus.

A-8.   Product of Inertia Is Zero with Respect to Axes of Symmetry

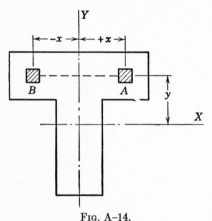

FIG. A-14.

Consideration of the symmetrical T section shown in Fig. A-14 will disclose that for any differential area like that at A, an equal differential area will be located at B if Y is an axis of symmetry. Since the x coordinates of A and B are of opposite signs, it follows that the products xy dA for areas A and B will cancel each other. Hence, the value of $\int xy\, dA$ for the entire area will be zero.

As a general rule, if either or both reference axes are axes of symmetry, the product of inertia will be zero.

A-9.   Transfer Formula for Product of Inertia

Consider any irregular area, such as that in Fig. A-15, whose cross-sectional area is A and whose product of inertia relative to the centroidal axes is denoted by $P_{x_o y_o}$. Let a parallel set of axes X and Y be located so that the coordinates of the centroid of the given irregular area are $\bar{x}$ and $\bar{y}$ relative to these axes. The signs of $\bar{x}$ and $\bar{y}$ depend on the location of the centroid relative to the X and Y axes.

From the fundamental definition of product of inertia we have, with respect to centroidal axes,

$$P_{x_o y_o} = \int x'y'\, dA \qquad (a)$$

and with respect to any parallel set of X and Y axes

$$P_{xy} = \int (x' + \bar{x})(y' + \bar{y})\, dA \qquad (b)$$

Expanding Eq. (b) gives

$$P_{xy} = \int x'y'\, dA + \bar{x}\int y'\, dA + \bar{y}\int x'\, dA + \bar{x}\bar{y}\int dA \qquad (c)$$

Note that the two middle terms represent the moment of area relative to the centroidal axes multiplied respectively by the constants $\bar{x}$ and $\bar{y}$. Since the moment of area relative to centroidal axes is zero, Eq. (c) finally reduces to

$$P_{xy} = P_{x_o y_o} + A\bar{x}\bar{y} \qquad \textbf{(A-8)}$$

This equation, which is known as the transfer formula for products of inertia, forms the basis of the method of computing products of inertia for areas composed of simple geometrical shapes. Remember that the signs of $\bar{x}$ and $\bar{y}$ in this equation depend on the position of the centroid with respect to the X and Y axes.

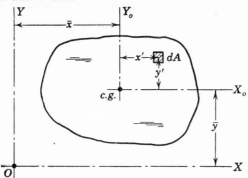

Fig. A–15. — Products of inertia between parallel sets of axes.

ILLUSTRATIVE PROBLEMS

A33. Determine the product of inertia of the right triangle shown in Fig. A–16 with respect to the X and Y axes.

Solution: In applying the definition of product of inertia, $P = \int xy \, dA$, observe that x and y represent the coordinates of the centroid of the differential area dA. For the right triangle illustrated, select the differential area as the shaded strip parallel to the base. The area of this strip is $dA = x \, dy$, and the coordinates of its centroid are $\frac{1}{2} x$ and y.

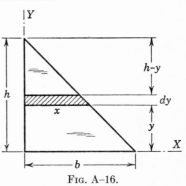

Fig. A–16.

From consideration of similar triangles, it is evident that $x = \dfrac{b}{h} (h - y)$. Hence $dA = x \, dy = \dfrac{b}{h} (h - y) \, dy$. Applying the definition of product of inertia, we obtain

$$[P = \int xy \cdot dy] \qquad P_{xy} = \int_0^h \left[\frac{1}{2} \frac{b}{h} (h - y) \right] \cdot y \cdot \left[\frac{b}{h} (h - y) \, dy \right]$$

$$= \frac{b^2}{2 \, h^2} \int_0^h (h^2 y - 2 \, hy^2 + y^3) \, dy$$

$$= \frac{b^2}{2 \, h^2} \left[\frac{h^2 y^2}{2} - \frac{2 \, hy^3}{3} + \frac{y^4}{4} \right]_0^h$$

$$P_{xy} = + \frac{b^2 h^2}{24} \quad Ans.$$

A34. Determine the product of inertia of the 8 by 6 by 1 in. angle section shown in Fig. A–17 with respect to the indicated X and Y axes.

Solution: The angle section can be considered composed of a 5 by 1 in. rectangle plus an 8 by 1 in. rectangle. For the first rectangle, the centroidal axes parallel to the X and Y axes are axes of symmetry; hence, from Art. A–8, $P_{x_0y_0}$ for this rectangle equals zero. The situation is similar for the other rectangle. Hence, for the composite area, we obtain

$$[P_{xy} = P_{x_0y_0} + A\bar{x}\bar{y}]$$

5 by 1 in. rectangle: $P_{xy} = (5 \times 1) \times .5 \times 3.5 = 8.78$ in.^{4}

8 by 1 in. rectangle: $P_{xy} = (8 \times 1) \times 4 \times .5 = 16.0$ in.^{4}

For the composite area: $P_{xy} = 8.78 + 16$

$$P_{xy} = 24.78 \text{ in.}^4 \quad Ans.$$

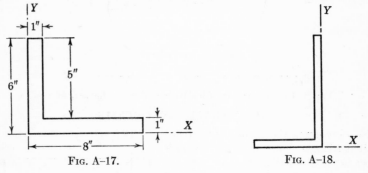

FIG. A–17.   FIG. A–18.

If the angle is rotated 90° counterclockwise to the position shown in Fig. A–18, the same value of P_{xy} but with opposite sign will be obtained, i.e., $P_{yx} = -24.78$ in.^{4} In so far as Fig. A–17 is concerned, this result is equivalent to stating that $P_{xy} = -P_{yx}$. The negative sign and interchange of subscripts follows from selecting the Y axis as the first axis; the second axis is the negative X axis 90° counterclockwise from Y. In this respect, products of inertia are analogous to shearing stresses on perpendicular planes, i.e., $S_{xy} = -S_{yx}$, as discussed in the footnote on page 300.

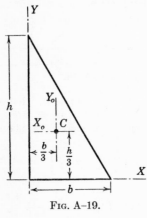

FIG. A–19.

$$[P_{xy} = P_{x_0y_0} + A\bar{x}\bar{y}]$$

A35 From the answer to Prob. A33, use the transfer formula to obtain the product of inertia of the right triangle shown in Fig. A–19 with respect to the indicated centroidal axes.

Solution: From the answer to Prob. A33 we have

$$P_{xy} = \frac{b^2h^2}{24}.$$ Applying the transfer formula, we obtain

$$\frac{b^2h^2}{24} = P_{x_0y_0} + \frac{bh}{2} \times \frac{b}{3} \times \frac{h}{3}$$

$$= P_{x_0y_0} + \frac{b^2h^2}{18}$$

$$P_{x_o y_o} = \frac{b^2 h^2}{24} - \frac{b^2 h^2}{18} = - \frac{b^2 h^2}{72} \quad Ans.$$

Note the minus sign carefully.   Will the product of inertia change sign if the triangle is rotated about the Y axis to lie in the second quadrant?

PROBLEMS

A36.   Compute the product of inertia of the semicircular area shown with respect to the X and Y axes.

A37.   Compute the product of inertia of the angle section shown in Prob. A17 (page 432), (*a*) with respect to the centroidal X and Y axes, (*b*) with respect to the horizontal and vertical axes whose origin is at the lower left-hand corner of the angle.   *Ans.*   (*a*) $P_{x_o y_o} = -20.46$ in.[4]

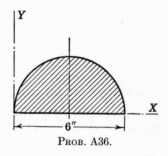

PROB. A36.

A38.   Determine the product of inertia of the Z section shown in Prob. A24 (page 433) with respect to the centroidal X and Y axes.
          Ans. $P_{xy} = -18.9$ in.[4]

A39.   Determine the product of inertia of an 8 by 6 by 1 in. angle section with respect to centroidal axes parallel to the legs.   Refer to Appendix B for the location of the centroid.   *Ans.* $P_{x_o y_o} = \pm 32.31$ in.[4]

A–10.   Moments of Inertia with Respect to Inclined Axes

In some cases, it is necessary to determine the moment of inertia with respect to axes that are inclined to the usual axes.   The moment of inertia in such cases can be obtained by formal integration, but a general formula is usually easier to use.

The problem may be stated as follows: Assuming the values of I_x, I_y and P_{xy} with respect to the X and Y axes to be known, determine the values of I_u, I_v, and P_{uv} with respect to the U and V axes inclined at an angle α with the X and Y axes, as shown in Fig. A–20.

The coordinates for a typical differential area dA are given by x and y with respect to the X and Y axes, and by u and v relative to the U and V axes.   The relations between these coordinates can be obtained by projecting x and y upon the U and V axes.   This gives

$$\left. \begin{array}{l} v = y \cos \alpha - x \sin \alpha \\ u = y \sin \alpha + x \cos \alpha \end{array} \right\} \tag{a}$$

By definition $(I = \int \rho^2 \, dA)$, the values of I_u and I_v are

$$I_u = \int v^2 \, dA \tag{b}$$
$$I_v = \int u^2 \, dA \tag{c}$$

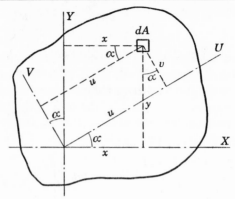

FIG. A–20. — Moments of inertia with respect to inclined axes.

Replacing v in Eq. (b) by its value in Eq. (a), we obtain

$$I_u = \int (y^2 \cos^2 \alpha - 2\,xy \sin \alpha \cos \alpha + x^2 \sin^2 \alpha)\,dA$$

Since

$$I_x = \int y^2\,dA, \quad I_y = \int x^2\,dA, \quad \text{and} \quad P_{xy} = \int xy\,dA,$$

this reduces to

$$I_u = I_x \cos^2 \alpha + I_y \sin^2 \alpha - P_{xy} \sin 2\alpha \qquad (d)$$

If the relations

$$\cos^2 \alpha = \frac{1 + \cos 2\alpha}{2} \quad \text{and} \quad \sin^2 \alpha = \frac{1 - \cos 2\alpha}{2} \qquad (e)$$

are substituted in Eq. (d), the result is

$$\mathbf{I_u = \frac{I_x + I_y}{2} + \frac{I_x - I_y}{2} \cos 2\alpha - P_{xy} \sin 2\alpha} \qquad \textbf{(A–9)}$$

Similarly, replacing u in Eq. (c) by its value in Eq. (a) gives

$$I_v = \int (y^2 \sin^2 \alpha + 2\,xy \sin \alpha \cos \alpha + x^2 \cos^2 \alpha)\,dA$$

This reduces to

$$I_v = I_x \sin^2 \alpha + I_y \cos^2 \alpha + P_{xy} \sin 2\alpha \qquad (f)$$

The relations in Eq. (e) transform Eq. (f) into

$$\mathbf{I_v = \frac{I_x + I_y}{2} - \frac{I_x - I_y}{2} \cos 2\alpha + P_{xy} \sin 2\alpha} \qquad \textbf{(A–10)}$$

When values of I_x, I_y, and P_{xy} are known, Eqs. (A–9) and (A–10) permit the values of I_u and I_v, with respect to the U and V axes inclined at an angle α to the X and Y axes, to be determined without further integration. In a sense, these equations do for inclined axes what the transfer formula does for parallel axes.

Adding Eqs. (A–9) and (A–10) gives the relation

$$I_u + I_v = I_x + I_y$$

which shows that the sum of the moments of inertia with respect to any set of rectangular axes through the same point is a constant quantity. This conclusion could also have been obtained from Art. A–2, which shows that the polar moment of inertia J_z is the sum of the moments of inertia with respect to rectangular axes passing through the polar axis. Hence, since J_z is a constant, we obtain as before

$$J_z = I_x + I_y = I_u + I_v$$

To determine the product of inertia relative to the U and V axes, we note that P_{uv} is defined as

$$P_{uv} = \int uv \, dA \tag{g}$$

Substituting the values of u and v given in Eq. (a), we have

$$
\begin{aligned}
P_{uv} &= \int (y^2 \sin \alpha \cos \alpha + xy \cos^2 \alpha - xy \sin^2 \alpha - x^2 \sin \alpha \cos \alpha) \, dA \\
&= \frac{I_x}{2} \sin 2\alpha + P_{xy} \cos^2 \alpha - P_{xy} \sin^2 \alpha - \frac{I_y}{2} \sin 2\alpha \tag{h}
\end{aligned}
$$

whence by using the relation $\cos^2 \alpha - \sin^2 \alpha = \cos 2\alpha$, we obtain

$$P_{uv} = \frac{I_x - I_y}{2} \sin 2\alpha + P_{xy} \cos 2\alpha \tag{A–11}$$

A–11. Mohr's Circle for Moments of Inertia

Except for a change of symbols, Eqs. (A–9) and (A–11) are identical with Eqs. (9–5) and (9–6), which express the variation in normal and shearing stress. It follows that the method described in Art. 9–7 for Mohr's circle of stress may be similarly applied to obtain a Mohr's circle of inertia. This construction will give a visual representation of all the possible values of I and P with respect to all axes passing through a specified point in an area. For convenience, the rules in Art. 9–7 are rephrased as follows to apply to moments of inertia:

1. On a set of rectangular coordinate axes, choose one axis on which to plot numerical values of moments of inertia, and the other on which to plot products of inertia; call these the I and P axes. Plot points having the coordinates (I_x, P_{xy}) and $(I_y, -P_{xy})$. The values for I_x, I_y, and P_{xy} are assumed to be already known. Note carefully that the value for P_{xy} with its real sign is associated with the value of I_x, and that the value of P_{xy} with the opposite sign is associated with I_y. Actually P_{yx} should be paired with I_y, but $P_{yx} = -P_{xy}$, as we saw in Prob. A34.

2. Draw a straight line through the two points thus determined. This

line is the diameter of Mohr's circle. The center of this circle is on the I coordinate axis. Draw the circle.

3. The *radius* of the circle drawn through any point on the circumference represents the axis of inertia corresponding to the I coordinate of this point.

4. The coordinates of any point on the circumference represent the values for I and P with respect to the axis of inertia corresponding to the radius of the circle drawn through this point.

5. The angle between any two radii on Mohr's circle is double the actual angle between the two axes represented by the two radii. The rotational sense of this angle corresponds to the rotational sense of the actual angle between the axes; i.e., if the U axis is located at a counterclockwise angle α relative to the X axis, on Mohr's circle U is laid off as a counterclockwise angle $2\,\alpha$ from X.

ILLUSTRATIVE PROBLEM

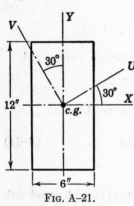

FIG. A-21.

A40. For the rectangle shown in Fig. A–21, compute the values of I_u, I_v, and P_{uv} with respect to the U and V axes. These axes are inclined 30° counterclockwise to the X and Y axes.

Solution: The moments of inertia and the product of inertia are first found with respect to the X and Y axes, as follows:

$$\left[I_x = \frac{bh^3}{12}\right] \qquad I_x = \frac{6 \times (12)^3}{12} = 864 \text{ in.}^4$$

$$\left[I_y = \frac{hb^3}{12}\right] \qquad I_y = \frac{12 \times (6)^3}{12} = 216 \text{ in.}^4$$

$P_{xy} = 0$ because X and Y are axes of symmetry

Following the rules given above, draw a set of rectangular coordinate axes and label them I and P, as shown in Fig. A–22. Using the values of I_x, I_y, and P_{xy}, plot the points A and B whose coordinates are (864, 0) and (216, 0).

According to Rule 2, the diameter of Mohr's circle is AB. Its center C is midway between A and B. The I coordinate of C is 540 in.⁴ The radius of the circle is the distance $CA = 864 - 540 = 324$ in.⁴

From Rule 3, the radius CA represents the axis of inertia corresponding to the I coordinate of A; in this case, the X axis. Applying Rule 5, we find that the U axis of inertia is represented by the radius CD laid off 60° counterclockwise from the X axis (CA). Also, since V is actually 90° from U, the V axis (CE) is laid off 180° (i.e., double scale) from the U axis. D, C, and E form a straight line.

From Rule 4, the coordinates of D represent I_u and P_{uv}; the coordinates of E represent I_v and P_{uv} with the opposite sign. Accordingly, from the diagram we obtain

$[I_u = OC + CD \cos 60°] \qquad I_u = 540 + 324 \cos 60° = 540 + 162$

$$I_u = 702 \text{ in.}^4 \quad Ans.$$

$[I_v = OC - CE \cos 60°]$ $\quad I_v = 540 - 324 \cos 60°$ $\quad I_v = 378 \text{ in.}^4$ *Ans.*

$[P_{uv} = CD \sin 60°]$ $\quad P_{uv} = 324 \sin 60°$ $\quad P_{uv} = 281 \text{ in.}^4$ *Ans.*

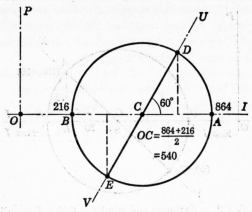

Fig. A–22. — Application of Mohr's circle.

A–12. Maximum and Minimum Moments of Inertia. Principal Axes

An inspection of Mohr's circle will show that the points whose co-ordinates indicate maximum and minimum moments of inertia are located on the I axis and have a zero product of inertia. Conversely, axes that have a zero product of inertia must be axes of maximum or minimum inertia. Such axes are called *principal axes*.

As we have already seen (Art. A–8), the products of inertia relative to axes of symmetry are zero. Hence, we conclude that axes of symmetry must be principal axes, because they always yield values of maximum and minimum moments of inertia. But many figures do not have axes of symmetry, although they do have principal axes with respect to which the product of inertia is zero. *Axes of symmetry are always principal axes, but the converse is not necessarily true.*

ILLUSTRATIVE PROBLEM

A41. A certain area is found to have the following values with respect to the X and Y axes: $I_x = 100 \text{ in.}^4$, $I_y = 60 \text{ in.}^4$, and $P_{xy} = 15 \text{ in.}^4$ Determine the maximum and minimum moments of inertia and illustrate the position of the principal axes relative to the X and Y axes.

Solution: On a set of I and P axes, as shown in Fig. A–23, plot points having the following coordinates:

$$\begin{pmatrix} I_x = 100 \\ P_{xy} = 15 \end{pmatrix} \quad \begin{pmatrix} I_y = 60 \\ -P_{xy} = -15 \end{pmatrix}$$

Note that the given value of P_{xy} is associated with I_x and that the value of P_{xy} with the opposite sign is associated with I_y. If P_{xy} had been negative originally, this value would have been associated with I_x, and the positive value of P_{xy} with I_y.

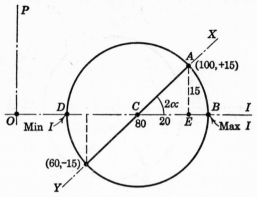

FIG. A–23. — Maximum and minimum moments of inertia.

Plotting these points gives two points on Mohr's circle. Joining them gives the diameter of the circle shown in Fig. A–23. Obviously the radius of the circle is $CA = 25$. The maximum and minimum moments of inertia are located at B and D; hence

$[\text{Max. } I = OC + CB]$ Max. $I = 80 + 25 = 105$ in.[4]   *Ans.*

$[\text{Min. } I = OC - CD]$ Min. $I = 80 - 25 = 55$ in.[4]   *Ans.*

To go from the X axis to the axis of maximum inertia CB, we must rotate clockwise through an angle 2α. From the diagram

$$\left[\tan 2\alpha = \frac{AE}{CE}\right] \qquad \tan 2\alpha = \frac{15}{20} = 0.75$$

$$2\alpha = 36° 52' \text{ and } \alpha = 18° 26'   \textit{Ans.}$$

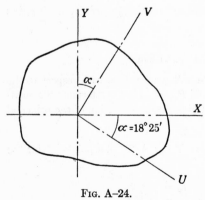

FIG. A–24.

Angle α, which locates the axis of the maximum moment of inertia (the U axis), is also rotated clockwise on the original reference axes; this gives the position shown in Fig. A–24. The axis of minimum moment of inertia (i.e., the V axis) is at 90° to the U axis.

PROBLEMS

A42. For a certain area it is known that $I_x = 60$ in.[4], $I_y = 20$ in.[4], and $P_{xy} = 0$. Referring to the figure that shows this area and the reference axes, determine the moment of inertia with respect to the U axis.   *Ans.* $I_u = 50$ in.[4]

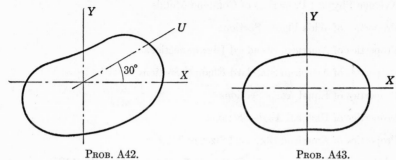

PROB. A42.   PROB. A43.

A43. The area shown has the following properties: $I_x = 100$ in.[4], $I_y = 40$ in.[4], $P_{xy} = 40$ in.[4] Determine the values of the maximum and minimum moments of inertia, and also the angle that the axis of maximum inertia makes with the X axis. Illustrate by a diagram.   *Ans.* Max. $I = 120$ in.[4]; min. $I = 20$ in.[4]; $\theta = 26° 35'$

A44. In Prob. A43, determine the moments of inertia and the product of inertia with respect to U and V axes inclined 30° clockwise to X and Y respectively.

A45. A right triangle has a base of 6 in. and an altitude of 9 in. Determine the maximum and minimum moments of inertia with respect to the principal axes passing through the centroid.

A46. Determine the minimum radius of gyration of the 6 by 6 by 1 in. angle section described in Prob. A17 (page 432). It is known that $I_{x_0} = 35.5$ in.[4] and that $P_{x_0y_0} = -20.5$ in.[4]

A47. Determine the maximum and minimum moments of inertia of the Z section shown in Prob. A24 (page 433), with respect to the principal axes passing through the centroid.   *Ans.* Max. $I = 52.0$ in.[4]; min. $I = 5.61$ in.[4]

A48. Show that the moment of inertia for the area of any regular polygon is a constant with respect to all axes in the plane of the area that pass through its centroid.

Appendix B

TABLES

B-1. Average Physical Properties of Common Metals

B-2. Properties of Wide Flange Sections

B-3. Properties of American Standard I-beam Sections

B-4. Properties of American Standard Channel Sections

B-5. Properties of Equal Angle Sections

B-6. Properties of Unequal Angle Sections

B-7. Properties of American Standard Sizes of Timber

Acknowledgement: Data for Tables B-2 to B-7 are taken from the AISC manual *Steel Construction* by permission of the American Institute of Steel Construction.

TABLE B-1. Average Physical Properties of Common Metals

Metal	Weight Lb/cu. ft.	Temp. Coeff. of Linear Expansion per Degree Fahr.	Proportional Limit, psi[a]		Ultimate Strength psi			Modulus of Elasticity, psi[a]		% Elongation (in 2 in.)
			Tension	Shear	Tension	Comp.	Shear	Tension, E	Shear, G	
Steel, 0.2% carbon, hot rolled	490		35,000	21,000	60,000	b	45,000	30×10^6	12×10^6	35
0.2% carbon cold rolled	490	Varies from 6.1×10^{-6} to 7.3×10^{-6}	60,000	36,000	80,000	b	60,000	30×10^6	12×10^6	18
0.6% carbon hot rolled	490	Average is 6.5×10^{-6}	60,000	36,000	100,000	b	80,000	30×10^6	12×10^6	15
0.8% carbon hot rolled	490		70,000	42,000	120,000	b	105,000	30×10^6	12×10^6	10
Gray cast iron	450	6×10^{-6}	c	d	20,000	75,000	d	15×10^6	6×10^6	Slight
Malleable cast iron	450	6.6×10^{-6}	36,000	23,000	54,000	b	48,000	25×10^6	12.5×10^6	18
Wrought iron	480	6.7×10^{-6}	30,000	18,000	50,000	b	35,000	27×10^6	10×10^6	35
Aluminum, cast	165	12.8×10^{-6}	9,000		13,000	b	10,500	10×10^6	4×10^6	20
Aluminum Alloy 17ST	168	12.8×10^{-6}	32,000	21,000	56,000	b	32,000	10.3×10^6	4×10^6	
Brass, rolled (70% Cu) (30% Zn)	530	10.4×10^{-6}	25,000	15,000	55,000	b	48,000	14×10^6	6×10^6	30
Bronze, cast	510	10×10^{-6}	20,000		33,000	56,000		12×10^6	5×10^6	10
Copper, hard-drawn	550	9.3×10^{-6}	38,000	23,000	55,000	b		17×10^6	6×10^6	4

Notes: [a] The proportional limit and modulus of elasticity for compression may be assumed equal to these values for tension except for cast iron where proportional limit = 26,000 psi.
[b] The ultimate compressive strength for ductile materials may be taken as the yield point which is slightly greater than the proportional limit in tension.
[c] Not well defined; approximately 6000 psi.
[d] Cast iron fails by diagonal tension.

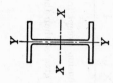

TABLE B-2. Properties of Wide Flange Sections
(Abridged List)

Section Index	Weight per Foot Lb.	Area In.²	Depth In.	Flange Width In.	Flange Thickness In.	Web Thickness In.	AXIS X-X I In.⁴	$Z=\frac{I}{c}$ In.³	k In.	AXIS Y-Y I In.⁴	$Z=\frac{I}{c}$ In.³	k In.	$\frac{d}{bt}$ In.⁻¹	L_u Unsupported Length Ft
36 WF 300	300	88.17	36.72	16.655	1.680	.945	20290.2	1105.1	15.17	1225.2	147.1	3.73	1.31	38
36 WF 230	230	67.73	35.88	16.475	1.260	.765	14988.4	835.5	14.88	870.9	105.7	3.59	1.73	28.5
36 WF 194	194	57.11	36.48	12.117	1.260	.770	12103.4	663.6	14.56	355.4	58.7	2.49	2.39	20.5
36 WF 150	150	44.16	35.84	11.972	.940	.625	9012.1	502.9	14.29	250.4	41.8	2.38	3.19	15.5
33 WF 240	240	70.52	33.50	15.865	1.400	.830	13585.1	811.1	13.88	874.3	110.2	3.52	1.51	33
33 WF 200	200	58.79	33.00	15.750	1.150	.715	11048.2	669.6	13.71	691.7	87.8	3.43	1.82	27
33 WF 152	152	44.71	33.50	11.565	1.055	.635	8147.6	486.4	13.50	256.1	44.3	2.39	2.74	18
33 WF 130	130	38.26	33.10	11.510	.855	.580	6699.0	404.8	13.23	201.4	35.0	2.29	3.36	15
30 WF 210	210	61.78	30.38	15.105	1.315	.775	9872.4	649.9	12.64	707.9	93.7	3.38	1.53	32.5
30 WF 172	172	50.65	29.88	14.985	1.065	.655	7891.5	528.2	12.48	550.1	73.4	3.30	1.87	26.5
30 WF 132	132	38.83	30.30	10.551	1.000	.615	5753.1	379.7	12.17	185.0	35.1	2.18	2.87	17.5
30 WF 108	108	31.77	29.82	10.484	.760	.548	4461.0	299.2	11.85	135.1	25.8	2.06	3.74	13
27 WF 177	177	52.10	27.31	14.090	1.190	.725	6728.6	492.8	11.36	518.9	73.7	3.16	1.63	30.5
27 WF 145	145	42.68	26.88	13.965	.975	.600	5414.3	402.9	11.26	406.9	58.3	3.09	1.97	25
27 WF 114	114	33.53	27.28	10.070	.932	.570	4080.5	299.2	11.03	149.6	29.7	2.11	2.91	17
27 WF 94	94	27.65	26.91	9.990	.747	.490	3266.7	242.8	10.87	115.1	23.0	2.04	3.61	13.5
24 WF 160	160	47.04	24.72	14.091	1.135	.656	5110.3	413.5	10.42	492.6	69.9	3.23	1.55	32
24 WF 130	130	38.21	24.25	14.000	.900	.565	4009.5	330.7	10.24	375.2	53.6	3.13	1.93	26

	Wt	A	d	b	t	w	I	S	r	I	S	r		
24 WF 120	120	35.29	24.31	12.088	.930	.556	3635.3	299.1	10.15	254.0	42.0	2.68	2.16	23
24 WF 100	100	29.43	24.00	12.000	.775	.468	2987.3	248.9	10.08	203.5	33.9	2.63	2.58	19
24 WF 94	94	27.63	24.29	9.061	.872	.516	2683.0	220.9	9.85	102.2	22.6	1.92	3.07	16
24 WF 84	84	24.71	24.09	9.015	.772	.470	2364.3	196.3	9.78	88.3	19.6	1.89	3.47	14.5
24 WF 76	76	22.37	23.91	8.985	.682	.440	2096.4	175.4	9.68	76.5	17.0	1.85	3.90	12.5
21 WF 142	142	41.76	21.46	13.132	1.095	.659	3403.1	317.2	9.03	385.9	58.8	3.04	1.49	33.5
21 WF 112	112	32.93	21.00	13.000	.865	.527	2620.6	249.6	8.92	289.7	44.6	2.96	1.87	27
21 WF 96	96	28.21	21.14	9.038	.935	.575	2088.9	197.6	8.60	109.3	24.2	1.97	2.50	20
21 WF 82	82	24.10	20.86	8.962	.795	.499	1752.4	168.0	8.53	89.6	20.0	1.93	2.93	17
21 WF 73	73	21.46	21.24	8.295	.740	.455	1600.3	150.7	8.64	66.2	16.0	1.76	3.46	14.5
21 WF 62	62	18.23	20.99	8.240	.615	.400	1326.8	126.4	8.53	53.1	12.9	1.71	4.15	12
18 WF 114	114	33.51	18.48	11.833	.991	.595	2033.8	220.1	7.79	255.6	43.2	2.76	1.58	31.5
18 WF 105	105	30.86	18.32	11.792	.911	.554	1852.5	202.2	7.75	231.0	39.2	2.73	1.71	29
18 WF 96	96	28.22	18.16	11.750	.831	.512	1674.7	184.4	7.70	206.8	35.2	2.71	1.86	27
18 WF 85	85	24.97	18.32	8.838	.911	.526	1429.9	156.1	7.57	99.4	22.5	2.00	2.28	22
18 WF 70	70	20.56	18.00	8.750	.751	.438	1153.9	128.2	7.49	78.5	17.9	1.95	2.74	18
18 WF 64	64	18.80	17.87	8.715	.686	.403	1045.8	117.0	7.46	70.3	16.1	1.93	2.99	16.5
18 WF 55	55	16.19	18.12	7.532	.630	.390	889.9	98.2	7.41	42.0	11.1	1.61	3.82	13
18 WF 50	50	14.71	18.00	7.500	.570	.358	800.6	89.0	7.38	37.2	9.9	1.59	4.22	12
16 WF 88	88	25.87	16.16	11.502	.795	.504	1222.6	151.3	6.87	185.2	32.2	2.67	1.77	28
16 WF 78	78	22.92	16.32	8.586	.875	.529	1042.6	127.8	6.74	87.5	20.4	1.95	2.17	23
16 WF 71	71	20.86	16.16	8.543	.795	.486	936.9	115.9	6.70	77.9	18.2	1.93	2.38	21
16 WF 64	64	18.80	16.00	8.500	.715	.443	833.8	104.2	6.66	68.4	16.1	1.91	2.63	19
16 WF 58	58	17.04	15.86	8.464	.645	.407	746.4	94.1	6.62	60.5	14.3	1.88	2.91	17
16 WF 50	50	14.70	16.25	7.073	.628	.380	655.4	80.7	6.68	34.8	9.8	1.54	3.66	13.5
16 WF 45	45	13.24	16.12	7.039	.563	.346	583.3	72.4	6.64	30.5	8.7	1.52	4.07	12
16 WF 36	36	10.59	15.85	6.992	.428	.299	446.3	56.3	6.49	22.1	6.3	1.45	5.30	9.5
14 WF 426	426	125.25	18.69	16.695	3.033	1.875	6610.3	707.4	7.26	2359.5	282.7	4.34	1.06	47
14 WF 342	342	100.59	17.56	16.365	2.468	1.545	4911.5	559.4	6.99	1806.9	220.8	4.24	1.13	44
14 WF 264	264	77.63	16.50	16.025	1.938	1.205	3526.0	427.4	6.74	1331.2	166.1	4.14		
14 WF 228	228	67.06	16.00	15.865	1.688	1.045	2942.4	367.8	6.62	1124.8	141.8	4.10		
14 WF 202	202	59.39	15.63	15.750	1.503	.930	2538.8	324.9	6.54	979.7	124.4	4.06		
14 WF 142	142	41.85	14.75	15.500	1.063	.680	1672.2	226.7	6.32	660.1	85.2	3.97		
14 WF 136	136	39.98	14.75	14.740	1.063	.660	1593.0	216.0	6.31	567.7	77.0	3.77		
14 WF 119	119	34.99	14.50	14.650	.938	.570	1373.1	189.4	6.26	491.8	67.1	3.75		
14 WF 111	111	32.65	14.37	14.620	.873	.540	1266.5	176.3	6.23	454.9	62.2	3.73		

TABLE B-2. Properties of Wide Flange Sections—*Continued*

(Abridged List)

Section Index	Weight per Foot Lb.	Area In.²	Depth In.	Flange Width In.	Flange Thickness In.	Web Thickness In.	AXIS X-X I In.⁴	AXIS X-X $Z=\frac{I}{c}$ In.³	AXIS X-X k In.	AXIS Y-Y I In.⁴	AXIS Y-Y $Z=\frac{I}{c}$ In.³	AXIS Y-Y k In.	$\frac{d}{bt}$ In.⁻¹	L_u Unsupported Length Ft
14 WF 95	95	27.94	14.12	14.545	.748	.465	1063.5	150.6	6.17	383.7	52.8	3.71	1.30	38
14 WF 87	87	25.56	14.00	14.500	.688	.420	966.9	138.1	6.15	349.7	48.2	3.70	1.40	35.5
14 WF 84	84	24.71	14.18	12.023	.778	.451	928.4	130.9	6.13	225.5	37.5	3.02	1.52	33
14 WF 78	78	22.94	14.06	12.000	.718	.428	851.2	121.1	6.09	206.9	34.5	3.00	1.63	30.5
14 WF 74	74	21.76	14.19	10.072	.783	.450	796.8	112.3	6.05	133.5	26.5	2.48	1.80	28
14 WF 68	68	20.00	14.06	10.040	.718	.418	724.1	103.0	6.02	121.2	24.1	2.46	1.95	25.5
14 WF 61	61	17.94	13.91	10.000	.643	.378	641.5	92.2	5.98	107.3	21.5	2.45	2.16	23
14 WF 53	53	15.59	13.94	8.062	.658	.370	542.1	77.8	5.90	57.5	14.3	1.92	2.63	19
14 WF 43	43	12.65	13.68	8.000	.528	.308	429.0	62.7	5.82	45.1	11.3	1.89	3.24	15.5
14 WF 38	38	11.17	14.12	6.776	.513	.313	385.3	54.6	5.87	24.6	7.3	1.49	4.06	12.5
14 WF 34	34	10.00	14.00	6.750	.453	.287	339.2	48.5	5.83	21.3	6.3	1.46	4.58	11
14 WF 30	30	8.81	13.86	6.733	.383	.270	289.6	41.8	5.73	17.5	5.2	1.41	5.37	9.5
12 WF 190	190	55.86	14.38	12.670	1.736	1.060	1892.5	263.2	5.82	589.7	93.1	3.25	1.29	38
12 WF 120	120	35.31	13.12	12.320	1.106	.710	1071.7	163.4	5.51	345.1	56.0	3.13		33
12 WF 106	106	31.19	12.88	12.230	.986	.620	930.7	144.5	5.46	300.9	49.2	3.11		33
12 WF 92	92	27.06	12.62	12.155	.856	.545	788.9	125.0	5.40	256.4	42.2	3.08		30
12 WF 85	85	24.98	12.50	12.105	.796	.495	723.3	115.7	5.38	235.5	38.9	3.07	1.52	26
12 WF 72	72	21.16	12.25	12.040	.671	.430	597.4	97.5	5.31	195.3	32.4	3.04	1.67	24
12 WF 65	65	19.11	12.12	12.000	.606	.390	533.4	88.0	5.28	174.6	29.1	3.02	1.90	
12 WF 58	58	17.06	12.19	10.014	.641	.359	476.1	78.1	5.28	107.4	21.4	2.51		
12 WF 53	53	15.59	12.06	10.000	.576	.345	426.2	70.7	5.23	96.1	19.2	2.48	2.90	

12 WF 50	50	14.71	12.19	8.077	.641	.371	394.5	64.7	5.18	56.4	14.0	1.96	2.35	21
12 WF 45	45	13.24	12.06	8.042	.576	.336	350.8	58.2	5.15	50.0	12.4	1.94	2.60	19
12 WF 40	40	11.77	11.94	8.000	.516	.294	310.1	51.9	5.15	44.1	11.0	1.94	2.89	17.5
12 WF 36	36	10.59	12.24	6.565	.540	.305	280.8	45.9	5.15	23.7	7.2	1.50	3.45	14.5
12 WF 27	27	7.97	11.95	6.500	.400	.240	204.1	34.1	5.06	16.6	5.1	1.44	4.50	10.5
10 WF 112	112	32.92	11.38	10.415	1.248	.755	718.7	126.3	4.67	235.4	45.2	2.67	1.37	36
10 WF 100	100	29.43	11.12	10.345	1.118	.685	625.0	112.4	4.61	206.6	39.9	2.65	1.63	30.5
10 WF 89	89	26.19	10.88	10.275	.998	.615	542.4	99.7	4.55	180.6	35.2	2.63	1.79	28
10 WF 77	77	22.67	10.62	10.195	.868	.535	457.2	86.1	4.49	153.4	30.1	2.60	2.04	24.5
10 WF 72	72	21.18	10.50	10.170	.808	.510	420.7	80.1	4.46	141.8	27.9	2.59	2.36	21
10 WF 66	66	19.41	10.38	10.117	.748	.457	382.5	73.7	4.44	129.2	25.5	2.58	2.83	17.5
10 WF 54	54	15.88	10.12	10.028	.618	.368	305.7	60.4	4.39	103.9	20.7	2.56	3.52	14
10 WF 49	49	14.40	10.00	10.000	.558	.340	272.9	54.6	4.35	93.0	18.6	2.54	4.08	12
10 WF 45	45	13.24	10.12	8.022	.618	.350	248.6	49.1	4.33	53.2	13.3	2.00		10
10 WF 39	39	11.48	9.94	7.990	.528	.318	209.7	42.2	4.27	44.9	11.2	1.98		
10 WF 33	33	9.71	9.75	7.964	.433	.292	170.9	35.0	4.20	36.5	9.2	1.94		
10 WF 29	29	8.53	10.22	5.799	.500	.289	157.3	30.8	4.29	15.2	5.2	1.34		
10 WF 25	25	7.35	10.08	5.762	.430	.252	133.2	26.4	4.26	12.7	4.4	1.31		
10 WF 21	21	6.19	9.90	5.750	.340	.240	106.3	21.5	4.14	9.7	3.4	1.25	5.07	
8 WF 67	67	19.70	9.00	8.287	.933	.575	271.8	60.4	3.71	88.6	21.4	2.12	2.05	24
8 WF 58	58	17.06	8.75	8.222	.808	.510	227.3	52.0	3.65	74.9	18.2	2.10	2.31	21.5
8 WF 48	48	14.11	8.50	8.117	.683	.405	183.7	43.2	3.61	60.9	15.0	2.08	2.66	18.5
8 WF 40	40	11.76	8.25	8.077	.558	.365	146.3	35.5	3.53	49.0	12.1	2.04	3.07	16
8 WF 35	35	10.30	8.12	8.027	.493	.315	126.5	31.1	3.50	42.5	10.6	2.03	4.08	12
8 WF 31	31	9.12	8.00	8.000	.433	.288	109.7	27.4	3.47	37.0	9.2	2.01	4.95	10
8 WF 28	28	8.23	8.06	6.540	.463	.285	97.8	24.3	3.45	21.6	6.6	1.62		
8 WF 24	24	7.06	7.93	6.500	.398	.245	82.5	20.8	3.42	18.2	5.6	1.61		
8 WF 20	20	5.88	8.14	5.268	.378	.248	69.2	17.0	3.43	8.5	3.2	1.20		
8 WF 17	17	5.00	8.00	5.250	.308	.230	56.4	14.1	3.36	6.7	2.6	1.16		

451

TABLE B-3. Properties of American Standard I-Beam Sections

Section Index	Weight per Foot Lb.	Area In.²	Depth In.	Flange Width In.	Flange Thickness In.	Web Thickness In.	AXIS X-X I In.⁴	AXIS X-X $Z=\frac{I}{c}$ In.³	AXIS X-X k In.	AXIS Y-Y I In.⁴	AXIS Y-Y $Z=\frac{I}{c}$ In.³	AXIS Y-Y k In.	$\frac{d}{bt}$ In.⁻¹	L_u Ft.
24 I 120	120.0	35.13	24.00	8.048	1.102	.798	3010.8	250.9	9.26	84.9	21.1	1.56	2.71	18.5
24 I 105.9	105.9	30.98	24.00	7.875	1.102	.625	2811.5	234.3	9.53	78.9	20.0	1.60	2.76	18
24 I 100	100.0	29.25	24.00	7.247	.871	.747	2371.8	197.6	9.05	48.4	13.4	1.29	3.81	13
24 I 90	90.0	26.30	24.00	7.124	.871	.624	2230.1	185.8	9.21	45.5	12.8	1.32	3.87	13
24 I 79.9	79.9	23.33	24.00	7.000	.871	.500	2087.2	173.9	9.46	42.9	12.2	1.36	3.94	12.5
20 I 95	95.0	27.74	20.00	7.200	.916	.800	1599.7	160.0	7.59	50.5	14.0	1.35	3.03	16.5
20 I 85	85.0	24.80	20.00	7.053	.916	.653	1501.7	150.2	7.78	47.0	13.3	1.38	3.09	16
20 I 75	75.0	21.90	20.00	6.391	.789	.641	1263.5	126.3	7.60	30.1	9.4	1.17	3.97	12.5
20 I 65.4	65.4	19.08	20.00	6.250	.789	.500	1169.5	116.9	7.83	27.9	8.9	1.21	4.05	12
18 I 70	70.0	20.46	18.00	6.251	.691	.711	917.5	101.9	6.70	24.5	7.8	1.09	4.17	12
18 I 54.7	54.7	15.94	18.00	6.000	.691	.460	795.5	88.4	7.07	21.2	7.1	1.15	4.35	11.5
15 I 50	50.0	14.59	15.00	5.640	.622	.550	481.1	64.2	5.74	16.0	5.7	1.05	4.28	11.5
15 I 42.9	42.9	12.49	15.00	5.500	.622	.410	441.8	58.9	5.95	14.6	5.3	1.08	4.39	11

Section														
12 I 50	50.0	14.57	12.00	5.477	.659	.687	301.6	50.3	4.55	16.0	5.8	1.05	3.32	15
12 I 40.8	40.8	11.84	12.00	5.250	.659	.460	268.9	44.8	4.77	13.8	5.3	1.08	3.47	14.5
12 I 35	35.0	10.20	12.00	5.078	.544	.428	227.0	37.8	4.72	10.0	3.9	.99	4.34	11.5
12 I 31.8	31.8	9.26	12.00	5.000	.544	.350	215.8	36.0	4.83	9.5	3.8	1.01	4.41	11.5
10 I 35	35.0	10.22	10.00	4.944	.491	.594	145.8	29.2	3.78	8.5	3.4	.91	4.12	12
10 I 25.4	25.4	7.38	10.00	4.660	.491	.310	122.1	24.4	4.07	6.9	3.0	.97	4.37	11.5
8 I 23	23.0	6.71	8.00	4.171	.425	.441	64.2	16.0	3.09	4.4	2.1	.81	4.51	11
8 I 18.4	18.4	5.34	8.00	4.000	.425	.270	56.9	14.2	3.26	3.8	1.9	.84	4.71	10.5
7 I 20	20.0	5.83	7.00	3.860	.392	.450	41.9	12.0	2.68	3.1	1.6	.74	4.62	11
7 I 15.3	15.3	4.43	7.00	3.660	.392	.250	36.2	10.4	2.86	2.7	1.5	.78	4.88	10
6 I 17¼	17.25	5.02	6.00	3.565	.359	.465	26.0	8.7	2.28	2.3	1.3	.68	4.69	10.5
6 I 12.5	12.5	3.61	6.00	3.330	.359	.230	21.8	7.3	2.46	1.8	1.1	.72	5.02	10
5 I 14¾	14.75	4.29	5.00	3.284	.326	.494	15.0	6.0	1.87	1.7	1.0	.63	4.67	10.5
5 I 10	10.0	2.87	5.00	3.000	.326	.210	12.1	4.8	2.05	1.2	.82	.65	5.11	10
4 I 9.5	9.5	2.76	4.00	2.796	.293	.326	6.7	3.3	1.56	.91	.65	.58	4.89	10
4 I 7.7	7.7	2.21	4.00	2.660	.293	.190	6.0	3.0	1.64	.77	.58	.59	5.13	9.5
3 I 7.5	7.5	2.17	3.00	2.509	.260	.349	2.9	1.9	1.15	.59	.47	.52	4.60	11
3 I 5.7	5.7	1.64	3.00	2.330	.260	.170	2.5	1.7	1.23	.46	.40	.53	4.95	10

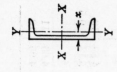

Table B-4. Properties of American Standard Channel Sections

Section Index	Weight per Foot Lb.	Area In.²	Depth In.	Flange Width In.	Flange Average Thickness In.	Web Thickness In.	AXIS X-X I In.⁴	AXIS X-X $Z=\frac{I}{c}$ In.³	AXIS X-X k In.	AXIS Y-Y I In.⁴	AXIS Y-Y $Z=\frac{I}{c}$ In.³	AXIS Y-Y k In.	AXIS Y-Y x In.
18 ⊐ 58	58.0	16.98	18.00	4.200	.625	.700	670.7	74.5	6.29	18.5	5.6	1.04	.88
18 ⊐ 51.9	51.9	15.18	18.00	4.100	.625	.600	622.1	69.1	6.40	17.1	5.3	1.06	.87
18 ⊐ 45.8	45.8	13.38	18.00	4.000	.625	.500	573.5	63.7	6.55	15.8	5.1	1.09	.89
18 ⊐ 42.7	42.7	12.48	18.00	3.950	.625	.450	549.2	61.0	6.64	15.0	4.9	1.10	.90
15 ⊐ 50	50.0	14.64	15.00	3.716	.650	.716	401.4	53.6	5.24	11.2	3.8	.87	.80
15 ⊐ 40	40.0	11.70	15.00	3.520	.650	.520	346.3	46.2	5.44	9.3	3.4	.89	.78
15 ⊐ 33.9	33.9	9.90	15.00	3.400	.650	.400	312.6	41.7	5.62	8.2	3.2	.91	.79
12 ⊐ 30	30.0	8.79	12.00	3.170	.501	.510	161.2	26.9	4.28	5.2	2.1	.77	.68
12 ⊐ 25	25.0	7.32	12.00	3.047	.501	.387	143.5	23.9	4.43	4.5	1.9	.79	.68
12 ⊐ 20.7	20.7	6.03	12.00	2.940	.501	.280	128.1	21.4	4.61	3.9	1.7	.81	.70
10 ⊐ 30	30.0	8.80	10.00	3.033	.436	.673	103.0	20.6	3.42	4.0	1.7	.67	.65

10 ⌐ 25	25.0	7.33	10.00	2.886	.436	.526	90.7	18.1	3.52	3.4	1.5	.68	.62
10 ⌐ 20	20.0	5.86	10.00	2.739	.436	.379	78.5	15.7	3.66	2.8	1.3	.70	.61
10 ⌐ 15.3	15.3	4.47	10.00	2.600	.436	.240	66.9	13.4	3.87	2.3	1.2	.72	.64
9 ⌐ 20	20.0	5.86	9.00	2.648	.413	.448	60.6	13.5	3.22	2.4	1.2	.65	.59
9 ⌐ 15	15.0	4.39	9.00	2.485	.413	.285	50.7	11.3	3.40	1.9	1.0	.67	.59
9 ⌐ 13.4	13.4	3.89	9.00	2.430	.413	.230	47.3	10.5	3.49	1.8	.97	.67	.61
8 ⌐ 18¾	18.75	5.49	8.00	2.527	.390	.487	43.7	10.9	2.82	2.0	1.0	.60	.57
8 ⌐ 13¾	13.75	4.02	8.00	2.343	.390	.303	35.8	9.0	2.99	1.5	.86	.62	.56
8 ⌐ 11.5	11.5	3.36	8.00	2.260	.390	.220	32.3	8.1	3.10	1.3	.79	.63	.58
7 ⌐ 14¾	14.75	4.32	7.00	2.299	.366	.419	27.1	7.7	2.51	1.4	.79	.57	.53
7 ⌐ 12¼	12.25	3.58	7.00	2.194	.366	.314	24.1	6.9	2.59	1.2	.71	.58	.53
7 ⌐ 9.8	9.8	2.85	7.00	2.090	.366	.210	21.1	6.0	2.72	.98	.63	.59	.55
6 ⌐ 13.0	13.0	3.81	6.00	2.157	.343	.437	17.3	5.8	2.13	1.1	.65	.53	.52
6 ⌐ 10.5	10.5	3.07	6.00	2.034	.343	.314	15.1	5.0	2.22	.87	.57	.53	.50
6 ⌐ 8.2	8.2	2.39	6.00	1.920	.343	.200	13.0	4.3	2.34	.70	.50	.54	.52
5 ⌐ 9.0	9.0	2.63	5.00	1.885	.320	.325	8.8	3.5	1.83	.64	.45	.49	.48
5 ⌐ 6.7	6.7	1.95	5.00	1.750	.320	.190	7.4	3.0	1.95	.48	.38	.50	.49
4 ⌐ 7¼	7.25	2.12	4.00	1.720	.296	.320	4.5	2.3	1.47	.44	.35	.46	.46
4 ⌐ 5.4	5.4	1.56	4.00	1.580	.296	.180	3.8	1.9	1.56	.32	.29	.45	.46
3 ⌐ 6.0	6.0	1.75	3.00	1.596	.273	.356	2.1	1.4	1.08	.31	.27	.42	.46
3 ⌐ 5.0	5.0	1.46	3.00	1.498	.273	.258	1.8	1.2	1.12	.25	.24	.41	.44
3 ⌐ 4.1	4.1	1.19	3.00	1.410	.273	.170	1.6	1.1	1.17	.20	.21	.41	.44

TABLE B-5 Properties of Equal Angle Sections
(Slightly Abridged List)

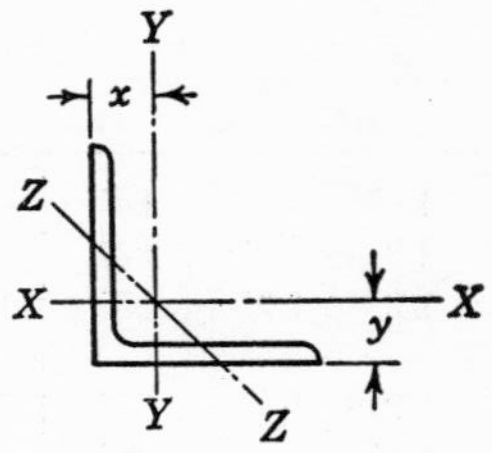

Size	Thickness	Weight per Foot	Area	AXIS X-X AND AXIS Y-Y				AXIS Z-Z
				I	I/c	k	x or y	k
In.	In.	Lb.	In.²	In.⁴	In.³	In.	In.	In.
8 × 8	1⅛	56.9	16.73	98.0	17.5	2.42	2.41	1.56
	1	51.0	15.00	89.0	15.8	2.44	2.37	1.56
	⅞	45.0	13.23	79.6	14.0	2.45	2.32	1.57
	¾	38.9	11.44	69.7	12.2	2.47	2.28	1.57
	⅝	32.7	9.61	59.4	10.3	2.49	2.23	1.58
	9⁄16	29.6	8.68	54.1	9.3	2.50	2.21	1.58
	½	26.4	7.75	48.6	8.4	2.50	2.19	1.59
6 × 6	1	37.4	11.00	35.5	8.6	1.80	1.86	1.17
	⅞	33.1	9.73	31.9	7.6	1.81	1.82	1.17
	¾	28.7	8.44	28.2	6.7	1.83	1.78	1.17
	⅝	24.2	7.11	24.2	5.7	1.84	1.73	1.18
	½	19.6	5.75	19.9	4.6	1.86	1.68	1.18
	7⁄16	17.2	5.06	17.7	4.1	1.87	1.66	1.19
	⅜	14.9	4.36	15.4	3.5	1.88	1.64	1.19
	5⁄16	12.5	3.66	13.0	3.0	1.89	1.61	1.19
5 × 5	⅞	27.2	7.98	17.8	5.2	1.49	1.57	.97
	¾	23.6	6.94	15.7	4.5	1.51	1.52	.97
	⅝	20.0	5.86	13.6	3.9	1.52	1.48	.98
	½	16.2	4.75	11.3	3.2	1.54	1.43	.98
	7⁄16	14.3	4.18	10.0	2.8	1.55	1.41	.98
	⅜	12.3	3.61	8.7	2.4	1.56	1.39	.99
	5⁄16	10.3	3.03	7.4	2.0	1.57	1.37	.99

Size	Thickness							
4 × 4	¾	18.5	5.44	7.7	2.8	1.19	1.27	.78
	⅝	15.7	4.61	6.7	2.4	1.20	1.23	.78
	½	12.8	3.75	5.6	2.0	1.22	1.18	.78
	⅜	9.8	2.86	4.4	1.5	1.23	1.14	.79
	5/16	8.2	2.40	3.7	1.3	1.24	1.12	.79
	¼	6.6	1.94	3.0	1.1	1.25	1.09	.80
3½ × 3½	½	11.1	3.25	3.6	1.5	1.06	1.06	.68
	⅜	8.5	2.48	2.9	1.2	1.07	1.01	.69
	5/16	7.2	2.09	2.5	.98	1.08	.99	.69
	¼	5.8	1.69	2.0	.79	1.09	.97	.69
3 × 3	½	9.4	2.75	2.2	1.1	.90	.93	.58
	⅜	7.2	2.11	1.8	.83	.91	.89	.58
	5/16	6.1	1.78	1.5	.71	.92	.87	.59
	¼	4.9	1.44	1.2	.58	.93	.84	.59
	3/16	3.71	1.09	.96	.44	.94	.82	.59
2½ × 2½	½	7.7	2.25	1.2	.72	.74	.81	.49
	⅜	5.9	1.73	.98	.57	.75	.76	.49
	¼	4.1	1.19	.70	.39	.77	.72	.49
	3/16	3.07	.90	.55	.30	.78	.69	.49
2 × 2	⅜	4.7	1.36	.48	.35	.59	.64	.39
	¼	3.19	.94	.35	.25	.61	.59	.39
	3/16	2.44	.71	.27	.19	.62	.57	.39
	⅛	1.65	.48	.19	.13	.63	.55	.40
1¾ × 1¾	¼	2.77	.81	.23	.19	.53	.53	.34
	3/16	2.12	.62	.18	.14	.54	.51	.34
	⅛	1.44	.42	.13	.10	.55	.48	.35
1½ × 1½	¼	2.34	.69	.14	.13	.45	.47	.29
	3/16	1.80	.53	.11	.10	.46	.44	.29
	⅛	1.23	.36	.08	.07	.47	.42	.30
1¼ × 1¼	¼	1.92	.56	.08	.09	.37	.40	.24
	3/16	1.48	.43	.06	.07	.38	.38	.24
	⅛	1.01	.30	.04	.05	.38	.36	.25
1 × 1	¼	1.49	.44	.04	.06	.29	.34	.20
	3/16	1.16	.34	.03	.04	.30	.32	.19
	⅛	.80	.23	.02	.03	.30	.30	.20

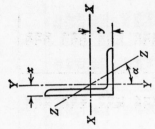

TABLE B–6. Properties of Unequal Angle Sections
(Slightly Abridged List)

Size	Thickness	Weight per Foot	Area	AXIS X–X				AXIS Y–Y				AXIS Z–Z	
				I	I/c	k	y	I	I/c	k	x	k	Tan α
In.	In.	Lb.	In.²	In.⁴	In.³	In.	In.	In.⁴	In.³	In.	In.	In.	
9 × 4	1	40.8	12.00	97.0	17.6	2.84	3.50	12.0	4.0	1.00	1.00	.83	.203
	¾	31.3	9.19	76.1	13.6	2.88	3.41	9.6	3.1	1.02	.91	.84	.212
	½	21.3	6.25	53.2	9.3	2.92	3.31	6.9	2.2	1.05	.81	.85	.220
8 × 6	1	44.2	13.00	80.8	15.1	2.49	2.65	38.8	8.9	1.73	1.65	1.28	.543
	¾	33.8	9.94	63.4	11.7	2.53	2.56	30.7	6.9	1.76	1.56	1.29	.551
	⅝	28.5	8.36	54.1	9.9	2.54	2.52	26.3	5.9	1.77	1.52	1.29	.554
	½	23.0	6.75	44.3	8.0	2.56	2.47	21.7	4.8	1.79	1.47	1.30	.558
	⁷⁄₁₆	20.2	5.93	39.2	7.1	2.57	2.45	19.3	4.2	1.80	1.45	1.31	.560
8 × 4	1	37.4	11.00	69.6	14.1	2.52	3.05	11.6	3.9	1.03	1.05	.85	.247
	⅞	33.1	9.73	62.5	12.5	2.53	3.00	10.5	3.5	1.04	1.00	.85	.253
	¾	28.7	8.44	54.9	10.9	2.55	2.95	9.4	3.1	1.05	.95	.85	.258
	⅝	24.2	7.11	46.9	9.2	2.57	2.91	8.1	2.6	1.07	.91	.86	.262
	½	19.6	5.75	38.5	7.5	2.59	2.86	6.7	2.2	1.08	.86	.86	.267
	⁷⁄₁₆	17.2	5.06	34.1	6.6	2.60	2.83	6.0	1.9	1.09	.83	.87	.269

Size	Thick.	Weight lb/ft	Area in²	I (x)	S (x)	r (x)	y	I (y)	S (y)	r (y)	x	r (z)	tan α
7 × 4	7/8	30.2	8.86	42.9	9.7	2.20	2.55	10.2	3.5	1.07	1.05	.86	.318
	3/4	26.2	7.69	37.8	8.4	2.22	2.51	9.1	3.0	1.09	1.01	.86	.324
	5/8	22.1	6.48	32.4	7.1	2.24	2.46	7.8	2.6	1.10	.96	.86	.329
	1/2	17.9	5.25	26.7	5.8	2.25	2.42	6.5	2.1	1.11	.92	.87	.335
	7/16	15.8	4.62	23.7	5.1	2.26	2.39	5.8	1.9	1.12	.89	.88	.337
	3/8	13.6	3.98	20.6	4.4	2.27	2.37	5.1	1.6	1.13	.87	.88	.339
6 × 4	7/8	27.2	7.98	27.7	7.2	1.86	2.12	9.8	3.4	1.11	1.12	.86	.421
	3/4	23.6	6.94	24.5	6.3	1.88	2.08	8.7	3.0	1.12	1.08	.86	.428
	5/8	20.0	5.86	21.1	5.3	1.90	2.03	7.5	2.5	1.13	1.03	.86	.435
	1/2	16.2	4.75	17.4	4.3	1.91	1.99	6.3	2.1	1.15	.99	.87	.440
	7/16	14.3	4.18	15.5	3.8	1.92	1.96	5.6	1.9	1.16	.96	.87	.443
	3/8	12.3	3.61	13.5	3.3	1.93	1.94	4.9	1.6	1.17	.94	.88	.446
	5/16	10.3	3.03	11.4	2.8	1.94	1.92	4.2	1.4	1.17	.92	.88	.449
6 × 3½	1/2	15.3	4.50	16.6	4.2	1.92	2.08	4.3	1.6	.97	.83	.76	.344
	3/8	11.7	3.42	12.9	3.2	1.94	2.04	3.3	1.2	.99	.79	.77	.350
	5/16	9.8	2.87	10.9	2.7	1.95	2.01	2.9	1.0	1.00	.76	.77	.352
	1/4	7.9	2.31	8.9	2.2	1.96	1.99	2.3	0.85	1.01	.74	.78	.355
5 × 3½	3/4	19.8	5.81	13.9	4.3	1.55	1.75	5.6	2.2	.98	1.00	.75	.464
	5/8	16.8	4.92	12.0	3.7	1.56	1.70	4.8	1.9	.99	.95	.75	.472
	1/2	13.6	4.00	10.0	3.0	1.58	1.66	4.1	1.6	1.01	.91	.75	.479
	7/16	12.0	3.53	8.9	2.6	1.59	1.63	3.6	1.4	1.01	.88	.76	.482
	3/8	10.4	3.05	7.8	2.3	1.60	1.61	3.2	1.2	1.02	.86	.76	.486
	5/16	8.7	2.56	6.6	1.9	1.61	1.59	2.7	1.0	1.03	.84	.76	.489
	1/4	7.0	2.06	5.4	1.6	1.61	1.56	2.2	.83	1.04	.81	.76	.492
5 × 3	1/2	12.8	3.75	9.5	2.9	1.59	1.75	2.6	1.1	.83	.75	.65	.357
	7/16	11.3	3.31	8.4	2.6	1.60	1.73	2.3	1.0	.84	.73	.65	.361
	3/8	9.8	2.86	7.4	2.2	1.61	1.70	2.0	.89	.84	.70	.65	.364
	5/16	8.2	2.40	6.3	1.9	1.61	1.68	1.8	.75	.85	.68	.66	.368
	1/4	6.6	1.94	5.1	1.5	1.62	1.66	1.4	.61	.86	.66	.66	.371

Angles — continued

TABLE B-6. Properties of Unequal Angle Sections—Continued

(Slightly Abridged List)

Size	Thick-ness	Weight per Foot	Area	AXIS X-X				AXIS Y-Y				AXIS Z-Z	
				I	I/c	k	y	I	I/c	k	x	k	Tan α
In.	In.	Lb.	In.^{2}	In.^{4}	In.^{3}	In.	In.	In.^{4}	In.^{3}	In.	In.	In.	
4 × 3½	5/8	14.7	4.30	6.4	2.4	1.22	1.29	4.5	1.8	1.03	1.04	.72	.745
	1/2	11.9	3.50	5.3	1.9	1.23	1.25	3.8	1.5	1.04	1.00	.72	.750
	7/16	10.6	3.09	4.8	1.7	1.24	1.23	3.4	1.4	1.05	.98	.72	.753
	3/8	9.1	2.67	4.2	1.5	1.25	1.21	3.0	1.2	1.06	.96	.73	.755
	5/16	7.7	2.25	3.6	1.3	1.26	1.18	2.6	1.0	1.07	.93	.73	.757
	1/4	6.2	1.81	2.9	1.0	1.27	1.16	2.1	.81	1.07	.91	.73	.759
4 × 3	5/8	13.6	3.98	6.0	2.3	1.23	1.37	2.9	1.4	.85	.87	.64	.534
	1/2	11.1	3.25	5.1	1.9	1.25	1.33	2.4	1.1	.86	.83	.64	.543
	3/8	8.5	2.48	4.0	1.5	1.26	1.28	1.9	.87	.88	.78	.64	.551
	5/16	7.2	2.09	3.4	1.2	1.27	1.26	1.7	.73	.89	.76	.65	.554
	1/4	5.8	1.69	2.8	1.0	1.28	1.24	1.4	.60	.90	.74	.65	.558
3½ × 3	1/2	10.2	3.00	3.5	1.5	1.07	1.13	2.3	1.1	.88	.88	.62	.714
	3/8	7.9	2.30	2.7	1.1	1.09	1.08	1.9	.85	.90	.83	.62	.721
	5/16	6.6	1.93	2.3	.95	1.10	1.06	1.6	.72	.90	.81	.63	.724
	1/4	5.4	1.56	1.9	.78	1.11	1.04	1.3	.59	.91	.79	.63	.727
3½ × 2½	1/2	9.4	2.75	3.2	1.4	1.09	1.20	1.4	.76	.70	.70	.53	.486
	3/8	7.2	2.11	2.6	1.1	1.10	1.16	1.1	.59	.72	.66	.54	.496
	5/16	6.1	1.78	2.2	.93	1.11	1.14	.94	.50	.73	.64	.54	.501
	1/4	4.9	1.44	1.8	.75	1.12	1.11	.78	.41	.74	.61	.54	.506

Size	Thick.	Wt.												
3 × 2½	½	8.5	2.50	2.1	1.0	.91	1.00	1.3	.74	.72	.75	.52	.667
	⅜	6.6	1.92	1.7	.81	.93	.96	1.0	.58	.74	.71	.52	.676
	5⁄16	5.6	1.62	1.4	.69	.94	.93	.90	.49	.74	.68	.53	.680
	¼	4.5	1.31	1.2	.56	.95	.91	.74	.40	.75	.66	.53	.684
3 × 2	½	7.7	2.25	1.9	1.0	.92	1.08	.67	.47	.55	.58	.43	.414
	⅜	5.9	1.73	1.5	.78	.94	1.04	.54	.37	.56	.54	.43	.428
	5⁄16	5.0	1.47	1.3	.66	.95	1.02	.47	.32	.57	.52	.43	.435
	¼	4.1	1.19	1.1	.54	.95	.99	.39	.26	.57	.49	.43	.440
	3⁄16	3.07	.90	.84	.41	.97	.97	.31	.20	.58	.47	.44	.446
2½ × 2	⅜	5.3	1.55	.91	.55	.77	.83	.51	.36	.58	.58	.42	.614
	5⁄16	4.5	1.31	.79	.47	.78	.81	.45	.31	.58	.56	.42	.620
	¼	3.62	1.06	.65	.38	.78	.79	.37	.25	.59	.54	.42	.626
	3⁄16	2.75	.81	.51	.29	.79	.76	.29	.20	.60	.51	.43	.631
2½ × 1½	⅜	4.7	1.36	.82	.52	.78	.92	.22	.20	.40	.42	.32	.340
	5⁄16	3.92	1.15	.71	.44	.79	.90	.19	.17	.41	.40	.32	.349
	¼	3.19	.94	.59	.36	.79	.88	.16	.14	.41	.38	.32	.357
	3⁄16	2.44	.72	.46	.28	.80	.85	.13	.11	.42	.35	.33	.364
2 × 1½	¼	2.77	.81	.32	.24	.62	.66	.15	.14	.43	.41	.32	.543
	3⁄16	2.12	.62	.25	.18	.63	.64	.12	.11	.44	.39	.32	.551
	⅛	1.44	.42	.17	.13	.64	.62	.09	.08	.45	.37	.33	.558
1¾ × 1¼	¼	2.34	.69	.20	.18	.54	.60	.09	.10	.35	.35	.27	.486
	3⁄16	1.80	.53	.16	.14	.55	.58	.07	.08	.36	.33	.27	.496
	⅛	1.23	.36	.11	.09	.56	.56	.05	.05	.37	.31	.27	.506

TABLE B-7. Properties of American Standard Sizes of Timber

Nominal Size In.	American Standard Dressed Size In.	Area of Section In.²	Weight per Foot Lb.	Moment of Inertia In.⁴	Section Modulus In.³
2 × 4	1⅝ × 3⅝	5.89	1.64	6.45	3.56
6	5⅝	9.14	2.54	24.1	8.57
8	7½	12.2	3.39	57.1	15.3
10	9½	15.4	4.29	116	24.4
12	11½	18.7	5.19	206	35.8
14	13½	21.9	6.09	333	49.4
16	15½	25.2	6.99	504	65.1
18	17½	28.4	7.90	726	82.9
3 × 4	2⅝ × 3⅝	9.52	2.64	10.4	5.75
6	5⅝	14.8	4.10	38.9	13.8
8	7½	19.7	5.47	92.3	24.6
10	9½	24.9	6.93	188	39.5
12	11½	30.2	8.39	333	57.9
14	13½	35.4	9.84	538	79.7
16	15½	40.7	11.3	815	105
18	17½	45.9	12.8	1172	134
4 × 4	3⅝ × 3⅝	13.1	3.65	14.4	7.94
6	5⅝	20.4	5.66	53.8	19.1
8	7½	27.2	7.55	127	34.0
10	9½	34.4	9.57	259	54.5
12	11½	41.7	11.6	459	79.9

Nominal Size In.	American Standard Dressed Size In.	Area of Section In.²	Weight per Foot Lb.	Moment of Inertia In.⁴	Section Modulus In.³
10 × 10	9½ × 9½	90.3	25.0	679	143
12	11½	109	30.3	1204	209
14	13½	128	35.6	1948	289
16	15½	147	40.9	2948	380
18	17½	166	46.1	4243	485
20	19½	185	51.4	5870	602
22	21½	204	56.7	7868	732
24	23½	223	62.0	10274	874
12 × 12	11½ × 11½	132	36.7	1458	253
14	13½	155	43.1	2358	349
16	15½	178	49.5	3569	460
18	17½	201	55.9	5136	587
20	19½	224	62.3	7106	729
22	21½	247	68.7	9524	886
24	23½	270	75.0	12437	1058
14 × 14	13½ × 13½	182	50.6	2768	410
16	15½	209	58.1	4189	541
18	17½	236	65.6	6029	689
20	19½	263	73.1	8342	856
22	21½	290	80.6	11181	1040
24	23½	317	88.1	14600	1243

Nominal Size	Dressed Size				
4 × 14	3⅝ × 13½	48.9	13.6	743	110
16	15½	56.2	15.6	1125	145
18	17½	63.4	17.6	1619	185
6 × 6	5½ × 5½	30.3	8.40	76.3	27.7
8	7½	41.3	11.4	193	51.6
10	9½	52.3	14.5	393	82.7
12	11½	63.3	17.5	697	121
14	13½	74.3	20.6	1128	167
16	15½	85.3	23.6	1707	220
18	17½	96.3	26.7	2456	281
20	19½	107.3	29.8	3398	349
8 × 8	7½ × 7½	56.3	15.6	264	70.3
10	9½	71.3	19.8	536	113
12	11½	86.3	23.9	951	165
14	13½	101.3	28.0	1538	228
16	15½	116.3	32.0	2327	300
18	17½	131.3	36.4	3350	383
20	19½	146.3	40.6	4634	475
22	21½	161.3	44.8	6211	578

Nominal Size	Dressed Size				
16 × 16	15½ × 15½	240	66.7	4810	621
18	17½	271	75.3	6923	791
20	19½	302	83.9	9578	982
22	21½	333	92.5	12837	1194
24	23½	364	101	16763	1427
18 × 18	17½ × 17½	306	85.0	7816	893
20	19½	341	94.8	10813	1109
22	21½	376	105	14493	1348
24	23½	411	114	18926	1611
26	25½	446	124	24181	1897
20 × 20	19½ × 19½	380	106	12049	1236
22	21½	419	116	16150	1502
24	23½	458	127	21089	1795
26	25½	497	138	26945	2113
28	27½	536	149	33795	2458
24 × 24	23½ × 23½	552	153	25415	2163
26	25½	599	166	32472	2547
28	27½	646	180	40727	2962
30	29½	693	193	50275	3408

NATIONAL LUMBER MANUFACTURERS ASSOCIATION

All properties and weights given are for dressed size only.
The weights given above are based on assumed average weight of 40 pounds per cubic foot.

Index